FORD | RANGER PICK-UPS
2000-11 REPAIR MANUAL

MW00991930

CHILTON'S

Covers U.S. and Canadian models of
Ford Ranger (2000 through 2011) and Mazda B2300,
B2500, B3000 and B4000 pick-ups
(2000 through 2009)

by Eric Jorgensen
and Alan Ahlstrand

CHILTON *Automotive Books*

PUBLISHED BY **HAYNES NORTH AMERICA, Inc.**

Printed in Malaysia
© 2006, 2010, 2013 Haynes North America, Inc.
ISBN-10: 1-62092-048-4
ISBN-13: 978-1-62092-048-0
Library of Congress Control Number 2013946628

Haynes Publishing Group
Sparkford Nr Yeovil
Somerset BA22 7JJ England

Haynes North America, Inc
859 Lawrence Drive
Newbury Park
California 91320 USA

ABCD

10V10

Contents

About this manual

ITS PURPOSE

The purpose of this manual is to help you get the best value from your vehicle. It can do so in several ways. It can help you decide what work must be done, even if you choose to have it done by a dealer service department or a repair shop; it provides information and procedures for routine maintenance and servicing; and it offers diagnostic and repair procedures to follow when trouble occurs.

We hope you use the manual to tackle the work yourself. For many simpler jobs, doing it yourself may be quicker than arranging an appointment to get the vehicle into a shop and making the trips to leave it and pick it up. More importantly, a lot of money can be saved by avoiding the expense the shop must pass on to you to cover its labor and overhead costs. An added benefit is the sense of satisfaction and accomplishment that you feel after doing the job yourself.

USING THE MANUAL

The manual is divided into Chapters. Each Chapter is divided into numbered Sections. Each Section consists of consecutively numbered paragraphs.

At the beginning of each numbered Section you will be referred to any illustrations which apply to the procedures in that Section. The reference numbers used in illustration captions pinpoint the pertinent Section and the Step within that Section. That is, illustration 3.2 means the illustration refers to Section 3 and Step (or paragraph) 2 within that Section.

Procedures, once described in the text, are not normally repeated. When it's necessary to refer to another Chapter, the reference will be given as Chapter and Section number. Cross references given without use of the word "Chapter" apply to Sections and/or paragraphs in the same Chapter. For example, "see Section 8" means in the same Chapter.

References to the left or right side of the vehicle assume you are sitting in the driver's seat, facing forward.

Even though we have prepared this manual with extreme care, neither the publisher nor the author can accept responsibility for any errors in, or omissions from, the information given.

➡NOTE

A *Note* provides information necessary to properly complete a procedure or information which will make the procedure easier to understand.

※※ CAUTION

A *Caution* provides a special procedure or special steps which must be taken while completing the procedure where the Caution is found. Not heeding a Caution can result in damage to the assembly being worked on.

※※ WARNING

A *Warning* provides a special procedure or special steps which must be taken while completing the procedure where the Warning is found. Not heeding a Warning can result in personal injury.

Introduction

The models covered by this manual are available in a variety of trim options.

Engine options include the inline four, 3.0L V6 and 4.0L V6.

Chassis layout is conventional, with the engine mounted at the front and the power being transmitted through either a manual or automatic transmission to a driveshaft and solid rear axle on 2WD models. On 4WD models a transfer case transmits power to the front axle by way of a driveshaft. Transmissions used are a five-speed overdrive manual and four- or five-speed overdrive automatic.

The front suspension consists of upper and lower control arms, shock absorbers, coil springs (2WD models) or torsion bars (4WD models) and a stabilizer bar. All models use semi-elliptical leaf springs at the rear.

All models are equipped with power assisted front disc and rear drum brakes. Rear anti-lock brakes are used on some models; others are equipped with four-wheel anti-lock brakes. 2010 and later models have four-wheel disc brakes.

VEHICLE IDENTIFICATION NUMBERS

Modifications are a continuing and unpublicized process in vehicle manufacturing. Since spare parts manuals and lists are compiled on a numerical basis, the individual vehicle numbers are necessary to correctly identify the component required.

VEHICLE IDENTIFICATION NUMBER (VIN)

This very important identification number is located on a plate attached to the left side dashboard just inside the windshield (see illustration). The VIN also appears on the Vehicle Certificate of Title and Registration. It contains information such as where and when the vehicle was manufactured, engine type, the model year and the body style.

VEHICLE CERTIFICATION LABEL

The Vehicle Certification label (VC label, also referred to as the Truck Safety Compliance Certification label) is attached to the end of the left (driver's side) door (see illustration). The upper half of the label contains the name of the manufacturer, the month and year of production, the Gross Vehicle Weight Rating (GVWR), the Gross Axle Weight Rating (GAWR) and the certification statement.

The Vehicle Identification Number (VIN) is visible through the driver's side of the windshield

The VC label also contains the VIN number, which is used for warranty identification of the vehicle, and provides such information as manufacturer, type of restraint system, body type, engine, transmission, model year and vehicle serial number.

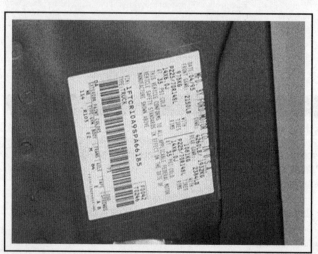

The Vehicle Certification label, also known as the Truck Safety Compliance Certification label is located on the left front door pillar

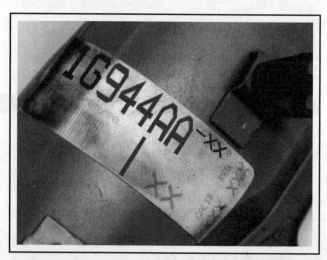

An engine identification label can usually be found on the valve cover

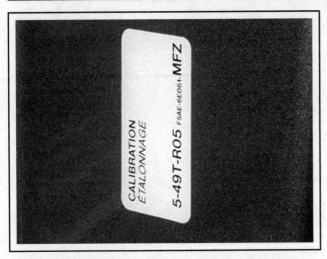

The calibration label is located on the driver's door pillar

The manual transmission identification label is mounted on the side of the transmission case

ENGINE NUMBERS

Labels containing the engine code, calibration and serial numbers, as well as plant name, can be found on the valve cover, as well as stamped on the engine itself (see illustration).

VIN ENGINE AND MODEL YEAR CODES

Two particularly important pieces of information found in the VIN are the engine code and model year code. Counting from the left, the engine code letter designation is the eighth digit and the model year code letter designation is the 10th digit.

On the models covered by this manual the engine codes are:

D .... 2.3L DOHC four-cylinder
C .... 2.5L SOHC four-cylinder
U .... 3.0L V6 (pushrod)
V .... 3.0L V6 (pushrod) flex fuel
X .... 4.0L V6 (pushrod)
E .... 4.0L V6 SOHC

On the models covered by this manual the model year codes are:

Y 2000
1 2001
2 2002
3 2003
4 2004
5 2005
6 2006
7 2007
8 2008
9 2009
A 2010
B 2011

CALIBRATION LABEL

This label (see illustration), found on the driver's door pillar, contains information that will be required when purchasing fuel or emissions components

MANUAL TRANSMISSION NUMBERS

The manual transmission identification number and serial numbers can be found on a tag on the left or right side of the transmission main case (see illustration).

AUTOMATIC TRANSMISSION NUMBERS

Tags with the automatic transmission serial number, build date and other information are attached with a bolt, usually at the extension housing.

VEHICLE EMISSIONS CONTROL INFORMATION (VECI) LABEL

This label is found under the hood (see Chapter 6).

Buying parts

Replacement parts are available from many sources, which generally fall into one of two categories - authorized dealer parts departments and independent retail auto parts stores. Our advice concerning these parts is as follows:

Retail auto parts stores: Good auto parts stores will stock frequently needed components which wear out relatively fast, such as clutch components, exhaust systems, brake parts, tune-up parts, etc. These stores often supply new or reconditioned parts on an exchange basis, which can save a considerable amount of money. Discount auto parts stores are often very good places to buy materials and parts needed for general vehicle maintenance such as oil, grease, filters, spark plugs, belts, touch-up paint, bulbs, etc. They also usually sell

tools and general accessories, have convenient hours, charge lower prices and can often be found not far from home.

Authorized dealer parts department: This is the best source for parts which are unique to the vehicle and not generally available elsewhere (such as major engine parts, transmission parts, trim pieces, etc.).

Warranty information: If the vehicle is still covered under warranty, be sure that any replacement parts purchased - regardless of the source - do not invalidate the warranty!

To be sure of obtaining the correct parts, have engine and chassis numbers available and, if possible, take the old parts along for positive identification.

Maintenance techniques, tools and working facilities

MAINTENANCE TECHNIQUES

There are a number of techniques involved in maintenance and repair that will be referred to throughout this manual. Application of these techniques will enable the home mechanic to be more efficient, better organized and capable of performing the various tasks properly, which will ensure that the repair job is thorough and complete.

Fasteners

Fasteners are nuts, bolts, studs and screws used to hold two or more parts together. There are a few things to keep in mind when working with fasteners. Almost all of them use a locking device of some type, either a lockwasher, locknut, locking tab or thread adhesive. All threaded fasteners should be clean and straight, with undamaged threads and undamaged corners on the hex head where the wrench fits. Develop the habit of replacing all damaged nuts and bolts with new ones. Special locknuts with nylon or fiber inserts can only be used once. If they are removed, they lose their locking ability and must be replaced with new ones.

Rusted nuts and bolts should be treated with a penetrating fluid to ease removal and prevent breakage. Some mechanics use turpentine in a spout-type oil can, which works quite well. After applying the rust penetrant, let it work for a few minutes before trying to loosen the nut or bolt. Badly rusted fasteners may have to be chiseled or sawed off or removed with a special nut breaker, available at tool stores.

If a bolt or stud breaks off in an assembly, it can be drilled and removed with a special tool commonly available for this purpose. Most automotive machine shops can perform this task, as well as other repair procedures, such as the repair of threaded holes that have been stripped out.

Flat washers and lockwashers, when removed from an assembly, should always be replaced exactly as removed. Replace any damaged washers with new ones. Never use a lockwasher on any soft metal surface (such as aluminum), thin sheet metal or plastic.

Fastener sizes

For a number of reasons, automobile manufacturers are making wider and wider use of metric fasteners. Therefore, it is important to be able to tell the difference between standard (sometimes called U.S.

Grade 1 or 2   Grade 5   Grade 8

Bolt strength marking (standard/SAE/USS; bottom - metric)

Grade	Identification	Grade	Identification
Hex Nut Grade 5	3 Dots	Hex Nut Property Class 9	Arabic 9
Hex Nut Grade 8	6 Dots	Hex Nut Property Class 10	Arabic 10

Standard hex nut strength markings

Metric hex nut strength markings

Class 10.9   Class 9.8   Class 8.8

Metric stud strength markings

00-1 HAYNES

or SAE) and metric hardware, since they cannot be interchanged.

All bolts, whether standard or metric, are sized according to diameter, thread pitch and length. For example, a standard 1/2 - 13 x 1 bolt is 1/2 inch in diameter, has 13 threads per inch and is 1 inch long. An M12 - 1.75 x 25 metric bolt is 12 mm in diameter, has a thread pitch of 1.75 mm (the distance between threads) and is 25 mm long. The two bolts are nearly identical, and easily confused, but they are not interchangeable.

In addition to the differences in diameter, thread pitch and length, metric and standard bolts can also be distinguished by examining the bolt heads. To begin with, the distance across the flats on a standard bolt head is measured in inches, while the same dimension on a metric bolt is sized in millimeters (the same is true for nuts). As a result, a standard wrench should not be used on a metric bolt and a metric wrench should not be used on a standard bolt. Also, most standard bolts have

slashes radiating out from the center of the head to denote the grade or strength of the bolt, which is an indication of the amount of torque that can be applied to it. The greater the number of slashes, the greater the strength of the bolt. Grades 0 through 5 are commonly used on automobiles. Metric bolts have a property class (grade) number, rather than a slash, molded into their heads to indicate bolt strength. In this case, the higher the number, the stronger the bolt. Property class numbers 8.8, 9.8 and 10.9 are commonly used on automobiles.

Strength markings can also be used to distinguish standard hex nuts from metric hex nuts. Many standard nuts have dots stamped into one side, while metric nuts are marked with a number. The greater the number of dots, or the higher the number, the greater the strength of the nut.

Metric studs are also marked on their ends according to property class (grade). Larger studs are numbered (the same as metric bolts), while smaller studs carry a geometric code to denote grade.

Metric thread sizes

	Ft-lbs	Nm
M-6	6 to 9	9 to 12
M-8	14 to 21	19 to 28
M-10	28 to 40	38 to 54
M-12	50 to 71	68 to 96
M-14	80 to 140	109 to 154

Pipe thread sizes

	Ft-lbs	Nm
1/8	5 to 8	7 to 10
1/4	12 to 18	17 to 24
3/8	22 to 33	30 to 44
1/2	25 to 35	34 to 47

U.S. thread sizes

	Ft-lbs	Nm
1/4 - 20	6 to 9	9 to 12
5/16 - 18	12 to 18	17 to 24
5/16 - 24	14 to 20	19 to 27
3/8 - 16	22 to 32	30 to 43
3/8 - 24	27 to 38	37 to 51
7/16 - 14	40 to 55	55 to 74
7/16 - 20	40 to 60	55 to 81
1/2 - 13	55 to 80	75 to 108

Standard (SAE and USS) bolt dimensions/grade marks

G   *Grade marks (bolt strength)*
L   *Length (in inches)*
T   *Thread pitch (number of threads per inch)*
D   *Nominal diameter (in inches)*

Metric bolt dimensions/grade marks

P   *Property class (bolt strength)*
L   *Length (in millimeters)*
T   *Thread pitch (distance between threads in millimeters)*
D   *Diameter*

It should be noted that many fasteners, especially Grades 0 through 2, have no distinguishing marks on them. When such is the case, the only way to determine whether it is standard or metric is to measure the thread pitch or compare it to a known fastener of the same size.

Standard fasteners are often referred to as SAE, as opposed to metric. However, it should be noted that SAE technically refers to a non-metric fine thread fastener only. Coarse thread non-metric fasteners are referred to as USS sizes.

Since fasteners of the same size (both standard and metric) may have different strength ratings, be sure to reinstall any bolts, studs or nuts removed from your vehicle in their original locations. Also, when replacing a fastener with a new one, make sure that the new one has a strength rating equal to or greater than the original.

Tightening sequences and procedures

Most threaded fasteners should be tightened to a specific torque value (torque is the twisting force applied to a threaded component such as a nut or bolt). Overtightening the fastener can weaken it and cause it to break, while undertightening can cause it to eventually come loose. Bolts, screws and studs, depending on the material they are made of and their thread diameters, have specific torque values, many of which are noted in the Specifications at the end of each Chapter. Be sure to follow the torque recommendations closely. For fasteners not assigned a specific torque, a general torque value chart is presented here as a guide. These torque values are for dry (unlubricated) fasteners threaded into steel or cast iron (not aluminum). As was previously mentioned, the size and grade of a fastener determine the amount of torque that can

Micrometer set

Dial indicator set

safely be applied to it. The figures listed here are approximate for Grade 2 and Grade 3 fasteners. Higher grades can tolerate higher torque values.

Fasteners laid out in a pattern, such as cylinder head bolts, oil pan bolts, differential cover bolts, etc., must be loosened or tightened in sequence to avoid warping the component. This sequence will normally be shown in the appropriate Chapter. If a specific pattern is not given, the following procedures can be used to prevent warping.

Initially, the bolts or nuts should be assembled finger-tight only. Next, they should be tightened one full turn each, in a criss-cross or diagonal pattern. After each one has been tightened one full turn, return to the first one and tighten them all one-half turn, following the same pattern. Finally, tighten each of them one-quarter turn at a time until each fastener has been tightened to the proper torque. To loosen and remove the fasteners, the procedure would be reversed.

Component disassembly

Component disassembly should be done with care and purpose to help ensure that the parts go back together properly. Always keep track of the sequence in which parts are removed. Make note of special characteristics or marks on parts that can be installed more than one way, such as a grooved thrust washer on a shaft. It is a good idea to lay the disassembled parts out on a clean surface in the order that they were removed. It may also be helpful to make sketches or take instant photos of components before removal.

When removing fasteners from a component, keep track of their locations. Sometimes threading a bolt back in a part, or putting the washers and nut back on a stud, can prevent mix-ups later. If nuts and bolts cannot be returned to their original locations, they should be kept in a compartmented box or a series of small boxes. A cupcake or muffin tin is ideal for this purpose, since each cavity can hold the bolts and nuts from a particular area (i.e. oil pan bolts, valve cover bolts, engine mount bolts, etc.). A pan of this type is especially helpful when working on assemblies with very small parts, such as the carburetor, alternator, valve train or interior dash and trim pieces. The cavities can be marked with paint or tape to identify the contents.

Whenever wiring looms, harnesses or connectors are separated, it is a good idea to identify the two halves with numbered pieces of masking tape so they can be easily reconnected.

Gasket sealing surfaces

Throughout any vehicle, gaskets are used to seal the mating surfaces between two parts and keep lubricants, fluids, vacuum or pressure contained in an assembly.

Many times these gaskets are coated with a liquid or paste-type gasket sealing compound before assembly. Age, heat and pressure can sometimes cause the two parts to stick together so tightly that they are very difficult to separate. Often, the assembly can be loosened by striking it with a soft-face hammer near the mating surfaces. A regular hammer can be used if a block of wood is placed between the hammer and the part. Do not hammer on cast parts or parts that could be easily damaged. With any particularly stubborn part, always recheck to make sure that every fastener has been removed.

Avoid using a screwdriver or bar to pry apart an assembly, as they can easily mar the gasket sealing surfaces of the parts, which must remain smooth. If prying is absolutely necessary, use an old broom handle, but keep in mind that extra clean up will be necessary if the wood splinters.

After the parts are separated, the old gasket must be carefully scraped off and the gasket surfaces cleaned. Stubborn gasket material can be soaked with rust penetrant or treated with a special chemical to soften it so it can be easily scraped off.

�֎ CAUTION:

Never use gasket removal solutions or caustic chemicals on plastic or other composite components.

A scraper can be fashioned from a piece of copper tubing by flattening and sharpening one end. Copper is recommended because it is usually softer than the surfaces to be scraped, which reduces the chance of gouging the part. Some gaskets can be removed with a wire brush, but regardless of the method used, the mating surfaces must be left clean and smooth. If for some reason the gasket surface is gouged, then a gasket sealer thick enough to fill scratches will have to be used during reassembly of the components. For most applications, a non-drying (or semi-drying) gasket sealer should be used.

Dial caliper

Hand-operated vacuum pump

Timing light

Compression gauge with spark plug hole adapter

Hose removal tips

> ※※ **WARNING:**
>
> **If the vehicle is equipped with air conditioning, do not disconnect any of the A/C hoses without first having the system depressurized by a dealer service department or a service station.**

Hose removal precautions closely parallel gasket removal precautions. Avoid scratching or gouging the surface that the hose mates against or the connection may leak. This is especially true for radiator hoses. Because of various chemical reactions, the rubber in hoses can bond itself to the metal spigot that the hose fits over. To remove a hose, first loosen the hose clamps that secure it to the spigot. Then, with slip-joint pliers, grab the hose at the clamp and rotate it around the spigot. Work it back and forth until it is completely free, then pull it off. Silicone or other lubricants will ease removal if they can be applied between the hose and the outside of the spigot. Apply the same lubricant to the inside of the hose and the outside of the spigot to simplify installation.

As a last resort (and if the hose is to be replaced with a new one anyway), the rubber can be slit with a knife and the hose peeled from the spigot. If this must be done, be careful that the metal connection is not damaged.

If a hose clamp is broken or damaged, do not reuse it. Wire-type clamps usually weaken with age, so it is a good idea to replace them with screw-type clamps whenever a hose is removed.

TOOLS

A selection of good tools is a basic requirement for anyone who plans to maintain and repair his or her own vehicle. For the owner who has few tools, the initial investment might seem high, but when compared to the spiraling costs of professional auto maintenance and repair, it is a wise one.

To help the owner decide which tools are needed to perform the tasks detailed in this manual, the following tool lists are offered: *Maintenance and minor repair, Repair/overhaul* and *Special.*

The newcomer to practical mechanics should start off with the *maintenance and minor repair* tool kit, which is adequate for the simpler jobs performed on a vehicle. Then, as confidence and experience grow, the owner can tackle more difficult tasks, buying additional tools as they are needed. Eventually the basic kit will be expanded into the *repair and overhaul* tool set. Over a period of time, the experienced do-it-yourselfer will assemble a tool set complete enough for most repair and overhaul procedures and will add tools from the special category when it is felt that the expense is justified by the frequency of use.

Damper/steering wheel puller

General purpose puller

Hydraulic lifter removal tool

Valve spring compressor

Valve spring compressor

Ridge reamer

Maintenance and minor repair tool kit

The tools in this list should be considered the minimum required for performance of routine maintenance, servicing and minor repair work. We recommend the purchase of combination wrenches (box-end and open-end combined in one wrench). While more expensive than open end wrenches, they offer the advantages of both types of wrench.

> *Combination wrench set (1/4-inch to 1 inch or 6 mm to 19 mm)*
> *Adjustable wrench, 8 inch*
> *Spark plug wrench with rubber insert*
> *Spark plug gap adjusting tool*
> *Feeler gauge set*
> *Brake bleeder wrench*
> *Standard screwdriver (5/16-inch x 6 inch)*
> *Phillips screwdriver (No. 2 x 6 inch)*
> *Combination pliers - 6 inch*
> *Hacksaw and assortment of blades*
> *Tire pressure gauge*
> *Grease gun*
> *Oil can*
> *Fine emery cloth*
> *Wire brush*
> *Battery post and cable cleaning tool*
> *Oil filter wrench*
> *Funnel (medium size)*
> *Safety goggles*
> *Jackstands (2)*
> *Drain pan*

➡**Note: If basic tune-ups are going to be part of routine maintenance, it will be necessary to purchase a good quality stroboscopic timing light and combination tachometer/dwell meter. Although they are included in the list of special tools, it is mentioned here because they are absolutely necessary for tuning most vehicles properly.**

Repair and overhaul tool set

These tools are essential for anyone who plans to perform major repairs and are in addition to those in the maintenance and minor repair tool kit. Included is a comprehensive set of sockets which, though expensive, are invaluable because of their versatility, especially when various extensions and drives are available. We recommend the 1/2-inch drive over the 3/8-inch drive. Although the larger drive is bulky and more expensive, it has the capacity of accepting a very wide range of large sockets. Ideally, however, the mechanic should have a 3/8-inch drive set and a 1/2-inch drive set.

> *Socket set(s)*
> *Reversible ratchet*
> *Extension - 10 inch*
> *Universal joint*
> *Torque wrench (same size drive as sockets)*
> *Ball peen hammer - 8 ounce*
> *Soft-face hammer (plastic/rubber)*
> *Standard screwdriver (1/4-inch x 6 inch)*
> *Standard screwdriver (stubby - 5/16-inch)*
> *Phillips screwdriver (No. 3 x 8 inch)*
> *Phillips screwdriver (stubby - No. 2)*
> *Pliers - vise grip*

Piston ring groove cleaning tool

Ring removal/installation tool

Ring compressor

Cylinder hone

Brake hold-down spring tool

Pliers - lineman's
Pliers - needle nose
Pliers - snap-ring (internal and external)
Cold chisel - 1/2-inch
Scribe
Scraper (made from flattened copper tubing)
Centerpunch
Pin punches (1/16, 1/8, 3/16-inch)
Steel rule/straightedge - 12 inch
Allen wrench set (1/8 to 3/8-inch or 4 mm to 10 mm)
A selection of files
Wire brush (large)
Jackstands (second set)
Jack (scissor or hydraulic type)

➡️**Note: Another tool which is often useful is an electric drill with a chuck capacity of 3/8-inch and a set of good quality drill bits.**

Special tools

The tools in this list include those which are not used regularly, are expensive to buy, or which need to be used in accordance with their manufacturer's instructions. Unless these tools will be used frequently, it is not very economical to purchase many of them. A consideration would be to split the cost and use between yourself and a friend or friends. In addition, most of these tools can be obtained from a tool rental shop on a temporary basis.

This list primarily contains only those tools and instruments widely available to the public, and not those special tools produced by the vehicle manufacturer for distribution to dealer service depart-

ments. Occasionally, references to the manufacturer's special tools are included in the text of this manual. Generally, an alternative method of doing the job without the special tool is offered. However, sometimes there is no alternative to their use. Where this is the case, and the tool cannot be purchased or borrowed, the work should be turned over to the dealer service department or an automotive repair shop.

Valve spring compressor
Piston ring groove cleaning tool
Piston ring compressor
Piston ring installation tool
Cylinder compression gauge
Cylinder ridge reamer
Cylinder surfacing hone
Cylinder bore gauge
Micrometers and/or dial calipers
Hydraulic lifter removal tool
Balljoint separator
Universal-type puller
Impact screwdriver
Dial indicator set
Stroboscopic timing light (inductive pick-up)
Hand operated vacuum/pressure pump
Tachometer/dwell meter
Universal electrical multimeter
Cable hoist
Brake spring removal and installation tools
Floor jack

Torque angle gauge

Clutch plate alignment tool

Tap and die set

Buying tools

For the do-it-yourselfer who is just starting to get involved in vehicle maintenance and repair, there are a number of options available when purchasing tools. If maintenance and minor repair is the extent of the work to be done, the purchase of individual tools is satisfactory. If, on the other hand, extensive work is planned, it would be a good idea to purchase a modest tool set from one of the large retail chain stores. A set can usually be bought at a substantial savings over the individual tool prices, and they often come with a tool box. As additional tools are needed, add-on sets, individual tools and a larger tool box can be purchased to expand the tool selection. Building a tool set gradually allows the cost of the tools to be spread over a longer period of time and gives the mechanic the freedom to choose only those tools that will actually be used.

Tool stores will often be the only source of some of the special tools that are needed, but regardless of where tools are bought, try to avoid cheap ones, especially when buying screwdrivers and sockets, because they won't last very long. The expense involved in replacing cheap tools will eventually be greater than the initial cost of quality tools.

Care and maintenance of tools

Good tools are expensive, so it makes sense to treat them with respect. Keep them clean and in usable condition and store them properly when not in use. Always wipe off any dirt, grease or metal chips before putting them away. Never leave tools lying around in the work area. Upon completion of a job, always check closely under the hood for tools that may have been left there so they won't get lost during a test drive.

Some tools, such as screwdrivers, pliers, wrenches and sockets, can be hung on a panel mounted on the garage or workshop wall, while others should be kept in a tool box or tray. Measuring instruments, gauges, meters, etc. must be carefully stored where they cannot be damaged by weather or impact from other tools.

When tools are used with care and stored properly, they will last a very long time. Even with the best of care, though, tools will wear out if used frequently. When a tool is damaged or worn out, replace it. Subsequent jobs will be safer and more enjoyable if you do.

HOW TO REPAIR DAMAGED THREADS

Sometimes, the internal threads of a nut or bolt hole can become stripped, usually from overtightening. Stripping threads is an all-too-common occurrence, especially when working with aluminum parts, because aluminum is so soft that it easily strips out.

Usually, external or internal threads are only partially stripped. After they've been cleaned up with a tap or die, they'll still work. Sometimes, however, threads are badly damaged. When this happens, you've got three choices:

1) *Drill and tap the hole to the next suitable oversize and install a larger diameter bolt, screw or stud.*
2) *Drill and tap the hole to accept a threaded plug, then drill and tap the plug to the original screw size. You can also buy a plug already threaded to the original size. Then you simply drill a hole to the specified size, then run the threaded plug into the hole with a bolt and jam nut. Once the plug is fully seated, remove the jam nut and bolt.*
3) *The third method uses a patented thread repair kit like Heli-Coil or Slimsert. These easy-to-use kits are designed to repair damaged threads in straight-through holes and blind holes. Both are available as kits which can handle a variety of sizes and thread*

patterns. Drill the hole, then tap it with the special included tap. Install the Heli-Coil and the hole is back to its original diameter and thread pitch.

Regardless of which method you use, be sure to proceed calmly and carefully. A little impatience or carelessness during one of these relatively simple procedures can ruin your whole day's work and cost you a bundle if you wreck an expensive part.

WORKING FACILITIES

Not to be overlooked when discussing tools is the workshop. If anything more than routine maintenance is to be carried out, some sort of suitable work area is essential.

It is understood, and appreciated, that many home mechanics do not have a good workshop or garage available, and end up removing an engine or doing major repairs outside. It is recommended, however, that the overhaul or repair be completed under the cover of a roof.

A clean, flat workbench or table of comfortable working height is an absolute necessity. The workbench should be equipped with a vise that has a jaw opening of at least four inches.

As mentioned previously, some clean, dry storage space is also required for tools, as well as the lubricants, fluids, cleaning solvents, etc. which soon become necessary.

Sometimes waste oil and fluids, drained from the engine or cooling system during normal maintenance or repairs, present a disposal problem. To avoid pouring them on the ground or into a sewage system, pour the used fluids into large containers, seal them with caps and take them to an authorized disposal site or recycling center. Plastic jugs, such as old antifreeze containers, are ideal for this purpose.

Always keep a supply of old newspapers and clean rags available. Old towels are excellent for mopping up spills. Many mechanics use rolls of paper towels for most work because they are readily available and disposable. To help keep the area under the vehicle clean, a large cardboard box can be cut open and flattened to protect the garage or shop floor.

Whenever working over a painted surface, such as when leaning over a fender to service something under the hood, always cover it with an old blanket or bedspread to protect the finish. Vinyl covered pads, made especially for this purpose, are available at auto parts stores.

Booster battery (jump) starting

Observe these precautions when using a booster battery to start a vehicle:

a) *Before connecting the booster battery, make sure the ignition switch is in the Off position.*

b) *Turn off the lights, heater and other electrical loads.*

c) *Your eyes should be shielded. Safety goggles are a good idea.*

d) *Make sure the booster battery is the same voltage as the dead one in the vehicle.*

e) *The two vehicles MUST NOT TOUCH each other!*

f) *Make sure the transaxle is in Neutral (manual) or Park (automatic).*

g) *If the booster battery is not a maintenance-free type, remove the vent caps and lay a cloth over the vent holes.*

Connect the red jumper cable to the positive (+) terminals of each battery (see illustration).

Connect one end of the black jumper cable to the negative (-) terminal of the booster battery. The other end of this cable should be connected to a good ground on the vehicle to be started, such as a bolt or bracket on the body.

Start the engine using the booster battery, then, with the engine running at idle speed, disconnect the jumper cables in the reverse order of connection.

Make the booster battery cable connections in the numerical order shown (note that the negative cable of the booster battery is NOT attached to the negative terminal of the dead battery)

Jacking and towing

JACKING

> ❋❋ **WARNING:**
>
> **On vehicles equipped with a limited slip differential, do not run the engine with the vehicle on a jack.**

When lifting the vehicle with either the supplied jack or a floor jack, block the wheel that is diagonally opposite the one being lifted to prevent the vehicle from moving.

> ❋❋ **WARNING:**
>
> **If equipped with an under-chassis mounted spare tire, remove the tire or tire carrier from the rack before the vehicle is raised in order to avoid sudden weight release from the chassis.**

When using the vehicle jack, the manufacturer recommends positioning the jack under the outer end of the rear axle housing or under the projection on the lower control arm (see illustrations).

If you're using a floor jack to raise the vehicle, place the jack under the outer end of the control arm (front) or under the outer end of the axle housing (rear).

> ❋❋ **CAUTION:**
>
> **Don't raise the rear of the vehicle with a floor jack positioned under the differential. The cover could become distorted or cracked, resulting in lubricant leakage.**

When raising the vehicle for service, always place jackstands under the frame rails. NEVER work under the vehicle when it is supported only by a jack!

TOWING

When the vehicle is towed with the rear wheels raised, the steering wheel must be clamped in the straight ahead position with a special device designed for use during towing.

> ❋❋ **WARNING:**
>
> **Don't use the steering lock to keep the front wheels pointed straight ahead. It's not strong enough for this purpose.**

The vehicle can be towed with all four wheels on the ground, provided the following conditions are met (depending on drivetrain):

2WD models with an automatic transmission

    a) *Parking brake released*
    b) *Transmission in Neutral (N)*
    c) *Maximum speed of 35 mph**
    d) *Maximum distance of 50 miles**

*If this speed or distance will be exceeded, disconnect the driveshaft at the differential and support it securely under the vehicle.

2WD models with a manual transmission

    a) *Parking brake released*
    b) *Transmission in Neutral (N)*
    c) *Maximum speed of 55 mph*

4WD models with a manual shift transfer case

    a) *Parking brake released*
    b) *Transmission in Neutral (N)*
    c) *Transfer case in Neutral (N)*
    d) *Manual locking hubs in the FREE position*
    e) *Maximum speed of 55 mph*

4WD with an electric shift transfer case

    a) *Parking brake released*
    b) *Transmission in Neutral (N)*
    c) *Transfer case placed in the 2H position*
    d) *Hubs unlocked*
    e) *If the vehicle is equipped with an automatic transmission, limit speed to 35 mph and distance to 50 miles**

*If this speed or distance will be exceeded, disconnect the driveshaft at the differential and support it securely under the vehicle.

Equipment specifically designed for towing should be used. It should be attached to the frame members of the vehicle, not the bumpers or brackets.

Safety is a major consideration when towing and all applicable state and local laws must be obeyed. A safety chain system must be used at all times. Remember that power steering and power brakes will not work with the engine off.

Front jacking location

Rear jacking location

Automotive chemicals and lubricants

A number of automotive chemicals and lubricants are available for use during vehicle maintenance and repair. They include a wide variety of products ranging from cleaning solvents and degreasers to lubricants and protective sprays for rubber, plastic and vinyl.

CLEANERS

Carburetor cleaner and choke cleaner is a strong solvent for gum, varnish and carbon. Most carburetor cleaners leave a dry-type lubricant film which will not harden or gum up. Because of this film it is not recommended for use on electrical components.

Brake system cleaner is used to remove brake dust, grease and brake fluid from the brake system, where clean surfaces are absolutely necessary. It leaves no residue and often eliminates brake squeal caused by contaminants.

Electrical cleaner removes oxidation, corrosion and carbon deposits from electrical contacts, restoring full current flow. It can also be used to clean spark plugs, carburetor jets, voltage regulators and other parts where an oil-free surface is desired.

Demoisturants remove water and moisture from electrical components such as alternators, voltage regulators, electrical connectors and fuse blocks. They are non-conductive and non-corrosive.

Degreasers are heavy-duty solvents used to remove grease from the outside of the engine and from chassis components. They can be sprayed or brushed on and, depending on the type, are rinsed off either with water or solvent.

LUBRICANTS

Motor oil is the lubricant formulated for use in engines. It normally contains a wide variety of additives to prevent corrosion and reduce foaming and wear. Motor oil comes in various weights (viscosity ratings) from 0 to 50. The recommended weight of the oil depends on the season, temperature and the demands on the engine. Light oil is used in cold climates and under light load conditions. Heavy oil is used in hot climates and where high loads are encountered. Multi-viscosity oils are designed to have characteristics of both light and heavy oils and are available in a number of weights from 0W-20 to 20W-50.

Gear oil is designed to be used in differentials, manual transmissions and other areas where high-temperature lubrication is required.

Chassis and wheel bearing grease is a heavy grease used where increased loads and friction are encountered, such as for wheel bearings, ball-joints, tie-rod ends and universal joints.

High-temperature wheel bearing grease is designed to withstand the extreme temperatures encountered by wheel bearings in disc brake equipped vehicles. It usually contains molybdenum disulfide (moly), which is a dry-type lubricant.

White grease is a heavy grease for metal-to-metal applications where water is a problem. White grease stays soft under both low and high temperatures (usually from -100 to +190-degrees F), and will not wash off or dilute in the presence of water.

Assembly lube is a special extreme pressure lubricant, usually containing moly, used to lubricate high-load parts (such as main and rod bearings and cam lobes) for initial start-up of a new engine. The assembly lube lubricates the parts without being squeezed out or washed away until the engine oiling system begins to function.

Silicone lubricants are used to protect rubber, plastic, vinyl and nylon parts.

Graphite lubricants are used where oils cannot be used due to contamination problems, such as in locks. The dry graphite will lubricate metal parts while remaining uncontaminated by dirt, water, oil or acids. It is electrically conductive and will not foul electrical contacts in locks such as the ignition switch.

Moly penetrants loosen and lubricate frozen, rusted and corroded fasteners and prevent future rusting or freezing.

Heat-sink grease is a special electrically non-conductive grease that is used for mounting electronic ignition modules where it is essential that heat is transferred away from the module.

SEALANTS

RTV sealant is one of the most widely used gasket compounds. Made from silicone, RTV is air curing, it seals, bonds, waterproofs, fills surface irregularities, remains flexible, doesn't shrink, is relatively easy to remove, and is used as a supplementary sealer with almost all low and medium temperature gaskets.

Anaerobic sealant is much like RTV in that it can be used either to seal gaskets or to form gaskets by itself. It remains flexible, is solvent resistant and fills surface imperfections. The difference between an anaerobic sealant and an RTV-type sealant is in the curing. RTV cures when exposed to air, while an anaerobic sealant cures only in the absence of air. This means that an anaerobic sealant cures only after the assembly of parts, sealing them together.

Thread and pipe sealant is used for sealing hydraulic and pneumatic fittings and vacuum lines. It is usually made from a Teflon compound, and comes in a spray, a paint-on liquid and as a wrap-around tape.

CHEMICALS

Anti-seize compound prevents seizing, galling, cold welding, rust and corrosion in fasteners. High-temperature anti-seize, usually made with copper and graphite lubricants, is used for exhaust system and exhaust manifold bolts.

Anaerobic locking compounds are used to keep fasteners from vibrating or working loose and cure only after installation, in the absence of air. Medium strength locking compound is used for small nuts, bolts and screws that may be removed later. High-strength locking compound is for large nuts, bolts and studs which aren't removed on a regular basis.

Oil additives range from viscosity index improvers to chemical treatments that claim to reduce internal engine friction. It should be noted that most oil manufacturers caution against using additives with their oils.

Gas additives perform several functions, depending on their chemical makeup. They usually contain solvents that help dissolve gum and varnish that build up on carburetor, fuel injection and intake parts. They also serve to break down carbon deposits that form on the inside surfaces of the combustion chambers. Some additives contain upper cylinder lubricants for valves and piston rings, and others contain chemicals to remove condensation from the gas tank.

MISCELLANEOUS

Brake fluid is specially formulated hydraulic fluid that can withstand the heat and pressure encountered in brake systems. Care must be taken so this fluid does not come in contact with painted surfaces or plastics. An opened container should always be resealed to prevent contamination by water or dirt.

Weatherstrip adhesive is used to bond weatherstripping around doors, windows and trunk lids. It is sometimes used to attach trim pieces.

Undercoating is a petroleum-based, tar-like substance that is designed to protect metal surfaces on the underside of the vehicle from corrosion. It also acts as a sound-deadening agent by insulating the bottom of the vehicle.

Waxes and polishes are used to help protect painted and plated surfaces from the weather. Different types of paint may require the use of different types of wax and polish. Some polishes utilize a chemical or abrasive cleaner to help remove the top layer of oxidized (dull) paint on older vehicles. In recent years many non-wax polishes that contain a wide variety of chemicals such as polymers and silicones have been introduced. These non-wax polishes are usually easier to apply and last longer than conventional waxes and polishes.

CONVERSION FACTORS

LENGTH (distance)
Inches (in)	X 25.4	= Millimeters (mm)	X 0.0394	= Inches (in)	
Feet (ft)	X 0.305	= Meters (m)	X 3.281	= Feet (ft)	
Miles	X 1.609	= Kilometers (km)	X 0.621	= Miles	

VOLUME (capacity)
Cubic inches (cu in; in³)	X 16.387	= Cubic centimeters (cc; cm³)	X 0.061	= Cubic inches (cu in; in³)
Imperial pints (Imp pt)	X 0.568	= Liters (l)	X 1.76	= Imperial pints (Imp pt)
Imperial quarts (Imp qt)	X 1.137	= Liters (l)	X 0.88	= Imperial quarts (Imp qt)
Imperial quarts (Imp qt)	X 1.201	= US quarts (US qt)	X 0.833	= Imperial quarts (Imp qt)
US quarts (US qt)	X 0.946	= Liters (l)	X 1.057	= US quarts (US qt)
Imperial gallons (Imp gal)	X 4.546	= Liters (l)	X 0.22	= Imperial gallons (Imp gal)
Imperial gallons (Imp gal)	X 1.201	= US gallons (US gal)	X 0.833	= Imperial gallons (Imp gal)
US gallons (US gal)	X 3.785	= Liters (l)	X 0.264	= US gallons (US gal)

MASS (weight)
Ounces (oz)	X 28.35	= Grams (g)	X 0.035	= Ounces (oz)
Pounds (lb)	X 0.454	= Kilograms (kg)	X 2.205	= Pounds (lb)

FORCE
Ounces-force (ozf; oz)	X 0.278	= Newtons (N)	X 3.6	= Ounces-force (ozf; oz)
Pounds-force (lbf; lb)	X 4.448	= Newtons (N)	X 0.225	= Pounds-force (lbf; lb)
Newtons (N)	X 0.1	= Kilograms-force (kgf; kg)	X 9.81	= Newtons (N)

PRESSURE
Pounds-force per square inch (psi; lbf/in²; lb/in²)	X 0.070	= Kilograms-force per square centimeter (kgf/cm²; kg/cm²)	X 14.223	= Pounds-force per square inch (psi; lbf/in²; lb/in²)
Pounds-force per square inch (psi; lbf/in²; lb/in²)	X 0.068	= Atmospheres (atm)	X 14.696	= Pounds-force per square inch (psi; lbf/in²; lb/in²)
Pounds-force per square inch (psi; lbf/in²; lb/in²)	X 0.069	= Bars	X 14.5	= Pounds-force per square inch (psi; lbf/in²; lb/in²)
Pounds-force per square inch (psi; lbf/in²; lb/in²)	X 6.895	= Kilopascals (kPa)	X 0.145	= Pounds-force per square inch (psi; lbf/in²; lb/in²)
Kilopascals (kPa)	X 0.01	= Kilograms-force per square centimeter (kgf/cm²; kg/cm²)	X 98.1	= Kilopascals (kPa)

TORQUE (moment of force)
Pounds-force inches (lbf in; lb in)	X 1.152	= Kilograms-force centimeter (kgf cm; kg cm)	X 0.868	= Pounds-force inches (lbf in; lb in)
Pounds-force inches (lbf in; lb in)	X 0.113	= Newton meters (Nm)	X 8.85	= Pounds-force inches (lbf in; lb in)
Pounds-force inches (lbf in; lb in)	X 0.083	= Pounds-force feet (lbf ft; lb ft)	X 12	= Pounds-force inches (lbf in; lb in)
Pounds-force feet (lbf ft; lb ft)	X 0.138	= Kilograms-force meters (kgf m; kg m)	X 7.233	= Pounds-force feet (lbf ft; lb ft)
Pounds-force feet (lbf ft; lb ft)	X 1.356	= Newton meters (Nm)	X 0.738	= Pounds-force feet (lbf ft; lb ft)
Newton meters (Nm)	X 0.102	= Kilograms-force meters (kgf m; kg m)	X 9.804	= Newton meters (Nm)

VACUUM
Inches mercury (in. Hg)	X 3.377	= Kilopascals (kPa)	X 0.2961	= Inches mercury
Inches mercury (in. Hg)	X 25.4	= Millimeters mercury (mm Hg)	X 0.0394	= Inches mercury

POWER
Horsepower (hp)	X 745.7	= Watts (W)	X 0.0013	= Horsepower (hp)

VELOCITY (speed)
Miles per hour (miles/hr; mph)	X 1.609	= Kilometers per hour (km/hr; kph)	X 0.621	= Miles per hour (miles/hr; mph)

FUEL CONSUMPTION *
Miles per gallon, Imperial (mpg)	X 0.354	= Kilometers per liter (km/l)	X 2.825	= Miles per gallon, Imperial (mpg)
Miles per gallon, US (mpg)	X 0.425	= Kilometers per liter (km/l)	X 2.352	= Miles per gallon, US (mpg)

TEMPERATURE
Degrees Fahrenheit = (°C x 1.8) + 32   Degrees Celsius (Degrees Centigrade; °C) = (°F - 32) x 0.56

*It is common practice to convert from miles per gallon (mpg) to liters/100 kilometers (l/100km), where mpg (Imperial) x l/100 km = 282 and mpg (US) x l/100 km = 235

0-20

FRACTION/DECIMAL/MILLIMETER EQUIVALENTS

DECIMALS to MILLIMETERS

Decimal	mm	Decimal	mm
0.001	0.0254	0.500	12.7000
0.002	0.0508	0.510	12.9540
0.003	0.0762	0.520	13.2080
0.004	0.1016	0.530	13.4620
0.005	0.1270	0.540	13.7160
0.006	0.1524	0.550	13.9700
0.007	0.1778	0.560	14.2240
0.008	0.2032	0.570	14.4780
0.009	0.2286	0.580	14.7320
		0.590	14.9860
0.010	0.2540		
0.020	0.5080		
0.030	0.7620		
0.040	1.0160	0.600	15.2400
0.050	1.2700	0.610	15.4940
0.060	1.5240	0.620	15.7480
0.070	1.7780	0.630	16.0020
0.080	2.0320	0.640	16.2560
0.090	2.2860	0.650	16.5100
		0.660	16.7640
0.100	2.5400	0.670	17.0180
0.110	2.7940	0.680	17.2720
0.120	3.0480	0.690	17.5260
0.130	3.3020		
0.140	3.5560		
0.150	3.8100	0.700	17.7800
0.160	4.0640	0.710	18.0340
0.170	4.3180	0.720	18.2880
0.180	4.5720	0.730	18.5420
0.190	4.8260	0.740	18.7960
		0.750	19.0500
0.200	5.0800	0.760	19.3040
0.210	5.3340	0.770	19.5580
0.220	5.5880	0.780	19.8120
0.230	5.8420	0.790	20.0660
0.240	6.0960		
0.250	6.3500		
0.260	6.6040	0.800	20.3200
0.270	6.8580	0.810	20.5740
0.280	7.1120	0.820	21.8280
0.290	7.3660	0.830	21.0820
0.300	7.6200	0.840	21.3360
0.310	7.8740	0.850	21.5900
0.320	8.1280	0.860	21.8440
0.330	8.3820	0.870	22.0980
0.340	8.6360	0.880	22.3520
0.350	8.8900	0.890	22.6060
0.360	9.1440		
0.370	9.3980		
0.380	9.6520		
0.390	9.9060	0.900	22.8600
0.400	10.1600	0.910	23.1140
0.410	10.4140	0.920	23.3680
0.420	10.6680	0.930	23.6220
0.430	10.9220	0.940	23.8760
0.440	11.1760	0.950	24.1300
0.450	11.4300	0.960	24.3840
0.460	11.6840	0.970	24.6380
0.470	11.9380	0.980	24.8920
0.480	12.1920	0.990	25.1460
0.490	12.4460	1.000	25.4000

FRACTIONS to DECIMALS to MILLIMETERS

Fraction	Decimal	mm	Fraction	Decimal	mm
1/64	0.0156	0.3969	33/64	0.5156	13.0969
1/32	0.0312	0.7938	17/32	0.5312	13.4938
3/64	0.0469	1.1906	35/64	0.5469	13.8906
1/16	0.0625	1.5875	9/16	0.5625	14.2875
5/64	0.0781	1.9844	37/64	0.5781	14.6844
3/32	0.0938	2.3812	19/32	0.5938	15.0812
7/64	0.1094	2.7781	39/64	0.6094	15.4781
1/8	0.1250	3.1750	5/8	0.6250	15.8750
9/64	0.1406	3.5719	41/64	0.6406	16.2719
5/32	0.1562	3.9688	21/32	0.6562	16.6688
11/64	0.1719	4.3656	43/64	0.6719	17.0656
3/16	0.1875	4.7625	11/16	0.6875	17.4625
13/64	0.2031	5.1594	45/64	0.7031	17.8594
7/32	0.2188	5.5562	23/32	0.7188	18.2562
15/64	0.2344	5.9531	47/64	0.7344	18.6531
1/4	0.2500	6.3500	3/4	0.7500	19.0500
17/64	0.2656	6.7469	49/64	0.7656	19.4469
9/32	0.2812	7.1438	25/32	0.7812	19.8438
19/64	0.2969	7.5406	51/64	0.7969	20.2406
5/16	0.3125	7.9375	13/16	0.8125	20.6375
21/64	0.3281	8.3344	53/64	0.8281	21.0344
11/32	0.3438	8.7312	27/32	0.8438	21.4312
23/64	0.3594	9.1281	55/64	0.8594	21.8281
3/8	0.3750	9.5250	7/8	0.8750	22.2250
25/64	0.3906	9.9219	57/64	0.8906	22.6219
13/32	0.4062	10.3188	29/32	0.9062	23.0188
27/64	0.4219	10.7156	59/64	0.9219	23.4156
7/16	0.4375	11.1125	15/16	0.9375	23.8125
29/64	0.4531	11.5094	61/64	0.9531	24.2094
15/32	0.4688	11.9062	31/32	0.9688	24.6062
31/64	0.4844	12.3031	63/64	0.9844	25.0031
1/2	0.5000	12.7000	1	1.0000	25.4000

Safety first!

Regardless of how enthusiastic you may be about getting on with the job at hand, take the time to ensure that your safety is not jeopardized. A moment's lack of attention can result in an accident, as can failure to observe certain simple safety precautions. The possibility of an accident will always exist, and the following points should not be considered a comprehensive list of all dangers. Rather, they are intended to make you aware of the risks and to encourage a safety conscious approach to all work you carry out on your vehicle.

ESSENTIAL DOS AND DON'TS

DON'T rely on a jack when working under the vehicle. Always use approved jackstands to support the weight of the vehicle and place them under the recommended lift or support points.

DON'T attempt to loosen extremely tight fasteners (i.e. wheel lug nuts) while the vehicle is on a jack - it may fall.

DON'T start the engine without first making sure that the transmission is in Neutral (or Park where applicable) and the parking brake is set.

DON'T remove the radiator cap from a hot cooling system - let it cool or cover it with a cloth and release the pressure gradually.

DON'T attempt to drain the engine oil until you are sure it has cooled to the point that it will not burn you.

DON'T touch any part of the engine or exhaust system until it has cooled sufficiently to avoid burns.

DON'T siphon toxic liquids such as gasoline, antifreeze and brake fluid by mouth, or allow them to remain on your skin.

DON'T inhale brake lining dust - it is potentially hazardous (see Asbestos below).

DON'T allow spilled oil or grease to remain on the floor - wipe it up before someone slips on it.

DON'T use loose fitting wrenches or other tools which may slip and cause injury.

DON'T push on wrenches when loosening or tightening nuts or bolts. Always try to pull the wrench toward you. If the situation calls for pushing the wrench away, push with an open hand to avoid scraped knuckles if the wrench should slip.

DON'T attempt to lift a heavy component alone - get someone to help you.

DON'T rush or take unsafe shortcuts to finish a job.

DON'T allow children or animals in or around the vehicle while you are working on it.

DO wear eye protection when using power tools such as a drill, sander, bench grinder, etc. and when working under a vehicle.

DO keep loose clothing and long hair well out of the way of moving parts.

DO make sure that any hoist used has a safe working load rating adequate for the job.

DO get someone to check on you periodically when working alone on a vehicle.

DO carry out work in a logical sequence and make sure that everything is correctly assembled and tightened.

DO keep chemicals and fluids tightly capped and out of the reach of children and pets.

DO remember that your vehicle's safety affects that of yourself and others. If in doubt on any point, get professional advice.

STEERING, SUSPENSION AND BRAKES

These systems are essential to driving safety, so make sure you have a qualified shop or individual check your work. Also, compressed suspension springs can cause injury if released suddenly - be sure to use a spring compressor.

AIRBAGS

Airbags are explosive devices that can CAUSE injury if they deploy while you're working on the vehicle. Follow the manufacturer's instructions to disable the airbag whenever you're working in the vicinity of airbag components.

ASBESTOS

Certain friction, insulating, sealing, and other products - such as brake linings, brake bands, clutch linings, torque converters, gaskets, etc. - may contain asbestos or other hazardous friction material. Extreme care must be taken to avoid inhalation of dust from such products, since it is hazardous to health. If in doubt, assume that they do contain asbestos.

FIRE

Remember at all times that gasoline is highly flammable. Never smoke or have any kind of open flame around when working on a vehicle. But the risk does not end there. A spark caused by an electrical short circuit, by two metal surfaces contacting each other, or even by static electricity built up in your body under certain conditions, can ignite gasoline vapors, which in a confined space are highly explosive. Do not, under any circumstances, use gasoline for cleaning parts. Use an approved safety solvent.

Always disconnect the battery ground (-) cable at the battery before working on any part of the fuel system or electrical system. Never risk spilling fuel on a hot engine or exhaust component. It is strongly recommended that a fire extinguisher suitable for use on fuel and electrical fires be kept handy in the garage or workshop at all times. Never try to extinguish a fuel or electrical fire with water.

FUMES

Certain fumes are highly toxic and can quickly cause unconsciousness and even death if inhaled to any extent. Gasoline vapor falls into this category, as do the vapors from some cleaning solvents. Any draining or pouring of such volatile fluids should be done in a well ventilated area.

When using cleaning fluids and solvents, read the instructions on the container carefully. Never use materials from unmarked containers.

Never run the engine in an enclosed space, such as a garage. Exhaust fumes contain carbon monoxide, which is extremely poisonous. If you need to run the engine, always do so in the open air, or at least have the rear of the vehicle outside the work area.

THE BATTERY

Never create a spark or allow a bare light bulb near a battery. They normally give off a certain amount of hydrogen gas, which is highly explosive.

Always disconnect the battery ground (-) cable at the battery before working on the fuel or electrical systems.

If possible, loosen the filler caps or cover when charging the battery from an external source (this does not apply to sealed or maintenance-free batteries). Do not charge at an excessive rate or the battery may burst.

Take care when adding water to a non maintenance-free battery and when carrying a battery. The electrolyte, even when diluted, is very corrosive and should not be allowed to contact clothing or skin.

Always wear eye protection when cleaning the battery to prevent the caustic deposits from entering your eyes.

HOUSEHOLD CURRENT

When using an electric power tool, inspection light, etc., which operates on household current, always make sure that the tool is correctly connected to its plug and that, where necessary, it is properly grounded. Do not use such items in damp conditions and, again, do not create a spark or apply excessive heat in the vicinity of fuel or fuel vapor.

SECONDARY IGNITION SYSTEM VOLTAGE

A severe electric shock can result from touching certain parts of the ignition system (such as the spark plug wires) when the engine is running or being cranked, particularly if components are damp or the insulation is defective. In the case of an electronic ignition system, the secondary system voltage is much higher and could prove fatal.

HYDROFLUORIC ACID

This extremely corrosive acid is formed when certain types of synthetic rubber, found in some O-rings, oil seals, fuel hoses, etc. are exposed to temperatures above 750-degrees F (400-degrees C). The rubber changes into a charred or sticky substance containing the acid. *Once formed, the acid remains dangerous for years. If it gets onto the skin, it may be necessary to amputate the limb concerned.*

When dealing with a vehicle which has suffered a fire, or with components salvaged from such a vehicle, wear protective gloves and discard them after use.

Troubleshooting

CONTENTS

This section provides an easy reference guide to the more common problems which may occur during the operation of your vehicle. These problems and possible causes are grouped under various components or systems; i.e. Engine, Cooling System, etc., and also refer to the Chapter and/or Section which deals with the problem.

Remember that successful troubleshooting is not a mysterious black art practiced only by professional mechanics. It's simply the result of a bit of knowledge combined with an intelligent, systematic approach to the problem. Always work by a process of elimination, starting with the simplest solution and working through to the most complex - and never overlook the obvious. Anyone can forget to fill the gas tank or leave the lights on overnight, so don't assume that you are above such oversights.

Finally, always get clear in your mind why a problem has occurred and take steps to ensure that it doesn't happen again. If the electrical system fails because of a poor connection, check all other connections in the system to make sure that they don't fail as well. If a particular fuse continues to blow, find out why - don't just go on replacing fuses. Remember, failure of a small component can often be indicative of potential failure or incorrect functioning of a more important component or system.

ENGINE

1 Engine will not rotate when attempting to start

1 Battery terminal connections loose or corroded. Check the cable terminals at the battery. Tighten the cable or remove corrosion as necessary.
2 Battery discharged or faulty. If the cable connections are clean and tight on the battery posts, turn the key to the On position and switch on the headlights and/or windshield wipers. If they fail to function, the battery is discharged.
3 Automatic transmission not completely engaged in Park or Neutral or clutch pedal not completely depressed.
4 Broken, loose or disconnected wiring in the starting circuit. Inspect all wiring and connectors at the battery, starter solenoid and ignition switch.
5 Starter motor pinion jammed in flywheel ring gear. If manual transmission, place transmission in gear and rock the vehicle to manually turn the engine. Remove starter and inspect pinion and flywheel at earliest convenience (Chapter 5).
6 Starter solenoid faulty (Chapter 5).
7 Starter motor faulty (Chapter 5).
8 Ignition switch faulty (Chapter 12).

2 Engine rotates but will not start

1 Fuel tank empty.
2 Fault in the fuel injection system (Chapter 4).
3 Battery discharged (engine rotates slowly). Check the operation of electrical components as described in the previous Section.
4 Battery terminal connections loose or corroded (see previous Section).
5 Fuel pump faulty (Chapter 4).
6 Excessive moisture on, or damage to, ignition components (see Chapter 5).

7 Worn, faulty or incorrectly gapped spark plugs (Chapter 1).
8 Broken, loose or disconnected wiring in the starting circuit (see previous Section).
9 Broken, loose or disconnected wires at the ignition coil pack or faulty coil pack (Chapter 5).
10 Broken, loose or damaged timing belt (Chapter 2A).

3 Starter motor operates without rotating engine

1 Starter pinion sticking. Remove the starter (Chapter 5) and inspect.
2 Starter pinion or flywheel teeth worn or broken. Remove the flywheel/driveplate access cover and inspect.

4 Engine hard to start when cold

1 Battery discharged or low. Check as described in Section 1.
2 Fault in the fuel or electrical systems (Chapters 4 and 5).

5 Engine hard to start when hot

1 Air filter clogged (Chapter 1).
2 Fault in the fuel or electrical systems (Chapters 4 and 5).
3 Fuel not reaching the injectors (see Chapter 4).

6 Starter motor noisy or excessively rough in engagement

1 Pinion or flywheel gear teeth worn or broken. Remove the cover at the rear of the engine (if equipped) and inspect.
2 Starter motor mounting bolts loose or missing.

7 Engine starts but stops immediately

1 Loose or faulty electrical connections at distributor, coil or alternator.
2 Fault in the fuel or electrical systems (Chapters 4 and 5).
3 Vacuum leak at the gasket surfaces of the intake manifold or throttle body. Make sure all mounting bolts/nuts are tightened securely and all vacuum hoses connected to the manifold are positioned properly and in good condition.

8 Engine lopes while idling or idles erratically

1 Vacuum leakage. Check the mounting bolts/nuts at the throttle body and intake manifold for tightness. Make sure all vacuum hoses are connected and in good condition. Use a stethoscope or a length of fuel hose held against your ear to listen for vacuum leaks while the engine is running. A hissing sound will be heard. A soapy water solution will also detect leaks.
2 Fault in the fuel or electrical systems (Chapters 4 and 5).
3 Plugged PCV valve (see Chapters 1 and 6).
4 Air filter clogged (Chapter 1).
5 Fuel pump not delivering sufficient fuel to the fuel injectors (see Chapter 4).
6 Leaking head gasket. Perform a compression check (Chapter 2F).
7 Camshaft lobes worn (Chapter 2).

9 Engine misses at idle speed

1 Spark plugs worn, fouled or not gapped properly (Chapter 1).
2 Fault in the fuel or electrical systems (Chapters 4 and 5).
3 Faulty spark plug wires (Chapter 1).
4 Vacuum leaks at intake or hose connections. Check as described in Section 8.
5 Uneven or low cylinder compression. Check compression as described in Chapter 2F.

10 Engine misses throughout driving speed range

1 Fuel filter clogged and/or impurities in the fuel system (Chapter 1).
2 Faulty or incorrectly gapped spark plugs (Chapter 1).
3 Fault in the fuel or electrical systems (Chapters 4 and 5).
4 Defective spark plug wires (Chapter 1).
5 Faulty emissions system components (Chapter 6).
6 Low or uneven cylinder compression pressures. Remove the spark plugs and test the compression with a gauge (Chapter 2).
7 Weak or faulty ignition system (Chapter 5).
8 Vacuum leaks at the throttle body, intake manifold or vacuum hoses (see Section 8).

11 Engine stalls

1 Idle speed incorrect. Refer to the VECI label.
2 Fuel filter clogged and/or water and impurities in the fuel system (Chapter 1).
3 Fault in the fuel system or sensors (Chapters 4 and 6).
4 Faulty emissions system components (Chapter 6).
5 Faulty or incorrectly gapped spark plugs (Chapter 1). Also check the spark plug wires (Chapter 1).
6 Vacuum leak at the throttle body, intake manifold or vacuum hoses. Check as described in Section 8.

12 Engine lacks power

1 Fault in the fuel or electrical systems (Chapters 4 and 5).
2 Faulty or incorrectly gapped spark plugs (Chapter 1).
3 Faulty coil (Chapter 5).
4 Brakes binding (Chapter 1).
5 Automatic transmission fluid level incorrect (Chapter 1).
6 Clutch slipping (Chapter 8).
7 Fuel filter clogged and/or impurities in the fuel system (Chapter 1).
8 Emissions control system not functioning properly (Chapter 6).
9 Use of substandard fuel. Fill the tank with the proper octane fuel.
10 Low or uneven cylinder compression pressures. Test with a compression tester, which will detect leaking valves and/or a blown head gasket (Chapter 2F).

13 Engine backfires

1 Emissions system not functioning properly (Chapter 6).
2 Fault in the fuel or electrical systems (Chapters 4 and 5).
3 Faulty secondary ignition system (cracked spark plug insulator or faulty plug wires) (Chapters 1 and 5).
4 Fuel injection system malfunction (Chapter 4).
5 Vacuum leak at the throttle body, intake manifold or vacuum hoses. Check as described in Section 8.
6 Valves sticking (Chapter 2).
7 Crossed plug wires (Chapter 1).

14 Pinging or knocking engine sounds during acceleration or uphill

1 Incorrect grade of fuel. Fill the tank with fuel of the proper octane rating.
2 Fault in the fuel or electrical systems (Chapters 4 and 5).
3 Improper spark plugs. Check the plug type against the VECI label located in the engine compartment. Also check the plugs and wires for damage (Chapter 1).
4 Faulty emissions system (Chapter 6).
5 Vacuum leak. Check as described in Section 8.

15 Engine continues to run after switching off

1 Idle speed too high. Refer to Chapter 1.
2 Fault in the fuel or electrical systems (Chapters 4 and 5).
3 Excessive engine operating temperature. Probable causes of this are a low coolant level (see Chapter 1), malfunctioning thermostat, clogged radiator or faulty water pump (see Chapter 3).

ENGINE ELECTRICAL SYSTEM

16 Battery will not hold a charge

1 Alternator drivebelt defective or not adjusted properly (Chapter 1).
2 Electrolyte level low or battery discharged (Chapter 1).
3 Battery terminals loose or corroded (Chapter 1).
4 Alternator not charging properly (Chapter 5).
5 Loose, broken or faulty wiring in the charging circuit (Chapter 5).
6 Short in the vehicle wiring causing a continuous drain on the battery (refer to Chapter 12 and the Wiring Diagrams).
7 Battery defective internally.

17 Ignition light fails to go out

1 Fault in the alternator or charging circuit (Chapter 5).
2 Alternator drivebelt defective or not properly adjusted (Chapter 1).

18 Ignition light fails to come on when key is turned on

1 Instrument cluster warning light bulb defective (Chapter 12).
2 Alternator faulty (Chapter 5).
3 Fault in the instrument cluster printed circuit, dashboard wiring or bulb holder (Chapter 12).

FUEL SYSTEM

19 Excessive fuel consumption

1 Dirty or clogged air filter element (Chapter 1).
2 Emissions system not functioning properly (Chapter 6).
3 Fault in the fuel or electrical systems (Chapters 4 and 5).

4   Fuel injection system malfunction (Chapter 4).
5   Low tire pressure or incorrect tire size (Chapter 1).

20   Fuel leakage and/or fuel odor

1   Leak in a fuel feed or vent line (Chapter 4).
2   Tank overfilled. Fill only to automatic shut-off.
3   Evaporative emissions system canister clogged (Chapter 6).
4   Vapor leaks from system lines (Chapter 4).
5   Fuel injection system malfunction (Chapter 4).

COOLING SYSTEM

21   Overheating

1   Insufficient coolant in the system (Chapter 1).
2   Water pump drivebelt defective or not adjusted properly (Chapter 1).
3   Radiator core blocked or radiator grille dirty and restricted (see Chapter 3).
4   Thermostat faulty (Chapter 3).
5   Fan blades broken or cracked (Chapter 3).
6   Radiator cap not maintaining proper pressure. Have the cap pressure tested by gas station or repair shop.

22   Overcooling

1   Thermostat faulty (Chapter 3).
2   Inaccurate temperature gauge (Chapter 12).

23   External coolant leakage

1   Deteriorated or damaged hoses or loose clamps. Replace hoses and/or tighten the clamps at the hose connections (Chapter 1).
2   Water pump seals defective. If this is the case, water will drip from the weep hole in the water pump body (Chapter 3).
3   Leakage from the radiator core or side tank(s). This will require the radiator to be professionally repaired (see Chapter 3 for removal procedures).
4   Engine drain plug leaking (Chapter 1) or water jacket core plugs leaking (see Chapter 2).

24   Internal coolant leakage

➡Note: Internal coolant leaks can usually be detected by examining the oil. Check the dipstick and inside of the valve cover for water deposits and an oil consistency like that of a milkshake.

1   Leaking cylinder head gasket. Have the cooling system pressure tested.
2   Cracked cylinder bore or cylinder head. Dismantle the engine and inspect (Chapter 2).
3   Intake manifold gasket leaking (Chapter 2).

25   Coolant loss

1   Too much coolant in the system (Chapter 1).
2   Coolant boiling away due to overheating (see Section 15).
3   External or internal leakage (see Sections 23 and 24).
4   Faulty radiator cap. Have the cap pressure tested.

26   Poor coolant circulation

1   Inoperative water pump. A quick test is to pinch the top radiator hose closed with your hand while the engine is idling, then let it loose. You should feel the surge of coolant if the pump is working properly (see Chapter 1).
2   Restriction in the cooling system. Drain, flush and refill the system (Chapter 1). If necessary, remove the radiator (Chapter 3) and have it reverse flushed.
3   Water pump drivebelt defective or not adjusted properly (Chapter 1).
4   Thermostat sticking (Chapter 3).

CLUTCH

27   Fails to release (pedal pressed to the floor - shift lever does not move freely in and out of Reverse)

1   Leak in the clutch hydraulic system. Check the master cylinder, slave cylinder and lines (Chapter 8).
2   Clutch plate warped or damaged (Chapter 8).

28   Clutch slips (engine speed increases with no increase in vehicle speed)

1   Clutch plate oil soaked or lining worn. Remove clutch (Chapter 8) and inspect.
2   Clutch plate not seated.
3   Pressure plate worn (Chapter 8).

29   Grabbing (chattering) as clutch is engaged

1   Oil on clutch plate lining. Remove (Chapter 8) and inspect. Correct any leakage source.
2   Worn or loose engine or transmission mounts. These units move slightly when the clutch is released. Inspect the mounts and bolts (Chapter 2).
3   Worn splines on clutch plate hub. Remove the clutch components (Chapter 8) and inspect.
4   Warped pressure plate or flywheel. Remove the clutch components and inspect.

30   Squeal or rumble with clutch fully engaged (pedal released)

Release bearing binding on transmission bearing retainer. Remove clutch components (Chapter 8) and check bearing. Remove any burrs or nicks; clean and relubricate bearing retainer before installing.

31 Squeal or rumble with clutch fully disengaged (pedal depressed)

1   Worn, defective or broken release bearing (Chapter 8).
2   Worn or broken pressure plate springs (or diaphragm fingers) (Chapter 8).

32 Clutch pedal stays on floor when disengaged

1   Linkage or release bearing binding. Inspect the linkage or remove the clutch components as necessary.
2   Make sure proper pedal stop (bumper) is installed.

MANUAL TRANSMISSION

➡Note: All the following references are in Chapter 7A, unless noted.

33 Noisy in Neutral with engine running

1   Input shaft bearing worn.
2   Damaged main drive gear bearing.
3   Worn countershaft bearings.
4   Worn or damaged countershaft endplay shims.

34 Noisy in all gears

1   Any of the above causes, and/or:
2   Insufficient lubricant (see the checking procedures in Chapter 1).

35 Noisy in one particular gear

1   Worn, damaged or chipped gear teeth for that particular gear.
2   Worn or damaged synchronizer for that particular gear.

36 Slips out of high gear

1   Transmission loose on clutch housing.
2   Dirt between the transmission case and engine or misalignment of the transmission.

37 Difficulty in engaging gears

1   Clutch not releasing completely (see Chapter 8).
2   Loose, damaged or out-of-adjustment shift linkage. Make a thorough inspection, replacing parts as necessary.

38 Oil leakage

1   Excessive amount of lubricant in the transmission (see Chapter 1 for correct checking procedures). Drain lubricant as required.
2   Driveaxle oil seal or speedometer oil seal in need of replacement.

AUTOMATIC TRANSMISSION

➡Note: Due to the complexity of the automatic transmission, it's difficult for the home mechanic to properly diagnose and service this component. For problems other than the following, the vehicle should be taken to a dealer service department or a transmission shop.

39 General shift mechanism problems

1   Chapter 7B deals with checking and adjusting the shift linkage on automatic transmissions. Common problems which may be attributed to poorly adjusted linkage are:
    a) *Engine starting in gears other than Park or Neutral.*
    b) *Indicator on shifter pointing to a gear oth-er than the one actually being selected.*
    c) *Vehicle moves when in Park.*
2   Refer to Chapter 7B to adjust the linkage.

40 Transmission will not downshift with accelerator pedal pressed to the floor

Kickdown cable misadjusted.

41 Transmission slips, shifts rough, is noisy or has no drive in forward or reverse gears

1   There are many probable causes for the above problems, but the home mechanic should be concerned with only one possibility - fluid level.
2   Before taking the vehicle to a repair shop, check the level and condition of the fluid as described in Chapter 1. Correct fluid level as necessary or change the fluid and filter if needed. If the problem persists, have a professional diagnose the probable cause.
3   If the transmission shifts late and the shifts are harsh, suspect a faulty vacuum diaphragm, if equipped (Chapter 7B).

42 Fluid leakage

1   Automatic transmission fluid is a deep red color. Fluid leaks should not be confused with engine oil, which can easily be blown by air flow to the transmission.
2   To pinpoint a leak, first remove all built-up dirt and grime from around the transmission. Degreasing agents and/or steam cleaning will achieve this. With the underside clean, drive the vehicle at low speeds so air flow will not blow the leak far from its source. Raise the vehicle and determine where the leak is coming from. Common areas of leakage are:
    a) *Pan: Tighten the mounting bolts and/or replace the pan gasket as necessary (see Chapter 7B).*
    b) *Filler pipe: Replace the rubber seal where the pipe enters the transmission case.*
    c) *Transmission oil lines: Tighten the connectors where the lines enter the transmission case and/or replace the lines.*
    d) *Vent pipe: Transmission overfilled and/or water in fluid (see checking procedures, Chapter 1).*
    e) *Speedometer connector: Replace the O-ring where the speedometer cable enters the transmission case (if equipped).*

TRANSFER CASE

43 Transfer case is difficult to shift into the desired range

1 Speed may be too great to permit engagement. Stop the vehicle and shift into the desired range.
2 Shift linkage loose, bent or binding. Check the linkage for damage or wear and replace or lubricate as necessary (Chapter 7C).
3 If the vehicle has been driven on a paved surface for some time, the driveline torque can make shifting difficult. Stop and shift into two-wheel drive on paved or hard surfaces.
4 Insufficient or incorrect grade of lubricant. Drain and refill the transfer case with the specified lubricant. (Chapter 1).
5 Worn or damaged internal components. Disassembly and overhaul of the transfer case may be necessary (Chapter 7C).

44 Transfer case noisy in all gears

Insufficient or incorrect grade of lubricant. Drain and refill (Chapter 1).

45 Noisy or jumps out of four-wheel drive Low range

1 Transfer case not fully engaged. Stop the vehicle, shift into Neutral and then engage 4L.
2 Shift linkage loose, worn or binding. Tighten, repair or lubricate linkage as necessary.
3 Shift fork cracked, inserts worn or fork binding on the rail. Disassemble and repair as necessary (Chapter 7C).

46 Lubricant leaks from the vent or output shaft seals

1 Transfer case is overfilled. Drain to the proper level (Chapter 1).
2 Vent is clogged or jammed closed. Clear or replace the vent.
3 Output shaft seal incorrectly installed or damaged. Replace the seal and check contact surfaces for nicks and scoring.

DRIVESHAFT

47 Oil leak at seal end of driveshaft

Defective transmission or transfer case oil seal. See Chapter 7 for replacement procedures. While this is done, check the splined yoke for burrs or a rough condition which may be damaging the seal. Burrs can be removed with crocus cloth or a fine whetstone.

48 Knock or clunk when the transmission is under initial load (just after transmission is put into gear)

1 Loose or disconnected rear suspension components. Check all mounting bolts, nuts and bushings (see Chapter 10).
2 Loose driveshaft bolts. Inspect all bolts and nuts and tighten them to the specified torque.
3 Worn or damaged universal joint bearings. Check for wear (see Chapter 8).

49 Metallic grinding sound consistent with vehicle speed

Pronounced wear in the universal joint bearings. Check as described in Chapter 8.

50 Vibration

➡Note: Before assuming that the driveshaft is at fault, make sure the tires are perfectly balanced and perform the following test.

1 Install a tachometer inside the vehicle to monitor engine speed as the vehicle is driven. Drive the vehicle and note the engine speed at which the vibration (roughness) is most pronounced. Now shift the transmission to a different gear and bring the engine speed to the same point.
2 If the vibration occurs at the same engine speed (rpm) regardless of which gear the transmission is in, the driveshaft is NOT at fault since the driveshaft speed varies.
3 If the vibration decreases or is eliminated when the transmission is in a different gear at the same engine speed, refer to the following probable causes.
4 Bent or dented driveshaft. Inspect and replace as necessary (see Chapter 8).
5 Undercoating or built-up dirt, etc. on the driveshaft. Clean the shaft thoroughly and recheck.
6 Worn universal joint bearings. Remove and inspect (see Chapter 8).
7 Driveshaft and/or companion flange out of balance. Check for missing weights on the shaft. Remove the driveshaft (see Chapter 8) and reinstall 180-degrees from original position, then retest. Have the driveshaft professionally balanced if the problem persists.

AXLES

51 Noise

1 Road noise. No corrective procedures available.
2 Tire noise. Inspect tires and check tire pressures (Chapter 1).
3 Rear wheel bearings loose, worn or damaged (Chapter 8).

52 Vibration

See probable causes under Driveshaft. Proceed under the guidelines listed for the driveshaft. If the problem persists, check the rear wheel bearings by raising the rear of the vehicle and spinning the rear wheels by hand. Listen for evidence of rough (noisy) bearings. Remove and inspect (see Chapter 8).

53 Oil leakage

1 Pinion seal damaged (see Chapter 8).
2 Axleshaft oil seals damaged (see Chapter 8).
3 Differential inspection cover leaking. Tighten the bolts or replace the gasket as required (see Chapters 1 and 8).

BRAKES

➡Note: Before assuming that a brake problem exists, make sure that the tires are in good condition and inflated properly (see Chapter 1), that the front end alignment is correct and that the vehicle is not loaded with weight in an unequal manner.

54   Vehicle pulls to one side during braking

1   Defective, damaged or oil contaminated disc brake pads or shoes on one side. Inspect as described in Chapter 9.
2   Excessive wear of brake shoe or pad material or drum/disc on one side. Inspect and correct as necessary.
3   Loose or disconnected front suspension components. Inspect and tighten all bolts to the specified torque (Chapter 10).
4   Defective drum brake or caliper assembly. Remove the drum or caliper and inspect for a stuck piston or other damage (Chapter 9).
5   Inadequate lubrication of front brake caliper slide rails. Remove caliper and lubricate slide rails (Chapter 9).

55   Noise (high-pitched squeal with the brakes applied)

1   Disc brake pads worn out. The noise comes from the wear sensor rubbing against the disc (does not apply to all vehicles) or the actual pad backing plate itself if the material is completely worn away. Replace the pads with new ones immediately (Chapter 9). If the pad material has worn completely away, the brake discs should be inspected for damage as described in Chapter 9.
2   Missing or damaged brake pad insulators (disc brakes). Replace pad insulators (see Chapter 9).
3   Linings contaminated with dirt or grease. Replace pads or shoes.
4   Incorrect linings. Replace with correct linings.

56   Excessive brake pedal travel

1   Partial brake system failure. Inspect the entire system (Chapter 9) and correct as required.
2   Insufficient fluid in the master cylinder. Check (Chapter 1), add fluid and bleed the system if necessary (Chapter 9).
3   Rear brakes not adjusting properly. Make a series of starts and stops while the vehicle is in Reverse. If this does not correct the situation, remove the drums and inspect the self-adjusters (Chapter 9).

57   Brake pedal feels spongy when depressed

1   Air in the hydraulic lines. Bleed the brake system (Chapter 9).
2   Faulty flexible hoses. Inspect all system hoses and lines. Replace parts as necessary.
3   Master cylinder mounting bolts/nuts loose.
4   Master cylinder defective (Chapter 9).

58   Excessive effort required to stop vehicle

1   Power brake booster not operating properly (Chapter 9).
2   Excessively worn linings or pads. Inspect and replace if necessary (Chapter 9).
3   One or more caliper pistons or wheel cylinders seized or sticking. Inspect and rebuild as required (Chapter 9).

4   Brake linings or pads contaminated with oil or grease. Inspect and replace as required (Chapter 9).
5   New pads or shoes installed and not yet seated. It will take a while for the new material to seat against the drum (or rotor).

59   Pedal travels to the floor with little resistance

1   Little or no fluid in the master cylinder reservoir caused by leaking wheel cylinder(s), leaking caliper piston(s), loose, damaged or disconnected brake lines. Inspect the entire system and correct as necessary.
2   Worn master cylinder seals (Chapter 9).

60   Brake pedal pulsates during brake application

1   Caliper improperly installed. Remove and inspect (Chapter 9).
2   Disc or drum defective. Remove (Chapter 9) and check for excessive lateral runout and parallelism. Have the disc or drum resurfaced or replace it with a new one.

SUSPENSION AND STEERING SYSTEMS

61   Vehicle pulls to one side

1   Tire pressures uneven (Chapter 1).
2   Defective tire (Chapter 1).
3   Excessive wear in suspension or steering components (Chapter 10).
4   Front end in need of alignment.
5   Front brakes dragging. Inspect the brakes as described in Chapter 9.

62   Shimmy, shake or vibration

1   Tire or wheel out-of-balance or out-of-round. Have professionally balanced.
2   Loose, worn or out-of-adjustment rear wheel bearings (Chapter 1).
3   Shock absorbers and/or suspension components worn or damaged (Chapter 10).

63   Excessive pitching and/or rolling around corners or during braking

1   Defective shock absorbers. Replace as a set (Chapter 10).
2   Broken or weak springs and/or suspension components. Inspect as described in Chapter 10.

64   Excessively stiff steering

1   Lack of fluid in power steering fluid reservoir (Chapter 1).
2   Incorrect tire pressures (Chapter 1).
3   Lack of lubrication at steering joints (see Chapter 1).
4   Front end out of alignment.
5   Lack of power assistance (see Section 66).

65 Excessive play in steering

1 Loose front wheel bearings (Chapters 1 and 10).
2 Excessive wear in suspension or steering components (Chapter 10).
3 Steering gearbox damaged or out of adjustment (Chapter 10).

66 Lack of power assistance

1 Steering pump drivebelt faulty or not adjusted properly (Chapter 1).
2 Fluid level low (Chapter 1).
3 Hoses or lines restricted. Inspect and replace parts as necessary.
4 Air in power steering system. Bleed the system (Chapter 10).

67 Excessive tire wear (not specific to one area)

1 Incorrect tire pressures (Chapter 1).
2 Tires out-of-balance. Have professionally balanced.
3 Wheels damaged. Inspect and replace as necessary.
4 Suspension or steering components excessively worn (Chapter 10).

68 Excessive tire wear on outside edge

1 Inflation pressures incorrect (Chapter 1).
2 Excessive speed in turns.
3 Front end alignment incorrect (excessive toe-in). Have professionally aligned.
4 Suspension arm bent or twisted (Chapter 10).

69 Excessive tire wear on inside edge

1 Inflation pressures incorrect (Chapter 1).
2 Front end alignment incorrect (toe-out). Have professionally aligned.
3 Loose or damaged steering components (Chapter 10).

70 Tire tread worn in one place

1 Tires out-of-balance.
2 Damaged or buckled wheel. Inspect and replace if necessary.
3 Defective tire (Chapter 1).

Notes

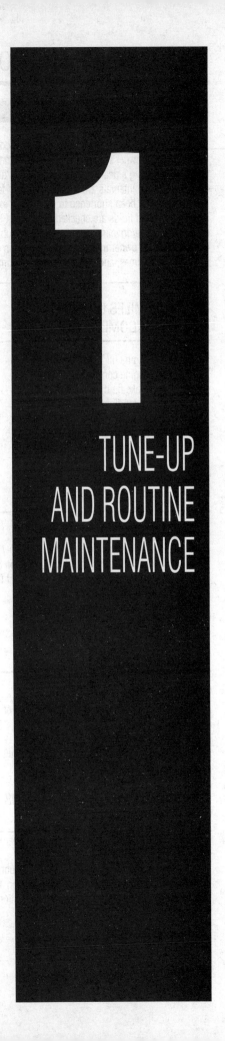

1

TUNE-UP AND ROUTINE MAINTENANCE

Section

Reference to other Chapters
CHECK ENGINE light - See Chapter 6

1 Maintenance schedule

The following maintenance intervals are based on the assumption that the vehicle owner will be doing the maintenance or service work, as opposed to having a dealer service department do the work. Although the time/mileage intervals are loosely based on factory recommendations, most have been shortened to ensure, for example, that such items as lubricants and fluids are checked/changed at intervals that promote maximum engine/driveline service life. Also, subject to the preference of the individual owner interested in keeping his or her vehicle in peak condition at all times, and with the vehicle's ultimate resale in mind,

many of the maintenance procedures may be performed more often than recommended in the following schedule. We encourage such owner initiative.

Because off-road use necessitates more frequent maintenance, a separate schedule is included for vehicles used off road.

When the vehicle is new it should be serviced initially by a factory authorized dealer service department to protect the factory warranty. In many cases the initial maintenance check is done at no cost to the owner (check with your dealer service department for more information).

EVERY 250 MILES OR WEEKLY, WHICHEVER COMES FIRST

Check the engine oil level (Section 4)
Check the engine coolant level (Section 4)
Check the brake fluid level (Section 4)
Check the clutch fluid level (Section 4)
Check the windshield washer fluid level (Section 4)
Check the tires and tire pressures (Section 5)
Perform owner safety checks (Section 6)

EVERY 3,000 MILES OR 3 MONTHS, WHICHEVER COMES FIRST

All items listed above, plus . . .

Change the engine oil and oil filter (Section 7)
Check the power steering fluid level (Section 8)
Check the automatic transmission fluid level (Section 9)
Rotate the tires (Section 10)
Check the air filter (Section 28)

EVERY 6,000 MILES OR 6 MONTHS, WHICHEVER COMES FIRST

All items listed above, plus . . .

Inspect/replace the underhood hoses (Section 11)
Check the drivebelt (Section 12)
Check/service the battery (Section 13)
Inspect/lubricate automatic transmission shift linkage (Section 15)
Lubricate the chassis (Section 16)

EVERY 12,000 MILES OR 12 MONTHS, WHICHEVER COMES FIRST

All items listed above, plus . . .

Check/replenish the manual transmission lubricant (Section 17)
Check the differential lubricant level (Section 18)
Check the transfer case lubricant level (Section 19)
Check/replace the PCV valve (Section 20)

Check the fuel system (Section 21)
Inspect the cooling system (Section 22)
Inspect the exhaust system (Section 23)
Inspect the steering and suspension components (Section 24)
Inspect the brakes and lubricate caliper friction points (Section 25)
Inspect/replace the windshield wiper blades (Section 26)
Adjust rear brakes

EVERY 24,000 MILES OR 24 MONTHS, WHICHEVER COMES FIRST

All items listed above, plus . . .

Change the automatic transmission fluid and filter (Section 9)
Service the cooling system (drain, flush and refill) (Section 27)
Check/replace the spark plug wires (Section 14)

EVERY 30,000 MILES OR 30 MONTHS, WHICHEVER COMES FIRST

Replace the air filter (Section 28)
Check/replace the fuel filter (Section 29)
Change the differential lubricant (Section 18)
Change the transfer case lubricant (Section 19)
Lubricate the driveshaft slip yokes (Section 30)
Lubricate right front driveaxle slip yoke (4WD) (Section 30)

EVERY 60,000 MILES OR 60 MONTHS, WHICHEVER COMES FIRST

Replace the spark plugs (Section 14)

OFF-ROAD OPERATION

If the vehicle is driven off road, perform the following maintenance items every 1,000 miles. If the vehicle is driven in mud or water, perform the items daily.

Inspect the brakes (Section 25)
Inspect exhaust system (Section 23)
Lubricate driveshaft slip yoke and U-joints (if equipped with grease fittings) (Sections 16 and 30)

Typical four-cylinder engine compartment component locations

1	Power distribution (fuse and relay) box	6A	Engine oil dipstick (early models)	10	Windshield washer reservoir
2	Air cleaner housing	6B	Engine oil dipstick (later models)	11	Radiator cap
3	Engine oil filler cap	7	Brake master cylinder reservoir	12	Upper radiator hose
4	Ignition coil pack	8	Clutch fluid reservoir	13	Battery
5	Ignition wires	9	Engine coolant reservoir		

Typical V6 engine compartment component locations

1	Brake fluid reservoir	6	Drivebelt	10	Windshield washer fluid reservoir
2	Power distribution box (fuses and relays)	7	Upper radiator hose	11	Engine oil filler cap
3	Power steering fluid reservoir	8	Air filter housing	12	Automatic transmission fluid dipstick
4	Battery	9	Coolant reservoir	13	Ignition coil pack/spark plug wires
5	Radiator cap				

Typical engine compartment underside components

1 Radiator drain fitting (obscured by lower support)   3 Grease fittings
2 Lower radiator hose

Typical rear underside components

1 Rear shock absorber   3 Muffler   5 Rear differential
2 Leaf spring assembly   4 Fuel tank

2 Introduction

This Chapter is designed to help the home mechanic maintain his or her vehicle with the goals of maximum performance, economy, safety and reliability in mind.

Included is a master maintenance schedule, followed by procedures dealing specifically with each item on the schedule. Visual checks, adjustments, component replacement and other helpful items are included. Refer to the accompanying illustrations of the engine compartment and the underside of the vehicle for the locations of various components. Servicing the vehicle, in accordance with the mileage/time maintenance schedule and the step-by-step procedures will result in a planned maintenance program that should produce a long and reliable service life. Keep in mind that it is a comprehensive plan, so maintaining some items but not others at specified intervals will not produce the same results.

As you service the vehicle, you will discover that many of the procedures can - and should - be grouped together because of the nature of the particular procedure you're performing or because of the close proximity of two otherwise unrelated components to one another.

For example, if the vehicle is raised for chassis lubrication, you should inspect the exhaust, suspension, steering and fuel systems while you're under the vehicle. When you're rotating the tires, it makes good sense to check the brakes since the wheels are already removed. Finally, let's suppose you have to borrow or rent a torque wrench. Even if you only need it to tighten the spark plugs, you might as well check the torque of as many critical fasteners as time allows.

The first step in this maintenance program is to prepare yourself before the actual work begins. Read through all the procedures you're planning to do, then gather up all the parts and tools needed. If it looks like you might run into problems during a particular job, seek advice from a mechanic or an experienced do-it-yourselfer.

3 Tune-up general information

The term tune-up is used in this manual to represent a combination of individual operations rather than one specific procedure.

If, from the time the vehicle is new, the routine maintenance schedule is followed closely and frequent checks are made of fluid levels and high wear items, as suggested throughout this manual, the engine will be kept in relatively good running condition and the need for additional work will be minimized.

More likely than not, however, there will be times when the engine is running poorly due to a lack of regular maintenance. This is even more likely if a used vehicle, which has not received regular and frequent maintenance checks, is purchased. In such cases, an engine tune-up will be needed outside of the regular maintenance intervals.

The first step in any tune-up or diagnostic procedure to help correct a poor running engine is a cylinder compression check. A compression check (see Chapter 2, Part F) will help determine the condition of internal engine components and should be used as a guide for tune-up and repair procedures. If, for instance, a compression check indicates serious internal engine wear, a conventional tune-up will not improve the performance of the engine and would be a waste of time and money. Because of its importance, the compression check should be done by someone with the right equipment and the knowledge to use it properly.

The following procedures are those most often needed to bring as generally poor running engine back into a proper state of tune.

MINOR TUNE-UP

Check all engine related fluids (see Section 4)
Check all underhood hoses (see Section 11)
Check and adjust the drivebelt (see Section 12)
Clean, inspect and test the battery (see Section 13)
Replace the spark plugs (see Section 14)
Inspect the spark plug wires (see Section 14)
Check the PCV valve (see Section 20)
Check the cooling system (see Section 22)
Check the air filter (see Section 28)

MAJOR TUNE-UP

All items listed under minor tune-up, plus . . .

Replace the spark plug wires (see Section 14)
Check the fuel system (see Chapter 4)
Check the ignition system (see Chapter 5)
Check the charging system (see Chapter 5)

4 Fluid level checks (every 250 miles or weekly, whichever comes first)

▶ Refer to illustrations 4.4a, 4.4b, 4.6, 4.8 and 4.15

➡Note: The following are fluid level checks to be done on a 250 mile or weekly basis. Additional fluid level checks can be found in specific maintenance procedures which follow. Regardless of intervals, be alert to fluid leaks under the vehicle which would indicate a fault to be corrected immediately.

1 Fluids are an essential part of the lubrication, cooling, brake and windshield washer systems. Because the fluids gradually become depleted and/or contaminated during normal operation of the vehicle, they must be periodically replenished. See *Recommended lubricants and fluids* at the end of this Chapter before adding fluid to any of the following components.

➡Note: The vehicle must be on level ground when fluid levels are checked.

ENGINE OIL

2 Engine oil is checked with a dipstick, which is located on the side of the engine (refer to the underhood illustration at the front of this Chapter for dipstick location). The dipstick extends through a metal tube down into the oil pan.

3 The engine oil should be checked before the vehicle has been driven, or about 10 to 15 minutes after the engine has been shut off. If the oil is checked immediately after driving the vehicle, some of the oil

4.4a Remove the engine oil dipstick, wipe it clean, then reinsert it all the way before withdrawing it for an accurate oil level check

4.4b The oil level should appear between the ADD 1 QT and SAFE or FULL marks; don't overfill the engine with oil

will remain in the upper part of the engine, resulting in an inaccurate reading on the dipstick.

4   Pull the dipstick out of the tube (see illustration) and wipe all of the oil away from the end with a clean rag or paper towel. Insert the clean dipstick all the way back into the tube and pull it out again. Note the oil at the end of the dipstick. At its highest point, the oil should be above the ADD mark, in the SAFE range (see illustration).

5   It takes one quart of oil to raise the level from the ADD mark to the FULL or MAX mark on the dipstick. Do not allow the level to drop below the ADD mark or oil starvation may cause engine damage. Conversely, overfilling the engine (adding oil above the FULL or MAX mark) may cause oil fouled spark plugs, oil leaks or oil seal failures.

6   To add oil, remove the filler cap located on the valve cover or filler neck (see illustration). After adding oil, wait a few minutes to allow the level to stabilize, then pull the dipstick out and check the level again. Add more oil if required. Install the filler cap and tighten it by hand only.

7   Checking the oil level is an important preventive maintenance step. A consistently low oil level indicates oil leakage through damaged seals, defective gaskets or past worn rings or valve guides. The condition of the oil should also be noted. If the oil looks milky in color or has water droplets in it, the cylinder head gasket(s) may be blown or the head(s) or block may be cracked. The engine should be repaired immediately. Whenever you check the oil level, slide your thumb and index finger up the dipstick before wiping off the oil. If you see

small dirt or metal particles clinging to the dipstick, the oil should be changed (see Section 4).

ENGINE COOLANT

✻✻ WARNING:

Do not allow antifreeze to come in contact with your skin or painted surfaces of the vehicle. Flush contaminated areas immediately with plenty of water. Don't store new coolant or leave old coolant lying around where it's accessible to children or pets - they're attracted by its sweet smell. Ingestion of even a small amount of coolant can be fatal! Wipe up garage floor and drip pan spills immediately. Keep antifreeze containers covered and repair cooling system leaks as soon as they're noticed.

8   All vehicles covered by this manual are equipped with a pressurized coolant recovery system. A white plastic coolant reservoir or expansion tank is located in the engine compartment (see illustration).

9   The coolant level in the tank should be checked regularly.

✻✻ WARNING:

Do not remove the pressure cap or expansion tank cap to check the coolant level when the engine is warm!

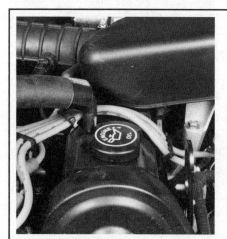

4.6 To add oil, remove the filler cap from the valve cover or filler neck

4.8 The coolant recovery reservoir is combined with the windshield washer fluid reservoir (there are separate compartments for the two fluids)

The level in the tank varies with the temperature of the engine. When the engine is cold, the coolant level should be at or slightly above the COLD or MIN mark on the reservoir or expansion tank. Once the engine has warmed up, the level should be at or near the HOT or FULL mark. If it isn't, allow the engine to cool, then remove the cap from the tank and add a 50/50 mixture of the specified coolant and water.

➡Note: Some models do not have a HOT mark on the tank.

10 Drive the vehicle and recheck the coolant level. If only a small amount of coolant is required to bring the system up to the proper level, water can be used. However, repeated additions of water will dilute the antifreeze and water solution. In order to maintain the proper ratio of antifreeze and water, always top up the coolant level with the correct mixture. Don't use rust inhibitors or additives. An empty plastic milk jug or bleach bottle makes an excellent container for mixing coolant.

11 If the coolant level drops consistently, there may be a leak in the system. Inspect the radiator, hoses, filler cap, drain plugs and water pump (see Section 22). If no leaks are noted, have the pressure cap or expansion tank cap pressure tested by a service station.

12 If you have to remove the radiator cap or expansion tank cap, wait until the engine has cooled completely, then wrap a thick cloth around the cap and turn it to the first stop. If coolant or steam escapes, or if you hear a hissing noise, let the engine cool down longer, then remove the cap.

13 Check the condition of the coolant as well. It should be relatively clear. If it's brown or rust colored, the system should be drained, flushed and refilled. Even if the coolant appears to be normal, the corrosion inhibitors wear out, so it must be replaced at the specified intervals.

BRAKE AND CLUTCH FLUID

> ✳✳ **WARNING:**
>
> **Brake fluid can harm your eyes and damage painted surfaces, so use extreme caution when handling or pouring it. Do not use brake fluid that has been standing open or is more than one year old. Brake fluid absorbs moisture from the air, which can cause a dangerous loss of brake effectiveness. Use only the specified type of brake fluid. Mixing different types (such as DOT 3 or 4 and DOT 5) can cause brake failure.**

14 The brake master cylinder is mounted at the left (driver's side) rear corner of the engine compartment. The clutch fluid reservoir (used on models with manual transmissions) is mounted adjacent to it.

15 To check the clutch fluid level, observe the level through the translucent reservoir. The level should be at or near the step molded into the reservoir. If the level is low, remove the reservoir cap to add the specified fluid (see illustration).

16 The brake fluid level is checked by looking through the plastic reservoir mounted on the master cylinder. The fluid level should be between the MAX and MIN lines on the reservoir (see illustration 4.15). If the fluid level is low, wipe the top of the reservoir and the cap with a clean rag to prevent contamination of the system as the cap is unscrewed. Top up with the recommended brake fluid, but do not over-fill.

17 While the reservoir cap is off, check the master cylinder reservoir for contamination. If rust deposits, dirt particles or water droplets are present, the system should be drained and refilled by a dealer service department or repair shop.

18 After filling the reservoir to the proper level, make sure the cap is seated to prevent fluid leakage and/or contamination.

19 The fluid level in the master cylinder will drop slightly as the disc brake pads wear. A very low level may indicate worn brake pads. Check for wear (see Section 25).

20 If the brake fluid level drops consistently, check the entire system for leaks immediately. Examine all brake lines, hoses and connections, along with the calipers, wheel cylinders and master cylinder (see Section 25).

21 When checking the fluid level, if you discover one or both reservoirs empty or nearly empty, the brake or clutch hydraulic system should be checked for leaks and bled (see Chapters 8 and 9).

WINDSHIELD WASHER FLUID

22 Fluid for the windshield washer system is stored in a plastic reservoir in the engine compartment. The windshield washer reservoir is combined with the coolant reservoir (there are separate compartments for the two different fluids) (see illustration 4.9).

23 In milder climates, plain water can be used in the reservoir, but it should be kept no more than 2/3 full to allow for expansion if the water freezes. In colder climates, use windshield washer system antifreeze, available at any auto parts store, to lower the freezing point of the fluid. This comes in concentrated or pre-mixed form. If you purchase concentrated antifreeze, mix the antifreeze with water in accordance with the manufacturer's directions on the container.

> ✳✳ **CAUTION:**
>
> **Do not use cooling system antifreeze - it will damage the vehicle's paint.**

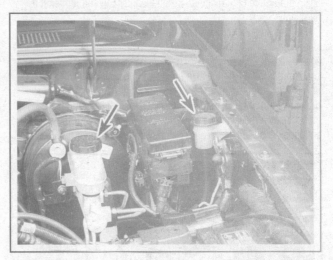

4.15 Clutch fluid is contained in a separate reservoir (right arrow) next to the brake master cylinder (left arrow) - clean the rubber-lined cap(s) before returning it to the reservoir

5   Tire and tire pressure checks (every 250 miles or weekly, whichever comes first)

▶ **Refer to illustrations 5.2, 5.3, 5.4a, 5.4b and 5.8**

1   Periodic inspection of the tires may save you the inconvenience of being stranded with a flat tire. It can also provide you with vital information regarding possible problems in the steering and suspension systems before major damage occurs.

2   Tires are equipped with 1/2-inch wide bands that will appear when tread depth reaches 1/16-inch, which is when the tires are worn out. Tread wear can be monitored with a simple, inexpensive device known as a tread depth indicator (see illustration).

3   Note any abnormal tire wear (see illustration). Tread pattern irregularities such as cupping, flat spots and more wear on one side that the other are indications of front end alignment and/or balance problems. If any of these conditions are noted, take the vehicle to a tire shop or service station to correct the problem.

5.2 Use a tire tread depth indicator to monitor tire wear - they are available at auto parts stores and service stations and cost very little

UNDERINFLATION

CUPPING

OVERINFLATION

Cupping may be caused by:

• Underinflation and/or mechanical irregularities such as out-of-balance condition of wheel and/or tire, and bent or damaged wheel.

• Loose or worn steering tie-rod or steering idler arm.

• Loose, damaged or worn front suspension parts.

INCORRECT TOE-IN OR EXTREME CAMBER

FEATHERING DUE TO MISALIGNMENT

5.3 This chart will help you determine the condition of the tires, the probable cause(s) of abnormal wear and the corrective action necessary

5.4a If a tire loses air on a steady basis, check the valve stem core first to make sure it's snug (special inexpensive wrenches are commonly available at auto parts stores)

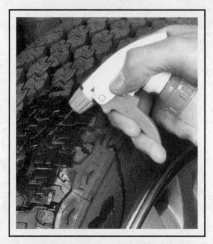

5.4b If the valve stem core is tight, raise the corner of the vehicle with the low tire and spray a soapy water solution onto the tread as the tire is turned slowly - leaks will cause small bubbles to appear

5.8 To extend the life of the tires, check the air pressure at least once a week with an accurate gauge (don't forget the spare!)

4 Look closely for cuts, punctures and embedded nails or tacks. Sometimes a tire will hold air pressure for a short time or leak down very slowly after a nail has embedded itself in the tread. If a slow leak persists, check the valve stem core to make sure it is tight (see illustration). Examine the tread for an object that may have embedded itself into the tire or for a "plug" that may have begun to leak (radial tire punctures are repaired with a plug that is installed in the puncture). If a puncture is suspected, it can be easily verified by spraying a solution of soapy water onto the puncture (see illustration). The soapy solution will bubble if there is a leak. Unless the puncture is unusually large, a tire shop or service station can usually repair the tire.

5 Carefully inspect the inner sidewall of each tire for evidence of brake fluid leakage. If you see any, inspect the brakes immediately.

6 Correct air pressure adds miles to the lifespan of the tires, improves mileage and enhances overall ride quality. Tire pressure cannot be accurately estimated by looking at a tire, especially if it's a radial. A tire pressure gauge is essential. Keep an accurate gauge in the glove compartment. The pressure gauges attached to the nozzles of air hoses at gas stations are often inaccurate.

7 Always check tire pressure when the tires are cold. Cold, in this case, means the vehicle has not been driven over a mile in the three hours preceding a tire pressure check. A pressure rise of four to eight pounds is not uncommon once the tires are warm.

8 Unscrew the valve cap protruding from the wheel or hubcap and push the gauge firmly onto the valve stem (see illustration). Note the reading on the gauge and compare the figure to the recommended tire pressure shown in your owner's manual or on the tire placard on the passenger side door or door pillar. Be sure to reinstall the valve cap to keep dirt and moisture out of the valve stem mechanism. Check all four tires and, if necessary, add enough air to bring them to the recommended pressure.

9 Don't forget to keep the spare tire inflated to the specified pressure (refer to your owner's manual or the placard attached to the door pillar). Note that the pressure recommended for temporary (mini) spare tires is higher than for the tires on the vehicle.

6 Safety checks (every 250 miles or weekly, whichever comes first)

1 Most of these checks can be easily performed while the vehicle is being driven, simply by paying attention to the specified items. The checks are intended to make the vehicle owner aware of potential safety problems before they occur.

2 Check the seat belts for wear, fraying and cuts. Make sure the buckles latch securely and that the automatic retractors function correctly. Do not try to repair seat belts; always replace them if any problems are found.

3 Make sure the ignition key cannot be removed when the transmission is in any gear other than Park (automatic) or Reverse (manual). Make sure the steering column locks when the key is removed from the ignition. It may be necessary to rotate the steering wheel slightly to lock the steering column.

4 Check the parking brake. The easiest way to do this is to park on a steep hill, set the parking brake and see if it keeps the vehicle from rolling. Stay in the vehicle during this check!

5 If equipped with an automatic transmission, also check the Park mechanism. Place the transmission in Park, release the parking brake and note whether the transmission holds the vehicle from rolling. If the vehicle rolls while in Park, the transmission should be taken to a qualified shop for repairs.

6 If equipped with an automatic transmission, see if the shift indicator shows the proper gear. If it doesn't, refer to Chapter 7B for linkage adjustment procedures.

7 If equipped with an automatic transmission, make sure the vehicle starts only in Park or Neutral. If it starts in any other gear, refer to Chapter 7B for switch adjustment procedures.

8 If equipped with a manual transmission, the starter should operate only when the clutch pedal is pressed to the floor. If the starter operates when it shouldn't, refer to Chapter 8 for clutch/starter interlock switch service.

9 Make sure the brakes do not pull to one side while stopping. The

brake pedal should feel firm, but excessive effort should not be required to stop the vehicle. If the pedal sinks too low, if you have to pump it more than once to get a firm pedal, or if pedal effort is too high, refer to Chapter 9 for repair procedures. A squealing sound from the front brakes may be caused by the pad wear indicators. Refer to Chapter 9 for pad replacement procedures.

10 Rearview mirrors should be clean and undamaged. They should hold their position when adjusted.

11 Sun visors should hold their position when adjusted. They should remain securely out of the way when lifted off the windshield.

12 Make sure the defroster blows heated air onto the windshield. If it doesn't, refer to Chapter 3 for heating system service.

13 The horn should sound with a clearly audible tone every time it is operated. If not, refer to Chapter 12.

14 Make sure the windows are clean and undamaged.

15 Turn on the lights, then walk around the car and make sure they work. Check headlights in both the high beam and low beam positions. Check the turn indicators for one side of the vehicle, then for the other side. If possible, have an assistant watch the brake lights while you push the pedal. If no assistant is available, the brake lights can be checked by backing up to a wall or garage door, then pressing the pedal. There should be two distinct patches of red light when the brake pedal is pressed.

16 Make sure locks operate smoothly when the key is turned. Lubricate locks if necessary with Ford Lock Lubricant or an equivalent product. Make sure all latches hold securely.

7 Engine oil and filter change (every 3,000 miles or 3 months, whichever comes first)

◆ Refer to illustrations 7.2, 7.7 and 7.16

1 Frequent oil changes are the most important preventive maintenance procedures that can be done by the home mechanic. As engine oil ages, it becomes diluted and contaminated, which leads to premature engine wear.

2 Make sure that you have all the necessary tools before you begin this procedure (see illustration). You should also have plenty of rags or newspapers handy for mopping up oil spills.

3 Start the engine and allow it to reach normal operating temperature - oil and sludge will flow more easily when warm. If new oil, a filter or tools are needed, use the vehicle to go get them and warm up the engine oil at the same time. Park on a level surface and shut off the engine when it's warmed up. Remove the oil filler cap from the valve cover.

4 Access to the oil drain plug and filter will be improved if the vehicle can be lifted on a hoist, driven onto ramps or supported by jackstands.

✳✳ WARNING:

DO NOT work under a vehicle supported only by a bumper, hydraulic or scissors-type jack - always use jackstands!

5 Raise the vehicle and support it on jackstands. Make sure it is safely supported!

6 If you haven't changed the oil on this vehicle before, get under it and locate the drain plug and the oil filter. The exhaust components will be hot as you work, so note how they are routed to avoid touching them.

7 Being careful not to touch the hot exhaust components, position a drain pan under the plug in the bottom of the engine. Clean the area around the plug, then remove the plug (see illustration). It's a good idea

7.2 These tools are required when changing the engine oil and filter

1 **Drain pan** - It should be fairly shallow in depth, but wide to prevent spills
2 **Rubber gloves** - When removing the drain plug and filter, you will get oil on your hands (the gloves will prevent burns)
3 **Breaker bar** - Sometimes the oil drain plug is tight and a long breaker bar is needed to loosen it
4 **Socket** - To be used with the breaker bar or a ratchet (must be the correct size to fit the drain plug - six-point preferred)
5 **Filter wrench** - This is a metal band-type wrench, which requires clearance around the filter to be effective
6 **Filter wrench** - This type fits on the bottom of the filter and can be turned with a ratchet or breaker bar (different size wrenches are available for different types of filters)

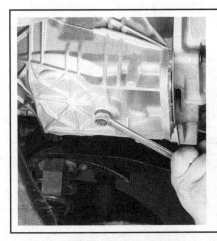

7.7 Remove the oil pan drain plug with a box-end wrench or socket - an open-end or adjustable wrench shouldn't be used, since it may round off the corners of the drain plug

to wear an old glove while unscrewing the plug the final few turns to avoid being scalded by hot oil. It will also help to hold the drain plug against the threads as you unscrew it, then pull it away from the drain hole suddenly. This will place your arm out of the way of the hot oil, as well as reducing the chances of dropping the drain plug into the drain pan.

8 It may be necessary to move the drain pan slightly as oil flow slows to a trickle. Inspect the old oil for the presence of metal particles.

9 After all the oil has drained, wipe off the drain plug with a clean rag. Any small metal particles clinging to the plug would immediately contaminate the new oil.

10 Reinstall the plug and tighten it securely, but don't strip the threads.

11 Move the drain pan into position under the oil filter.

12 Loosen the oil filter by turning it counterclockwise with a filter wrench. Any standard filter wrench will work.

13 Sometimes the oil filter is screwed on so tightly that it can't be loosened. If it is, punch a metal bar or long screwdriver directly through it, as close to the engine as possible, and use it as a T-bar to turn the filter. Be prepared for oil to spurt out of the canister as it's punctured.

14 Once the filter is loose, use your hands to unscrew it from the block. Just as the filter is detached from the block, immediately tilt the open end up to prevent oil inside the filter from spilling out.

15 Using a clean rag, wipe off the mounting surface on the block. Also, make sure that none of the old gasket remains stuck to the mounting surface. It can be removed with a scraper if necessary.

16 Compare the old filter with the new one to make sure they are the same type. Smear some engine oil on the rubber gasket of the new filter and screw it into place (see illustration). Overtightening the filter will damage the gasket, so don't use a filter wrench. Most filter manufacturers recommend tightening the filter by hand only. Normally, they should be tightened 3/4-turn after the gasket contacts the block, but be sure to follow the directions on the filter or container.

17 Remove all tools and materials from under the vehicle, being careful not to spill the oil in the drain pan, then lower the vehicle.

18 Add new oil to the engine through the oil filler cap in the rocker arm cover. Use a funnel to prevent oil from spilling onto the top of the engine. Pour four quarts of fresh oil into the engine. Wait a few minutes

7.16 Lubricate the oil filter gasket with clean engine oil before installing the filter on the engine

to allow the oil to drain into the pan, then check the level on the dipstick (see Section 4 if necessary). If the oil level is in the SAFE range, install the filler cap.

19 Start the engine and run it for about a minute. While the engine is running, look under the vehicle and check for leaks at the oil pan drain plug and around the oil filter. If either one is leaking, stop the engine and tighten the plug or filter slightly.

20 Wait a few minutes, then recheck the level on the dipstick. Add oil as necessary to bring the level into the SAFE range.

21 During the first few trips after an oil change, make it a point to check frequently for leaks and proper oil level.

22 The old oil drained from the engine cannot be reused in its present state and should be disposed of. Check with your local auto parts store, disposal facility or environmental agency to see if they will accept the oil for recycling. After the oil has cooled it can be drained into a container (capped plastic jugs, topped bottles, milk cartons, etc.) for transport to one of these disposal sites. Don't dispose of the oil by pouring it on the ground or down a drain!

8 Power steering fluid level check (every 3,000 miles or 3 months, whichever comes first)

8.2 The power steering fluid reservoir is located on the left side of the engine, just below the air conditioning compressor (if equipped) - SOHC four-cylinder engine shown, V6 engines similar

▶ Refer to illustrations 8.2 and 8.5

1 Check the power steering fluid level periodically to avoid steering system problems, such as damage to the pump.

✳ CAUTION:

DO NOT hold the steering wheel against either stop (extreme left or right turn) for more than five seconds. If you do, the power steering pump could be damaged.

2 The power steering pump, located at the left front corner of the engine on all models, is equipped with a twist-off cap with an integral fluid level dipstick or a reservoir with index marks on the side to check fluid level (see illustration).

3 Park the vehicle on level ground and apply the parking brake.

4 Run the engine until it has reached normal operating temperature. With the engine at idle, turn the steering wheel back-and-forth several times to get any air out of the steering system. Shut the engine off,

remove the cap by turning it counterclockwise, wipe the dipstick clean and reinstall the cap (make sure it is seated).

5   Remove the cap again and note the fluid level. It must be between the two lines designating the FULL HOT range (see illustration) (be sure to use the proper temperature range on the dipstick when checking the fluid level - the FULL COLD lines on the reverse side of the dipstick are only usable when the engine is cold).

6   Add small amounts of fluid until the level is correct.

✳✳ CAUTION:

Do not overfill the pump. If too much fluid is added, remove the excess with a clean syringe or suction pump.

7   Check the power steering hoses and connections for leaks and wear (see Section 11).

8.5 Check the power steering fluid level with the engine at normal operating temperature - fluid should not go above the Full Hot mark

8   Check the condition and tension of the serpentine drivebelt (see Section 12).

9   Automatic transmission fluid check/change

FLUID LEVEL CHECK (EVERY 3,000 MILES OR 3 MONTHS)

▶ Refer to illustrations 9.5 and 9.6

✳✳ CAUTION:

The use of transmission fluid other than the type listed in this Chapter's Specifications could result in transmission malfunctions or failure.

1   The automatic transmission fluid should be carefully maintained. Low fluid level can lead to slipping or loss of drive, while overfilling can cause foaming and loss of fluid. Either condition can cause transmission damage.

2   Since transmission fluid expands as it heats up, the fluid level should only be checked when the transmission is warm (at normal operating temperature). If the vehicle has just been driven over 20 miles (32 km), the transmission can be considered warm.

✳✳ CAUTION:

If the vehicle has just been driven for a long time at high speed or in city traffic, in hot weather, or if it has been pulling a trailer, an accurate fluid level reading cannot be obtained. Allow the transmission to cool down for about 30 minutes. You can also check the transmission fluid level when the transmission is cold. If the vehicle has not been driven for over five hours and the fluid is about room temperature (70 to 95-degrees F), the transmission is cold. However, the fluid level is normally checked with the transmission warm to ensure accurate results.

3   Immediately after driving the vehicle, park it on a level surface, set the parking brake and start the engine. While the engine is idling, depress the brake pedal and move the selector lever through all the gear ranges, beginning and ending in Park.

4   Locate the automatic transmission dipstick tube in the engine compartment (see the illustration at the front of this Chapter for dipstick location).

5   With the engine still idling, pull the dipstick away from the tube (see illustration), wipe it off with a clean rag, push it all the way back into the tube and withdraw it again, then note the fluid level.

6   If the transmission is cold, the level should be in the room temperature range on the dipstick (between the two circles); if it's warm, the

9.5 Make sure the area around the transmission dipstick is clean (arrow), then pull it out of the tube - fluid level is checked with the engine idling

9.6 Follow the directions stamped on the transmission dipstick to get an accurate reading

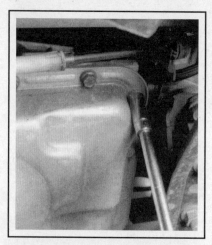

9.14 Remove the bolts around the front and sides of the transmission pan . . .

9.16 . . . and let the pan hang down so the fluid can drain

9.19 Once the pan is removed the filter is accessible

fluid level should be in the operating temperature range (between the two lines) (see illustration). If the level is low, add the specified automatic transmission fluid through the dipstick tube - use a clean funnel to prevent spills.

7   Add just enough of the recommended fluid to fill the transmission to the proper level. It takes about one pint to raise the level from the low mark to the high mark when the fluid is hot, so add the fluid a little at a time and keep checking the level until it's correct.

8   The condition of the fluid should also be checked along with the level. If the fluid is black or a dark reddish-brown color, or if it smells burned, it should be changed (see below). If you are in doubt about its condition, purchase some new fluid and compare the two for color and smell.

FLUID AND FILTER CHANGE (EVERY 24,000 MILES OR 24 MONTHS)

▶ **Refer to illustrations 9.14, 9.16 and 9.19**

➡**Note: On 2006 and later models, the automatic transmission is filled for life, and at-home fluid changes are not recommended by the manufacturer.**

9   At the specified intervals, the transmission fluid should be drained and replaced. Since the fluid will remain hot long after driving, perform this procedure only after the engine has cooled down completely.

10   Before beginning work, purchase the specified transmission fluid (see *Recommended lubricants and fluids* at the end of this Chapter), a new filter and gasket. Never reuse the old filter or gasket!

11   Other tools necessary for this job include jackstands to support the vehicle in a raised position, a drain pan capable of holding at least eight quarts, newspapers and clean rags.

12   Raise the vehicle and support it securely on jackstands. DO NOT crawl under the vehicle when it is supported only by a jack! Place the drain pan beneath the transmission.

13   If you're working on a vehicle with a 4.0L engine, pry the transmission heat shield loose from the edge of the transmission fluid pan (if equipped). It isn't necessary to remove the heat shield from the vehicle.

14   With the drain pan in place, remove the mounting bolts from the

front and sides of the transmission fluid pan (see illustration).

15   Loosen the rear pan bolts approximately four turns.

16   Carefully pry the transmission pan loose with a screwdriver. Let the pan hang down so the fluid can drain (see illustration). Don't damage the pan or transmission gasket surfaces or leaks could develop.

17   Remove the remaining bolts, pan and gasket. Carefully clean the gasket surface of the transmission to remove all traces of the old gasket and sealant.

18   Drain the fluid from the transmission pan, clean it with solvent and dry it with compressed air.

19   Remove the filter from the mount inside the transmission (see illustration).

20   Install a new filter and gasket. Tighten the mounting bolt securely. Remove the magnet (if equipped) from the pan, clean it and the pan, then attach the magnet back inside the pan.

21   Make sure the gasket surface on the transmission pan is clean, then install a new gasket.

➡**Note: On later models, the pan gasket is reusable, if not damaged during removal.**

Put the pan in place against the transmission and install the bolts. Working around the pan, tighten each bolt a little at a time until the torque listed in this Chapter's Specifications is reached. Don't overtighten the bolts!

22   Lower the vehicle and add automatic transmission fluid through the filler tube.

✳✳ CAUTION:

Refer to the Specifications at the end of this Chapter for the correct amount and type of transmission fluid. Use of the wrong type or the wrong amount can cause transmission damage.

23   With the transmission in Park and the parking brake set, run the engine at a fast idle, but don't race it.

24   Move the gear selector through each range and back to Park. Check the fluid level. Add fluid if needed to reach the correct level.

25   Check under the vehicle for leaks after the first few trips.

10 Tire rotation (every 3,000 miles or 3 months, whichever comes first)

▶ **Refer to illustrations 10.2a and 10.2b**

1   The tires should be rotated at the specified intervals and whenever uneven wear is noticed. Since the vehicle will be raised and the tires checked anyway, check the brakes also (see Section 25).

2   It is recommended that the tires be rotated in a specific pattern (see illustrations).

3   Refer to the information in *Jacking and towing* at the front of this manual for the proper procedure to follow when raising the vehicle and changing a tire. If the brakes must be checked, don't apply the parking brake as stated.

4   The vehicle must be raised on a hoist or supported on jackstands to get all four tires off the ground. Make sure the vehicle is safely supported!

5   After the rotation procedure is finished, check and adjust the tire pressures as necessary and be sure to check the lug nut tightness.

10.2a Tire rotation diagram (2010 and earlier models)

10.2b Tire rotation diagram (2011 models)

11 Underhood hose check and replacement (every 6,000 miles or 6 months, whichever comes first)

❈ CAUTION:

Replacement of air conditioning hoses must be left to a dealer service department or air conditioning shop that has the equipment to depressurize the system safely. Never disconnect air conditioning hoses or components until the system has been depressurized.

GENERAL

1   High temperatures under the hood can cause deterioration of the rubber and plastic hoses used for engine, accessory and emission systems operation. Periodic inspection should be made for cracks, loose clamps, material hardening and leaks.

2   Information specific to the cooling system can be found in Section 22.

3   Most (but not all) hoses are secured to the fitting with clamps. Where clamps are used, check to be sure they haven't lost their tension, allowing the hose to leak. If clamps aren't used, make sure the hose has not expanded and/or hardened where it slips over the fitting, allowing it to leak.

PCV SYSTEM HOSE

4   To reduce hydrocarbon emissions, crankcase blow-by gas is vented through the PCV valve to the intake manifold via a rubber hose on most models. The blow-by gases mix with incoming air in the intake manifold before being burned in the combustion chambers.

5   Check the PCV hose for cracks, leaks and other damage. Disconnect it from the valve cover and the intake manifold and check the inside for obstructions. If it's clogged, clean it out with solvent.

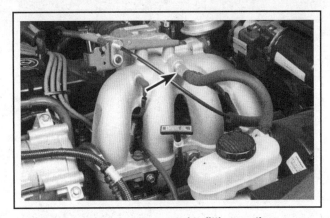

11.6 Vacuum hoses are connected to fittings on the intake manifold

VACUUM HOSES

▶ **Refer to illustration 11.6**

6   It's quite common for vacuum hoses, especially those in the emissions system, to be color coded or identified by colored stripes molded into them. Various systems require hoses with different wall thicknesses, collapse resistance and temperature resistance. When replacing hoses, be sure the new ones are made of the same material. A number of hoses connect to vacuum fittings on the intake manifold (see illustration).

7   Often the only effective way to check a hose is to remove it completely from the vehicle. If more than one hose is removed, be sure to

label the hoses and fittings to ensure correct installation.

8   When checking vacuum hoses, be sure to include any plastic T-fittings in the check. Inspect the fittings for cracks and the hose where it fits over each fitting for distortion, which could cause leakage.

9   A small piece of vacuum hose can be used as a stethoscope to detect vacuum leaks. Hold one end of the hose to your ear and probe around vacuum hoses and fittings, listening for the "hissing" sound characteristic of a vacuum leak.

※※ WARNING:

When probing with the vacuum hose stethoscope, be careful not to come into contact with moving engine components such as the drivebelt, cooling fan, etc.

FUEL HOSES

※※ WARNING:

There are certain precautions which must be taken when servicing or inspecting fuel system components. Work in a well ventilated area and do not allow open flames (cigarettes, appliance pilot lights, etc.) or bare light bulbs near the work area. Mop up any spills immediately and do not store fuel-soaked rags where they could ignite.

10 The fuel lines are usually under pressure, so if any fuel lines are to be disconnected be prepared to catch spilled fuel.

※※ WARNING:

These vehicles are equipped with fuel injection; you must relieve the fuel system pressure before servicing the fuel lines.

Refer to Chapter 4 for the fuel system pressure relief procedure.

11 Check all rubber fuel lines for deterioration and chafing. Check especially for cracks in areas where the hose bends and just before fittings, such as where a hose attaches to the fuel pump, fuel filter and carburetor or fuel injection system.

12 High quality fuel line, specifically designed for fuel-injection systems, must be used for fuel line replacement. Never, under any circumstances, use unreinforced vacuum line, clear plastic tubing or water hose for fuel lines.

13 Spring-type clamps are commonly used on fuel lines. These clamps often lose their tension over a period of time, and can be "sprung" during removal. Replace all spring-type clamps with screw clamps whenever a hose is replaced.

METAL LINES

14 Sections of metal line are often used for fuel line between the fuel pump and carburetor or fuel injection system. Check carefully to make sure the line isn't bent, crimped or cracked.

15 If a section of metal fuel line must be replaced, use seamless steel tubing only, since copper and aluminum tubing do not have the strength necessary to withstand the vibration caused by the engine.

16 Check the metal brake lines where they enter the master cylinder and brake proportioning unit (if used) for cracks in the lines and loose fittings. Any sign of brake fluid leakage calls for an immediate thorough inspection of the brake system.

NYLON FUEL LINES

17 Nylon fuel lines are used at several points in fuel injection systems. These lines require special materials and methods for repair. Refer to Chapter 4 for details.

POWER STEERING HOSES

18 Check the power steering hoses for leaks, loose connections and worn clamps. Tighten loose connections. Worn clamps or leaky hoses should be replaced.

12 Drivebelt check, adjustment and replacement (every 6,000 miles or 6 months, whichever comes first)

12.2 The belt's pathway is illustrated on a decal on the radiator support

♦ **Refer to illustrations 12.2, 12.3, 12.5a and 12.5b**

1   The accessory drivebelt is located at the front of the engine. The single serpentine belt drives the water pump, alternator, power steering pump and air conditioning compressor. The condition and tension of the drivebelt is critical to the operation of the engine and accessories. Excessive tension causes bearing wear, while insufficient tension produces slippage, noise, component vibration and belt failure. Because of their composition and the high stress to which they are subjected, drivebelts stretch and continue to deteriorate as they get older. As a result, they must be periodically checked. The serpentine belt has an automatic tensioner and requires no adjustment for the life of the belt.

CHECK

2   These vehicles use a single V-ribbed belt to drive all of the accessories. This is also known as a "serpentine" belt because of the winding path it follows between various drive, accessory and idler pulleys (see illustration).

Cracks Running Across
"V" Portions of Belt
ACCEPTABLE

1/2"

Missing Two or More Adjacent
Ribs 1/2" or longer

UNACCEPTABLE

Cracks Running Parallel
to "V" Portions of Belt

12.3 Small cracks in the underside of a V-ribbed belt are acceptable - lengthwise cracks, or missing pieces that cause the belt to make noise, are cause for replacement

12.5a To loosen the belt, place a 3/8-inch drive ratchet in the square-shaped hole (use a wrench on tensioners without a hole) . . .

12.5b . . . and rotate it against the spring force in the direction shown to move the tensioner off the belt

3   With the engine off, open the hood and locate the drivebelt at the front of the engine. With a flashlight, check the belt for separation of the rubber plies from each side of the core, a severed core, separation of the ribs from the rubber and torn or worn ribs. Also check for fraying and glazing, which gives the belt a shiny appearance. Cracks in the rib side of V-ribbed belts are acceptable, as are small chunks missing from the ribs. If a V-ribbed belt has lost chunks bigger than 1/2-inch (13 mm) from two adjacent ribs, or if the missing chunks cause belt noise, the belt should be replaced (see illustration). Both sides of the belt should be inspected, which means you'll have to twist it to check the underside. Use your fingers to feel the belt where you can't see it. If any of the above conditions are evident, replace the belt.

ADJUSTMENT

4   Tension is set by an automatic tensioner. Manual adjustment is not required.

REPLACEMENT

5   To replace a serpentine belt, rotate the tensioner counterclockwise (2.3L, 2.5L and 4.0L engines) or clockwise (3.0L engine) to lift it off the belt (see illustrations). Slip the belt off the pulleys.

6   Hold the tensioner in the released position. Install a new belt and make sure it is routed correctly. Be sure the ribs of the new belt engage the pulley ribs correctly. Release the tensioner.

DRIVEBELT TENSIONER REPLACEMENT

7   To replace a tensioner that can't properly tension the belt, or one that exhibits binding or worn-out bearing/pulley, remove the drivebelt (see Step 5), then unscrew the mounting bolt. On 2011 4.0L V6 models, the air filter intake duct must be removed first (see Chapter 4).

8   Installation of the tensioner is the reverse of removal. Tighten the bolt to the torque value listed in this Chapter's Specifications.

9   Install the drivebelt (see Steps 5 and 6). On 2011 models, install the air filter housing duct (see Chapter 4).

13 Battery check, maintenance and charging (every 6,000 miles or 6 months, whichever comes first)

CHECK AND MAINTENANCE

◆ Refer to illustrations 13.1, 13.4, 13.8a, 13.8b, 13.8c and 13.8d

❊❊ WARNING:

Certain precautions must be followed when checking and servicing the battery. Hydrogen gas, which is highly flammable, is always present in the battery cells, so keep lighted tobacco and all other flames and sparks away from it. The electrolyte inside the battery is actually dilute sulfuric acid, which will cause injury if splashed on your skin or in your eyes. It will also ruin clothes and painted surfaces. When removing the battery cables, always detach the negative cable first and hook it up last!

1 Battery maintenance is an important procedure which will help ensure that you are not stranded because of a dead battery. Several tools are required for this procedure (see illustration).

2 Before servicing the battery, always turn the engine and all accessories off and disconnect the cable from the negative terminal of the battery.

3 A sealed (sometimes called maintenance free) battery is standard equipment. The cell caps cannot be removed, no electrolyte checks are required and water cannot be added to the cells. However, if an aftermarket battery has been installed and it is a type that requires regular maintenance, the following procedures can be used.

4 If equipped with a maintenance-type battery, check the electrolyte level in each of the battery cells (see illustration). It must be above the plates. There's usually a split-ring indicator in each cell to indicate the correct level. If the level is low, add distilled water only, then install the cell caps.

❊❊ CAUTION:

Overfilling the cells may cause electrolyte to spill over during periods of heavy charging, causing corrosion and damage to nearby components.

5 If the positive terminal and cable clamp on your vehicle's battery is equipped with a rubber protector, make sure that it's not torn or damaged. It should completely cover the terminal.

6 The external condition of the battery should be checked periodically. Look for damage such as a cracked case.

7 Check the tightness of the battery cable clamps to ensure good electrical connections and inspect the entire length of each cable, looking for cracked or abraded insulation and frayed conductors.

8 If corrosion (visible as white, fluffy deposits) is evident, remove the cables from the terminals, clean them with a battery brush and rein-

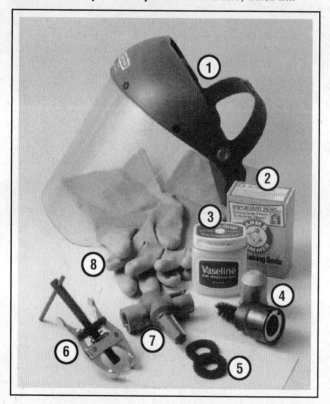

13.1 Tools and materials required for battery maintenance

1 *Face shield/safety goggles* - *When removing corrosion with a brush, the acidic particles can easily fly up into your eyes*
2 *Baking soda* - *A solution of baking soda and water can be used to neutralize corrosion*
3 *Petroleum jelly* - *A layer of this on the battery posts will help prevent corrosion*
4 *Battery post/cable cleaner* - *This wire brush cleaning tool will remove all traces of corrosion from the battery posts and cable clamps*
5 *Treated felt washers* - *Placing one of these on each post, directly under the cable clamps, will help prevent corrosion*
6 *Puller* - *Sometimes the cable clamps are very difficult to pull off the posts, even after the nut/bolt has been completely loosened. This tool pulls the clamp straight up and off the post without damage*
7 *Battery post/cable cleaner* - *Here is another cleaning tool which is a slightly different version of number 4 above, but it does the same thing*
8 *Rubber gloves* - *Another safety item to consider when servicing the battery; remember that's acid inside the battery!*

13.4 If equipped with a maintenance-type battery, remove the cell caps to check the water level in the battery - if the level is low, add distilled water only

stall them (see illustrations). Corrosion can be kept to a minimum by installing specially treated washers available at auto parts stores or by applying a layer of petroleum jelly or grease to the terminals and cable clamps after they are assembled.

9   Make sure that the battery carrier is in good condition and that the hold-down clamp bolt is tight. If the battery is removed (see Chapter 5 for the removal and installation procedure), make sure that no parts remain in the bottom of the carrier when it's reinstalled. When reinstalling the hold-down clamp, don't overtighten the bolt.

10 Corrosion on the carrier, battery case and surrounding areas can be removed with a solution of water and baking soda. Apply the mixture with a small brush, let it work, then rinse it off with plenty of clean water.

11 Any metal parts of the vehicle damaged by corrosion should be coated with a zinc-based primer, then painted.

12 Additional information on the battery and jump starting can be found in Chapter 5 and the front of this manual.

CHARGING

13 Remove all of the cell caps (if equipped) and cover the holes with a clean cloth to prevent spattering electrolyte. Disconnect the negative battery cable and hook the battery charger leads to the battery posts (positive to positive, negative to negative), then plug in the charger. Make sure it is set at 12-volts if it has a selector switch.

14 If you're using a charger with a rate higher than two amps, check the battery regularly during charging to make sure it doesn't overheat. If you're using a trickle charger, you can safely let the battery charge overnight after you've checked it regularly for the first couple of hours.

15 If the battery has removable cell caps, measure the specific gravity with a hydrometer every hour during the last few hours of the charging cycle. Hydrometers are available inexpensively from auto parts stores - follow the instructions that come with the hydrometer. Consider the battery charged when there's no change in the specific gravity reading for two hours and the electrolyte in the cells is gassing (bubbling) freely. The specific gravity reading from each cell should be very close to the others. If not, the battery probably has a bad cell(s).

16 Some batteries with sealed tops have built-in hydrometers on the top that indicate the state of charge by the color displayed in the hydrometer window. Normally, a bright-colored hydrometer indicates a full charge and a dark hydrometer indicates the battery still needs charging. Check the battery manufacturer's instructions to be sure you know what the colors mean.

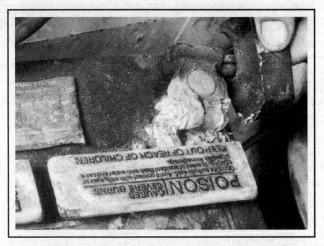

13.8a Battery terminal corrosion usually appears as light, fluffy powder

13.8b Removing the cable from a battery post with a wrench - sometimes special battery pliers are required for this procedure if corrosion has caused deterioration of the nut hex (always remove the ground cable first and hook it up last!)

17 If the battery has a sealed top and no built-in hydrometer, you can hook up a digital voltmeter across the battery terminals to check the charge. A fully charged battery should read 12.6-volts or higher.

18 Further information on the battery and jump starting can be found in Chapter 5 and at the front of this manual.

13.8c Regardless of the type of tool used on the battery posts, a clean, shiny surface should be the result

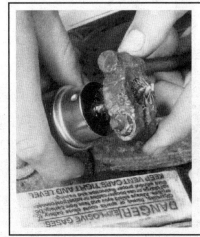

13.8d When cleaning the cable clamps, all corrosion must be removed (the inside of the clamp is tapered to match the taper on the post, so don't remove too much material)

14 Spark plugs and wires - check and replacement (every 30,000 miles or 30 months, whichever comes first)

SPARK PLUGS

◆ **Refer to illustrations 14.2, 14.5a, 14.5b, 14.7, 14.9 and 14.10**

1 The spark plugs are located on the sides of the engine.

➡**Note: The 2.5L (2000 and 2001) four-cylinder engine models are equipped with two spark plugs per cylinder, for a total of eight spark plugs. The spark plugs on the intake manifold side of the** engine are very difficult to access, requiring removal of intake system components and/or several special tools (long extensions, swivel socket, etc.). Refer to Chapter 4 for additional information on the intake system. The maximum replacement interval for spark plugs specified by the manufacturer is as follows:

a) *2000 four-cylinder engines - 60,000 miles*
b) *2000 through 2010 3.0L and 4.0L engines - 100,000 miles**
c) *2001 through 2010 four-cylinder engines - 100,000 miles*
d) *2011 models - 105,000 miles*

* While the manufacturer specifies a 100,000-mile interval for most late-model engines we recommend a 60,000-mile interval for these engines, since fouling and erosion can often cause misfiring before 100,000 miles.

2 In most cases, the tools necessary for spark plug replacement include a spark plug socket which fits into a ratchet (spark plug sockets are padded inside to prevent damage to the porcelain insulators on the new plugs and to hold the plugs in the socket during removal and installation), various extensions and a gap gauge to check and adjust the gaps on the new plugs (see illustration). A special plug wire removal tool is available for separating the wire boots from the spark plugs, but it isn't absolutely necessary. A torque wrench should be used to tighten the new plugs.

14.2 Tools required for changing spark plugs

1 **Spark plug socket -** *This will have special padding inside to protect the spark plug's ceramic insulator*
2 **Torque wrench -** *Although not mandatory, using this tool is the best way to ensure the plugs are tightened properly*
3 **Ratchet -** *Standard hand tool to fit the spark plug socket*
4 **Extension -** *Depending on model and accessories, you may need special extensions and universal joints to reach one or more of the plugs*
5 **Spark plug gap gauge -** *This gauge for checking the gap comes in a variety of styles. Make sure the gap for your engine is included.*

14.5a Spark plug manufacturers recommend using a wire type gauge when checking the gap - if the wire does not slide between the electrodes with a slight drag, adjustment is required

14.5b To change the gap, bend the side electrode only, as indicated by the arrows, and be very careful not to crack or chip the porcelain insulator surrounding the center electrode

TWIST AND PULL

14.7 When removing the spark plug wires, pull only on the boot and twist it back-and-forth

A **normally worn** spark plug should have light tan or gray deposits on the firing tip.

A **carbon fouled** plug, identified by soft, sooty, black deposits, may indicate an improperly tuned vehicle. Check the air cleaner, ignition components and engine control system.

An **oil fouled** spark plug indicates an engine with worn piston rings and/or bad valve seals allowing excessive oil to enter the chamber.

This spark plug has been **left in the engine too long**, as evidenced by the extreme gap- Plugs with such an extreme gap can cause misfiring and stumbling accompanied by a noticeable lack of power.

A **physically damaged** spark plug may be evidence of severe detonation in that cylinder. Watch that cylinder carefully between services, as a continued detonation will not only damage the plug, but could also damage the engine.

A **bridged or almost bridged** spark plug, identified by a build-up between the electrodes caused by excessive carbon or oil build-up on the plug.

14.9 Inspect the spark plug to determine engine running conditions

3   The best approach when replacing the spark plugs is to purchase the new ones in advance, adjust them to the proper gap and replace the plugs one at a time. When buying the new spark plugs, be sure to obtain the correct type for your particular engine. This information can be found in this Chapter's Specifications, on the *Vehicle Emission Control Information* label located under the hood and in the vehicle owner's manual. If differences exist between the plug specified on the emissions label and in the owner's manual or in this Chapter's Specifications, assume the emissions label is correct.

4   Allow the engine to cool completely before attempting to remove any of the plugs. While you are waiting for the engine to cool, check the new plugs for defects and adjust the gaps.

5   The gap is checked by inserting the proper thickness gauge between the electrodes at the tip of the plug (see illustration). The gap between the plugs should be the same as the one specified on the *Vehicle Emissions Control Information label* or in this Chapter's Specifications. The gauge wire should just slide between the electrodes with a slight amount of drag. If the gap is incorrect, use the adjuster on the gauge body to bend the curved side electrode slightly until the specified gap is obtained (see illustration). If the side electrode is not exactly over the center electrode, bend it with the adjuster until it is. Check for cracks in the porcelain insulator (if any are found, the plug should not be used).

6   On 2011 4.0L V6 models, loosen the right front wheel lug nuts, raise the front of the vehicle and support it securely on jackstands. Remove the right front wheel and the inner fenderwell liner (see Chapter 11, if necessary).

7   With the engine cool, remove the spark plug wire from one spark plug. Pull only on the boot at the end of the wire - do not pull on the wire. A plug wire removal tool should be used if available (see illustration). If compressed air is available, use it to blow any dirt or foreign material away from the spark plug hole. The idea here is to eliminate the possibility of debris falling into the cylinder as the spark plug is removed.

8   Place the spark plug socket over the plug and remove it from the

14.10 A length of snug-fitting rubber hose will save time and prevent damaged threads when installing the spark plugs

engine by turning in a counterclockwise direction.

9   Compare the spark plug to those shown in this spark plug condition chart (see illustration) to get an indication of the general running condition of the engine.

10 Thread one of the new plugs into the hole until you can no longer turn it with your fingers, then tighten it with a torque wrench (if available) or the ratchet. It's a good idea to slip a short length of rubber hose over the end of the plug to use as a tool to thread it into place, particularly if the cylinder head is made of aluminum (see illustration). The hose will grip the plug well enough to turn it, but will start to slip if the plug begins to cross-thread in the hole - this will prevent damaged threads and the accompanying repair costs.

11 Before pushing the spark plug wire onto the end of the plug, inspect it following the procedures outlined below.

12 Attach the plug wire to the new spark plug, again using a twisting motion on the boot until it is seated on the spark plug.

13 Repeat the procedure for the remaining spark plugs, replacing them one at a time to prevent mixing up the spark plug wires.

SPARK PLUG WIRES

→Note: Every time a spark plug wire is detached from a spark plug or the coil, silicone dielectric compound (a clear grease available at auto parts stores) should be applied to the inside of each boot before reconnection. Use a small standard screwdriver to coat the entire inside surface of each boot with a thin layer of the compound.

14 The spark plug wires should be checked and, if necessary, replaced at the same time new spark plugs are installed.

15 The easiest way to identify bad wires is to make a visual check while the engine is running. In a dark, well-ventilated garage, start the engine and look at each plug wire. Be careful not to come into contact with any moving engine parts. If there is a break in the wire, you will see arcing or a small spark at the damaged area. If arcing is noticed, make a note to obtain new wires.

16 The spark plug wires should be inspected one at a time, beginning with the spark plug for the number one cylinder, to prevent confusion. Clearly label each original plug wire with a piece of tape marked with the correct number. The plug wires must be reinstalled in the correct order to ensure proper engine operation.

→Note: 2000 2.5L engines have two spark plugs per cylinder, and two plug wires per cylinder.

17 Disconnect the spark plug wire from the first spark plug. A removal tool can be used (see illustration 14.7), or you can grab the wire boot, twist it slightly and pull the wire free. Do not pull on the wire itself, only on the rubber boot.

18 Push the wire and boot back onto the end of the spark plug. It should fit snugly. If it doesn't, detach the wire and boot once more and use a pair of pliers to carefully crimp the metal connector inside the wire boot until it does.

19 Using a clean rag, wipe the entire length of the wire to remove built-up dirt and grease.

20 Once the wire is clean, check for burns, cracks and other damage. Do not bend the wire sharply or you might break the conductor.

21 Disconnect the wire from the ignition coil pack or distributor. Squeeze the locking tabs together and pull the end of the wire out of the terminal. Check for corrosion and a tight fit. Replace the wire in the coil pack.

22 Inspect each of the remaining spark plug wires, making sure that each one is securely fastened at the coil pack or distributor and spark plug when the check is complete.

23 If new spark plug wires are required, purchase a set for your specific engine model. Pre-cut wire sets with the boots already installed are available. Remove and replace the wires one at a time to avoid mix-ups in the firing order.

15 Automatic transmission shift linkage lubrication (every 6,000 miles or 6 months, whichever comes first)

▶ Refer to illustrations 15.3a and 15.3b

1 Open the hood and locate the shift cable pivot point on the steering column. Also locate the cable end and pivot point on the transmission lever (raise the vehicle and support it securely on jackstands, if necessary).

2 Clean the cable ends and pivot points.

3 Carefully pry the cable ends off the pivot points and lubricate the pivot points with multi-purpose grease (see illustrations). Reconnect the cable(s).

15.3a The lubrication points are accessible between the transmission and the exhaust pipe on the driver's side of the vehicle

15.3b Carefully pry the kickdown cable end off the ballstud to lubricate the stud

16 Chassis lubrication (every 6,000 miles or 6 months, whichever comes first)

▶ Refer to illustrations 16.1, 16.6a, 16.6b, 16.6c, 16.14a and 16.14b

→Note: Many late-model vehicles have suspension components that are maintenance free. No grease fittings or lubrication ports (plugged) will be found on these vehicles for chassis lubrication.

1 Refer to *Recommended lubricants and fluids* at the end of this Chapter to obtain the necessary grease, etc. You'll also need a grease gun (see illustration). Occasionally plugs will be installed rather than grease fittings. If so, grease fittings will have to be purchased and installed.

2 Look under the vehicle and locate the grease fittings or plugs in

16.1 Materials required for chassis and body lubrication

1 *Engine oil* - Light engine oil in a can like this can be used for door and hood hinges
2 *Graphite spray* - Used to lubricate lock cylinders
3 *Grease* - Grease, in a variety of types and weights, is available for use in a grease gun. Check the Specifications for your requirements
4 *Grease gun* - A common grease gun, shown here with a detachable hose and nozzle, is needed for chassis lubrication. After use, clean it thoroughly!

the tie-rod ends. If there are plugs, remove them and buy grease fittings, which will thread into the component. A dealer or auto parts store will be able to supply the correct fittings. Straight, as well as angled, fittings are available.

3 For easier access under the vehicle, raise it with a jack and place jackstands under the frame. Make sure the vehicle is safely supported - DO NOT crawl under the vehicle when it is supported only by the jack!

If the wheels are to be removed at this interval for tire rotation or brake inspection, loosen the lug nuts slightly while the vehicle is still on the ground.

4 Before beginning, force a little grease out of the nozzle to remove any dirt from the end of the gun. Wipe the nozzle clean with a rag.

5 With the grease gun and plenty of clean rags, crawl under the vehicle.

6 Wipe the tie-rod end grease fitting nipple clean and push the nozzle firmly over it. Squeeze the trigger on the grease gun to force grease into the component (see illustrations). They should be lubricated until the rubber seal is firm to the touch. Don't pump too much grease into the fitting as it could rupture the seal. If grease escapes around the grease gun nozzle, the nipple is clogged or the nozzle is not completely seated on the fitting. Resecure the gun nozzle to the fitting and try again. If necessary, replace the fitting with a new one.

7 Wipe the excess grease from the components and the grease fitting. Repeat the procedure for the remaining fitting(s).

➡Note: Original equipment universal joints don't have grease fittings, but they may have been replaced with U-joints that do have grease fittings. Some models are equipped with a flush grease fitting on the driveshaft centering device. If this is the case, lubricate the fittings with a grease gun at the interval listed in the Maintenance schedule. You'll need an adapter to lubricate the flush fitting.

8 Open the hood and smear a little chassis grease on the hood latch mechanism. Have an assistant pull the hood release lever from inside the vehicle as you lubricate the cable at the latch.

9 Lubricate all the hinges (door, hood, etc.) with engine oil to keep them in proper working order.

10 The key lock cylinders can be lubricated with spray graphite or silicone lubricant, which is available at auto parts stores.

11 Lubricate the door weatherstripping with silicone spray. This will reduce chafing and retard wear.

12 Lubricate the parking brake linkage. Note that two different types of grease are required. Use multi-purpose grease on the linkage, adjuster assembly and connectors; use speedometer cable lubricant on parts of the cable that touch other parts of the vehicle. Lubricate the cable twice, once with the parking brake set and once with it released.

13 On manual transmission equipped models, lubricate the clutch linkage pivot points.

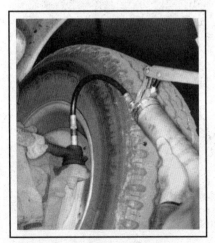

16.6a Lubricate the tie-rod ends (one on each side of the vehicle) . . .

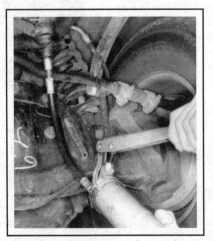

16.6b . . . the Pitman arm connection to the steering linkage . . .

16.6c . . . and the steering linkage cross rod

16.14a Remove the throttle linkage protective cover (2.3L engine shown)

16.14b After the cover is removed, carefully pry the linkage from the stud, grease the stud and reconnect the linkage

14 Remove the protective cover from the throttle lever ballstud (see illustration). Carefully unsnap the throttle linkage from the ballstud (see illustration). Lubricate the ballstud with multi-purpose grease, then reconnect the linkage and install the protective cover.

17 Manual transmission lubricant level check and change (every 12,000 miles or 12 monthswhichever comes first)

♦ **Refer to illustration 17.1**

➡**Note: The transmission lubricant level and quality should not deteriorate under normal driving conditions. However, it's recommended that you check the level occasionally. The most convenient time would be when the vehicle is raised for another reason, such as an engine oil change.**

LEVEL CHECK

1 The transmission has a check/fill plug which must be removed to check the lubricant level (see illustration). If the vehicle is raised to gain access to the plug, be sure to support it safely on jackstands - DO NOT crawl under a vehicle which is supported only by a jack!

2 Remove the plug from the transmission and use your little finger to reach inside the housing and feel the lubricant level. It should be at or very near the bottom of the plug hole.

3 If it isn't, add the recommended lubricant through the plug hole with a syringe or squeeze bottle.

4 Install and tighten the plug securely and check for leaks after the first few miles of driving.

LUBRICANT CHANGE

5 Manual transmission lubricant does not normally need changing during the life of the vehicle, but if you wish to do so, place a drain pan beneath the drain plug (see illustration 17.1). Remove the filler plug, then remove the drain plug and let the lubricant drain into a pan. Let the lubricant drain for 10 minutes or more, then reinstall the drain plug and tighten securely.

6 Fill the transmission to the bottom of the filler plug hole with the recommended lubricant.

7 Install and tighten the filler plug securely and check for leaks after the first few miles of driving.

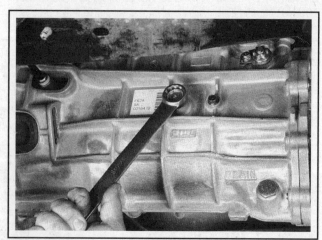

17.1 Manual transmission fill (upper) and drain (lower) plugs

18 Differential lubricant level check and change (every 12,000 miles or 12 months, whichever comes first)

▶ Refer to illustrations 18.2a, 18.2b, 18.3, 18.7, 18.8, 18.11a, 18.11b and 18.12

➡Note: This procedure applies to both the front and rear differential. The manufacturer recommends that differential lubricant be changed only at 100,000-mile intervals - and not checked between intervals - unless a leak is suspected or the differential has been submerged in water. Before starting this procedure, check for oil leaks at the differential pinion seal and cover gasket.

LEVEL CHECK

1   The differential has a check/fill plug which must be removed to check the lubricant level. If the vehicle is raised to gain access to the plug, be sure to support it safely on jackstands - DO NOT crawl under the vehicle when it's supported only by the jack!

2   Remove the lubricant check/fill plug from the differential (see illustrations). Use a 3/8-inch drive ratchet and short extension without a socket to unscrew the plug from the rear differential; use an open end wrench to unscrew the plug from the front differential.

3   Use your little finger as a dipstick to make sure the lubricant level is even with the bottom of the plug hole (see illustration). If not, use a syringe to add the recommended lubricant until it just starts to run out of the opening. On some models a tag is located in the area of the plug which gives information regarding lubricant type, particularly on models equipped with a limited slip differential.

4   Install the plug and tighten it securely.

LUBRICANT CHANGE

5   If it is necessary to change the differential lubricant, remove the check/fill plug (see illustration 18.2a or 18.2b), then drain the differential. Some differentials can be drained by removing the drain plug, while on some rear differentials it's necessary to remove the cover plate

18.2a The check/fill plug for the rear differential is located in the differential housing, facing the front of the vehicle

on the differential housing. As an alternative, a hand suction pump can be used to remove the differential lubricant through the filler hole. This is the only way to drain front axles which don't have a drain plug. If you remove the cover plate, obtain a tube of silicone sealant to be used when reinstalling the differential cover.

6   If equipped with a drain plug, remove the plug and allow the differential lubricant to drain completely. After the lubricant has drained, install the plug and tighten it securely.

7   If a suction pump is being used, insert the flexible hose (see illustration). Work the hose down to the bottom of the differential housing and pump the lubricant out.

8   If the differential is being drained by removing the cover plate, remove all of the bolts except the two near the top. Loosen the remain-

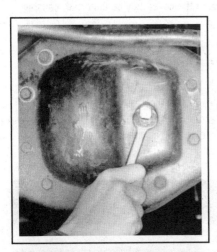

18.2b The check/fill plug for the front differential on 4WD models is located in the axle housing - use an open-end wrench to loosen it

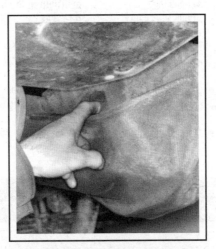

18.3 Reach into the filler hole with a finger to check the lubricant level

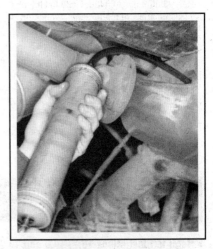

18.7 A suction pump can be used to remove the old lubricant from the differential - it's the only method for differentials that don't have cover or a drain plug

18.8 The rear differential can be drained by removing the cover if you don't have a suction pump

18.11a If you drain the differential by removing the cover, apply a thin film of RTV sealant to the differential cover just before installation . . .

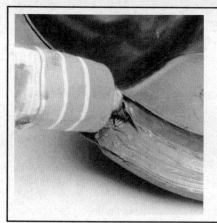

18.11b . . . then apply a thick bead all around the inside edge of the cover

18.12 Tighten the cover bolts in a criss-cross pattern - don't overtighten the bolts, or the cover may be distorted, causing it to leak

ing two bolts and use them to keep the cover loosely attached. Allow the lubricant to drain into the pan, then completely remove the cover (see illustration).

9   Using a lint-free rag, clean the inside of the cover and the accessible areas of the differential housing. As this is done, check for chipped gears and metal particles in the lubricant, indicating that the differential should be more thoroughly inspected and/or repaired.

10 Clean all old gasket material from the cover and differential housing.

11 Apply a thin film of RTV sealant to the cover mating surface, then run a thick bead all the way around inside the cover bolt holes (see illustrations).

12 Place the cover on the differential housing and install the bolts.

Tighten the bolts securely in a criss-cross pattern (see illustration). Don't overtighten them or the cover may be distorted and leaks may develop.

13 On all models, use a hand pump, syringe or funnel to fill the differential housing with the specified lubricant until it's level with the bottom of the plug hole.

14 Install the check/fill plug and tighten it securely.

---

19 Transfer case lubricant level check and change (every 12,000 miles or 12 months, whichever comes first)

▸ **Refer to illustrations 19.2, 19.6 and 19.7**

➡ **Note: This procedure applies to 4WD models only.**

LEVEL CHECK

1   The transfer case has a check/fill plug which must be removed

to check the lubricant level. If the vehicle is raised to gain access to the plug, be sure to support it safely on jackstands - DO NOT crawl under a vehicle which is supported only by a jack!

2   Remove the transfer case damper (if equipped) to gain access to the fill plug (see illustration).

3   Remove the plug from the transfer case and use your little finger

19.2 If the vehicle has a transfer case damper, unbolt it to gain access to the fill and drain plugs

19.6 If the vehicle's skid plate will obstruct removal of the drain plug, unbolt it from the frame rail to gain access to the plug

to reach inside the housing and feel the lubricant level. It should be at or very near the bottom of the plug hole.

4   If it isn't, add the recommended lubricant through the plug hole with a syringe or squeeze bottle.

5   Install and tighten the plug securely and check for leaks after the first few miles of driving.

LUBRICANT CHANGE

6   To change the lubricant, first note whether the transfer case skid plate will be in the way when the lubricant is drained. If it will be, remove it (see illustration).

7   Remove the fill plug first. This will speed draining. Remove the drain plug (see illustration) and let the lubricant drain.

8   Clean the drain plug threads, then reinstall the plug after the lubricant has finished draining.

9   Fill the transaxle to the bottom of the filler plug threads with the recommended lubricant listed in this Chapter's Specifications.

10   Install the filler plug and tighten it securely.

19.7 Location of the transfer case drain plug

20 Positive Crankcase Ventilation (PCV) valve check and replacement (every 12,000 miles or 12 months, whichever comes first)

♦ Refer to illustrations 20.1 and 20.2

➡Note: To maintain the efficiency of the PCV system, clean the hoses and check the PCV valve at the intervals recommended in the maintenance schedule. For additional information on the PCV system, refer to Chapter 6.

1   Locate the PCV valve (see illustration). The PCV valve on SOHC four-cylinder engines is mounted in the oil separator on the left side of the engine. On DOHC four-cylinder engines, remove the driver's-side inner fenderwell splash shield to access the PCV valve. On 2004 and later 3.0L and 4.0L engines, the PCV valve is located on the back of the camshaft cover. The valve is just behind the coolant bypass hose near the hose clip. Move the hose aside by removing it from the retainer clip. Carefully pry off the small round cap holding the PCV valve in place.

20.1 On 2001 and earlier models with 3.0L and 4.0L engines, the PCV valve is mounted in the valve cover near the brake booster (arrow)

2   To check the valve, first pull it out of the grommet in the oil separator (2.3L) or valve cover (3.0L and 4.0L). Shake the valve (see illustration). It should rattle, indicating that it is not clogged with deposits. If the valve does not rattle, replace it with a new one. If it does rattle, reinstall it.

3   Start the engine and allow it to idle, then disconnect the PCV hose. If vacuum is felt, the PCV valve system is working properly (see Chapter 6 for additional PCV system information).

4   If no vacuum is felt, the oil filler cap, hoses or valve cover gasket may be leaking or the PCV valve may be bad. Check for vacuum leaks at the valve, filler cap and all hoses.

5   Pull straight up on the valve to remove it. Check the rubber grommet for cracks and distortion. If it's damaged, replace it.

6   If the valve is clogged, the hose is also probably plugged. Remove the hose and clean with solvent.

7   After cleaning the hose, inspect it for damage, wear and deterioration. Make sure it fits snugly on the fittings.

8   If necessary, install a new PCV valve.

➡Note: The elbow (if equipped) is not part of the PCV valve. A new valve will not include the elbow. The original must be transferred to the new valve.

If a new elbow is purchased, it may be necessary to soak it in warm water for up to an hour to slip it onto the new valve. Do not attempt to

20.2 Shake the valve to test it - if it doesn't rattle, the valve is stuck and should be replaced

force the elbow onto the valve or it will break.

9   Install the clean PCV system hose. Make sure that the PCV valve and hose are secure.

21 Fuel system check (every 12,000 miles or 12 months, whichever comes first)

✳✳ WARNING:

Gasoline is extremely flammable, so take extra precautions when you work on any part of the fuel system. Don't smoke or allow open flames or bare light bulbs near the work area, and don't work in a garage where a gas-type appliance (such as a water heater or a clothes dryer) is present. Since gasoline is carcinogenic, wear latex gloves when there's a possibility of being exposed to fuel, and, if you spill any fuel on your skin, rinse it off immediately with soap and water. Mop up any spills immediately and do not store fuel-soaked rags where they could ignite. When you perform any kind of work on the fuel system, wear safety glasses and have a Class B type fire extinguisher on hand.

1   If you smell gasoline while driving or after the vehicle has been sitting in the sun, inspect the fuel system immediately.

2   Remove the fuel filler cap and inspect it for damage and corrosion. The gasket should have an unbroken sealing imprint. If the gasket is damaged or corroded, install a new cap.

3   Inspect the fuel feed and return lines for cracks. Make sure that the connections between the fuel lines and the fuel injection system and between the fuel lines and the in-line fuel filter are tight.

✳✳ WARNING:

The fuel system pressure must be relieved before servicing fuel system components. The fuel system pressure relief procedure is outlined in Chapter 4.

4   Since some components of the fuel system - the fuel tank and some of the fuel feed and return lines, for example - are underneath the vehicle, they can be inspected more easily with the vehicle raised on a hoist. If that's not possible, raise the vehicle and support it on jackstands.

5   With the vehicle raised and safely supported, inspect the gas tank and filler neck for punctures, cracks or other damage. The connection between the filler neck and the tank is particularly critical. Sometimes a rubber filler neck will leak because of loose clamps or deteriorated rubber. Inspect all fuel tank mounting brackets and straps to be sure the tank is securely attached to the vehicle.

✳✳ WARNING:

Do not, under any circumstances, try to repair a fuel tank (except rubber components). A welding torch or any open flame can easily cause fuel vapors inside the tank to explode.

6   Carefully check all rubber hoses and metal or nylon lines leading away from the fuel tank. Check for loose connections, deteriorated hoses, crimped lines and other damage. Repair or replace damaged sections as necessary (see Chapter 4).

22 Cooling system check (every 12,000 miles or 12 months, whichever comes first)

▶ **Refer to illustrations 22.3, 22.4a and 22.4b**

1   Many major engine failures can be attributed to a faulty cooling system. If the vehicle is equipped with an automatic transmission, the cooling system also plays an important role in prolonging transmission life because it cools the fluid.

2   The engine should be cold for the cooling system check, so perform the following procedure before the vehicle is driven for the day or after it has been shut off for at least three hours.

3   Remove the radiator cap (if equipped) (see illustration) and clean it thoroughly, inside and out, with clean water. Also clean the filler neck on the radiator. The presence of rust or corrosion in the filler neck means the coolant should be changed (see Section 27). The coolant inside the radiator should be relatively clean and transparent. If it's rust colored, drain the system and refill with new coolant.

4   Carefully check the radiator hoses and smaller diameter heater hoses (see illustrations). Inspect each coolant hose along its entire length, replacing any hose which is cracked, swollen or deteriorated. Cracks will show up better if the hose is squeezed. Pay close attention to hose clamps that secure the hoses to cooling system components. Hose clamps can pinch and puncture hoses, resulting in coolant leaks.

5   Make sure all hose connections are tight. A leak in the cooling system will usually show up as white or rust colored deposits on the area adjoining the leak. If wire-type clamps are used on the hoses, it may be a good idea to replace them with screw-type clamps.

6   Clean the front of the radiator and air conditioning condenser with compressed air, if available, or a soft brush. Remove all bugs, leaves, etc. embedded in the fins. Be extremely careful not to damage the cooling fins or cut your fingers on them.

7   If the coolant level has been dropping consistently and no leaks are detectable, have the radiator cap and cooling system pressure checked at a service station.

22.3 The radiator cap seals and the sealing surfaces in the radiator filler neck should be checked for built-up corrosion - the radiator cap should be replaced if the seals are brittle or deteriorated

Check for a chafed area that could fail prematurely.

Check for a soft area indicating the hose has deteriorated inside.

Overtightening the clamp on a hardened hose will damage the hose and cause a leak.

Check each hose for swelling and oil-soaked ends. Cracks and breaks can be located by squeezing the hose.

22.4b Hoses, like drivebelts, have a habit of failing at the worst possible time - to prevent the inconvenience of a blown radiator or heater hose, inspect them carefully as shown here

22.4a Radiator and heater hose locations (4.0L engine models) - the lower radiator hose, not shown, is connected to the bottom of the radiator

1	Heater return	3	Upper radiator hose
2	Heater supply	4	Coolant recovery hose

23 Exhaust system check (every 12,000 miles or 12 months, whichever comes first)

▶ **Refer to illustrations 23.4a, 23.4b, 23.4c and 23.4d**

1   With the engine cold (at least three hours after the vehicle has been driven), check the complete exhaust system from the engine to end of the tailpipe. Ideally, the inspection should be done with the vehicle on a hoist to permit unrestricted access. If a hoist isn't available, raise the vehicle and support it securely on jackstands.

2   Check the exhaust pipes and connections for evidence of leaks, severe corrosion and damage. Make sure that all brackets and hangers are in good condition and are tight.

3   At the same time, inspect the underside of the body for holes, corrosion, open seams, etc. which may allow exhaust gases to enter the passenger compartment. Seal all body openings with silicone or body putty.

4   Rattles and other noises can often be traced to the exhaust system, especially the mounts, hangers and heat shields. Try to move the pipes, muffler and catalytic converter (see illustrations). If the components can come in contact with the body or suspension parts, secure the exhaust system with new mounts.

5   Check the running condition of the engine by inspecting inside the end of the tailpipe. The exhaust deposits here are an indication of engine state-of-tune. If the pipe is black and sooty or coated with white deposits, the engine may need a tune-up, including a thorough fuel system inspection.

23.4a A catalytic converter is mounted beside the transmission - on automatic transmission models, the heat shield should be securely mounted in its clips

23.4b Also check the heat shield beneath the muffler

23.4c The catalytic converter and muffler should be securely attached to their brackets and the rubber mounts should be in good condition

23.4d The oxygen sensor(s) should be securely attached and the insulation on the sensor wires should be in good condition

24 Steering and suspension check (every 12,000 miles or 12 months, whichever comes first)

▶ **Refer to illustrations 24.10a, 24.10b, 24.11a and 24.11b**

➡**Note: The steering linkage and suspension components should be checked periodically. Worn or damaged suspension** and steering linkage components can result in excessive and abnormal tire wear, poor ride quality and vehicle handling and reduced fuel economy. For detailed illustrations of the steering and suspension components, refer to Chapter 10.

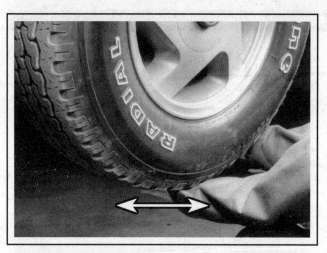

24.10a To check the suspension balljoints, try to move the lower edge of each front tire in-and-out while watching/feeling for movement at the top of the tire . . .

24.10b . . . if there's movement, repeat the test and look for looseness at the balljoints

SHOCK ABSORBER CHECK

1   Park the vehicle on level ground, turn the engine off and set the parking brake. Check the tire pressures.

2   Push down at one corner of the vehicle, then release it while noting the movement of the body. It should stop moving and come to rest in a level position with one or two bounces.

3   If the vehicle continues to move up-and-down or if it fails to return to its original position, a worn or weak shock absorber is probably the reason.

4   Repeat the above check at each of the three remaining corners of the vehicle.

5   Raise the vehicle and support it on jackstands.

6   Check the shock absorbers for evidence of fluid leakage. A light film of fluid is no cause for concern. Make sure that any fluid noted is from the shocks and not from any other source. If leakage is noted, replace the shocks as a set.

7   Check the shock absorbers to be sure that they are securely mounted and undamaged. Check the upper mounts for damage and wear. If damage or wear is noted, replace the shock absorbers as a set.

8   If the shock absorbers must be replaced, refer to Chapter 10 for the procedure.

STEERING AND SUSPENSION CHECK

9   Visually inspect the steering system components for damage and distortion (see Chapter 10). Look for leaks and damaged seals, boots and fittings.

10   Clean the lower end of the steering knuckle. Have an assistant grasp the lower edge of the tire and move the wheel in-and-out (see illustration) while you look for movement at the steering knuckle-to-axle arm balljoints (see illustration). If there is any movement, the balljoint(s) must be replaced.

11   Grasp each front tire at the front and rear edges, push in at the front, pull out at the rear and feel for play in the steering linkage (see illustrations). If any freeplay is noted, check the steering gear mounts and the tie-rod balljoints for looseness. If the steering gear mounts are loose, tighten them. If the tie-rods are loose, the balljoints may be worn (check to make sure the nuts are tight). Additional steering and suspension system illustrations can be found in Chapter 10.

24.11a To check the steering gear and idler arm mounts and tie-rod connections for play, grasp each front tire like this and try to move it back-and-forth . . .

24.11b . . . if play is noted, check the steering gear mounts and make sure that they're tight; look for looseness at the tie-rod ends (shown) and the steering linkage connections

25 Brake system check (every 12,000 miles or 12 months, whichever comes first)

♦ Refer to illustrations 25.7a, 25.7b, 25.11 and 25.17

❊❊❊ **WARNING:**

Dust produced by lining wear and deposited on brake components is hazardous to your health. DO NOT blow it out with compressed air and DO NOT inhale it! DO NOT use gasoline or solvents to remove the dust. Brake system cleaner should be used to flush the dust into a drain pan. After the brake components are wiped with a damp rag, dispose of the contaminated rag(s) and brake cleaner in a covered and labeled container. Try to use non-asbestos replacement parts whenever possible.

➡**Note: In addition to the specified intervals, the brake system should inspected each time the wheels are removed or a malfunction is indicated. Because of the obvious safety considerations, the following brake system checks are some of the most important maintenance procedures you can perform on your vehicle.**

SYMPTOMS OF BRAKE SYSTEM PROBLEMS

1   The disc brakes have built-in wear indicators which should make a high-pitched squealing or scraping noise when they're worn to the replacement point. When you hear this noise, replace the pads immediately or expensive damage to the brake discs could result.

2   Any of the following symptoms could indicate a potential brake system defect. The vehicle pulls to one side when the brake pedal is depressed, the brakes make squealing or dragging noises when applied, brake travel is excessive, the pedal pulsates and brake fluid leaks are noted (usually on the inner side of the tire or wheel). If any of these conditions are noted, inspect the brake system immediately. If the BRAKE light on the dash is on, a hydraulic system leak is indicated, which could be at the master cylinder, wheel cylinder, caliper, hose or line. Hydraulic leaks must be repaired immediately (see Chapter 9). If

the antilock brake system light on the dash is on, verify the brakes are functioning correctly, then carefully drive the vehicle to a dealer service department for repairs.

BRAKE LINES AND HOSES

➡**Note: Steel tubing is used throughout the brake system, with the exception of flexible, reinforced hoses at the front wheels and as connectors at the rear axle. Periodic inspection of these lines is very important.**

3   Park the vehicle on level ground and turn the engine off.

4   Remove the wheel covers. Loosen, but do not remove, the lug nuts on all four wheels.

5   Raise the vehicle and support it securely on jackstands (see *Jacking and towing* at the front of this book, or refer to your owner's manual, if necessary).

6   Remove the wheels.

7   Check all brake lines and hoses for cracks, chafing of the outer cover, leaks, blisters and distortion. Check the brake hoses at front and rear of the vehicle for softening, cracks, bulging, or wear from rubbing on other components (see illustrations). Check all threaded fittings for leaks and make sure the brake hose mounting bolts and clips are secure.

8   If leaks or damage are discovered, they must be fixed immediately. Refer to Chapter 9 for detailed brake system repair procedures.

DISC BRAKES

9   If it hasn't already been done, raise the vehicle and support it securely on jackstands. Remove the front wheels.

10 The disc brake calipers, which contain the pads, are now visible. Each caliper has an outer and an inner pad - all pads should be checked.

25.7a The brake hoses at the front of the vehicle (arrow) should be inspected and replaced if they show any defects

25.7b The rear brake hose meets the metal brake lines at a junction block on the axle housing - they should also be inspected and replaced if they show any defects

25.11 The lining thickness of the front disc brake pads (arrows) can be checked through the caliper inspection hole

25.17 Carefully peel back the rubber boot on each end of the wheel cylinder - if the exposed area is covered with brake fluid, or if fluid runs out, the wheel cylinder must be overhauled or replaced

11 Note the pad thickness by looking through the inspection hole in the caliper (see illustration). If the lining material is 1/8-inch thick or less, or if it is tapered from end-to-end, the pads should be replaced (see Chapter 9). Keep in mind that the lining material is riveted or bonded to a metal plate or shoe - the metal portion is not included in this measurement.

12 Check the condition of the brake disc. Look for score marks, deep scratches and overheated areas (they will appear blue or discolored). If damage or wear is noted, the disc can be removed and resurfaced by an automotive machine shop or replaced with a new one. Refer to Chapter 9 for more detailed inspection and repair procedures.

13 Remove the calipers without disconnecting the brake hoses (see Chapter 9). Lubricate the caliper slide rails and the inner pad slots on the steering knuckles with the special caliper slide grease listed in this Chapter's Specifications.

DRUM BRAKES

14 Refer to Chapter 9 and remove the rear brake drums.

15 Note the thickness of the lining material on the rear brake shoes and look for signs of contamination by brake fluid or grease. If the lining material is within 1/16-inch of the recessed rivets or metal shoes, replace the brake shoes with new ones. The shoes should also be replaced if they are cracked, glazed (shiny lining surfaces), or contaminated with brake fluid or grease. See Chapter 9 for the replacement procedure.

16 Check the shoe return and hold-down springs and the adjusting mechanism to make sure they are installed correctly and in good condi-

tion. Deteriorated or distorted springs, if not replaced, could allow the linings to drag and wear prematurely.

17 Check the wheel cylinders for leakage by carefully peeling back the rubber boots (see illustration). Slight moisture behind the boots is acceptable. If brake fluid is noted behind the boots or if it runs out of the wheel cylinder, the wheel cylinders must be overhauled or replaced (see Chapter 9).

18 Check the drums for cracks, score marks, deep scratches and hard spots, which will appear as small discolored areas. If imperfections cannot be removed with emery cloth, the drums must be resurfaced by an automotive machine shop (see Chapter 9 for more detailed information).

19 Refer to Chapter 9 and install the brake drums.

20 Install the wheels, but don't lower the vehicle yet.

PARKING BRAKE

➡**Note: The parking brake cable and linkage should be periodically lubricated (see Section 16). This maintenance procedure helps prevent the parking brake cable adjuster or the linkage from binding and adversely affecting the operation or adjustment of the parking brake.**

21 The easiest method of checking the parking brake is to park the vehicle on a steep hill with the parking brake set and the transmission in Neutral (stay in the vehicle for this check!). If the parking brake doesn't prevent the vehicle from rolling, refer to Chapter 9 and adjust it.

26 Windshield wiper blade check and replacement (every 12,000 miles or 12 months, whichever comes first)

1   Road film can build up on the wiper blades and affect their efficiency, so they should be washed regularly with a mild detergent solution.

CHECK

2   The windshield wiper and blade assembly should be inspected periodically. Even if you don't use your wipers, the sun and elements will dry out the rubber portions, causing them to crack and break apart. If inspection reveals hardened or cracked rubber, replace the wiper blades. If inspection reveals nothing unusual, wet the windshield, turn the wipers on, allow them to cycle several times, then shut them off. An uneven wiper pattern across the glass or streaks over clean glass indicate that the blades should be replaced.

3   The operation of the wiper mechanism can loosen the fasteners, so they should be checked and tightened, as necessary, at the same time the wiper blades are checked (see Chapter 12 for further information regarding the wiper mechanism).

WIPER BLADE REPLACEMENT

▶ Refer to illustrations 26.5a and 26.5b

4   Park the wiper blades in a convenient position to be worked on. To do this, run the wipers, then turn the ignition key to Off when the wiper blades reach the desired position.

5   Lift the blade slightly from the windshield. Squeeze the retaining lever to release the blade (see illustration), unhook the wiper arm from the blade (see illustration) and take the blade off.

☀ CAUTION:

Do not press too hard on the spring lock or it will be distorted.

6   Slide the new blade onto the wiper arm hook until the blade locks. Make sure the spring lock secures the blade to the pin.

WIPER ELEMENT REPLACEMENT

7   Insert a screwdriver blade between the wiper blade and element. Twist the screwdriver clockwise while pressing in and down to separate the element from the end retaining claw.

8   Slide the element out of the remaining retaining claws.

9   Starting at either end of the blade, slide a new element into the second retaining claw (not the one closest to the end of the blade). Slide it through the other retaining claws until it reaches the end of the blade.

10 Bend the element and slide it back into the claw at the end of the blade.

26.5a Squeeze the retaining lever . . .

26.5b . . . push the wiper blade down the arm to disengage the hook and separate the blade from the arm

27 Cooling system servicing (draining, flushing and refilling) (every 24,000 miles or 24 months, whichever comes first)

▶ **Refer to illustration 27.4**

> ❋❋ **WARNING:**
>
> **Do not allow antifreeze to come in contact with your skin or painted surfaces of the vehicle. Rinse off spills immediately with plenty of water. Antifreeze is highly toxic if ingested. Never leave antifreeze lying around in an open container or in puddles on the floor; children and pets are attracted by it's sweet smell and may drink it. Check with local authorities about disposing of used antifreeze. Many communities have collection centers which will see that antifreeze is disposed of safely.**

1 Periodically, the cooling system should be drained, flushed and refilled to replenish the antifreeze mixture and prevent formation of rust and corrosion, which can impair the performance of the cooling system and cause engine damage. When the cooling system is serviced, all hoses and the radiator cap should be checked and replaced if necessary

DRAINING

2 Apply the parking brake and block the wheels. If the vehicle has just been driven, wait several hours to allow the engine to cool down before beginning this procedure.

3 Once the engine is completely cool, remove the radiator cap.

4 Move a large container under the radiator drain to catch the coolant (see illustration). Attach a 3/8-inch diameter hose to the drain fitting to direct the coolant into the container, then open the drain fitting (a pair of pliers may be required to turn it).

5 While the coolant is draining, check the condition of the radiator hoses, heater hoses and clamps (see Section 22 if necessary).

6 Replace any damaged clamps or hoses (see Chapter 3 for detailed replacement procedures).

FLUSHING

7 Once the system is completely drained, flush the radiator with fresh water from a garden hose until the water runs clear at the drain. The flushing action of the water will remove sediments from the radiator but will not remove rust and scale from the engine and cooling tube surfaces.

8 These deposits can be removed by the chemical action of a cleaner available at your local auto parts store. Follow the procedure outlined in the manufacturer's instructions. If the radiator is severely corroded, damaged or leaking, it should be removed (see Chapter 3) and taken to a radiator repair shop.

9 The heater core should be back-flushed whenever the cooling system is flushed. To do this, disconnect the heater return hose from the thermostat housing or engine. Slide a female garden hose fitting into the heater hose and secure it with a clamp. This will allow you to attach a garden hose securely.

10 Attach the end of a garden hose to the fitting you installed in the

27.4 The radiator drain is located on the bottom of the radiator; connect a length of rubber hose to the drain and let it hang into the drain pan

heater hose.

11 Disconnect the heater inlet hose and position it to act as a drain.

12 Turn the water on and off several times to create a surging action through the heater core. Then turn the water on full force and allow it to run for approximately five minutes.

13 Turn off the water and disconnect the garden hose from the female fitting. Remove the fitting from the heater return hose, then reconnect the hoses to the engine.

14 Remove the overflow hose from the coolant recovery reservoir. Drain the reservoir and flush it with clean water, then reconnect the hose.

REFILLING

15 Close and tighten the radiator drain. Install and tighten the block drain plug(s).

16 Place the heater temperature control in the maximum heat position.

17 Slowly add new coolant (a 50/50 mixture of water and antifreeze) to the radiator until it is full. Add coolant to the reservoir up to the lower mark.

18 Leave the radiator cap on, but cocked open, and run the engine in a well-ventilated area until the thermostat opens (coolant will begin flowing through the radiator and the upper radiator hose will become hot).

19 Turn the engine off and let it cool. Add more coolant mixture to bring the coolant level back up to the lip on the radiator filler neck.

20 Squeeze the upper radiator hose to expel air, then add more coolant mixture if necessary. Replace the radiator cap.

21 Start the engine, allow it to reach normal operating temperature and check for leaks.

28 Air filter replacement (every 30,000 miles or 30 months, whichever comes first)

▶ Refer to illustration 28.6

⁕⁕ CAUTION:

All air filter cover assemblies must be installed correctly or engine damage could occur.

1   If the vehicle is driven in dust, the filter should be checked every 3,000 miles and replaced if it's dirty. In any case, the filter should be replaced at least every 30,000 miles, even if it looks clean.
2   Loosen the hose clamp on the air intake duct, just after the MAF sensor on most models.
3   Disconnect the MAF sensor electrical connector (where necessary).
4   Release the two locking clips/clamps on the cover.
5   Lift off the cover while separating it from the air intake duct.
6   Remove the air filter element by lifting it out from one edge.
7   Wipe the inside of the air filter housing with a clean cloth.
8   Place the new air filter element in the housing.
9   Reinstall the cover and reconnect the air intake duct (note the tabs on one side of the cover).

28.6 Lift the cover off and take the element out of the housing

10 Press down on the cover to engage the locking clips or secure the clamps.
11 Reconnect the MAF sensor, if necessary, and carefully tighten the hose clamp on the air intake duct.

29 Fuel filter replacement (every 30,000 miles or 30 months, whichever comes first)

▶ Refer to illustration 29.1

⁕⁕ WARNING:

Gasoline is extremely flammable, so take extra precautions when you work on any part of the fuel system. Don't smoke or allow open flames or bare light bulbs near the work area, and don't work in a garage where a gas-type appliance (such as a water heater or a clothes dryer) is present. Since gasoline is carcinogenic, wear latex gloves when there's a possibility of being exposed to fuel, and, if you spill any fuel on your skin, rinse it off immediately with soap and water. Mop up any spills immediately and do not store fuel-soaked rags where they could ignite. When you perform any kind of work on the fuel system, wear safety glasses and have a Class B type fire extinguisher on hand.

29.1 The inline fuel filter is mounted in the left frame rail; make sure the fuel line fittings are clean before disconnecting them (see Chapter 4 for disconnection procedures)

1   The fuel filter is mounted within the left frame rail (see illustration). The manufacturer states that replacement of the fuel filter at 30,000 miles is recommended, but not required, for California vehicles.
➡Note: **The fuel filters on later model vehicles may vary slightly in shape and fittings. Make certain that you match your new filter with the old one to confirm that it's correct.**
2   Obtain a new fuel filter before starting.

⁕⁕ WARNING:

Be sure the new filter is specifically designed for your engine.

Fuel injection system filters are built to withstand high pressure, and as a result, often cost more than filters meant for use in carbureted systems. Filters meant for carbureted systems may burst due to the high pressure if used on a fuel-injected engine. Also, be sure the new filter includes replacement hairpin clips (if used). The manufacturer recommends against reusing the clips.

⁕⁕ WARNING:

Before removing the fuel filter, the fuel system pressure must be relieved. See Chapter 4.

3   Position the front end of the vehicle higher than the rear to prevent fuel siphoning. Remove the gas cap, then reinstall it after relieving the fuel system pressure.
4   Inspect the hose fittings at both ends of the filter to see if they're clean. If more than a light coating of dust is present, clean the fittings before proceeding.

5   Disconnect the push-connect fittings from the filter (see Chapter 4).

➡**Note: On some models, it may be necessary to remove the fuel filter mounting bracket nut before the filter can be removed.**

6   Note which way the arrow on the filter is pointing - the new filter must be installed the same way. Loosen the clamp screw and detach the filter from the bracket.

7   Install the new filter in the bracket with the arrow pointing in the right direction and tighten the clamp screw securely.

8   Carefully connect each fuel line to the filter (see Chapter 4).

9   Start the engine and check for fuel leaks.

30   Driveshaft and driveaxle yoke lubrication (4WD models) (every 30,000 miles or 30 months, whichever comes first)

At the specified intervals, the slip yokes on the driveshafts and the right front driveaxle should be lubricated (see this Chapter's Specifications for the correct lubricant). This requires removal of the driveshafts and driveaxle (see Chapter 8 for the procedures).

Specifications

Recommended lubricants and fluids

➡**Note: Listed here are manufacturer recommendations at the time this manual was written. Manufacturers occasionally upgrade their fluid and lubricant specifications, so check with your local auto parts store for current recommendations.**

Engine oil	
Type	API grade SG or above
Viscosity	
2011 four-cylinder models	SAE 5W-20
All other models	See accompanying chart
Power steering fluid type	
2010 and earlier	MERCON® automatic transmission fluid
2011	MERCON® V automatic transmission fluid
Brake and clutch fluid type	DOT 3 heavy duty brake fluid
Automatic transmission fluid type*	MERCON® V automatic transmission fluid
Manual transmission lubricant type	
2010 and earlier	MERCON® automatic transmission fluid
2011	MERCON® V automatic transmission fluid
Transfer case lubricant type	
2010 and earlier	MERCON® automatic transmission fluid
2011	Motorcraft Transfer Case Lubricant
Coolant type**	50/50 mixture of Motorcraft Premium Engine Coolant (green colored) or Motorcraft Premium Gold Engine Coolant (yellow colored), or equivalent
Caliper slide rail grease	Disc brake caliper slide rail grease
Chassis grease	NLGI No. 2 lithium base grease containing polyethylene and molybdenum disulfide
Rear differential lubricant***	
2010 and earlier	API GL-5 SAE 90 Hypoid gear lubricant
2011	
RWD	SAE 80W-90 Premium Rear Axle lubricant
4WD	SAE 75W-140 synthetic rear axle lubricant
Front axle lubricant (4WD)	SAE 80W-90 gear lubricant

Be sure to use the correct type of transmission fluid. Do not mix MERCON® and MERCON® V.

**Do not mix coolants of different colors. Doing so might damage the cooling system and/or the engine. The manufacturer specifies either a green or a yellow colored coolant to be used in these systems.*

***Traction-Lock (limited slip) differentials add 4 oz. of friction modifier XL-3 or equivalent when lubricant is changed.*

Engine oil viscosity chart - for best fuel economy and cold-weather starting, select the lowest recommended viscosity rating for the operating temperature range (all except 2011 four-cylinder models)

Capacities (approximate)

Engine oil (including filter)		
2.3L engines		4 quarts
2.5L engines		5 quarts
3.0L engines		4.5 quarts
4.0L engines		5 quarts
Cooling system*		
2.3L		
2001 through 2010		11.2 quarts
2011		
	Automatic transmission models	10.9 quarts
	Manual transmission models	11.2 quarts
2.5L		10.5 quarts
4.0L		
2010 and earlier		13.5 quarts
2011		
	Automatic transmission models	13.2 quarts
	Manual transmission models	13.5 quarts
Transfer case (Warner 13-54)		1.25 quarts
Front axle differential		1.75 quarts
Dana 35 differential		3.5 pints
Rear axle differential		2.5 quarts
Automatic transmission (drain and refill)		3.0 quarts**
Manual transmission		2.8 quarts

*Capacity may vary +/- 15% due to equipment variations. Most service refills take only 80% of listed capacity because some coolant remains in the engine.

**Add more fluid as needed, 1/2 pint at a time, to bring it up to the correct level on the dipstick. Do not overfill. After overhaul, approximately 5 to 6 more quarts of fluid will be required.

Brakes

Disc brake pad thickness (minimum)	See Chapter 9
Drum brake shoe lining thickness (minimum)	See Chapter 9

Ignition system

Firing order

    Four-cylinder engine   1-3-4-2

    V6 engines   1-4-2-5-3-6

Ignition timing   Not adjustable

Spark plug type and gap

    Four-cylinder engines

        2.3L

            2001 through 2005

                Type   AGSF32FEM or equivalent

                Gap   0.041 to 0.045 inch

           2006 and later

                Type   AGSF32FEC or equivalent

                Gap   0.049 to 0.053 inch

        2.5L (2000 and 2001)

           Type   AWSTF32-F or equivalent

           Gap   0.042 to 0.046 inch

      3.0L V6 engine

        2000 through 2005

           Type   AWSF32PP

           Gap   0.042 to 0.046 inch

        2006 and later

           Type   AGSF-32FM or equivalent

           Gap   0.052 to 0.057 inch

      4.0L pushrod V6 engine

        Type   AGSF22PP

        Gap   0.052 to 0.056 inch

      4.0L SOHC V6 engine

        Type

           2008 and earlier models   AFS34FP or equivalent

           2009 and later models   AGSF24N

        Gap

           2010 and earlier models   0.052 to 0.057 inch

           2011 models   0.052 to 0.054 inch

Idle speed   Non adjustable

Cylinder and coil terminal locations - 2.3L DOHC four-cylinder engines

Cylinder and coil terminal locations - 2.5L SOHC four-cylinder engine

Cylinder and coil terminal locations - V6 engines

Torque specifications   Ft-lbs (unless otherwise indicated)

→Note: One foot-pound (ft-lb) of torque is equivalent to 12 inch-pounds (in-lbs) of torque. Torque values below approximately 15 ft-lbs are expressed in inch-pounds, since most foot-pound torque wrenches are not accurate at these smaller values.

Drivebelt tensioner bolt	
2010 and earlier	
3.0L engine	17 to 23
2.3L and 4.0L engines	30 to 40
2011	
2.3L engine	37
4.0L engine	35
Automatic transmission pan bolts	
2010 and earlier	96 to 120 in-lbs
2011	89 in-lbs
Spark plugs	
2010 and earlier	7 to 15
2011	
2.3L engine	106 in-lbs
4.0L engine	133 in-lbs
Wheel lug nuts	100*

* Whenever the lug nuts are removed, recheck lug nut torque after 500 miles.

Section

Reference to other Chapters

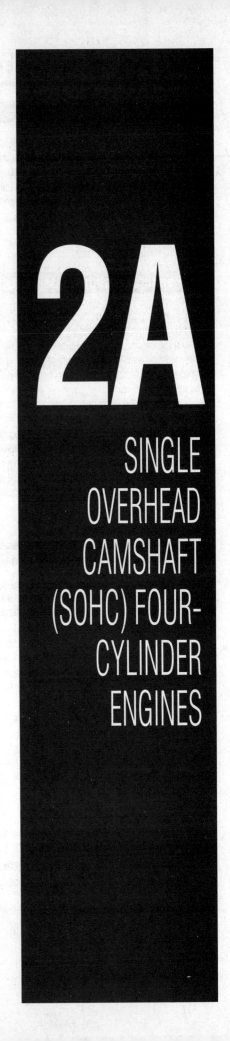

2A

SINGLE OVERHEAD CAMSHAFT (SOHC) FOUR-CYLINDER ENGINES

1 General information

This Part of Chapter 2 is devoted to in-vehicle repair procedures for the 2.3L and 2.5L SOHC four-cylinder engines.

Information concerning engine removal and installation, as well as engine block and cylinder head overhaul, is in Part F of this Chapter.

The following repair procedures are based on the assumption that the engine is installed in the vehicle. If the engine has been removed from the vehicle and mounted on a stand, many of the Steps included in this Part of Chapter 2 will not apply.

The Specifications included in this Part of Chapter 2 apply only to the engine and procedures in this Part. The specifications necessary for rebuilding the block and cylinder head are found in Part F.

2 Repair operations possible with the engine in the vehicle

Many major repair operations can be accomplished without removing the engine from the vehicle.

Clean the engine compartment and the exterior of the engine with some type of pressure washer before any work is done. A clean engine will make the job easier and will help keep dirt out of the internal areas of the engine.

Depending on the components involved, it may be a good idea to remove the hood and engine cover to improve access to the engine as repairs are performed (refer to Chapter 11 if necessary).

If vacuum, exhaust, oil or coolant leaks develop, indicating a need for gasket or seal replacement, the repairs can generally be made with the engine in the vehicle. The intake and exhaust manifold gaskets, oil pan gasket and cylinder head gasket are all accessible with the engine in place.

Engine components such as the intake and exhaust manifolds, the auxiliary shaft, the water pump, the starter motor, the alternator, the distributor and the fuel system components can be removed for repair with the engine in place.

Since the cylinder head can be removed without removing the engine, camshaft and valve component servicing can also be accomplished with the engine in the vehicle.

In extreme cases caused by a lack of necessary equipment, repair or replacement of piston rings, pistons, connecting rods and rod bearings is possible with the engine in the vehicle. However, this practice is not recommended because of the cleaning and preparation work that must be done to the components involved.

3 Top Dead Center (TDC) for number one piston - locating

→Note: **The four-cylinder engine is not equipped with a distributor. Piston position may be determined by feeling for compression at the number one spark plug hole, then aligning the timing marks as described in Step 5.**

1   Top Dead Center (TDC) is the highest point in the cylinder that each piston reaches as it travels up-and-down when the crankshaft turns. Each piston reaches TDC on the compression stroke and again on the exhaust stroke, but TDC generally refers to piston position on the compression stroke.

2   Positioning the piston at TDC is an essential part of many other repair procedures discussed in this manual.

3   Before beginning this procedure, be sure to place the transmission in Neutral and apply the parking brake or block the rear wheels. Remove the spark plugs (see Chapter 1). Disable the ignition system by disconnecting all wiring harness connectors from the ignition coil pack(s).

4   In order to bring any piston to TDC, the crankshaft must be turned using one of the methods outlined below. When looking at the front of the engine, normal crankshaft rotation is clockwise.

a) *The preferred method is to turn the crankshaft with a socket and ratchet attached to the bolt threaded into the front of the crankshaft.*

b) *A remote starter switch, which may save some time, can also be used. Follow the instructions included with the switch. Once the*

piston is close to TDC, use a socket and ratchet as described in the previous paragraph.

c) *If an assistant is available to turn the ignition switch to the Start position in short bursts, you can get the piston close to TDC without a remote starter switch. Make sure your assistant is out of the vehicle, away from the ignition switch, then use a socket and ratchet as described in Paragraph a) to complete the procedure.*

5   Remove the access plug(s) from the camshaft drivebelt cover. Rotate the crankshaft until the timing pointer aligns with the "TC" mark on the crankshaft pulley. Look through the access hole in the camshaft drivebelt cover and confirm that the camshaft timing pointer aligns with the timing mark on the camshaft sprocket. If the timing mark is not visible, the piston is at Bottom Dead Center (BDC). Rotate the crankshaft exactly 360-degrees, and look through the access hole again to confirm that the camshaft timing pointer aligns with the timing mark on the camshaft sprocket. TDC occurs when both camshaft and crankshaft pointers are aligned. Confirm that the diamond mark on the oil pump sprocket (visible through the lower access hole in the camshaft drivebelt cover) and the diamond pointer are aligned. TDC occurs when the camshaft, crankshaft and oil pump pointers are aligned.

6   After the number one piston has been positioned at TDC on the compression stroke, TDC for any of the remaining pistons can be located by turning the crankshaft 180-degrees at a time and following the firing order.

4   Valve cover - removal and installation

REMOVAL

1   Disconnect the negative cable from the battery.

2   Remove the accelerator control splash shield.

3   Remove EGR supply tube (see Chapter 6).

4   Identify and tag the various wires and hoses which cross over the valve cover, including the spark plug wires. Do this carefully as they all must be repositioned correctly during installation.

5   Remove the throttle linkage and the throttle body assembly (see Chapter 4).

6   Remove the bolts and separate the cover from the engine. It may be necessary to break the gasket seal by tapping the cover with a soft-face hammer. If it's really stuck, use a knife, gasket scraper or chisel to remove it, but be very careful not to damage the gasket sealing surfaces of the cover or head.

INSTALLATION

7   Place clean rags in the camshaft gallery to keep foreign material out of the engine.

8   Remove all traces of gasket material from the cover and head. Be careful not to nick or gouge the surfaces. Clean the mating surfaces with lacquer thinner or acetone.

9   Reinstall the cover with a new gasket - no sealant is required. Install the bolts and tighten them to the torque listed in this Chapter's Specifications in a crisscross pattern.

10   Reinstall the upper intake manifold (see Chapter 4) and the remaining components previously removed or disconnected.

11   Since the battery has been disconnected, the engine may not run properly for about 10 miles or so until the powertrain control module relearns its adaptive strategy and adjusts for current engine conditions.

5   Valve train components - removal and installation

➡Note: **Broken valve springs and defective valve stem seals can be replaced without removing the cylinder head. Two special tools and a compressed air source are normally required to perform this operation, so read through this Section carefully and rent or buy the tools before beginning the job. If compressed air isn't available, a length of nylon rope can be used to keep the valves from falling into the cylinder during this procedure.**

REMOVAL

1   Refer to Section 4 and remove the valve cover.

2   Remove the spark plug from the cylinder which has the defective component. If all of the valve stem seals are being replaced, all of the spark plugs should be removed (see Chapter 1).

3   Turn the crankshaft until the piston in the affected cylinder is at top dead center on the compression stroke (see Section 3 for instructions). If you're replacing all of the valve stem seals, begin with cylinder number one and work on the valves for one cylinder at a time. Move from cylinder-to-cylinder following the firing order sequence (1-3-4-2).

4   Thread an adapter into the spark plug hole and connect an air hose from a compressed air source to it. Most auto parts stores can supply the air hose adapter.

➡Note: **Many cylinder compression gauges utilize a screw-in fitting that may work with your air hose quick-disconnect fitting.**

5   Apply compressed air to the cylinder.

6   If you don't have access to compressed air, an alternative method can be used. Position the piston at a point just before TDC on the compression stroke, then feed a long piece of nylon rope through the spark plug hole until it fills the combustion chamber. Be sure to leave the end of the rope hanging out of the engine so it can be removed easily. Use a large breaker bar and socket to rotate the crankshaft in the normal direction of rotation until slight resistance is felt.

7   Stuff shop rags into the cylinder head holes above and below the valves to prevent parts and tools from falling into the engine, then use a valve spring compressor to compress the spring.

8   With the spring compressed, slide the cam follower over the lash adjuster to remove it. Also remove the lash adjuster, if necessary.

9   Still compressing the spring, remove the keepers. Release the valve spring tool and remove the spring retainer, damper assembly and valve spring.

10   Remove and discard the valve stem seal.

➡Note: **If air pressure fails to hold the valve in the closed position during this operation, the valve face or seat is probably damaged. If so, the cylinder head will have to be removed for additional repair operations.**

11   Wrap a rubber band or tape around the top of the valve stem so the valve will not fall into the cylinder, then release the air pressure.

12   Inspect the valve stem for damage. Rotate the valve in the guide and check the end for eccentric movement, which would indicate that the valve is bent.

13   Move the valve up-and-down in the guide and make sure it doesn't bind. If the valve stem binds, either the valve is bent or the guide is damaged. In either case, the head will have to be removed for repair.

INSTALLATION

14   Reapply air pressure to the cylinder to retain the valve in the closed position, then remove the tape or rubber band from the valve stem. Lubricate the valve stem with engine oil.

15   Place the plastic seal protector (provided with the valve seals) over the end of the valve stem.

16   Start the valve stem seal carefully over the cap and push the seal down until the seal body contacts the top of the guide.

17   Remove the plastic cap and use a seal installation tool to seat the seal onto the valve guide.

18   Install the valve spring, damper and retainer, compress the spring and install the keepers.

19   Disconnect the air hose and remove the adapter from the spark plug hole. If a rope was used in place of air pressure, pull it out of the cylinder.

�֎ CAUTION:

Do not turn the crankshaft backwards to release the rope. Turning the crankshaft backwards may cause the timing belt to jump time.

20   Using the spring compressor to compress the spring and valve, install the lash adjuster and cam follower. Make sure the lash adjuster has released completely before rotating the camshaft.

21   Reinstall the various components previously removed.

22   Start and run the engine, then check for oil leaks and unusual sounds coming from the valve cover area.

6 Timing belt - removal and installation

▶ Refer to illustration 6.14

REMOVAL

✳✳ CAUTION:

The timing system is complex. Severe engine damage will occur if you make any mistakes. Do not attempt this procedure unless you are highly experienced with this type of repair. If you are at all unsure of your abilities, consult an expert. Double-check all your work and be sure everything is correct before you attempt to start the engine.

1   Disconnect the negative cable from the battery.

2   Remove the spark plugs and position the number one piston at Top Dead Center (TDC) on the compression stroke (see Section 3). After positioning the number one piston at TDC, DO NOT turn the crankshaft until the timing belt is reinstalled.

3   Drain the cooling system (see Chapter 3).

4   Remove the drivebelts (see Chapter 1).

5   Remove the fan shroud, the fan and the water pump pulley (see Chapter 3).

6   Remove the upper radiator hose and the thermostat housing (see Chapter 3).

➡Note: Due to the lack of space at the front of the engine, access to the components may be difficult. If additional clearance is desired, remove the radiator.

7   Without disconnecting the hoses, unbolt the air conditioning compressor from the bracket and position the compressor aside. Unbolt the bracket from the engine and position the power steering pump and bracket assembly aside.

8   Remove outer timing belt cover.

9   Remove the crankshaft drivebelt pulley and belt guide.

10 Remove the four bolts and one screw and detach the outer timing belt cover.

11 Loosen the belt tensioner adjustment bolt and the tensioner pivot bolt. Position a belt tension releasing tool, available at most auto parts stores, on the tensioner and release the belt tension. Tighten the adjustment bolt just enough to hold the tensioner in the retracted position.

12 Remove the timing belt and inspect it for wear and damage. If it's worn or damaged, replace the belt. If in doubt about the belt condition, install a new one. If the belt breaks during engine operation, extensive damage may occur!

13 Check the sprockets for wear, cracks and burrs on the teeth. If the sprockets are worn or damaged, they can be replaced after removing the mounting bolts. Make sure the new sprockets are installed correctly. Tighten the mounting bolts to the torque listed in this Chapter's Specifications. Install a new camshaft sprocket bolt or use Teflon sealing tape on the old bolt.

INSTALLATION

✳✳ CAUTION:

Before starting the engine, carefully rotate the crankshaft by hand through at least two full revolutions (use a socket and breaker bar on the crankshaft pulley center bolt). If you feel any resistance, STOP! There is something wrong - most likely, valves are contacting the pistons. You must find the problem before proceeding. Check your work and see if any updated repair information is available.

14 Align the timing mark on the camshaft sprocket with the pointer on the inner timing belt cover. The marks will be triangles on 2.5L engines and will align at the top of the engine front cover. Make sure the crankshaft sprocket is still at TDC (the crankshaft sprocket keyway should be at the 12 o'clock position). Align the timing mark on the oil pump pulley with the pointer on the inner timing belt cover (see illustration). On 2.5L engines, the oil pump marks are diamond-shaped.

15 Install the timing belt over the crankshaft sprocket, then over the auxiliary shaft/oil pump sprocket. Pull the belt up (pulling slack from between camshaft sprocket and the auxiliary shaft/oil pump sprocket and install it on the camshaft sprocket in a counterclockwise direction so no slack will be between the two sprockets. Align the belt fore and aft on the sprockets.

16 Loosen the tensioner adjustment bolt to allow the tensioner to move against the belt. If the spring does not have enough tension to move the roller against the belt (the belt hangs loose), it may be necessary to insert a pry bar between the tensioner and roll pin and push the roller against the belt.

17 Slowly rotate the crankshaft two complete revolutions in the direction of normal rotation to make sure the belt is seated and to remove any slack. While turning the crankshaft, feel and listen for valve-to-piston contact. Don't force the crankshaft - if binding is felt, recheck all work or seek professional advice!

18 Rotate the tensioner assembly against the belt with approximately 30 to 33 ft-lbs of pressure and tighten the tensioner adjustment and pivot bolts to the torque listed in this Chapter's Specifications. Recheck the alignment of the timing marks.

19 Install the timing belt cover and tighten the mounting bolts to the torque listed in this Chapter's Specifications.

20 The remaining installation steps are the reverse of removal. Be sure to tighten the crankshaft pulley/sprocket bolt to the torque listed in this Chapter's Specifications.

21 Recheck the timing marks for proper alignment, one last time, before installing the belt cover access plugs.

Camshaft sprocket

Tensioner pulley

Oil pump sprocket marks

Pointer on timing belt cover

Crankshaft sprocket (keyway at 12 o'clock)

36071-2A-6.14 HAYNES

6.14 Timing mark details

7 Camshaft - removal and installation

REMOVAL

1 Disconnect the negative cable at the battery.

2 Remove the valve cover, the timing belt cover and the timing belt (see Sections 4 and 6).

3 Remove the spring clip from the hydraulic valve lash adjuster end of each cam follower, if equipped.

4 Using a valve spring compressor, compress the valve springs and remove all the cam followers (see Section 5). Keep the cam followers in order so they can be reinstalled in their original locations.

5 Lift out the hydraulic lash adjusters, keeping each one with its respective cam follower.

6 Remove the camshaft sprocket mounting bolt and washer. A long screwdriver placed through one of the holes in the sprocket will prevent the camshaft from turning.

7 Draw off the sprocket with a puller, then remove the belt guide (if equipped).

8 Remove the sprocket locating pin from the end of the camshaft.

9 Remove the camshaft retaining plate from the rear bearing pedestal.

10 Raise the vehicle and support it securely on jackstands.

11 Position a floor jack under the engine. Place a block of wood on the jack pad. Remove the left and right engine mount bolts and nuts. Raise the engine as high as it will go. Place wood blocks between the engine mounts and frame brackets. Lower the engine on the wood blocks and remove the jack.

✳✳ WARNING:

DO NOT place your hands under the engine where they would be crushed if the jack failed!

12 Remove the camshaft seal (see Section 9) and withdraw the camshaft. Be very careful not to damage the camshaft bearings and journals as it's pulled out.

INSTALLATION

13 Liberally coat the camshaft journals and bearings with engine assembly lube or moly-base grease, then carefully install the camshaft in the cylinder head.

14 Install the retaining plate and screws.

15 Lubricate the new camshaft oil seal with engine oil and carefully tap it into place at the front of the cylinder head with a large socket and a hammer. Make sure it enters the bore squarely and seats completely.

16 Install the belt guide and pin at the front end of the camshaft, then carefully tap on the sprocket.

17 Install a new sprocket bolt or use Teflon sealing tape on the threads of the old one.

18 Coat the hydraulic lash adjusters with engine assembly lube or moly-base grease, then install them in their original locations.

19 Coat the camshaft lobes and cam followers with engine assembly lube or moly-base grease.

20 Install the timing belt (see Section 6).

21 Compress each valve spring and position each cam follower on its respective valve end and adjuster. Install the retaining spring clips, if equipped.

22 Install the remaining components in the reverse order of removal.

8 Camshaft inspection

CAMSHAFT AND BEARINGS

1 After the camshaft has been removed from the engine, cleaned with solvent and dried, inspect the bearing journals for uneven wear, pits and galling. If the journals are damaged, the bearing inserts in the head are probably damaged as well. Both the camshaft and bearings will have to be replaced with new ones. Measure the inside diameter of each camshaft bearing and record the results (take two measurements, 90 degrees apart, at each bearing).

2 Measure the camshaft bearing journals with a micrometer to determine if they're excessively worn or out-of-round. If they're more than 0.005-inch out-of-round, the camshaft should be replaced with a new one. Subtract the bearing journal diameters from the corresponding bearing inside diameter measurements to obtain the oil clearance. If it's excessive, new bearings must be installed.

➡**Note: Camshaft bearing replacement requires special tools and expertise that place it outside the scope of the do-it-yourselfer. Take the head to an automotive machine shop to ensure that the job is done correctly.**

3 Check the camshaft lobes for heat discoloration, score marks, chipped areas, pitting and uneven wear. If the lobes are in good condition the camshaft can be reused. Refer to Chapter 2 Part F for further

camshaft inspection procedures.

4 Make sure the camshaft oil passages are clear and clean.

5 To check the thrust plate for wear, install the camshaft in the cylinder head and position the thrust plate at the rear. Using a dial indicator, check the total endplay by prying the camshaft carefully back-and-forth. If the endplay is outside the limit specified in this Chapter's Specifications, replace the thrust plate with a new one.

CAM FOLLOWERS

6 Check the faces, or rollers, of the cam followers (which bear on the camshaft lobes) for signs of pitting, score marks and other forms of wear. They should fit snugly on the lash adjuster.

7 Inspect the face which bears on the valve stem. If it's pitted, the cam follower must be replaced with a new one.

8 If excessive cam follower wear is evident (and possibly excessive camshaft lobe wear), it may be due to a malfunction of the lubrication system. If more than one cam follower is excessively worn, replace the camshaft and all the cam followers. This also applies where excessive camshaft lobe wear is found.

9 During any operation which requires removal of the cam followers, inspect the lash adjusters for damage or wear.

9 Front oil seals - replacement

→**Note: The camshaft, crankshaft, auxiliary shaft, and oil pump oil seals are all replaced the same way, using the same tools, after the appropriate sprocket has been removed.**

1 Disconnect the negative battery cable from the battery.
2 Remove the timing belt cover and timing belt (see Section 6).

→**Note: Due to the lack of space at the front of the engine, access to the components may be difficult. If additional clearance is desired, remove the radiator.**

3 To remove the camshaft sprocket or oil pump sprocket, refer to Section 7 or 14. A special puller is available for this purpose. To remove the crankshaft sprocket, use an appropriate gear puller.

4 A special tool, available at most auto parts stores, may be used to remove all the seals. When using the tool, be sure the jaws are gripping the thin edge of the seal very tightly before operating the screw portion of the tool. If the tool isn't available, a hammer and a small chisel may be used to remove the seal(s), if care is exercised.

5 Clean the seal bore and shaft surface prior to installation of the new seal. Apply a thin layer of grease to the outer edge of the new seal(s).

6 Install the seal(s) with a special tool made for this job, available at most auto parts stores. If the special tool isn't available, you may be able to use a large deep socket and a hammer or a short piece of pipe, the sprocket bolt and a large flat washer.

7 Install the components removed to gain access to the seals.

❊❊ CAUTION:

Always use a new camshaft sprocket bolt or seal the old bolt threads with Teflon sealing tape.

10 Intake manifold - removal and installation

REMOVAL

1 Relieve the fuel system pressure (see Chapter 4).
2 Disconnect the negative battery cable from the battery.
3 Remove the engine drivebelt (see Chapter 1). Drain the cooling system (see Chapter 1).
4 Remove the air cleaner and ducts (see Chapter 4). On 2.5L engines, remove the air conditioning compressor and mounting bracket (see Chapter 3) without disconnecting the high-pressure refrigerant lines.
5 Refer to Chapter 4, Section 12 and remove the upper intake manifold.
6 Remove the four bottom mounting bolts from the intake manifold.
7 Remove the four upper mounting bolts from the lower manifold. Note that the front two bolts also secure the engine lifting eye.
8 Detach the manifold from the engine.

INSTALLATION

9 Clean the manifold and head mating surfaces and check the manifold for cracks.

→**Note: The mating surfaces of the head and manifold must be perfectly clean when the manifold is installed. Gasket removal solvents in aerosol cans are available at most auto parts stores and may be helpful when removing old gasket material that's stuck to the head and manifold. Be careful not to scrape or gouge the sealing surfaces.**

10 Clean and oil the manifold mounting bolts.
11 Position the new intake manifold gasket on the head, using a light coat of gasket sealant to hold it in place.
12 Position the intake manifold, along with the lifting eye, on the head. Install the fasteners and tighten them, from the center outwards, to the torque listed in this Chapter's Specifications in two steps.
13 The remainder of installation is the reverse of removal.
14 Reconnect the battery and refill the cooling system.
15 Start the engine and let it run while checking for coolant, fuel and vacuum leaks.

11 Exhaust manifold - removal and installation

REMOVAL

1 Disconnect the negative battery cable from the battery.
2 Remove the air cleaner and duct assembly if needed to gain access.
3 Remove the EGR tube fitting at the exhaust manifold and loosen at the EGR tube (see Chapter 6).
4 Disconnect the oxygen sensor wiring harness connector.
5 Remove the bolt attaching the heater hoses to the valve cover, if equipped.
6 Raise the vehicle and support it securely on jackstands. Remove the two bolts attaching the exhaust pipe to the manifold (see Chapter 4).
7 Remove the eight exhaust manifold mounting bolts and detach the manifold from the engine.
8 Clean the manifold and cylinder head mounting surfaces with a gasket scraper, then wipe them off with a cloth saturated with lacquer thinner or acetone. Clean the bolt threads with a wire brush.

INSTALLATION

9   Using a new gasket, install the manifold and the eight bolts attaching it to the cylinder head. Tighten the bolts, from the center outwards, to the torque listed in this Chapter's Specifications.

10   Install the bolts attaching the exhaust pipe to the exhaust manifold.
11   Position the heater hoses on the valve cover.
12   Reconnect the oxygen sensor wire.
13   Install the EGR line at the exhaust manifold.
14   Install the air cleaner and duct assembly.
15   Reconnect the battery cable.

12 Cylinder head - removal and installation

♦ **Refer to illustrations 12.31 and 12.33**

REMOVAL

1   On 2.5L engines, have the air conditioning refrigerant recovered by a dealer service department or service station. Relieve the fuel system pressure (see Chapter 4). Disconnect the cable from the negative battery terminal and position the number one piston at Top Dead Center (TDC) on the compression stroke (see Section 3).
2   Drain the cooling system (see Chapter 1). Remove the air cleaner assembly and the air duct. Remove the drivebelt (see Chapter 1).
3   Remove the bolt retaining the heater hose to the valve cover, if equipped.
4   Remove the spark plug wires from the spark plugs and remove the ignition coil packs and wires as an assembly. Remove the spark plugs.
5   Label and disconnect any electrical connectors or vacuum hoses attached to components on the cylinder head.
6   Remove the dipstick tube.
7   Remove the upper intake manifold (see Chapter 4). Remove the lower intake manifold (see Section 10).
8   Remove the valve cover (see Section 4).
9   Remove the air conditioning compressor from its mounting bracket and set it aside without disconnecting the hoses. Remove the bracket and set it, and the power steering pump, aside. Remove the alternator bracket mounting bolts and set the alternator and bracket aside.
10   Disconnect the upper radiator hose at both ends and remove it from the engine.
11   Remove the radiator fan/clutch assembly, water pump pulley and timing belt front cover.
12   Confirm that all camshaft and crankshaft marks are still aligned, then loosen the timing belt tensioner (see Section 5).
13   Remove the timing belt from the camshaft or oil pump sprockets (see Section 6).
14   Remove the heat stove from the exhaust manifold.
15   Remove the exhaust manifold mounting bolts (see Section 11). The manifold itself can remain in place.
16   Remove the timing belt tensioner bolts.
17   Remove the timing belt tensioner spring stop from the cylinder head.
18   Disconnect the oil pressure sending unit wiring harness connector.
19   Refer to Section 10 and remove the intake manifold.
20   Using a new head gasket, outline the cylinders and bolt pattern on a piece of cardboard. Be sure to indicate the front of the engine for reference. Punch holes at the bolt locations.
21   Loosen the cylinder head mounting bolts in 1/4-turn increments until they can be removed by hand. Store the bolts in the cardboard holder as they're removed; this will ensure that they're reinstalled in their original locations.
22   Lift the head off the engine. If it's stuck, don't pry between the

head and block. Instead, rap the head with a soft-face hammer or a block of wood and a hammer to break the gasket seal.
23   Place the head on a block of wood to prevent damage to the gasket surface. Refer to Part F for cylinder head disassembly, inspection and valve service procedures. Make sure you check the cylinder head for warpage.

INSTALLATION

24   If a new cylinder head is being installed, transfer all external parts from the old cylinder head to the new one.
25   The mating surfaces of the cylinder head and block must be perfectly clean when the head is installed.
26   Use a gasket scraper to remove all traces of carbon and old gasket material, then clean the mating surfaces with lacquer thinner or acetone. If there's oil on the mating surfaces when the head is installed, the gasket may not seal correctly and leaks may develop. Use a vacuum cleaner to remove any debris that falls into the cylinders.
27   Check the block and head mating surfaces for nicks, deep scratches and other damage. If damage is slight, it can be removed with a file; if it's excessive, machining may be the only alternative.
28   Use a tap of the correct size to chase the threads in the head bolt holes. Mount each bolt in a vise and run a die down the threads to remove corrosion and restore the threads. Dirt, corrosion, sealant and damaged threads will affect critical head bolt torque readings.
29   Position the new gasket over the dowel pins in the block. Do not use a gasket sealer.
30   Confirm that the crankshaft is at TDC as described in Section 3. If it is not, rotate the crankshaft in the normal direction (see Section 3) until the "TC" mark aligns with the pointer. Pistons 1 and 4 should be at TDC.
31   Before installing the cylinder head, turn the camshaft until the pin is in the five o'clock position - this must be done to avoid damage to the valves when the head is installed (see illustration). Check the cam-

36071-2A-12.31 HAYNES

12.31 Be sure to turn the camshaft until the pin is in the 5 o'clock position as shown here before installing the head

12.33 Cylinder head bolt tightening sequence

shaft lobes to verify proper camshaft position. The lobes for Cylinders No. 1 and 4 should point almost directly out. The lobes for Cylinders No. 2 and 3 should point up at about a 45-degree angle. This ensures that all 8 valves are seated, and cannot collide with the pistons.

32 Carefully position the head on the block without disturbing the gasket.

33 Install the cylinder head bolts and tighten them in sequence (see illustration) to the torque listed in this Chapter's Specifications.

34 Return the camshaft to its original TDC position.

35 The remainder of installation is the reverse of the removal procedure.

36 Change the engine oil and filter (see Chapter 1).

13 Oil pan - removal and installation

➡Note: The engine must be removed from the vehicle to remove the oil pan.

REMOVAL

1 Drain the oil and remove the oil filter.

2 Remove the engine as described in Part F of this Chapter. Mount the engine in a suitable engine stand, right-side up.

3 Remove the oil pan mounting bolts and lower the pan.

INSTALLATION

4 Clean the oil pan and inspect for damage. Remove the spacers, if any, that are attached to the oil pan transmission mounting pad.

5 Clean the oil pan gasket surface on the cylinder block and the oil pan flange. These surfaces must be perfectly clean to prevent oil leaks.

6 Clean the oil pump pick-up tube screen.

7 Apply RTV sealant to six points; at the joints between the front cover and engine block and rear main bearing cap and engine block.

Position the gasket inside the channel of the oil pan.

8 Place the oil pan onto the engine and install the oil pan mounting bolts and hand tighten them only at this time. They will be tightened to final torque after the engine and transmission are mated to ensure correct alignment.

9 Install the engine in the vehicle as described in Part F of this Chapter.

10 Tighten the two oil pan-to-transmission bolts to the torque listed in this Chapter's Specifications, then loosen them 1/2 turn.

11 Tighten the oil pan-to-engine block bolts to the torque listed in this Chapter's Specifications. Work around the pan, tightening each bolt a little at a time.

12 Retighten the oil pan-to-transmission bolts to the torque listed in this Chapter's Specifications.

13 The remainder of the installation is the reverse of the removal procedure.

14 Be sure to refill the engine with the proper quantity and grade oil (see Chapter 1).

14 Oil pump - removal and installation

1 Remove the timing belt as described in Section 6.

2 Loosen the oil pump sprocket bolt. If the shaft turns, immobilize the sprocket by inserting a large screwdriver or 3/8-inch drive extension through one of the sprocket holes.

3 Pull off the sprocket (a puller may be required), and remove the key from the shaft.

4 Disconnect the camshaft position sensor (CMP) wiring connector.

5 Remove the two screws securing the CMP sensor and remove the sensor (see Chapter 6).

6 Remove the four oil pump mounting bolts.

7 Loosen the oil pump by prying between the cylinder block and the tab on the oil pump.

❈❈ **CAUTION:**

Do not pry on any sealing surfaces.

8 Remove the oil pump and the associated gasket.

9 Clean the exterior of the oil pump and the mating surface on the cylinder block.

10 Make sure the passage at the back of the oil pump bore in the cylinder block is clean and unobstructed.

11 Install new O-rings on the oil pump body and install a new gasket.

12 Pour 8 ounces of engine oil into the inlet passage to prime the oil pump.

13 Install the oil pump in the cylinder block being careful not to spill the primer oil.

14 Install the oil pump mounting bolts and tighten them to the torque listed in this Chapter's Specifications.

15 Insert the key in the oil pump shaft and install the oil pump sprocket. Install the bolt and washer and tighten the sprocket bolt to the torque listed in this Chapter's Specifications.

16 Check engine oil level on the dipstick. Top up as necessary.

17 Prime the oil pump by connecting it to a drill motor and rotating it until there is some resistance. This may take 10 or more revolutions of the sprocket.

18 Install the CMP sensor and connect the electrical connector.

19 Rotate the oil pump sprocket until the two timing marks align.

20 Verify that the crankshaft, camshaft and oil pump sprockets are properly aligned at TDC (see Section 3).

21 Install the timing belt and outer cover (see Section 6).

15 Flywheel/driveplate - removal and installation

1 Remove the transmission (see Chapter 7).

2 Remove the pressure plate and the clutch disc from the rear of the flywheel as described in Chapter 8 (manual transmission models).

3 Lock the flywheel/driveplate using a large screwdriver meshed with the starter ring gear and remove the six bolts securing the flywheel to the crankshaft. The bolts should be removed a quarter turn at a time in a diagonal and progressive manner.

4 Mark the mating position of the flywheel/driveplate and crank-shaft flange and then remove the flywheel.

5 If necessary, remove the engine rear cover plate bolts and ease the rear cover plate over the two dowel pins. Remove the cover plate.

6 If the flywheel ring gear is badly worn or has teeth missing, it should be replaced by an automotive machine shop.

7 Check for cracks and other damage.

8 Installation of the flywheel/driveplate and clutch is the reverse of the removal procedure with the following additions:

   a) *Apply oil-resistant sealer sparingly to the bolt threads.*

   b) *Tighten the mounting bolts to the torque listed in this Chapter's Specifications.*

9 For further information on clutch servicing and pilot bearing replacement, see Chapter 8.

16 Rear main oil seal - replacement

1 Remove the transmission (see Chapter 7) and clutch and pressure plate (if equipped - see Chapter 8) to access the oil seal in the back of the engine.

2 Remove the flywheel or driveplate (see Section 15).

3 Use a small punch to make two holes on opposite sides of the seal and install small sheet metal screws in the seal. Pry on the screws with two large screwdrivers until the seal is removed from the engine. It may be necessary to place small blocks of wood against the block to provide a fulcrum point for prying.

4 Apply a thin film of engine oil to the mating edges of the seal and the seal bore in the block, as well as the seal lips.

5 Position the seal on a seal installer, available at most auto parts stores, or its equivalent, then position the tool and seal at the rear of engine. Install the seal with the spring side toward the engine. Alternate tightening of the bolts to seat the seal properly.

6 If the special seal installer is not available, use a section of the appropriate diameter plastic pipe and gently tap the seal into place with a soft-face hammer.

7 The remainder of the installation is the reverse of the removal procedure.

✳✳ CAUTION:

Be careful not to scratch or otherwise damage the crankshaft oil seal surface.

17 Engine mounts - removal and installation

1 Engine mounts seldom require attention, but broken or dete-riorated mounts should be replaced immediately or the added strain placed on the driveline components may cause damage or wear.

CHECK

2 During the check, the engine must be raised slightly to remove the weight from the mounts.

3 Raise the vehicle and support it securely on jackstands, then position a jack under the engine oil pan. Place a large block of wood between the jack head and the oil pan, then carefully raise the engine just enough to take the weight of the mounts.

✳✳ WARNING:

DO NOT place any part of your body under the engine when it's supported only by a jack!

4 Check the mounts to see if the rubber is cracked, hardened or separated from the metal plates. Sometimes the rubber will split right down the center.

5 Check for relative movement between the mount plates and the engine or frame (use a large screwdriver or pry bar to attempt to move the mounts). If movement is noted, lower the engine and tighten the mount fasteners.

6   Rubber preservative should be applied to the mounts to slow deterioration.

REPLACEMENT

7   Disconnect the negative battery cable from the battery, then raise the vehicle and support it securely on jackstands (if not already done).

8   Remove the fasteners and detach the mount from the frame bracket.

9   Raise the engine slightly with a jack or hoist (make sure the fan doesn't hit the radiator or shroud). Remove the mount-to-block nuts/bolts and detach the mount.

10 Installation is the reverse of removal. Use thread locking compound on the mount fasteners and be sure to tighten them securely.

Specifications

General

Cylinder numbers (front-to-rear)	1-2-3-4
Firing order	1-3-4-2

Camshaft

Lobe lift (intake and exhaust)	
2007 and earlier	0.2163 inch
2008 and later	
Intake	0.234 inch
Exhaust	0.307 inch
Bearing journal diameter	1.7713 to 1.7720 inch
Bearing clearance	0.001 to 0.003 inch
Endplay	0.001 to 0.007 inch

36071-2A-SPECS HAYNES

Cylinder numbering and coil terminal location - 2000 and 2001 2.5L four-cylinder engines

Torque specifications   Ft-lbs (unless otherwise indicated)

➡**Note: One foot-pound (ft-lb) of torque is equivalent to 12 inch-pounds (in-lbs) of torque. Torque values below approximately 15 ft-lbs are expressed in inch-pounds, since most foot-pound torque wrenches are not accurate at these smaller values.**

Camshaft sprocket bolt	50 to 71
Camshaft position sensor bolt	62 in-lbs
Crankshaft pulley/sprocket bolt	103 to 133
Oil pump sprocket bolt	28 to 40
Rear camshaft retaining plate bolt	72 to 108 in-lbs
Timing belt outer cover bolts	72 to 108 in-lbs
Timing belt tensioner adjustment bolt	14 to 21
Timing belt tensioner pivot bolt	28 to 40
Valve cover bolts	72 to 108 in-lbs
Cylinder head bolts (in sequence - see illustration 12.33)	
Step 1	50
Step 2	Tighten additional 90 to 100-degrees
Flywheel/driveplate bolts	56 to 64
Intake manifold bolts	
Step 1	84 to 120 in-lbs
Step 2	19 to 28
Exhaust manifold bolts	
Step 1	15 to 22
Step 2	45 to 59
Oil pan-to-engine block bolts	127 to 141 in-lbs
Oil pan-to-transmission bolts	29 to 40
Oil pump bolts	127 to 141 in-lbs
Oil pump pick-up tube bolts	14 to 21
Engine mount-to-block bolts	45 to 60
Engine mount-to-frame bolts	
Left side	71 to 94
Right side	52 to 67

Notes

Section

Reference to other Chapters

2B

DUAL OVERHEAD CAMSHAFT (DOHC) FOUR-CYLINDER ENGINE

1 General information

This Part of Chapter 2 is devoted to in-vehicle repair procedures for the 2.3L DOHC four-cylinder engines. Since these procedures are based on the assumption that the engine is installed, if the engine has been removed from the vehicle and mounted on a stand, some of the preliminary disassembly steps outlined will not apply.

➡Note: Many of the photographs used in this Chapter were taken with the engine removed from the vehicle in order to aid our production. There is no need to remove the engine for any procedures in this Chapter unless we state otherwise.

Information concerning engine/transmission removal and replacement and engine overhaul can be found in Part F of this Chapter.

ENGINE DESCRIPTION

This engine has sixteen-valves, double overhead camshafts (DOHC), and an in-line four-cylinder block. It is longitudinally mounted at the front of the vehicle and followed directly by the transmission. It has a cast aluminum cylinder head, engine block, and oil pan.

The main bearing caps are integrated into a frame that holds the crankshaft solidly in place. This bearing configuration cannot be serviced. The pistons, connecting rods, crankshaft or engine block also cannot be serviced. Any failure of these components will require replacement of the entire engine block/crankcase as an assembly.

➡Note: This was the case at the time of writing. Check with an automotive machine shop to see if aftermarket components and service techniques have been developed if your engine requires repair.

The valvetrain uses bucket-style tappets which respond directly from head mounted camshafts. Any wear in this system may require replacement tappets which are sized individually to bring the valve clearances to specification.

The two camshafts (intake and exhaust) operate eight valves each and are driven by a single timing chain. Each camshaft rotates in five bearings that are line-bored directly in the cylinder head and the (bolted-on) bearing caps; this means that the bearing caps are not interchangeable. No replacement is designed to fit correctly based on this type of manufacturing.

The water pump is bolted to the right-hand end of the cylinder block and driven with the steering pump, A/C compressor and alternator by a multi-ribbed auxiliary drivebelt from the crankshaft pulley.

2 Repair operations possible with the engine in the vehicle

The following major repair operations can be accomplished without removing the engine from the vehicle. However, it should be noted that any operation involving the removal of the oil pan requires careful consideration. Level of skill, proper tools and facilities are all noteworthy factors. Refer to the relevant text for details.

a) Compression pressure - testing (see Chapter 2F).
b) Valve cover - removal and installation.
c) Manifolds - removal and installation.
d) Engine front cover - removal and installation.
e) Timing chain - replacement.
f) Timing chain tensioner and sprockets - removal and installation.
g) Camshafts and tappets - removal and installation.
h) Cylinder head - removal, overhaul and installation.
i) Crankshaft oil seals - replacement.
j) Flywheel/driveplate - removal and installation.
k) Engine/transmission mounts - removal and installation.

Clean the engine compartment and the exterior of the engine with some type of degreaser before any work is done (and/or clean the engine using a steam cleaner). It will make the job easier and will help to keep dirt out of the internal areas of the engine.

Depending on the components involved, it may be helpful to remove the hood to improve access to the engine (refer to Chapter 11 if necessary). Cover the fenders to prevent damage to the paint. An old bedspread or blanket works well in place of specialized fender covers available at auto supply stores.

3 Top Dead Center (TDC) for Number 1 piston - locating

▶ Refer to illustrations 3.6, 3.7, 3.8 and 3.10

1 Top Dead Center (TDC) is the highest point of the cylinder that each piston reaches as the crankshaft turns. Each piston reaches its TDC position at the end of its compression stroke, and then again at the end of its exhaust stroke. For the purpose of engine timing, TDC on the compression stroke for the Number 1 piston is used. The Number 1 cylinder is at the front of the engine.
2 Disconnect the negative battery cable (see Chapter 5).
3 Remove all the spark plugs (see Chapter 1).
4 Remove the valve cover (see Section 4).
5 Using a wrench or socket on the crankshaft pulley bolt, rotate the crankshaft clockwise until the intake valves for the Number 1 cylinder have opened and just closed again.

➡Note: The front lobes (at the very front of the engine) on both camshafts will be facing up and away from the valves when Cylinder #1 is at TDC.

6 Install the special camshaft alignment tool.

➡Note: The camshafts each have a machined slot at the transmission end of the engine; both slots will be completely horizontal, and at the same height as the cylinder head machined surface, when the engine is at TDC on the Number 1 cylinder. A special tool is used to check this position, and to positively locate the camshafts in position. Fortunately, a substitute tool can be made from a strip of metal 5 mm thick (while the strip's thickness is critical, its length and width are not, but should be approximately 180 to 230 mm long by 20 to 30 mm wide) (see illustration).

3.6 Slide the camshaft alignment tool into the slots in the ends of the camshafts

3.7 Remove the timing pin plug from the cylinder block

7   On the front of the engine block there is a plugged hole for a special tool used to locate the crankshaft to TDC (see illustration).

8   Unscrew the timing pin plug and screw in the special timing pin (obtainable from a dealer or specialty tool supplier) (see illustration). An alternative pin can be made from an M10 diameter bolt, cut down so that the length from the underside of the bolt head to the tip is exactly 63.4 mm. It may be necessary to turn the crankshaft slightly either way in order to fully insert the timing pin.

> ✳✳ **CAUTION:**
>
> **You must remove the timing pin and the camshaft alignment tool before turning the crankshaft.**

9   Turn the engine forwards gently until the crankshaft comes into contact with the timing pin - in this position, the engine is set to TDC on the Number 1 cylinder.

➡**Note: With the timing pin installed, the engine will be prevented from moving in the clockwise direction - but it can still move in the counterclockwise direction.**

10   There is also a bolt hole in the crankshaft pulley that aligns with a threaded hole in the front engine cover. These holes are used to locate

the crankshaft pulley at TDC but they can also be used to confirm that the engine is at TDC. Install a bolt (M6 x 18mm) through the pulley and into the cover to confirm that the crankshaft is in the TDC position (see illustration). Remove the bolt after confirming that the crankshaft pulley is at TDC.

➡**Note: If you cannot install this bolt easily, it is possible that the engine is not timed correctly.**

> ✳✳ **CAUTION:**
>
> **This bolt must be removed before the crankshaft pulley or crankshaft can be rotated.**

11   Before rotating the crankshaft again, make sure that the camshaft alignment tool, the timing pin and the TDC bolt in the crankshaft pulley are removed and the timing pin plug is replaced.

12   If the timing pin is not available, insert a length of wooden dowel (about 150 mm/6 in long) or similar into the Number 1 spark plug hole until it rests on the piston crown. Turn the engine back from its TDC position, then forward (taking care not to allow the dowel to be trapped in the cylinder) until the dowel stops rising - the piston is now at the top of its compression stroke and the dowel can be removed.

3.8 Installing the timing pin

3.10 Installing the M6 bolt to verify TDC

➥**Note: This method of locating TDC cannot be used to time the engine because it is not accurate enough.**

13 There is a dead area around TDC (as the piston stops rising, pauses and then begins to descend) which makes it difficult to find the exact location of TDC by this method; if accuracy is required, you'll need the special tools described above.

14 Once the Number 1 cylinder has been positioned at TDC on the compression stroke, TDC for any of the other cylinders can then be located by rotating the crankshaft clockwise 180-degrees at a time and following the firing order (see Specifications).

✳✳ CAUTION:

Do not turn the crankshaft with the timing pin installed.

---

4 Valve cover - removal and installation

◆ **Refer to illustration 4.11**

1 Disconnect the negative battery cable (see Chapter 5).

2 Remove the intake manifold (see Section 6).

3 Lift the boot to the CHT (cylinder head temperature) sensor (located between spark plug wires 2 and 3 on the valve cover) and then disconnect the electrical connector.

4 Detach the wiring harness fasteners from the studs on the side of the valve cover.

5 Disconnect the spark plug wires from the spark plugs by carefully withdrawing them from the valve cover. Use labels on the wires before removal.

➥**Note: Some wires are numbered by the manufacturer so labeling may not be necessary.**

6 Disconnect the ignition coil electrical connector and then remove the coil from the valve cover.

7 Disconnect the camshaft position sensor electrical connector, then remove the sensor (mounted on the valve cover).

8 Remove the crankcase ventilation hose from the valve cover.

9 Remove any other attached hoses, connectors or retainers that may be attached to the valve cover.

10 Remove the valve cover bolts and then the cover itself.

11 Installation is the reverse of removal noting the following points:

a) *Carefully inspect the valve cover gasket and replace it if necessary.*

b) *Make certain that the mating surfaces are clean.*

➥**Note: Do not use metal scrapers, wire brushes or abrasive wheels to clean mating surfaces - they can easily gouge the surfaces and cause leaks.**

c) *Follow the tightening sequence (see illustration) and the torque Specifications at the end of this Chapter.*

d) *After installation is complete, run the engine and check for any leaks.*

➥**Note: Make certain all electrical and hose connections are correct. Any poor connections may cause the Check engine warning light to illuminate, lead to poor engine performance or cause engine damage.**

4.11 The valve cover tightening sequence

---

5 Valve clearance - check and adjustment

5.3 Using a feeler gauge between the base of the cam lobe and the valve tappet to measure the valve clearance

➥**Note: There are no manufacturer recommended service intervals for checking valve clearances on this engine at the time this manual was written. High mileage or excessive noise in the valvetrain may determine the need to check the valve clearances.**

CHECK

◆ **Refer to illustration 5.3**

1 Remove the valve cover as described in Section 4.

2 Set the Number 1 cylinder to TDC on the compression stroke as described in Section 3. The intake and exhaust cam lobes of the Number 1 cylinder will be pointing upwards (though not vertical) and the valve clearances can be checked.

3 Working on each valve in turn, measure the clearance between the base of the cam lobe and the tappet (bucket-style) using a feeler gauge (see illustration). Record the thickness of the blade required to give a firm sliding fit on all four valves of the Number 1 cylinder.

4   Now turn the crankshaft clockwise 180° so that the valves of cylinder Number 3 are pointing upwards. Measure and record the valve clearances for cylinder Number 3. The clearances for cylinders 4 and 2 can be measured after turning the crankshaft 180° each time. Any measured valve clearances that do not fall in the specified range (see Specifications) must be adjusted.

5   Make a chart noting which valves need adjustment if any are out of specification.

➡**Note: Do not rely on memory alone.**

ADJUSTMENT

♦ **Refer to illustration 5.14**

➡**Note 1: For do-it-yourself purposes, note that while checking the valve clearances is relatively easy, adjusting the valve clearances on this engine is very involved and requires numerous steps before completing the actual adjustment procedure. The ability to obtain accurate measurements with a micrometer will also be necessary.**

➡**Note 2: If adjustments are required, replacement tappets of varying thicknesses are used to achieve the desired valve clearance. A formula is used to determine the correct replacement tappet needed for each valve in need of adjustment. Valve clearance measurements must be accurate in order to select the appropriate replacement tappet. Measuring twice is considered a good practice before beginning any valve adjustment.**

6   If the valve clearance was too small, a thinner-faced tappet must be installed. If the clearance was too large, a thicker-faced tappet must be installed. When the tappet thickness and the valve clearance are known, the required thickness of the new tappet can easily be calculated (see below).

➡**Note: The ideal valve clearance is the midrange between the Specifications given at the end of this Chapter.**

Sample calculation - clearance too small

Desired clearance (A) = 0.25 mm
Measured clearance (B) = 0.09 mm
Tappet thickness found (C) = 2.55 mm
Thickness required (D) = 2.39
C + B - A = 2.39 mm

Sample calculation - clearance too large

Desired clearance (A) = 0.30 mm
Measured clearance (B) = 0.36 mm
Tappet thickness found (C) = 2.19 mm
Thickness required (D) = 2.25
C + B - A = 2.25 mm

5.14 The tappet measurement is found underneath

7   After determining the replacement tappets necessary for all valves in need of adjustment, you'll need to purchase these special parts from your local dealership.

8   Set the engine to TDC (see Section 3).

9   Remove the valve cover (see Section 5).

10 Remove the engine front cover (see Section 7).

11 Remove the timing chain and camshaft sprockets (see Section 8).

12 Remove both camshafts (see Section 11).

13 Remove a single tappet with a valve lapping tool or a magnet.

➡**Note: To avoid confusion, remove and replace tappets one at a time only. Tappets that are not being replaced should be left alone.**

14 Note the thickness (measured in mm) of the tappet face which is engraved underneath (see illustration). If the marking is missing or illegible, a micrometer will be needed to establish its thickness.

15 Use liberal amounts of oil on the replacement tappets when installing them.

16 After all replacement tappets are installed, reassembly may begin.

17 Installation is the reverse of removal noting the following points:

  a) *Use liberal amounts of oil on the cam lobes and journals before installing the camshafts.*

  b) *Carefully measure the valve clearances again before installing the valve cover to assure that they are correct.*

  c) *Follow all tightening sequences and the torque specifications.*

  d) *Make certain all electrical and hose connections are correct.*

➡**Note: Any poor connections may cause the Check engine warning light to illuminate, lead to poor engine performance or cause engine damage.**

  e) *After installation is complete, run the engine and check for any leaks.*

---

6 Manifolds - removal and installation

✳✳ WARNING:

Wait until the engine is completely cool before beginning this procedure.

INTAKE MANIFOLD

➡**Note: This procedure involves many hoses and connections. We recommend using labels to aid installation.**

1   Disconnect the negative battery cable (see Chapter 5).

2   Clamp-off the coolant hose to the intake manifold and then remove the hose from its fitting.

3   Remove the cover from the top of the throttle body.

4   Remove the air intake tube from the throttle body and air cleaner housing.

5   Disconnect the throttle cable(s) from the throttle control linkage and then from the cable bracket on the intake manifold.

6   Disconnect the TP sensor electrical connector (located on the

throttle body) (see Chapter 6).

7   Disconnect the MAP, IAC and any remaining electrical connectors (see Chapter 6).

8   Disconnect all hoses and clips along with any engine wiring harness retainers from the manifold.

☀ WARNING:

The fuel system pressure must be relieved before disconnecting the fuel supply hose from the manifold (see Section 4).

9   Remove the bolt for the EGR tube bracket, then the EGR tube flange.

10   Detach the large 42-pin harness connector (square with a fastener on top) from its bracket and move it aside.

11   Remove any other brackets, hoses or connectors near the intake manifold which may hinder removal.

12   Remove the five bolts that attach the intake manifold and carefully remove it from the engine.

13   Installation is the reverse of removal noting the following points:

a)   *Carefully inspect the manifold gasket and replace it if necessary.*

b)   *Make certain that the mating surfaces are clean.*

➡**Note: Do not use metal scrapers, wire brushes or abrasive wheels to clean mating surfaces - they can easily gouge the surfaces and cause leaks.**

c)   *Use the torque Specifications at the end of this Chapter for installation.*

EXHAUST MANIFOLD

14   Disconnect the negative battery cable (see Chapter 5).

15   Raise the vehicle and support it securely on jackstands.

16   Remove the exhaust pipe-to-exhaust manifold nuts. If the nuts are rusty and stuck, spray them with penetrating oil and wait a half-hour

or so, then try again.

17   Lower the vehicle, then drain the cooling system (see Chapter 1).

18   Remove the drivebelt (see Chapter 1).

19   Disconnect the upper radiator hose and the expansion tank hose from the coolant pipe.

20   Remove the air conditioning compressor and set it aside, without disconnecting the refrigerant lines.

21   Disconnect the heater hose from the coolant pipe.

22   Remove the engine oil dipstick, then unscrew the bolts and remove the dipstick tube.

23   Unscrew the bolts and remove the coolant pipe.

24   Loosen the right front wheel lug nuts, then raise the front of the vehicle and support it securely on jackstands. Remove the wheel.

25   Remove the right inner fender splash shield.

26   Detach the electrical connectors from the alternator.

27   Remove the bolts securing the lower portion of the accessory drive bracket.

28   Install the wheel and lower the vehicle.

29   Remove the bolts securing the upper portion of the accessory drive bracket, then remove the bracket.

30   Unscrew the exhaust manifold retaining nuts and remove the manifold and gasket.

31   Installation is the reverse of removal noting the following points:

a)   *Make certain that the mating surfaces are clean.*

➡**Note: Do not use metal scrapers, wire brushes or abrasive wheels to clean mating surfaces - they can easily gouge the surfaces and cause leaks.**

b)   *Check the exhaust manifold for cracks and warpage. If the manifold is warped, an automotive machine shop may be able to resurface it.*

c)   *Install a new exhaust manifold gasket.*

d)   *Use the torque Specifications at the end of this Chapter for installation.*

e)   *Tighten the wheel lug nuts to the torque listed in the Chapter 1 Specifications.*

7   Crankshaft pulley - removal and installation

36071-2B-7.5 HAYNES

7.5 The crankshaft pulley holding tool installed

REMOVAL

▶ **Refer to illustration 7.5**

☀ CAUTION:

Once the crankshaft pulley is loosened the crankshaft (timing) sprocket will be loosened as well. The engine is considered out-of-time at this point. The installation procedure in this Section must be followed exactly to re-time the engine properly. Severe engine damage may occur otherwise.

1   Remove the cooling fan and shroud (see Chapter 3).

2   Remove the auxiliary drivebelt (see Chapter 1).

3   Remove the valve cover (see Section 4).

4   Set the engine to TDC (see Section 3).

5   The crankshaft must be held to prevent its rotation while the pulley bolt is unscrewed. A special tool to hold the crankshaft pulley is needed for this (see illustration), and is available at most auto supply stores or equipment rental locations. A suitable equivalent can be fabricated from a length of strap steel.

✳ CAUTION:

Use of a pry bar or similar tool can damage the crankshaft pulley.

6   Insert the service tool into the spaces in the front face of the pulley to hold it in place while turning the crankshaft pulley bolt with a large wrench or socket/breaker-bar combination.

✳ CAUTION:

Failure to hold the crankshaft pulley securely while removing the pulley bolt could result in engine damage. Moreover, NEVER rely on the timing pin or the camshaft service tool as a means of locking the crankshaft - they are designed for calibration only. Engine damage could occur by not using these tools for their intended purpose.

7   Unscrew the pulley bolt and remove the holding tool.
8   Remove the pulley and label or mark which side is installed towards the engine.

INSTALLATION

▶ **Refer to illustration 7.20**

9   Lightly coat the crankshaft front seal with clean engine oil, then install the crankshaft pulley.

➡**Note: If the seal shows signs of leakage, you may want to replace it before installing the crankshaft pulley (see Section 16).**

10   Install a new crankshaft pulley bolt and hand tighten only. Attempt to closely align the hole in the pulley with the threaded hole in the engine front cover.
11   Install a crankshaft pulley alignment bolt (M6 x 18mm) through the pulley and into the front engine cover. Rotate the pulley as necessary to do this (see illustration 3.10).

➡**Note: This aligns the pulley correctly with the crankshaft.**

12   Insert the large holding tool into the pulley and tighten the crankshaft pulley bolt to the torque listed in this Chapter's Specifications.

7.20 The camshaft alignment tool installed

13   Remove the crankshaft pulley holding tool and the threaded crankshaft alignment bolt from the pulley and front engine cover.
14   Remove the timing pin from the cylinder block.
15   Remove the camshaft alignment tool installed as part of Step 4.
16   Rotate the engine clockwise two complete revolutions by turning the crankshaft pulley bolt with a wrench or large socket.
17   Rotate the engine again to achieve TDC (see Section 3).

➡**Note: Rotate the engine in the clockwise direction only.**

18   Install the timing pin into the cylinder block.
19   Install the crankshaft pulley alignment bolt (M6 x 18mm). If it cannot be installed, the crankshaft pulley must be removed and aligned so that it can. Repeat Steps 9 through 18 until crankshaft pulley alignment is correct.
20   With the crankshaft pulley alignment bolt (M6 x 18mm) installed, install the camshaft alignment tool and check the position of the camshafts (see illustration). If the tool cannot be installed, the engine timing must be corrected by repeating Steps 9 through 19.
21   The correct engine timing is achieved when the camshaft alignment tool, timing pin and the crankshaft pulley alignment bolt tool can be placed simultaneously.
22   Once correct engine timing is achieved, remove all the alignment tools and bolts and install the timing pin plug.
23   The rest of the installation is the reverse of removal.

8   Engine front cover - removal and installation

REMOVAL

▶ **Refer to illustration 8.3**

1   Disconnect the negative battery cable (see Chapter 5).
2   Remove the crankshaft pulley (see Section 7).
3   Disconnect the crankshaft position (CKP) sensor electrical connector (see illustration). Move the wiring harness away from the engine cover by removing the harness retainers.
4   Remove the (CKP) sensor (see Chapter 6).

➡**Note: Unfortunately with this engine, anytime this sensor is removed, a new sensor must be installed. The new sensor is packaged with a special sensor alignment tool that is critical for installation.**

5   Remove the drivebelt and the tensioner (see Chapter 1).

8.3 The crankshaft position (CKP) sensor is adjacent to the crankshaft pulley

8.11a Using two wrenches, hold the bolt head while turning the nut clockwise (towards the washers) to drive the pulley onto the new engine front cover

6   Remove the water pump pulley (see Chapter 3).

7   Disconnect the electrical connector to the power steering pressure switch. The switch is located on a high pressure hose within the power steering system.

8   Remove the single bolt on the lower left corner of the power steering pump and move the pump aside.

9   Remove the cooling fan drive pulley (if equipped) by using a three-jaw puller.

➡Note 1: The pulley can remain installed if the engine cover is not being replaced with a new one.

➡Note 2: There is a mounting bolt for the engine cover underneath this pulley that can be accessed through one of the pulley holes.

10 Remove the bolts and the engine cover.

INSTALLATION

◗ Refer to illustrations 8.11a and 8.11b

11 Installation is the reverse of removal noting the following:

8.11b The engine front cover bolt tightening sequence

a) Install the cooling fan drive pulley (if removed) onto the engine front cover.

➡Note: This can easily be accomplished by using flat washers, a bolt and nut. By placing the bolt through the pulley and threading it to the cover along with the nut and washers, drive the pulley onto the engine front cover using wrenches (see illustration).

b) Clean the mating surfaces of all material.

➡Note: Be careful not to gouge or use any abrasives on the mating surfaces.

c) Install the engine cover within four minutes of applying a 2.5mm bead of silicone sealant.

d) Tighten all bolts to the specified torque settings (using a three-stage sequence - see Specifications) and also using the sequence pattern provided (see illustration).

e) Be sure to re-time the engine as described in Section 7 and also use a new crankshaft position sensor which includes the necessary alignment tool.

---

9   Timing chain and tensioner - removal and installation

REMOVAL

◗ Refer to illustrations 9.3a and 9.3b

✳✳ CAUTION:

The timing system is complex. Severe engine damage will occur if you make any mistakes. Do not attempt this procedure unless you are highly experienced with this type of repair. If you are at all unsure of your abilities, consult an expert. Double-check all your work and be sure everything is correct before you attempt to start the engine.

1   Apply the parking brake, then carefully jack up the front of the vehicle and support the lifted portion on jackstands.

2   Remove the engine front cover (see Section 7).

3   Carefully compress the timing chain tensioner and place a pin (a drill bit or paper clip will work) into the hole to hold it in the com-

9.3a Compressing the timing chain tensioner and placing the lock pin

pressed position (see illustration).

➡Note: The tensioner contacts the right-hand chain guide.

※※ CAUTION:

Compress only the round plunger on the tensioner and not the ratchet mechanism. The ratchet is next to the plunger and has square sides. If the ratchet needs to be reset, do the following (see illustration):

a) *Remove the tensioner and place it lightly in a vise using the plunger and tensioner housing.*
b) *Place a pick-type tool in the hole closest to the ratchet to relieve the tension on the ratchet mechanism.*
c) *While holding the pick tool in place, move the ratchet back into the tensioner and then install a pin into the other hole to keep the plunger and ratchet compressed.*
d) *Remove the tensioner from the vise.*

4   Remove the two tensioner mounting bolts and then the tensioner itself.
5   Remove the loose timing chain guide (right)
6   Remove the timing chain.
7   The left chain guide and camshaft sprockets can now be removed if necessary (see Section 10).

INSTALLATION

▶ **Refer to illustration 9.13**

※※ CAUTION:

Before starting the engine, carefully rotate the crankshaft by hand through at least two full revolutions (use a socket and breaker bar on the crankshaft pulley center bolt). If you feel any resistance, STOP! There is something wrong -
most likely, valves are contacting the pistons. You must find the problem before proceeding. Check your work and see if any updated repair information is available.

8   Remove the camshaft alignment tool (if installed).
9   Loosen both camshaft sprocket bolts but don't remove them. Use a wrench on the hexagonal area of the camshaft to hold it while turning the camshaft sprocket bolt.

➡**Note: The hexagonal portion of the camshaft is located just after the second lobe from the front.**

※※ CAUTION:

Damage to the valves or pistons may occur if the camshafts are rotated during this procedure.

10   Install the left chain guide (if removed).

9.3b Timing chain tensioner details

9.13 Compressing the tensioner to release the lock pin

11   Install the timing chain.
12   Install the right chain guide.
13   Install the timing chain tensioner and tighten the fasteners to the torque listed in this Chapter's Specifications. Then remove the pin to release the tensioner to engage the chain guide (see illustration).
14   Install the camshaft alignment tool.
15   Torque the camshaft sprocket bolts to specification (see Specifications) while holding the camshafts in place with a wrench.

※※ CAUTION:

Do not rely on the camshaft alignment tool to hold the camshafts while tightening the camshaft sprocket bolts. Tool and engine damage may occur.

16   The engine front cover can now be installed (see Section 8).

10 Timing chain sprockets - removal and installation

CAMSHAFT SPROCKETS

Removal

1   Remove the timing chain (see Section 9).
2   Remove the camshaft alignment tool (if installed).

3   Use a wrench on the hexagonal area of the camshaft to hold it while turning the camshaft sprocket bolt (see illustration 10.11).

➡**Note: The hexagonal portion of the camshaft is located just after the second lobe from the front.**

4   Remove and label each camshaft sprocket so that they can be installed in the original place and direction.

Installation

♦ **Refer to illustration 10.11**

5   Place the camshaft sprockets back on their original camshafts and loosely install the sprocket bolts.

6   Install the left chain guide (if removed).

7   Install the timing chain.

8   Install the right chain guide.

9   Install the timing chain tensioner and tighten it to the torque

10.11 Tightening the camshaft sprocket bolt while holding the camshaft stationary with a wrench

listed in this Chapter's Specifications. Then remove the pin to engage the tensioner to the chain guide.

10   Install the camshaft alignment tool.

11   Tighten the camshaft sprocket bolts to the torque listed in this Chapter's Specifications while holding the camshafts in place with a wrench (see illustration).

❋❋ CAUTION:

Do not rely on the camshaft alignment tool to hold the camshafts while tightening the camshaft sprocket bolts. Tool and camshaft damage may occur.

12   The engine front cover can now be installed (see Section 8).

CRANKSHAFT SPROCKET

13   The crankshaft sprocket integrates with the oil pump drive sprocket as well. It can easily be pulled from the crankshaft once the oil pump drive chain is removed (see Section 14).

❋❋ CAUTION:

Use only factory parts if replacing the washers on either side of the crankshaft sprocket otherwise major engine damage could occur.

11   Camshafts and tappets - removal, inspection and installation

REMOVAL

♦ **Refer to illustrations 11.3, 11.4, 11.6 and 11.7**

1   Remove the timing chain (see Section 9).

2   Remove the camshaft sprockets (see Section 10).

3   Note the identifying numbers on the bearing caps (see illustration). Create a chart to match the bearing cap markings EXACTLY as they appear. If the markings are illegible or missing, you'll need to make your own.

11.3 Note the markings on the bearing caps

❋❋ CAUTION:

These bearing caps cannot be interchanged and must be replaced in their original positions otherwise engine damage may occur.

4   Loosen the camshaft bearing cap bolts progressively by half a turn at a time in the provided sequence only (see illustration). Gradually and evenly release the pressure of the valve springs on the caps.

11.4 Camshaft bearing cap loosening sequence - loosen each pair of bolts in sequence

11.6 The intake camshaft can be distinguished by the reference lobe for the camshaft position sensor

11.7 Removing the valve tappet (bucket-type) with a valve lapping tool

5   Remove the caps one at a time, noting their markings and locating dowels.

6   Before removing the camshafts, draw the position of the lobes for the number one cylinder on your chart. Carefully remove the camshafts.

➡**Note: The intake camshaft can be identified by the reference lobe for the camshaft position sensor (see illustration); use this to tell them apart.**

7   Get sixteen small containers that are clean and number them 1 through 16. Apply the numbers to the chart made for the bearing caps or make another chart for the valves. Remove each tappet one at a time using a valve lapping tool or a magnet (see illustration). Place them in the numbered containers for storage.

❊❊ CAUTION:

The valve tappets are individually sized for valve clearance (see Section 5) and must be placed back in their original position.

INSPECTION

▶ **Refer to illustrations 11.11, 11.14a and 11.14b**

8   Check each camshaft for signs of obvious wear (scoring, pitting, etc) and for roundness and replace if necessary.

9   Measure the outside diameter of each tappet - take measurements at the top and bottom of each one, then a second set at right-angles to the first; if any measurement is significantly different from the others, the tappet is tapered or oval (as applicable) and must be replaced. If the necessary equipment is available, measure the inside diameter of the corresponding cylinder head bore. No manufacturer's specifications were available at time of writing; if the tappets or the cylinder head bores are excessively worn, new tappets and/or a new cylinder head may be required.

10 If the engine had noisy valves or high mileage, look carefully for any signs of camshaft or tappet wear.

11 Visually examine the camshaft lobes for score marks, pitting, galling (wear due to rubbing) and evidence of overheating (blue, discolored areas). Look for flaking away of the hardened surface layer of each lobe. If any such signs are evident, replace the component concerned (see illustration).

12 Examine the camshaft bearing journals and the cylinder head bearing surfaces for signs of obvious wear or pitting. If any such signs are evident, consult an automotive machine shop for advice. Also check that the bearing oilways in the cylinder head are clear.

13 Using a micrometer, measure the diameter of each journal at several points. If the diameter of any one journal is less than the specified value, replace the camshaft.

14 To check the bearing journal running clearance, remove the tap-

11.11 Check the cam lobes for pitting, wear and score marks - if scoring is excessive, as shown here, replace the camshaft

11.14a Lay a strip of Plastigage on each camshaft journal

11.14b Compare the width of the crushed Plastigage to the scale on the envelope to determine the running clearance

11.23 Camshaft bearing cap tightening sequence - tighten each pair of bolts in sequence

pets, use a suitable solvent and a clean lint-free rag to clean carefully all bearing surfaces, then install the camshafts and bearing caps with a strand of Plastigage across each journal. Tighten the bearing cap bolts in the given sequence (see Installation) to the specified torque setting (do not rotate the camshafts), then remove the bearing caps and use the scale provided to measure the width of the compressed strands. Scrape off the Plastigage with your fingernail or the edge of a credit card - don't scratch or nick the journals or bearing caps (see illustrations).

15 If the running clearance of any bearing is found to be worn to beyond the specified service limits, install a new camshaft and repeat the check; if the clearance is still excessive, the cylinder head must be replaced.

16 To check camshaft endplay, remove the tappets, clean the bearing surfaces carefully and install the camshafts and bearing caps. Tighten the bearing cap bolts to the specified torque wrench setting, then measure the endplay using a dial indicator mounted on the cylinder head so that its tip bears on the camshaft right-hand end.

17 Tap the camshaft fully towards the gauge, zero the gauge, then tap the camshaft fully away from the gauge and note the gauge reading. If the endplay measured is found to be at or beyond the specified service limit, install a new camshaft and repeat the check; if the clearance is still excessive, the cylinder head must be replaced.

INSTALLATION

◆ **Refer to illustrations 11.21 and 11.23**

18 On reassembly, liberally oil the cylinder head tappet bores and tappets. Carefully install the tappets into the cylinder head making sure that each one is placed into its original bore. Some care will be required to place the tappets squarely into their bores.

19 Liberally oil the camshaft journals, bearing caps and lobes and place them in position. Use the chart (created during removal) to position the lobes for the number one cylinder and check that the slots in the rear for the camshaft alignment tool are level.

20 Install the camshaft alignment tool to assure that the slots in the rear are level.

21 Ensure that the locating dowels are pressed firmly into their recesses and check that all mating surfaces are completely clean, unmarked and free from oil. Apply a thin film of anaerobic sealant to the mating surfaces of each camshaft's front bearing cap.

22 Apply a little oil to the camshaft, then install each of the camshaft bearing caps to its original position using the chart created during removal.

23 Ensuring that each cap is kept square to the cylinder head as it is tightened down and working in the sequence shown, tighten the camshaft bearing cap bolts slowly and by one turn at a time, until each cap touches the cylinder head (see illustration).

24 Next, go round again in the same sequence, tightening the bolts to the specified Stage 1 torque setting.

25 Continue the tightening sequence patterns until all three tightening stages are complete.

26 Wipe off all surplus sealant, so that none is left to find its way into any oilways. Follow the sealant manufacturer's instructions as to the time needed for curing; usually, at least an hour must be allowed between application of the sealant and starting the engine (including turning the engine for further reassembly work).

27 Install the camshaft sprockets and timing chain (see Sections 9 and 10).

28 The rest of reassembly is the reverse of removal. Follow the procedures in each section carefully.

➡**Note: Be certain to check to valve clearances before installing the valve cover (see Section 5).**

12 Cylinder head - removal and installation

REMOVAL

1 Disconnect the negative battery cable (see Chapter 5). Drain the cooling system (see Chapter 1).

2 Remove the camshafts (see Section 11).

3 Remove the fuel rail and injectors noting the spacers beneath the rail (see Chapter 4).

4 Remove the intake and exhaust manifold (see Section 6).

5 Disconnect the electrical connectors for the engine coolant temperature sender and the EGR valve.

12.17 Apply sealant to these two spots on the engine block

Sealant   Sealant

36071-2B-12.17 HAYNES

← Front

36071-2B-12.20a HAYNES

12.20a Cylinder head bolt tightening sequence

➥Note: These components are located at the rear of the cylinder head.

6   Disconnect the coolant hose from the EGR unit and remove the hose from its bracket.

7   Disconnect the cooling system bypass hose.

8   Remove the cylinder head bolts and discard all but one.

➥Note: Compare the one old bolt with the new bolts to confirm that they are correct.

9   Carefully lift off the cylinder head.

10 Before removing the cylinder head gasket from the engine block, label it so you know which side is the top (if it's not already).

11 Remove the cylinder head gasket and set aside.

➥Note: Compare the old gasket with the new one to confirm that it is correct.

INSPECTION

➥Note: For disassembling the cylinder head, and other procedures relating to the valves, refer to Chapter 2F.

12 The mating faces of the cylinder head and cylinder block must be perfectly clean before installing the head. Use a hard plastic or wood scraper to remove all traces of gasket and carbon; also clean the piston crowns.

13 Take particular care during the cleaning operations, as aluminum alloy is easily damaged. Also, make sure that the carbon is not allowed to enter the oil and water passages - this is particularly important for the lubrication system, as carbon could block the oil supply to the engine's components. Using adhesive tape and paper, seal the water, oil and bolt holes in the cylinder block.

14 To prevent carbon entering the gap between the pistons and bores, smear a little grease in the gap. After cleaning each piston, use a small brush to remove all traces of grease and carbon from the gap, then wipe away the remainder with a clean rag.

15 Check the mating surfaces of the cylinder block and the cylinder head for nicks, deep scratches and other damage. If slight, they may be removed carefully with a file, but if excessive, replacement is necessary as it is not optional to machine the surfaces.

16 If warpage of the cylinder head gasket surface is suspected, use a straight-edge to check it for distortion. Refer to Part F of this Chapter if necessary.

12.20b Using the angle gauge for the third and fourth tightening stages

INSTALLATION

▶ Refer to illustrations 12.17, 12.20a and 12.20b

17 Apply a small amount of suitable silicone sealant to two areas of the cylinder block (see illustration).

18 Install a new head gasket on the cylinder block noting which side faces up.

19 Lubricate the new replacement cylinder head bolts with clean engine oil then place them in position.

20 First hand tighten all bolts, then tighten them in five stages (see this Chapter's Specifications) while following the proper sequence (see illustrations).

21 Reassembly is the reverse of removal noting the following points:

a) *Install the manifolds with reference to Section 5. Use new gaskets and fasteners.*

b) *Install the camshafts as described in Section 11, and the timing chain as described in Section 9.*

c) *Tighten all fasteners to the specified torque, where given, and use new gaskets.*

d) *Ensure that all hoses and wiring are correctly routed, and that hose clips and wiring connectors are securely installed.*

e) *Refill the cooling system as described in Chapter 1.*

f) *Change the engine oil and filter (see Chapter 1).*

g) *Check all disturbed joints for signs of oil or coolant leakage once the engine has been restarted and warmed-up to normal operating temperature.*

13 Oil pan - removal and installation

REMOVAL

➡Note: Removing the oil pan on this engine requires engine removal. Refer to Chapter 2F for the engine removal procedure.

➡Note: On 2006 and later models, the oil pan can be removed by disconnecting the left-side engine mount and raising only the left side of the engine.

1   Drain the engine oil then clean and install the oil drain plug (see Chapter 1).

➡Note: Make a note to yourself to replace the oil filter before refilling the engine with oil.

On 2011 models, remove the cooling fan (see Chapter 3).

2   Remove the engine oil dipstick, dipstick tube mounting bolts and the tube itself (if not removed during engine removal).

3   Remove all oil pan bolts. Disconnect any wiring harnesses that interfere with removal. If necessary for access, loosen the transmission-to-block bolts just enough to move the transmission slightly.

4   Separate the oil pan from the engine block by carefully prying them apart, using casting protrusions only. Do not damage the mating surfaces.

➡Note: The oil pan and engine block are joined by sealant

without the use of a gasket. This can make separating them a bit more difficult.

INSTALLATION

▶ Refer to illustrations 13.7a and 13.7b

5   Thoroughly clean the oil pan, the mating surfaces of the engine block and the bolts. Remove all traces of sealant and oil.

6   When all the parts are clean and ready to install, apply a 2.5 mm bead of sealant to the oil pan.

➡Note: The oil pain must be assembled to the engine block within four minutes of applying the sealant. The process will have to be repeated otherwise.

7   Install and torque all the bolts to specification (see Specifications) using the proper tightening sequence (see illustrations).

8   Install the dipstick tube and dipstick (unless removal is necessary for engine installation).

➡Note: Use clean engine oil on the O-ring gasket on the tube before installation.

9   Install the engine (see Chapter 2F).

10 Refill the crankcase with oil and install a new oil filter. Refill the cooling system (see Chapter 1).

13.7a Oil pan bolt tightening sequence - 2005 and earlier models

13.7b Oil pan bolt tightening sequence - 2006 and later models

14 Oil pump - removal and installation

▶ Refer to illustrations 14.3, 14.4, 14.6, 14.8

➡Note: Removing the oil pump on this engine requires engine removal. Refer to Chapter 2F for the engine removal procedure. Also, the oil pump is serviced as a complete unit without any sub-assembly or internal inspection.

1   With the engine removed, remove the timing chain (see Section 9).

2   Remove the oil pan (see Section 13).

3   Remove the oil pick-up mounting bolts and then remove the pick-up tube (see illustration).

4   Remove the chain tensioner mounting bolt and the tensioner, noting the spring location (see illustration).

5   Remove the two mounting bolts for the chain guide and remove

the guide (see illustration 14.4).

6   While holding the oil pump drive sprocket with a suitable tool, remove the sprocket bolt from the oil pump, then remove the sprocket (see illustration).

7   Slide the oil pump drive sprocket (and timing chain sprocket) and chain from the end of the crankshaft (if necessary).

✲✲ CAUTION:

The special washers on each side of the sprocket must be placed back in their original position or engine timing will not be maintained after assembly. This may result in engine damage or failure.

14.3 The oil pump pick-up tube is held by two mounting bolts

14.4 The tensioner is secured by one mounting bolt while the guide is held by two

14.6 Using a holding tool on the oil pump drive sprocket to remove the retaining bolt

14.8 Remove the four mounting bolts for the oil pump

8   Remove the oil pump mounting bolts, then remove the pump (see illustration).

9   Installation is the reverse of removal noting the following points:

a) *Replace all gaskets with new ones.*

b) *Torque the oil pump mounting bolts to specification (see Specifications) while using a criss-cross pattern.*

c) *After installing the engine, refill the crankcase with oil and the cooling system with the proper type and mixture of antifreeze (see Chapter 1).*

d) *Be certain to check for any oil warning lights in the instrument panel after the vehicle has been started and idling.*

15 Oil pressure warning light switch - removal and installation

REMOVAL

1   The switch is screwed into an oil filter adapter located at the oil filter.

2   With the vehicle parked on firm level ground, open the hood and disconnect the negative battery cable (see Chapter 5).

3   Raise the front of the vehicle and support it securely on jackstands.

4   Unplug the wiring from the switch and unscrew it; be prepared for some oil loss.

INSTALLATION

5   Installation is the reverse of removal noting the following points:

a) *Apply a small amount of pipe sealant (Teflon type) to the switch threads and install it securely.*

b) *Check the engine oil level and top it off as necessary (see Chapter 1).*

c) *Check for correct oil warning light operation and for signs of oil leaks once the engine has been started and fully warmed-up.*

16 Crankshaft oil seals - replacement

FRONT OIL SEAL

▶ **Refer to illustrations 16.5 and 16.6**

1 Remove the crankshaft pulley (see Section 7)
2 Use a screwdriver or hook tool to carefully pry out the seal.

➡**Note: Be careful not to damage the engine front cover bore where the seal is seated or the nose and sealing surface of the crankshaft.**

3 Another procedure for removing the seal is to drill a small hole on each side of the seal and place a self-tapping screw in each hole. Use these screws as a means of pulling the seal out without having to pry on it.
4 Wipe the sealing surfaces in the engine cover and on the crankshaft. Clean and coat them with clean engine oil.
5 Start installing the new seal by pressing it into the engine front cover (see illustration).

16.5 Make certain that the oil seal is kept square as it is placed in the bore

16.6 A socket of the correct size can be used to install the new seal

6 Once started, use a seal driver or a suitable socket of the correct size to carefully drive the seal squarely into place (see illustration).
7 The seal should be flush with the engine cover and remain square when installed.
8 Coat the lip of the seal (where it contacts the crankshaft) with clean engine oil.

REAR OIL SEAL

▶ **Refer to illustration 16.18**

➡**Note: At the time of writing, the oil seal and carrier are serviced as an assembly only.**

9 Remove the transmission (see Chapter 7), and clutch assembly (if equipped - see Chapter 8).
10 Remove the flywheel (or driveplate) (see Section 17).
11 Remove the oil pan (see Section 13).
12 Unbolt the oil seal and carrier.
13 Clean the mating surface for the oil seal carrier on the cylinder block and the crankshaft. Carefully remove and polish any burrs or raised edges on the crankshaft that may have caused the seal to fail.
14 Lightly coat the inside lip of the new seal with clean engine oil. Then use a thin (but durable) two-inch wide plastic strip (or a two-liter plastic beverage bottle cut to size) around the inside circumference of the seal to act as a liner for installation.
15 With the plastic seal liner in place, carefully move the new oil seal and carrier into position by sliding it onto the contact surface of the crankshaft.
16 Install the oil seal carrier bolts and finger tighten them while holding the carrier in place.
17 Carefully remove the plastic liner or bottle so that the new seal contacts the crankshaft mating surface correctly.
18 Tighten the oil seal carrier to the torque listed in this Chapter's Specifications using the proper sequence (see illustration).
19 The seal is now fully installed. Be sure to check for signs of oil leakage when the engine is operable.

16.18 The rear oil seal carrier tightening sequence

17 Flywheel/driveplate - removal, inspection and installation

➡**Note: On 2011 automatic transmission-equipped models, the driveplate is referred to as a flexplate by the manufacturer.**

REMOVAL

▶ **Refer to illustration 17.5**

1 Remove the transmission as described in Chapter 7.
2 Remove the clutch (if equipped) as described in Chapter 8.

➡**Note: If any clutch components show signs of wear or the vehicle has high mileage, it's recommended that it be replaced at this time.**

3 Mark the flywheel/driveplate to the crankshaft with paint or a center-punch so that it can be replaced in the same position.
4 Hold the flywheel/driveplate from turning by installing one transmission mounting bolt into the cylinder block. Have an assistant firmly hold a prybar (or similar tool) into the starter ring gear teeth and against the mounting bolt like a lever while the bolts are loosened.
5 Remove all bolts except one; leave it installed halfway (see illustration).
6 Pull the flywheel/driveplate away from the crankshaft flange to make sure that it comes off easily. Use a mallet to break it free if necessary.
7 Support the flywheel/driveplate while removing the last bolt. Carefully remove the flywheel/driveplate.

✳ CAUTION:

The flywheel is very heavy and has sharp edges along the ring-gear. Gloves and careful attention are recommended to avoid injury.

➡**Note: If the rear oil seal shows signs of leakage or the vehicle has high mileage, replacing the seal is highly recommended before re-installing the flywheel/driveplate.**

INSPECTION

8 Clean the flywheel/driveplate to remove any grease or oil. Inspect the surface for cracks, rivet grooves, burned areas and score marks.

17.5 Flywheel mounting bolts

Light scoring can be removed with emery cloth. Check for cracked and broken ring gear teeth. Lay the flywheel/driveplate on a flat surface and use a straight-edge to check for warpage.

➡**Note: It is common to have the flywheel/driveplate resurfaced by a professional machine shop if there are signs of severe wear or damage. Also, clutch replacement is recommended if the flywheel is resurfaced.**

9 Clean and inspect the mating surfaces of the flywheel/driveplate and the crankshaft.

INSTALLATION

10 Install the engine/transmission adapter plate (if removed). Place the flywheel/driveplate on the crankshaft so that all bolt holes align (it fits in one position only). Install the proper bolts and tighten them by hand.
11 Torque the flywheel/driveplate mounting bolts in a crisscross pattern and in three stages (see Specifications).
12 The remainder of installation is the reverse of removal.

18 Engine mounts - inspection and replacement

Refer to Chapter 2A for these procedures, but use the Specifications found in this Chapter.

General

Displacement	2.3L (140.3 cubic inches)
Bore	3.444 inches
Stroke	3.700 inches
Firing order	1-3-4-2

```
COIL
PACK

        ④
        ③
②  ③
④  ①    ②

        ①    ↓
             FRONT

36071-2A-SPECS HAYNES
```

Cylinder and coil terminal locations - 2001 and later four-cylinder engine

Camshafts

Camshaft bearing journal diameter	0.982 to 0.983 inch
Camshaft bearing journal-to-cylinder head running clearance	0.001 to 0.003 inch
Camshaft endplay	0.003 to 0.009 inch

Valves

Valve clearances (cold)	
Intake	0.008 to 0.011 inch
Exhaust	0.010 to 0.013 inch

Cylinder head

Maximum permissible gasket surface distortion	0.003 inch

Lubrication

Engine oil capacity	See Chapter 1
Oil pressure (engine at operating temperature)	
At 2000 rpm	29 to 39 psi

→**Note:** One foot-pound (ft-lb) of torque is equivalent to 12 inch-pounds (in-lbs) of torque. Torque values below approximately 15 ft-lbs are expressed in inch-pounds, since most foot-pound torque wrenches are not accurate at these smaller values.

Camshaft bearing cap bolts (in sequence - see illustration 11.23)	
Stage 1	*See Below
Stage 2	62 in-lbs
Stage 3	142 to144 in-lbs
Camshaft sprocket bolts	
2001 through 2006	48
2007 and later	53

Torque specifications	Ft-lbs (unless otherwise indicated)
Connecting rod cap bolts (2011)	
Step 1	21
Step 2	Tighten and additional 90 degrees
Crankshaft pulley bolt	
Stage 1	74
Stage 2	Rotate an additional 90-degrees (1/4 turn)
Crankshaft rear oil seal carrier bolts (in sequence -	
see illustration 16.18)	89 in-lbs
**Cylinder head bolts (in sequence - see illustration 12.20a)	
Stage 1	44 in-lbs
Stage 2	132 in-lbs
Stage 3	33
Stage 4	Rotate an additional 90-degrees (1/4 turn)
Stage 5	Angle-tighten another 90-degrees
Valve cover bolts	89 in-lbs
Exhaust manifold nuts	40
Flywheel/driveplate bolts	
Stage 1	37
Stage 2	59
Stage 3	83
Intake manifold bolts	156 in-lbs
Jackshaft retainer plate bolts (2011)	89 in-lbs
Main bearing cap bolts (2011)	
Step 1	44 in-lbs
Step 2	18
Step 3	Tighten an additional 90-degrees
Oil pick-up pipe bolts	89 in-lbs
Oil pump mounting bolts	
Stage 1	89 in-lbs
Stage 2	15
Oil pump sprocket bolt	
Models through 2006	28 to 40
2007 and later	18
Oil pan bolts (in sequence - see illustration 13.7a or 13.7b)	
Bolts to block	18
Bolts to transmission	35
Bolt to front cover	89 in-lbs
Engine front cover (in sequence - see illustration 8.11b)	
Stage 1	89 in-lbs
Stage 2	18
Stage 3	35
Timing chain guide bolts	89 in-lbs
Timing chain tensioner bolts	89 in-lbs
Transaxle-to-engine bolts	35

* **Note: Tighten the camshaft bearing caps by turning each bolt one turn at a time until tight.**

** **Note: Lubricate the new cylinder head bolts with clean engine oil before installing them.**

Notes

Section

Reference to other Chapters

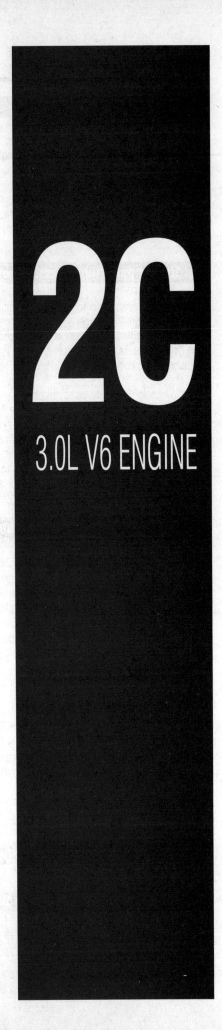

2C

3.0L V6 ENGINE

1 General information

This Part of Chapter 2 is devoted to in-vehicle repair procedures for 3.0L V6 engines. All information concerning engine removal and installation and engine block and cylinder head servicing can also be found in Part F of this Chapter.

The repair procedures included in this Part are based on the assumption that the engine is still installed in the vehicle. Therefore, if this information is being used during a complete engine overhaul - with the engine already out of the vehicle and on a stand - many of the Steps included here will not apply.

The Specifications included in this Part of Chapter 2 apply only to the engine and procedures found here. Part F of Chapter 2 contains the specifications necessary for engine block and cylinder head rebuilding procedures.

2 Repair operations possible with the engine in the vehicle

Many major repair operations can be accomplished without removing the engine from the vehicle.

Clean the engine compartment and the exterior of the engine with some type of pressure washer before any work is done. A clean engine will make the job easier and will help keep dirt out of the internal areas of the engine.

If oil or coolant leaks develop, indicating a need for gasket or seal replacement, the repairs can generally be made with the engine in the vehicle. The cylinder head gaskets, intake and exhaust manifold gaskets, timing cover gaskets and the crankshaft oil seals are accessible with the engine in place. The engine must be removed first.

Exterior engine components, such as the water pump, the starter motor, the alternator, the distributor and the EFI components, as well as the intake and exhaust manifolds, can be removed for repair with the engine in place.

Since the cylinder heads can be removed without removing the engine, valve component servicing can also be accomplished with the engine in the vehicle.

Replacement of, repairs to or inspection of the timing chain and sprockets and the oil pump are all possible with the engine in place (except on 4WD models).

In extreme cases caused by a lack of necessary equipment, repair or replacement of piston rings, pistons, connecting rods and rod bearings is possible with the engine in the vehicle. However, this practice is not recommended because of the cleaning and preparation work that must be done to the components involved.

3 Top Dead Center (TDC) for number one piston - locating

1 Top Dead Center (TDC) is the highest point in the cylinder that each piston reaches as it travels up-and-down when the crankshaft turns. Each piston reaches TDC on the compression stroke and again on the exhaust stroke, but TDC generally refers to piston position on the compression stroke. The timing marks on the vibration damper installed on the front of the crankshaft are referenced to the number one piston at TDC.

2 Positioning the piston(s) at TDC is an essential part of many procedures such as rocker arm removal, timing chain and sprocket replacement.

3 In order to bring any piston to TDC, the crankshaft must be turned using one of the methods outlined below. When looking at the front of the engine, normal crankshaft rotation is clockwise.

   a) *The preferred method is to turn the crankshaft with a large socket and breaker bar attached to the vibration damper bolt that is threaded into the front of the crankshaft.*

   b) *A remote starter switch, which may save some time, can also be used. Attach the switch leads to the switch and battery terminals on the solenoid. Once the piston is close to TDC, use a socket and breaker bar as described in the previous paragraph.*

   c) *If an assistant is available to turn the ignition switch to the Start*

position in short bursts, you can get the piston close to TDC without a remote starter switch. Use a socket and breaker bar as described in Paragraph a) to complete the procedure.

➡ **Note: The 3.0L engine is not equipped with a distributor. Piston position must be determined by feeling for compression at the number one spark plug hole, then aligning the ignition timing marks as described in Step 5.**

4 Before beginning this procedure, be sure to place the transmission in Neutral and apply the parking brake or block the rear wheels. Remove the spark plugs (see Chapter 1). Disable the ignition system by disconnecting the wiring harness connector from the ignition coil pack, mounted to the intake manifold.

5 Hold your finger over the number one spark plug hole. Slowly turn the crankshaft (see Step 3 above) until you feel compression at the number one spark plug hole, then continue to turn the crankshaft until the TDC notch is aligned with the pointer (located at the front of the engine).

6 After the number one piston has been positioned at TDC on the compression stroke, TDC for any of the remaining pistons can be located by turning the crankshaft 120-degrees at a time and following the firing order shown in the Specifications for this Chapter.

4 Valve covers - removal and installation

REMOVAL

1 Disconnect the negative cable at the battery.
2 Disconnect the spark plug wires on the side(s) you are taking off,

leaving them attached to the wire separators. If they are not numbered, tag them so they won't get mixed up on reassembly.

3 Remove the spark plug wire separators from the valve cover studs.

4   If the right valve cover is being removed, disconnect the engine harness connectors, remove the fuel charging wiring standoffs from the inboard valve cover studs and remove the PCV closure hose from the oil fill adapter.

5   If the left cover is being removed, remove the throttle body or the upper intake manifold as required (see Chapter 4), the PCV valve and the fuel charging wiring standoffs from the inboard valve cover studs.

6   Make a sketch noting the location of the valve cover bolts and studs so that they can be installed correctly later, then remove them. Use a deep socket to remove the studs.

7   Try bumping the valve cover with a rubber mallet to loosen it. If that doesn't work easily, use a thin-bladed knife to cut the RTV sealant.

✳✳ CAUTION:

Do not cut the integral gasket. Cut the RTV sealant only.

Gently lift the cover off and make sure that the RTV sealant does not pull the integral gasket from the cover. Cut the RTV as necessary to protect the gasket.

8   Carefully roll the integral gasket from its channel in the valve cover. If in good condition, the gasket can be reused indefinitely.

INSTALLATION

9   Clean the gasket channel thoroughly to remove oil and dirt. Clean the mating surface on the cylinder head. Make sure to remove all residual RTV sealant. Lightly oil all fastener threads.

10 Install the original gasket or a new one in the valve cover channel and carefully align the stud and bolt holes. Install the bolts and studs in their holes according to the sketch you make earlier. Hold the fastener with a socket and gently push the gasket down around the fastener until it seats fully in the channel.

➡**Note: Make sure the gasket lies flat in the valve cover channel, with no bulges, or it will leak.**

11 Apply a bead of RTV sealant at the cylinder head to intake manifold rail step (two places per rail).

12 Install the valve cover straight onto the cylinder head. If it shifts after contacting the sealant, the gasket could be pulled from the channel and leak.

13 Tighten all fasteners to the torque listed in this Chapter's Specifications. Work around the cover in several steps.

14 The remainder of the installation is the reverse of removal.

15 Reconnect the battery, start the engine and check for oil and vacuum leaks.

5   Rocker arms and pushrods - removal, inspection and installation

♦ **Refer to illustrations 5.3a and 5.3b**

REMOVAL

1   Remove the valve covers as described in Section 4.

2   Remove the rocker arm fulcrum bolts.

3   Remove the rocker arms. If only the pushrods are being removed, loosen the fulcrum bolts and rotate the rocker arms out of the way of the pushrods (see illustration). Keep the pushrods organized to ensure that they are reinstalled in their original locations (see illustration).

INSPECTION

4   Check the rocker arms for excessive wear, cracks and other dam-age, especially where the pushrods and valve stems contact the rocker arm faces.

5   Make sure the hole at the pushrod end of the rocker arm is open.

6   Check the rocker arm fulcrum contact area for wear and galling. If the rocker arms are worn or damaged, replace them with new ones and use new fulcrum seats as well.

7   Inspect the pushrods for cracks and excessive wear at the ends. Roll each pushrod across a flat surface to see if they are bent.

INSTALLATION

8   Apply engine oil or assembly lube to the top of the valve stem and the pushrod guide in the cylinder head.

9   Apply engine oil to the rocker arm fulcrum seat and the fulcrum

5.3a Loosen the bolt (arrow) and pivot the rocker arm to the side to remove the pushrod

5.3b A perforated cardboard box can be used to store the pushrods to ensure installation in their original locations

seat socket in the rocker arm.

10 Install the pushrods.

11 Install the rocker arms, fulcrums, and fulcrum bolts.

12 Turn the crankshaft until the lifter is all the way down.

13 Tighten the fulcrum bolts to the torque listed in this Chapter's Specifications in two stages.

14 Replace the valve covers and gaskets as described in Section 4.

15 Start the engine and check for roughness and/or noise.

6 Valve springs, retainers and seals - replacement

▶ **Refer to illustrations 6.8 and 6.14**

➡**Note: Broken valve springs and defective valve stem seals can be replaced without removing the cylinder head. Two special tools and a compressed air source are normally required to perform this operation, so read through this Section carefully and rent or buy the tools before beginning the job. If compressed air is not available, a length of nylon rope can be used to keep the valves from falling into the cylinder during this procedure.**

1 Refer to Section 4 and remove the valve cover from the affected cylinder head. If all of the valve stem seals are being replaced, remove both valve covers.

2 Remove the spark plug from the cylinder which has the defective component. If all of the valve stem seals are being replaced, all of the spark plugs should be removed.

3 Turn the crankshaft until the piston in the affected cylinder is at top dead center on the compression stroke (refer to Section 3 for instructions). If you are replacing all of the valve stem seals, begin with cylinder number one and work on the valves for one cylinder at a time. Move from cylinder-to-cylinder following the firing order sequence.

4 Thread an adapter into the spark plug hole and connect an air hose from a compressed air source to it. Most auto parts stores can supply the air hose adapter.

➡**Note: Many cylinder compression gauges utilize a screw-in fitting that may work with your air hose quick-disconnect fitting.**

5 Remove the bolt, pivot and rocker arm for the valve with the defective part and pull out the pushrod. If all of the valve stem seals are being replaced, all of the rocker arms and pushrods should be removed (refer to Section 5).

6 Apply compressed air to the cylinder. The valves should be held in place by the air pressure.

7 If you do not have access to compressed air, an alternative method can be used. Position the piston at a point approximately 45-degrees before TDC on the compression stroke, then feed a long piece of nylon rope through the spark plug hole until it fills the combustion chamber.

Be sure to leave the end of the rope hanging out of the engine so it can be removed easily. Use a large breaker bar and socket to rotate the crankshaft in the normal direction of rotation until slight resistance is felt.

8 Stuff shop rags into the cylinder head holes above and below the valves to prevent parts and tools from falling into the engine, then use a valve spring compressor to compress the spring/damper assembly (see illustration). Remove the keepers with small needle-nose pliers or a magnet.

➡**Note: A couple of different types of tools are available for compressing the valve springs with the head in place. One type grips the lower spring coils and presses on the retainer as the knob is turned, while the other type utilizes the rocker arm bolt for leverage. Both types work very well, although the lever type is usually less expensive.**

9 Remove the spring retainer and valve spring assembly, then remove the umbrella-type guide seal

➡**Note: If air pressure fails to hold the valve in the closed position during this operation, the valve face or seat is probably damaged. If so, the cylinder head will have to be removed for additional repair operations.**

10 Wrap a rubber band or tape around the top of the valve stem so the valve will not fall into the combustion chamber, then release the air pressure.

➡**Note: If a rope was used instead of air pressure, turn the crankshaft slightly in the direction opposite normal rotation.**

11 Inspect the valve stem for damage. Rotate the valve in the guide and check the end for eccentric movement, which would indicate that the valve is bent.

12 Move the valve up-and-down in the guide and make sure it does not bind. If the valve stem binds, either the valve is bent or the guide is damaged. In either case, the head will have to be removed for repair.

13 Reapply air pressure to the cylinder to retain the valve in the closed position, then remove the tape or rubber band from the valve stem. If a rope was used instead of air pressure, rotate the crankshaft in the normal direction of rotation until slight resistance is felt.

14 Lubricate the valve stem with engine oil and install a new seal onto the guide (see illustration).

6.14 Carefully place the seal in position, then tap it into place with a deep socket and light hammer

6.8 Apply air pressure to the cylinder, compress the valve spring and remove the keepers

✳✳ CAUTION:

The intake and exhaust seals are different. Make sure you install the correct seal on each valve. The intake valve seal has a silver band and the exhaust seal has a red band.

15 Install the spring/damper assembly in position over the valve.
16 Install the valve spring retainer. Compress the valve spring assembly.
17 Position the keepers in the upper groove. Apply a small dab

of grease to the inside of each keeper to hold it in place if necessary. Remove the pressure from the spring tool and make sure the keepers are seated.
18 Disconnect the air hose and remove the adapter from the spark plug hole. If a rope was used in place of air pressure, pull it out of the cylinder.
19 Refer to Section 5 and install the rocker arm(s) and pushrod(s).
20 Install the spark plug(s) and hook up the wire(s).
21 Refer to Section 4 and install the valve cover(s).
22 Start the engine, then check for oil leaks and unusual sounds coming from the valve cover area.

7   Intake manifold - removal and installation

♦ **Refer to illustrations 7.11, 7.13, 7.14, 7.15, and 7.18**

REMOVAL

1   Relieve the fuel pressure (see Chapter 4).
2   Disconnect the negative cable at the battery.
3   Drain the cooling system (see Chapter 1).
4   Disconnect the fuel rails and lines. Cap the lines to prevent entry of dirt.
5   Remove the throttle body (see Chapter 4).
6   Label and disconnect all wiring, vacuum and coolant hoses from the intake manifold.
7   Remove the camshaft position sensor (see Chapter 6).
8   Remove the pushrod from number three cylinder intake valve (see Section 5). On 2006 and later models, loosen the rocker arms enough to remove all the pushrods.
➡**Note: Each pushrod should be marked so that it can be returned to its original location during assembly.**

9   Remove the manifold attaching bolts/studs (this requires a Torx driver bit), noting the location of studs for reinstallation.
10 Remove the intake manifold. It may be necessary to pry between the manifold and block, using the water pump lug as a fulcrum. Use care to avoid damaging the machined surfaces. a

✳✳ CAUTION:

Do not pry between the gasket surfaces or leaks will develop.

The fuel rails and injectors may remain in place. Lift the manifold out of the engine compartment.

INSTALLATION

11 Clean all traces of old gasket material from the mating surfaces (see illustration). Use a solvent such as lacquer thinner or acetone, if necessary.
12 Lightly oil all threaded fasteners prior to assembly.
13 Apply RTV sealant to the intersections of the cylinder head and block (see illustration).
14 Position the intake manifold gaskets in place over the tabs on the cylinder heads (see illustration).

7.11 Use a scraper to remove the intake manifold gaskets

7.13 Apply RTV sealant in the areas where the cylinder heads meet the ridges at the front and rear of the cylinder block before installing the end seals

7.14 Be sure the locking tabs on the gaskets are engaged

7.15 The end seals have locating pins which must be pressed into place

7.18 Intake manifold bolt tightening sequence

15 Install the front and rear manifold end seals (see illustration).

16 Apply RTV sealer on top of the end seals.

➡**Note: Do not allow the sealer to dry prior to installation.**

17 Carefully lower the manifold into place. Avoid displacing the seals and gaskets.

18 Install the bolts and studs, tightening them in the sequence shown to the torque listed in this Chapter's Specifications (see illustration).

19 If removed, install the thermostat housing with a new gasket (see Chapter 3).

20 The remainder of the installation is the reverse of the removal procedure. If equipped with a camshaft position sensor, install it as described in Chapter 6, Section 5.

21 Refill the cooling system and connect the battery.

22 Run the engine and check for vacuum and fluid leaks.

8 Exhaust manifolds - removal and installation

REMOVAL

✳✳ WARNING:

Allow the engine to cool completely before following this procedure.

1 Disconnect the negative cable at the battery.

2 Raise the vehicle and support it securely on jackstands.

3 Spray the exhaust pipe fasteners and exhaust manifold fasteners with rust penetrant and allow it to soak in for about 10 minutes. If there is any resistance during removal, stop and respray the fasteners to prevent them from breaking off.

4 Unbolt the exhaust pipe(s) from the appropriate manifold(s) as described in Chapter 4.

Right side

5 Remove the right side spark plugs and secure the wires out of the way (see Chapter 1).

6 Unbolt and remove the manifold.

Left side

7 Remove the oil dipstick tube bracket nut and either rotate the tube out of the way or remove it completely.

8 Remove the EGR tube (see Chapter 6).

9 Unbolt and remove the manifold.

INSTALLATION

10 Clean the mating surfaces of the head and manifold.

11 Clean and lightly oil the threads of all fasteners.

12 Install the manifold and tighten all fasteners snugly. Starting in the center and working out to the ends, tighten the bolts to the torque listed in this Chapter's Specifications.

13 Reinstall all parts removed for access. If the dipstick was removed, apply RTV sealant to the base of the dipstick tube. Be sure to press the dipstick tube all the way into the block until seated.

14 Connect the exhaust pipe to the manifold(s).

15 Lower the vehicle and connect the battery cable.

16 Run the engine and check for exhaust leaks.

9 Cylinder heads - removal and installation

◆ **Refer to illustrations 9.14, 9.19 and 9.20**

REMOVAL

1 Disconnect the negative cable at the battery.

2 Drain the cooling system (see Chapter 1), including removing the engine block drain plugs.

3 Remove the air cleaner outlet tube and air cleaner assembly (see Chapter 4).

4 Remove the intake manifold (see Section 7).

5 Remove the drivebelts (see Chapter 1).

6 If removing the left cylinder head, remove the air conditioning compressor mounting bolts from the bracket. Without disconnecting the hoses, carefully lift the compressor off and secure it aside.

7 Remove the power steering pump mounting bracket bolts. Leave the pump and hoses connected and secure the pump and bracket assembly aside.

8 Remove the ignition coil bracket and dipstick tube.

9 Remove the alternator and the mounting bracket from the right cylinder head (see Chapter 4).

10 Remove the ground strap and throttle cable bracket.

11 Remove the exhaust manifold(s) (see Section 8).

12 Remove the valve cover(s) (see Section 4).

13 Loosen the rocker arms and remove pushrods (see Section 5).

14 Unbolt and remove the cylinder heads. Pry them up at the point shown (see illustration).

✳✳ CAUTION:

Do not pry the heads at the sealing surfaces.

INSTALLATION

15 Thoroughly clean and inspect the gasket mating surfaces for cracks and warpage. It well help to lay a shop cloth over the lifters and other exposed engine areas to prevent old gasket material and other debris from falling in the engine.

16 Service the head(s) as needed (see Chapter 2F).

17 Be sure all bolt and bolt hole threads are clean, dry and in good condition.

18 Lightly oil all bolt and stud threads prior to installation.

19 Carefully position the head gaskets on the block using the dowels for alignment (see illustration). Notice that the left and right head gaskets are different.

✳✳ CAUTION:

Do not use any kind of gasket sealant material on the head gaskets.

9.14 Once the bolts are removed, pry the head loose at a point where the gasket surfaces won't be damaged

20 Install the heads and head bolts and tighten them in two steps following the sequence shown (see illustration) to the torque listed in this Chapter's Specifications.

21 Installation of the remaining parts is the reverse of removal.

22 Refill the cooling system (see Chapter 1).

23 Run the engine and check for leaks and proper operation.

9.19 Position the new gasket over the dowels - make sure the UP (shown) or TOP mark is visible

9.20 Cylinder head bolt tightening sequence

10 Crankshaft front oil seal - replacement

▶ **Refer to illustrations 10.4, 10.8 and 10.9**

1 Disconnect the negative cable at the battery.

10.4 Remove the vibration damper with the appropriate puller

10.8 A piece of pipe, a bolt and several large washers can be used to fabricate a seal installation tool

2 Remove the radiator (see Chapter 3).

3 Remove the drivebelts (see Chapter 1) and the crankshaft pulley.

4 Remove the vibration damper bolt. Install a puller and remove the vibration damper (see illustration).

5 Carefully pry the old seal from the cover using a seal remover or a screwdriver. Do not nick or scratch the crankshaft or seal bore.

6 Thoroughly clean the seal area.

7 Apply engine oil to the seal lips. Slide the seal into place with the spring side facing the engine.

8 Press the seal into place using a seal installer or a large socket and hammer. A suitable installation tool can be fabricated as shown (see illustration). Be sure the seal seats against the timing chain cover.

9 Reinstall the vibration damper using a damper installation tool (see illustration). Tighten the bolt to the torque listed in this Chapter's Specifications.

10 The remainder of the installation is the reverse of removal.

11 Refill the cooling system and run the engine, checking for leaks.

10.9 Press the crankshaft damper into place with an installation tool

11 Timing chain cover - removal and installation

▶ **Refer to illustration 11.10**

REMOVAL

➡**Note: The engine must be removed from the vehicle to gain access to the oil pan on 4WD models.**

1 Disconnect the negative cable at the battery.

2 Drain the oil and coolant and remove the drivebelt (see Chapter 1).

3 Remove the fan shroud, fan/clutch assembly, water pump pulley and lower radiator hose (see Chapter 3).

4 Remove the air cleaner intake duct.

5 Remove the air conditioning compressor mounting bolts from the bracket. Without disconnecting the hoses, carefully lift the compressor off and secure it aside. Remove the power steering pump mounting bracket bolts. Leave the pump and hoses connected and secure the pump and bracket assembly aside.

6 Remove the alternator (see Chapter 5) and the alternator bracket.

7 Remove the water pump (see Chapter 3).

➡**Note: It's possible to leave the water pump bolted to the timing cover and remove them both together.**

8 Remove the crankshaft pulley and damper (see Section 10).

9 Remove the oil pan-to-timing chain cover bolts.

10 Unbolt the timing chain cover and remove it (see illustration).
➡**Note: The bolts are of various sizes and lengths; keep them in order to ensure they are installed in their proper locations.**

INSTALLATION

11 While the cover is off, replace the front oil seal. Drive the old one out from the rear. Place the cover on a block of wood and install a new seal using a hammer and a suitable driver.

12 Install the cover and tighten all fasteners to the torque listed in this Chapter's Specifications. All the 6mm diameter bolts are the same length. However, the 8mm are of several different lengths.

➡**Note: Use Teflon pipe sealant (Ford D6AZ-19558-A or equivalent) on the cover bolts which go into the water jacket (bolts marked "A" in illustration 11.10). Apply a light film of oil to the other fasteners.**

13 The remainder of the installation is the reverse of removal.
14 Refill the cooling system and run the engine, checking for leaks.

11.10 Timing chain cover bolt and stud locations (the bolts that go in holes marked "A" require sealant)

12 Timing chain and sprockets - check, removal and installation

◆ **Refer to illustrations 12.3 and 12.14**

CHECK

1 Remove the left (driver's side) valve cover (see Section 4).
2 Loosen the number 5 cylinder exhaust valve rocker arm (4th one back) and rotate it aside.
3 Mount a dial indicator on the end of the pushrod (see illustration).
4 Turn the crankshaft clockwise until the number 1 piston is at Top Dead Center (see Section 3). The damper timing mark should point to TDC on the timing degree indicator. This will take up slack on the right side of the chain.
5 Zero the dial indicator.
6 Slowly turn the crankshaft counterclockwise until the slightest movement is seen on the dial indicator. Check to see how far the damper TDC timing mark has moved away from the pointer.
7 If the reading on the timing indicator exceeds 6-degrees, replace the timing chain and sprockets.

REMOVAL

8 Turn the crankshaft clockwise until the number one piston is at Top Dead Center (see Section 3).

12.3 Mount a dial indicator on the pushrod to detect valve lifter movement

9 Disconnect the negative cable at the battery.
10 Remove the timing chain cover (see Section 11).
11 Unbolt the camshaft sprocket. Be sure the engine does not turn during bolt removal. Carefully remove the sprocket with the chain still on it.
12 Pry the crankshaft sprocket off. Do not lose the small crankshaft key.
13 Check the timing chain and sprockets for visible wear and damage. Replace as a set if necessary.

INSTALLATION

14 Slide both sprockets and the chain onto the camshaft and crankshaft with the timing marks aligned (see illustration). Tap the crankshaft sprocket into place with a brass drift and hammer.
15 Install the camshaft bolt and washer and tighten the bolts to the torque listed in this Chapter's Specifications.

12.14 Align the timing marks on the camshaft and crankshaft sprockets

---

※※ **CAUTION:**

The camshaft bolt has a drilled oil passage. Be sure that passage is open before installation. DO NOT substitute any other type bolt.

16 Apply oil to the timing chain and sprockets.
17 Install the timing chain cover (see Section 11) and the remaining components removed for installation.

---

13 Valve lifters - removal, inspection and installation

▸ **Refer to illustrations 13.3, 13.4, 13.7a and 13.7b**

REMOVAL AND INSTALLATION

1   Remove the intake manifold (see Section 7) and pushrods (see Section 5).
2   Loosen the two bolts securing the roller lifter guide plate retainer and lift the retainer off. Remove all the guide plates.
3   Remove the lifters with a magnet and place them in a rack in sequence so they can be replaced in their original location (see illustration).

13.3 A clearly labeled box with subdividers is a handy way to keep the lifters in order so that they can be reinstalled in the lifter bores they were removed from

4   If stuck, carefully use a lifter puller tool to remove them by rotating them back and forth to loosen them from gum or varnish deposits (see illustration). Carburetor cleaner can be used to loosen these deposits.

※※ **CAUTION:**

Do no use pliers to remove the lifers unless you are replacing them. Pliers can easily damage the lifters.

---

5   Clean the lifters and apply engine oil to both the lifters and bores before installing. Be sure to install the lifters in their original bores. Align the flats on the lifter body and install the guide plates. Install the retainer and tighten the retainer bolts to the torque listed in this Chapter's Specifications.
6   Install the pushrods and the intake manifold.

LIFTER INSPECTION

7   Check that the roller on each lifter turns freely and shows no signs of pitting, scoring or other wear (see illustration). Check the pushrod seat in each lifter for wear. Also make sure each lifter fits in its original bore without excessive looseness (see illustration). Wear is only normally encountered at very high mileages or in cases of neglected engine lubrication.
8   Press down on the plunger using a Phillips screwdriver to make sure it operates freely without binding.
9   If the lifters show signs of wear or binding they must be replaced.
10 See Chapter 2 Part D for further information.

13.4 The lifters in an engine that has vbe removed with a special tool

13.7a The roller on roller lifters mustturn freely - check for wear and excessive play as well

13.7b Check the pushrod seat in the top of each lifter for wear

14 Camshaft - removal, inspection and installation

→**Note: Refer to Chapter 2F and check the camshaft lobe lift as described, before removing the camshaft from the engine block.**

REMOVAL

1 Remove the intake manifold (see Section 7).
2 Remove the valve covers (see Section 4).
3 Loosen the rocker arm bolts and rotate the rocker arms to the side.
4 If the pushrods are to be reused, remove them from the engine and place them in a holder to keep them in order (see Section 5).
5 Remove the valve lifters from the engine (see Section 13).
6 Remove the timing chain cover (see Section 11).
7 Unbolt the camshaft sprocket. Be sure you do not turn the engine while doing so.
8 Remove the timing chain and sprockets (see Section 12).
9 Remove the bolts securing the camshaft thrust plate to the engine block.
10 Slowly withdraw the camshaft from the engine, being careful not to nick, scrape or otherwise damage the bearings with the cam lobes.

INSPECTION

11 See Chapter 2, Part F for the camshaft and lifter inspection procedures.

INSTALLATION

12 Lubricate the camshaft journals liberally with engine oil and apply engine assembly lube to the cam lobes.
13 Slide the camshaft into position, being careful not to scrape or nick the bearings.
14 Install the camshaft thrust plate. Tighten the thrust plate retaining bolts to the torque listed in this Chapter's Specifications. Install the timing chain and sprockets.
15 Install the hydraulic valve lifters in their original bores if the original lifters are being used. Make sure they are coated with engine assembly lube.
16 The remainder of the installation procedure is the reverse of removal. On models equipped with a camshaft position sensor, install it as described in Chapter 6, Section 5.

15 Oil pan - removal and installation

2WD MODELS

1 Disconnect the negative cable at the battery.
2 Remove the oil dipstick.
3 Unbolt the fan shroud and lay it over the fan (see Chapter 3).
4 Detach the engine mounts from the frame.
5 Raise the vehicle and support it securely on jackstands.
6 If equipped, disconnect the low oil level sensor by removing the retainer clip at the sensor and then separating the connector from the sensor.
7 Drain the oil and install a new oil filter (see Chapter 1).
8 Remove the starter motor (see Chapter 5).
9 Remove the inspection cover from the front of the transmission. Remove the nuts from the engine mounts and raise the engine two inches with a three-bar engine support fixture (these can be rented at tool rental yards). Refer to Chapter 7 and remove the transmission, then the engine flywheel/driveplate.
10 Remove the passenger side axle beam (see Chapter 10).

✳✳ CAUTION:

Be sure to remove the brake caliper and tie it up out of the way.

11 Unbolt the oil pan. Using a hoist, raise the engine approximately two inches to allow enough clearance to remove the oil pan. If it is stuck on, gently pry it off, taking care not to bend or distort the pan sealing flange.

✳✳ CAUTION:

The oil pan is a tight fit between the transmission spacer plate and the oil pump pick-up tube. Be careful not to damage the pick-up tube when you remove the pan. If necessary, remove the oil pump mounting bolt and lower the oil pump into the oil pan.

12 Thoroughly clean the gasket surfaces of the block and pan.
13 Install a new gasket on the oil pan using contact adhesive to hold it in place.
14 Apply a 4 to 5 mm (1/4-inch) bead of RTV sealer to the junctions of the rear main bearing cap and engine block and also to the timing chain cover-to-block surface. Instructions are included with the new gasket. Don't allow the sealant to cure before installing the pan.
15 Position the pan on the engine. Install the oil pan bolts and tighten them to the torque listed in this Chapter's Specifications.
16 Reinstall any parts removed and refill with engine oil.
17 Run the engine and check for leaks.

4WD MODELS

→**Note: The engine must be removed from the vehicle to gain access to the oil pan on 4WD models.**

18 Remove the engine as described in Part F of this Chapter. Mount the engine on a suitable engine stand, right-side up.
19 Unbolt the oil pan. If it is stuck on, gently pry it off, taking care not to bend or distort the pan sealing flange.
20 Thoroughly clean the gasket surfaces of the block and pan.
21 Install a new gasket on the oil pan using contact adhesive to hold it in place.
22 Apply a 4 to 5 mm (1/4-inch) bead of RTV sealer to the junctions of the rear main bearing cap and engine block and also to the timing chain cover-to-block. Instructions are included with the new gasket. Don't allow the sealant to cure before installing the pan.
23 Position the pan on the engine. Install the oil pan bolts and

tighten them to the torque listed in this Chapter's Specifications. Tighten the front and rear bolts first, then work from the center bolts out to the ends until all are tightened.

24 Install the engine.
25 Reinstall any parts removed and refill with engine oil.
26 Run the engine and check for leaks.

16 Oil pump and pick-up - removal and installation

➡**Note: We recommend oil pump replacement any time the engine is rebuilt and when the pump has high mileage or is otherwise suspect.**

1 Remove the oil pan as described in Section 15.
2 While supporting the oil pump, remove the pump-to-rear main bearing cap bolt.
3 Lower the pump and remove it along with the pump driveshaft.
4 If a new oil pump is installed, make sure the pump driveshaft is mated with the shaft inside the pump.

5 Position the pump on the engine and make sure the hex in the upper end of the driveshaft is aligned with the lower end of the distributor or camshaft position sensor shaft. The distributor or camshaft position sensor drives the oil pump, so it is absolutely essential that the components mate properly.
6 Install the mounting bolt and tighten it to the torque listed in this Chapter's Specifications.
7 Install the oil pan and add oil.
8 The remainder of installation is the reverse of removal.

17 Rear main oil seal - replacement

▸ **Refer to illustration 17.4, 17.6 and 17.10**

1 Remove the transmission (see Chapter 7).

2 On manual transmission equipped vehicles, remove the clutch assembly (see Chapter 8).
3 Remove the flywheel/driveplate.
4 Using a sharp awl, carefully punch one hole into the seal between the lip and the engine block (see illustration).
5 Screw in the threaded end of a slide hammer available at most auto parts stores, or equivalent. Pull the seal out with the tool.
6 If the special tool is not available, you may be able to carefully pry out the old seal using a screwdriver (see illustration). Take care to prevent nicking or scratching the seal bore or crankshaft.
7 Thoroughly clean and inspect the oil seal area.
8 Lubricate the new seal with engine oil.
9 Start the seal into its recess with the spring side facing engine.
10 Press the seal into place with a special tool available at most auto parts stores. You can also tap the seal in place using a hammer and hardwood drift or section of the appropriate size plastic pipe (see illustration). Work slowly around the seal until it is flush with the rear face of the block.
11 Install the flywheel/driveplate.
12 The remainder of installation is the reverse of removal.
13 Run the engine and check for leaks.

17.4 Do not scratch the crankshaft when punching a hole in the seal

17.6 You may be able to gently pry the seal out, but don't scratch the sealing surfaces

17.10 If a seal installation tool isn't available, tap around the seal, slowly working it into position

18 Flywheel/driveplate - removal and installation

Refer to Chapter 2 Part D for the flywheel/driveplate removal and installation procedures, but use the torque specifications found in this Chapter's Specifications.

19 Engine mounts - removal and installation

Refer to Chapter 2A for these procedures, but use the Specifications found in this Chapter.

Specifications

General

Cylinder numbers (front-to-rear)	
Left (driver's) side	4-5-6
Right side	1-2-3
Firing order	1-4-2-5-3-6

Camshaft

Lobe lift (intake and exhaust)	0.260 inch
Endplay	0.007 inch
Journal diameter	2.0074 to 2.0084 inches
Bearing inside diameter	2.0094 to 2.0104 inches
Bearing oil clearance	0.001 to 0.003 inch

36071-2B-HAYNES

Cylinder numbering and coil terminal location

Torque specifications
Ft-lbs (unless otherwise indicated)

➡**Note: One foot-pound (ft-lb) of torque is equivalent to 12 inch-pounds (in-lbs) of torque. Torque values below approximately 15 ft-lbs are expressed in inch-pounds, since most foot-pound torque wrenches are not accurate at these smaller values.**

Camshaft sprocket bolt	40 to 51
Camshaft thrust plate bolts	89 in-lbs
Crankshaft pulley-to-vibration damper bolts	39-53
Cylinder head bolts (in sequence - **see illustration 9.20**)	
2000 models	
Step 1	59
Step 2	Loosen 1 full turn
Step 3	37
Step 4	Tighten an additional 90-degrees
Step 5	Tighten an additional 90-degrees
2001 through 2008 models	
Step 1	37
Step 2	Loosen 1 full turn
Step 3	22
Step 4	Tighten an additional 90-degrees
Step 5	Tighten an additional 90-degrees
Flywheel/driveplate bolts	54 to 64
Engine mount-to-block bolts	33 to 44
Engine mount-to-crossmember nuts	52 to 54
Exhaust manifold bolts	
Step 1	96 in-lbs
Step 2	15 to 22
Intake manifold bolts	
Step 1	132 in-lbs
Step 2	19 to 24
Lifter guide plate retainer bolts	84 to 120 in-lbs
Oil pan bolts	84 to 108 in-lbs
Oil pump-to-block bolts	15 to 22
Oil pump pick-up tube-to-oil pump	15 to 22
Rocker arm fulcrum bolts	
Step 1	60 to 132 in-lbs
Step 2	18 to 26
Timing chain cover bolts	
6mm bolts	72 to 96 in-lbs
8mm bolts	15 to 22
Valve cover bolts	84 to 108 in-lbs
Vibration damper bolt	92 to 122

Section

Reference to other Chapters

2D

**4.0L PUSHROD
V6 ENGINE**

---

1 General information

This Part of Chapter 2 is devoted to in-vehicle repair procedures for the 4.0L pushrod V6 engine. Procedures such as timing chain and sprocket and oil pan removal are also included, however they require removal of the engine from the vehicle. All information concerning engine removal and installation and engine block and cylinder head overhaul can be found in Part F of this Chapter.

The following repair procedures are based on the assumption that the engine is installed in the vehicle. If the engine has been removed from the vehicle and mounted on a stand, many of the steps outlined in this Part of Chapter 2 will not apply.

The Specifications included in this Part of Chapter 2 apply only to the procedures contained in this Part. Part F of Chapter 2 contains the Specifications necessary for cylinder head and engine block rebuilding.

---

2 Repair operations possible with the engine in the vehicle

Many major repair operations can be accomplished without removing the engine from the vehicle.

Clean the engine compartment and the exterior of the engine with some type of degreaser before any work is done. It will make the job easier and help keep dirt out of the internal areas of the engine.

Depending on the components involved, it may be helpful to remove the hood to improve access to the engine as repairs are performed (refer to Chapter 11 if necessary). Cover the fenders to prevent damage to the paint. Special pads are available, but an old bedspread or blanket will also work.

If vacuum, exhaust, oil or coolant leaks develop, indicating a need for gasket or seal replacement, the repairs can generally be made with the engine in the vehicle. The intake and exhaust manifold gaskets and cylinder head gaskets are all accessible with the engine in place.

➡ **Note: Removing the oil pan on a 4.0L engine requires removing the engine from the vehicle.**

Exterior engine components, such as the intake and exhaust manifolds, the water pump, the starter motor, the alternator, the distributor and the fuel system components can be removed for repair with the engine in place.

Since the cylinder heads can be removed without pulling the engine, valve component servicing can also be accomplished with the engine in the vehicle. Replacement of the timing chain and sprockets requires removal of the oil pan, so it is not possible with the engine in the vehicle.

---

3 Top Dead Center (TDC) for number one piston - locating

◆ **Refer to illustrations 3.5a and 3.5b**

➡ **Note: These engines are not equipped with a distributor. Piston position must be determined by feeling for compression at the number one spark plug hole, then aligning the ignition timing marks as described in Step 5.**

1 Top Dead Center (TDC) is the highest point in the cylinder that each piston reaches as it travels up-and-down when the crankshaft turns. Each piston reaches TDC on the compression stroke and again on the exhaust stroke, but TDC generally refers to piston position on the compression stroke.

2 Positioning the piston(s) at TDC is an essential part of many other repair procedures discussed in this manual.

3 Before beginning this procedure, be sure to place the transmission in Neutral and apply the parking brake or block the rear wheels. Remove the spark plugs (see Chapter 1). Disable the ignition system by disconnecting the electrical connector from the ignition coil pack, located above the left valve cover.

4 In order to bring any piston to TDC, the crankshaft must be turned using one of the methods outlined below. When looking at the front of the engine, normal crankshaft rotation is clockwise.

a) The preferred method is to turn the crankshaft with a socket and ratchet attached to the bolt threaded into the front of the crankshaft.

b) A remote starter switch, which may save some time, can also be used. Follow the instructions included with the switch. Once the piston is close to TDC, use a socket and ratchet as described in the previous paragraph.

c) If an assistant is available to turn the ignition switch to the Start position in short bursts, you can get the piston close to TDC without a remote starter switch. Make sure your assistant is out of the vehicle, away from the ignition switch, then use a socket and ratchet as described in Paragraph a) to complete the procedure.

5 The crankshaft pulley has 35 teeth, evenly spaced every 10-degrees around the pulley, and a gap where a 36th tooth would be. The gap is located at 60-degrees Before Top Dead Center (BTDC) (see

3.5a The crankshaft pulley has a gap at 60-degrees BTDC - TDC for number one and five cylinders is located at the sixth tooth from the gap

illustration). Turn the crankshaft (see Paragraph 4) until you feel compression at the number one spark plug hole, then turn it slowly until the sixth tooth from the missing tooth is aligned with the Crankshaft Position (CKP) sensor and the TDC notch is aligned with the pointer (located at the front of the engine) (see illustration).

6   After the number one piston has been positioned at TDC on the compression stroke, TDC for any of the remaining pistons can be located by turning the crankshaft and following the firing order.

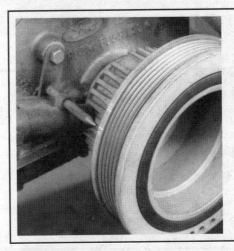

3.5b The pointer on the front of the engine lines up with a notch in the crankshaft pulley to indicate TDC

4   Valve covers - removal and installation

▶ Refer to illustrations 4.7, 4.8, 4.9a, 4.9b, 4.12, 4.16, 4.20 and 4.22

REMOVAL

1   Disconnect the negative cable from the battery.
2   Remove the accelerator control splash shield and air cleaner outlet tube.

Right valve cover

3   Remove the alternator and ignition coil pack (refer to Chapter 5).
4   Remove the bolt that secures the air conditioning line above the upper intake manifold (if not already done when removing the coil pack).
5   Detach the spark plug wires from the valve cover clips.
6   Carefully pry the two wiring harnesses loose from the valve cover with a tool such as a door panel clip remover (available at auto parts stores).
7   Disconnect the vacuum hose at the coupling above the valve cover (see illustration).
8   Carefully lift the engine wiring harness clip with your thumb at

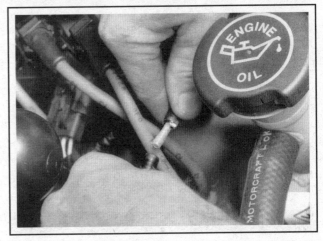

4.7 On the passenger's side, disconnect the vacuum hose at the coupling above the valve cover

the point shown to separate it from the valve cover (see illustration). Don't pull on the harness.
9   Remove the valve cover bolts and reinforcing plates. Lift the valve

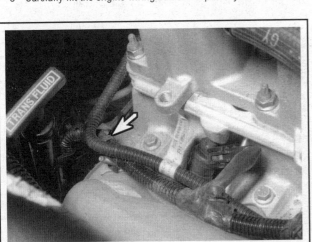

4.8 Lift the wiring harness off the stud with a thumbnail - don't pry it

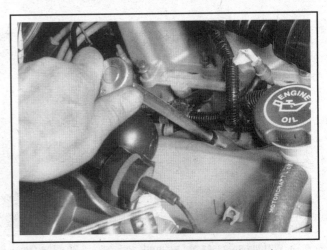

4.9a Remove the valve cover bolts with a ratchet and extension . . .

4.9b . . . and lift the cover off - you may have to angle it out, as show here - tap it gently with a soft-face mallet if necessary to break the gasket seal

4.12 Disconnect the compressor electrical connector from the back of the compressor, then remove the mounting bolts and shift the compressor forward as shown - DO NOT disconnect any refrigerant lines

cover off. Tap it gently with a soft-face hammer if necessary to break the gasket seal (see illustrations).

Left valve cover

10 If you haven't already done so, remove the bolt from the air conditioning line above the upper intake manifold.

11 Disconnect the electrical connector for the air conditioning compressor clutch. Carefully pry the wiring harness from the back of the compressor with a door panel clip remover or similar tool.

12 Remove the mounting bolts from the air conditioning compressor (see Chapter 3). Lift the air conditioning compressor, then position it out of the way (see illustration).

> ✳✳ **WARNING:**
>
> DO NOT disconnect any refrigerant lines!

13 Disconnect the brake booster vacuum hose.

14 Label and disconnect the vacuum hoses from the tee on the plenum. Remove the upper intake manifold (see Chapter 4).

15 Detach the PCV hose. Remove the PCV hose and valve (see

Chapter 1).

16 Carefully pry the wiring harnesses away from the valve cover with a door trim panel remover or similar tool (see illustration). Place the harnesses out of the way.

17 Disconnect the driver's side spark plug wires from the plugs and detach them from the clips on the valve cover. Position the wires out of the way.

18 Carefully lift the engine wiring harness clip with your thumb to separate it from the valve cover. Don't pull on the harness.

19 Remove the bolt that secures the fuel line clip to the front of the engine. Move the fuel line just enough to provide access to the front valve cover bolt.

> ✳✳ **WARNING:**
>
> DO NOT disconnect any fuel lines without first relieving fuel pressure (see Chapter 4).

20 Remove the valve cover bolts and reinforcing plates (see illustration 4.9a). Lift the valve cover off (see illustration). Tap it gently with a soft-face hammer if necessary to break the gasket seal.

4.16 Wiring harnesses are secured to the valve cover by clips

4.20 Move the wiring harnesses out of the way and lift the valve cover off

4.22 Just before installing the new gasket, peel the plastic film off the self-sticking sealant on the valve-cover side of the gasket

INSTALLATION

21 Clean the gasket surfaces on the intake manifold, cylinder head and valve cover. Use a scraper to remove the pieces of old gasket material, then wipe off all residue with lacquer thinner or acetone.

22 Most valve cover gaskets are equipped with self-sticking sealant on the valve cover side. Pull the plastic film off the gasket (see illustration) and stick the gasket to the valve cover.

➡ **Note: In the following step, apply silicone sealant to one side of the engine at a time (if both valve covers were removed), then install the valve cover.**

23 Apply silicone sealant to the seam where the cylinder head joins the intake manifold.

24 The remainder of installation is the reverse of the removal Steps. Tighten the valve cover bolts evenly, starting with the center bolts and working out, to the torque listed in this Chapter's Specifications.

---

5 Rocker arms and pushrods - removal, inspection and installation

REMOVAL

▸ **Refer to illustrations 5.2, 5.3, 5.4a and 5.4b**

1 Refer to Section 4 and remove the valve cover(s).

2 Loosen the rocker arm shaft support bolts two turns at a time, starting with the center bolt and working out, until the bolts can be removed by hand (see illustration).

3 Lift the rocker shaft assembly off the cylinder head (see illustration). The pins will hold the components together. Mark each shaft assembly so it can be returned to it's original location.

4 Lift the pushrods out of the engine (see illustration). Place the pushrods in order in a holder (see illustration) so they can be returned to their original positions. Be sure to store them so you can reinstall them with the same end facing up.

INSPECTION

5 Remove the pins and disassemble the rocker arm assembly. Place the parts in order on a clean workbench. Be sure you don't mix up the parts - they must be reassembled in exactly the same order they were before disassembly.

6 Check each rocker arm for wear, cracks and other damage, especially where the pushrods and valve stems contact the rocker arm faces.

7 Make sure all oil holes are open and not plugged. Plugging can be cleared with a piece of wire.

8 Check each rocker arm bore, and its corresponding position on the rocker shaft, for wear, cracks and galling. If the rocker arms or shaft are damaged, replace them with new ones.

5.2 Remove the bolts evenly, two turns at a time, to prevent the shafts from being bent by valve spring pressure

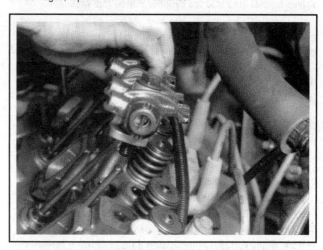

5.3 Once the bolts are loose, lift the rocker assembly off the engine

5.4a Pull the pushrods out of the lifters . . .

5.4b . . . and place them in a labeled holder so they can be returned to their original positions

9   Inspect the pushrods for cracks and excessive wear at the ends. Roll each pushrod across a piece of plate glass to see if it's bent (if it wobbles, it's bent).

10 If necessary, remove the plug from each end of the rocker shaft. Drill into one plug and insert a long steel rod through it to knock out the other plug. Knock out the first plug in the same manner.

11 If the rocker arm shaft plugs were removed, tap in new ones with a hammer and suitable drift.

12 Assemble the rocker assembly. Lubricate at friction points (pushrod ends, rocker arm bores and ends) with engine assembly lube.

13 Install new cotter pins in the ends of the rocker shaft. Be sure the rocker shaft oil holes will face down when the shaft is installed. The position of the oil holes is indicated by a notch on the front of each shaft.

INSTALLATION

14 Coat each end of each pushrod with assembly lube, then install them in the engine. If you are reinstalling the original pushrods, be sure to return them to their original positions.

15 Coat the rocker arm pads with assembly lube.

16 Install the rocker arm assembly on the engine. The notch on the front end of each shaft should face down.

17 Position the rocker arm ball ends in the pushrods.

18 Tighten the rocker shaft support bolts two turns at a time, working from the center bolt out, to the torque listed in this Chapter's Specifications.

19 The remainder of installation is the reverse of the removal Steps.

6   Valve springs, retainers and seals - replacement

▶ **Refer to illustrations 6.4, 6.9, 6.15a and 6.15b**

➡**Note: Broken valve springs and defective valve stem seals can be replaced without removing the cylinder heads. Two special tools and a compressed air source are normally required to perform this operation, so read through this Section carefully and rent or buy the tools before beginning the job. If compressed air isn't available, a length of nylon rope can be used to keep the valves from falling into the cylinder during this procedure.**

1   Refer to Section 4 and remove the valve cover from the affected cylinder head. If all of the valve stem seals are being replaced, remove both valve covers.

2   Remove the spark plug from the cylinder which has the defective component. If all of the valve stem seals are being replaced, all of the spark plugs should be removed.

3   Turn the crankshaft until the piston in the affected cylinder is at top dead center on the compression stroke (refer to Section 3 for instructions). If you're replacing all of the valve stem seals, begin with cylinder number one and work on the valves for one cylinder at a time. Move from cylinder-to-cylinder following the firing order sequence (see this Chapter's Specifications).

4   Thread an adapter into the spark plug hole and connect an air hose from a compressed air source to it. Most auto parts stores can supply the air hose adapter (see illustration).

➡**Note: Many cylinder compression gauges utilize a screw-in fitting that may work with your air hose quick-disconnect fitting.**

5   Remove the rocker assembly on the affected side of the engine (see Section 5). If all of the valve stem seals are being replaced, remove both rocker assemblies.

6   Apply compressed air to the cylinder.

✳✳ WARNING:

The piston may be forced down by compressed air, causing the crankshaft to turn suddenly. If the wrench used when positioning the number one piston at TDC is still attached to the bolt in the crankshaft nose, it could cause damage or injury when the crankshaft moves.

7   The valves should be held in place by the air pressure.

8   If you don't have access to compressed air, an alternative method can be used. Position the piston at a point approximately 45-degrees before TDC on the compression stroke, then feed a long piece of nylon rope through the spark plug hole until it fills the combustion chamber. Be sure to leave the end of the rope hanging out of the engine so it can be removed easily. Use a large ratchet and socket to rotate the crankshaft in the normal direction of rotation until slight resistance is felt.

9   Stuff shop rags into the cylinder head holes above and below the valves to prevent parts and tools from falling into the engine, then use

6.4 Thread the air hose adapter into the spark plug hole - adapters are commonly available from auto parts stores

6.9 Compress the valve spring, then remove the keepers

Max. gap = 0.019 in.

36071-2C-6.10 HAYNES

6.15a The valve stem seal must be installed to the proper height on the valve guide

6.15b The valve stem seal can be driven (carefully) into place with a hammer and deep socket

a valve spring compressor to compress the spring. Remove the keepers with small needle-nose pliers or a magnet (see illustration).

➡Note: A couple of different types of tools are available for compressing the valve springs with the head in place. One type grips the lower spring coils and presses on the retainer as the knob is turned, while the other type utilizes a bar installed in place of the rocker arm shaft for leverage.

10 Remove the spring retainer and valve spring, then remove the valve stem seal.

➡Note: If air pressure fails to hold the valve in the closed position during this operation, the valve face or seat is probably damaged. If so, the cylinder head will have to be removed for additional repair operations.

11 Wrap a rubber band or tape around the top of the valve stem so the valve won't fall into the combustion chamber, then release the air pressure.

➡Note: If a rope was used instead of air pressure, turn the crankshaft slightly in the direction opposite normal rotation.

12 Inspect the valve stem for damage. Rotate the valve in the guide and check the end for eccentric movement, which would indicate that the valve is bent.

13 Move the valve up-and-down in the guide and make sure it doesn't bind. If the valve stem binds, either the valve is bent or the guide is damaged. In either case, the head will have to be removed for repair.

14 Reapply air pressure to the cylinder to retain the valve in the closed position, then remove the tape or rubber band from the valve stem. If a rope was used instead of air pressure, rotate the crankshaft in the normal direction of rotation until slight resistance is felt.

15 Lubricate the valve stem with engine oil and install a new stem seal over the valve guide to the depth shown (see illustration). Use a special tool, available at most auto parts stores, or a deep socket of the appropriate size and gently tap the seal into place (see illustration).

16 Install the spring in position over the valve.

17 Install the valve spring retainer. Compress the valve spring and carefully position the keepers in the groove. Apply a small dab of grease to the inside of each lock to hold it in place.

18 Remove the pressure from the spring tool and make sure the keepers are seated.

19 Disconnect the air hose and remove the adapter from the spark plug hole. If a rope was used in place of air pressure, pull it out of the cylinder.

20 Refer to Section 5 and install the rocker arm assembly.

21 Install the spark plugs and hook up the wires.

22 Refer to Section 4 and install the valve covers.

23 Start the engine, then check for oil leaks and unusual sounds coming from the valve cover area.

7 Intake manifold - removal and installation

♦ **Refer to illustrations 7.6, 7.8, 7.9 and 7.11**

REMOVAL

1 Relieve the fuel system pressure (see Chapter 4). Disconnect the negative cable from the battery.

2 Remove the ignition coil and mounting bracket (see Chapter 5). Remove the upper intake manifold (see Chapter 4).

3 Remove the valve covers (see Section 4). If it's in the way, remove the camshaft position sensor, if equipped (see Chapter 6, Section 5).

4 Disconnect the electrical connectors from the various sensors threaded into the intake manifold. Disconnect the electrical connectors from the fuel injectors and disconnect the fuel lines to the fuel rail (see Chapter 4).

5 Disconnect the heater hose from the front of the intake manifold. Either remove the thermostat and housing (see Chapter 3) or disconnect the upper radiator hose from the outlet fitting.

7.6 Remove the eight intake manifold bolts and nuts

6   Remove the intake manifold nuts and bolts and lift the manifold off (see illustration). If it's stuck, tap it lightly with a soft-face hammer to break the gasket seal. If necessary, pry the manifold off, but pry between a casting protrusion and the engine - don't pry against gasket surfaces.

INSTALLATION

7   Clean away all traces of old gasket material. Remove oil and dirt with a cloth and solvent, such as acetone or lacquer thinner.

8   Apply RTV sealant around the coolant ports (the smaller ports at the ends of the heads) and to the front sealing surface. Also apply a bead of sealant to the four corners where the manifold meets the engine (see the accompanying illustration and illustration 7.6).

7.9 As soon as the sealant is applied, install the gasket and apply a bead of sealant around the coolant ports and in the four corners

7.8 Before installing the intake manifold gasket, apply a film of RTV sealant around the coolant ports as well as the front sealing surface - be sure to apply a bead to the corners (arrows) at the front and rear of the manifold

➡ **Note: Install the manifold gasket immediately after applying the sealant. If allowed to set up (approximately 15 minutes), the sealant won't work properly.**

9   Install the manifold gasket (see illustration), then apply RTV sealant onto the gasket, around the coolant ports and to the four corners.

10 Install the manifold over the studs. Install the nuts and bolts and tighten them finger-tight.

11 Tighten the nuts and bolts in the four stages listed in this Chapter's Specifications, following the sequence (see illustration).

12 The remainder of installation is the reverse of the removal steps.

13 Run the engine and check for oil, coolant and vacuum leaks.

7.11 Intake manifold bolt tightening sequence

8   Exhaust manifolds - removal and installation

REMOVAL

♦ **Refer to illustration 8.7**

✳✳ WARNING:

Allow the engine to cool completely before beginning this procedure.

1   Disconnect the cable from the negative battery terminal.
2   Spray the exhaust pipe fasteners and exhaust manifold fasteners with rust penetrant and allow it to soak in for about 10 minutes. If there is any resistance during removal, stop and respray the fasteners to prevent them from breaking off.
3   Remove the spark plug wires from the spark plugs and secure them out of the way (see Chapter 1). Be sure to mark the spark plug wires so they don't get mixed-up.
4   Unbolt the exhaust pipe from the manifold as described in Chapter 4.

➡**Note: For access to the exhaust pipe nuts, it may be necessary to raise the vehicle and support it securely on jackstands.**

Left manifold

5   Remove the oil dipstick tube bracket from the engine.
6   If the power steering pump hoses obstruct manifold removal, disconnect them (see Chapter 10). Cap the hoses and fittings to keep out dirt and place the hose ends out of the way.
7   Unbolt and remove the manifold from the cylinder head (see illustration).

Right manifold

8   Detach the heater hose bracket and disconnect the heater hoses (see Chapter 3).
9   Unbolt and remove the manifold from the cylinder head (see illustration 8.7).

INSTALLATION

10   Using a scraper, thoroughly clean the mating surfaces on the cylinder head, manifold and exhaust pipe. Remove residue with a solvent such as acetone or lacquer thinner.

➡**Note: These engines were originally assembled without exhaust manifold gaskets and can be reassembled the same way so long as the mating surfaces are perfectly flat and not damaged in any way. Warped or damaged manifolds may require a gasket or machining.**

11   Apply some graphite grease to the cylinder head mating surface and place the manifold on the cylinder head. Tighten the bolts evenly to the torque listed in this Chapter's Specifications.
12   Connect the exhaust pipe to the manifold and tighten the nuts evenly to the torque listed in this Chapter's Specifications.
13   The remainder of installation is the reverse of the removal steps. If the heater hoses were disconnected, fill the cooling system (see Chapter 1).
14   Run the engine and check for exhaust leaks.

8.7 Remove the exhaust manifold bolts (arrows)

9   Cylinder heads - removal and installation

REMOVAL

♦ **Refer to illustrations 9.12 and 9.13**

➡**Note: Head bolt removal requires a Torx bit. Obtain the necessary tool before starting. DO NOT try to use an Allen wrench since it may round out the bolt head.**

1   Disconnect the negative cable from the battery.
2   Drain the cooling system (see Chapter 3).
3   Remove the valve covers (see Section 4).
4   Remove the rocker arms and pushrods (see Section 5).
5   Remove the intake manifold (see Section 7).
6   Remove the drivebelt (see Chapter 1).
7   If removing the left cylinder head, detach the air conditioning

compressor from the engine and place it out of the way (see illustration 4.12).

✳✳ CAUTION:

DO NOT disconnect any refrigerant lines!

Detach the power steering pump and bracket and set them out of the way (see Chapter 10). Don't disconnect the power steering hoses.
8   If removing the right cylinder head, remove the alternator and bracket (see Chapter 5).
9   If there's a wiring harness attached to the rear of either cylinder head, unwrap or cut the tape to detach the harness from the retainer.
10   Remove the spark plugs (see Chapter 1).

9.12 Remove the head bolts with a T55 Torx bit - don't use an Allen wrench, since it may round out the bolt heads

11 Remove the exhaust manifolds (see Section 8).

12 Remove and discard the cylinder head bolts (see illustration). The bolts must be replaced with new ones whenever they are removed. Loosen the bolts in several stages.

13 Lift the cylinder head off the engine. If it's difficult to remove, carefully pry it off. Pry against a casting protrusion, not against gasket surfaces (see illustration).

INSTALLATION

▶ **Refer to illustrations 9.14, 9.17 and 9.18**

14 Thoroughly remove all traces of gasket material with a gasket scraper and clean all parts with solvent (see illustration). Use a rag and acetone or lacquer thinner to remove any traces of oil from the gasket mating surfaces. See Chapter 2, Part F for cylinder head inspection procedures.

15 Use a tap of the correct size to chase the threads in the head bolt holes.

16 Recheck all head bolt holes and cylinder bores for any traces of coolant, oil or other foreign matter. Remove as needed.

17 Position the new gaskets over the dowel pins on the block. Don't use sealant on the gaskets. Be sure the FRONT TOP marks are positioned correctly (see illustration).

18 Install the heads and new head bolts. Tighten the bolts to the torque listed in this Chapter's Specifications in the sequence shown (see illustration).

19 Refer to Section 7 and apply silicone sealant to the block and

9.13 If necessary, pry the head loose; pry against a casting protrusion so the gasket surfaces won't be damaged

9.14 Remove all traces of the old gasket with a scraper, taking care not to gouge the sealing surfaces

cylinder head mating surfaces. Install the intake manifold gasket, then apply silicone sealant to the gasket at the same locations.

20 Position the intake manifold on the engine (see Section 7). Install the intake manifold bolts and tighten them to the torque listed in this Chapter's Specifications, in the sequence shown in illustration 7.11.

21 The remainder of installation is the reverse of the removal steps.

22 Run the engine and check for oil, coolant and vacuum leaks.

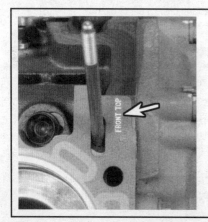

9.17 Be sure the FRONT TOP mark on the head gasket is positioned correctly

9.18 Cylinder head bolt tightening sequence

10 Crankshaft pulley and front oil seal - removal and installation

CRANKSHAFT PULLEY REMOVAL AND INSTALLATION

▶ **Refer to illustrations 10.3a and 10.3b**

1   Remove the drivebelt (see Chapter 1).

2   Remove the crankshaft pulley bolt.

3   Insert a longer, smaller-diameter bolt into the crankshaft so the puller will have something to bottom against, then remove the crankshaft pulley with a puller, designed for this job, available at most auto parts stores. (see illustrations). DO NOT pry the pulley off or use an impact puller!

4   Using clean engine oil, lubricate the surface of the pulley where the front seal rides. Install the crankshaft pulley. Don't hammer the pulley on. Tighten the pulley bolt to the torque listed in this Chapter's Specifications.

FRONT OIL SEAL REPLACEMENT

▶ **Refer to illustration 10.5**

5   Remove the crankshaft pulley (see Steps 1 through 3). Carefully pry the oil seal out with a screwdriver (see illustration).

10.3a To remove the crankshaft pulley, remove the pulley bolt (A) and install a longer bolt that's smaller in diameter (B) into the crankshaft . . .

6   Clean the seal bore and check it for nicks or gouges.

7   Coat the lip of the new seal with clean engine oil and drive it into the bore with a socket or large piece of pipe slightly smaller in diameter than the seal. The open side of the seal faces into the engine. Install the crankshaft pulley (see Step 4).

10.3b . . . so the puller screw (arrow) will have something to push against

10.5 To remove the front cover seal with the cover on the engine, pry it out with a screwdriver, taking care not to gouge the cover

11 Timing chain cover - removal and installation

REMOVAL

▶ **Refer to illustrations 11.5 and 11.6**

➡**Note: This procedure requires the engine be removed from the vehicle to properly reseal the timing chain cover-to-oil pan joint.**

1   Disconnect the cable from the negative battery terminal. Drain the engine oil and cooling system (see Chapter 1).

2   Remove the engine as described in Chapter 2F.

3   Remove the crankshaft pulley (see Section 10). Also remove the crankshaft position sensor (see Chapter 6).

4   Remove the water pump (see Chapter 3).

5   Remove the brackets, studs and cover bolts (see illustration).

11.5 Label the studs and brackets so they can be returned to their original locations

➡Note: The bolts are different lengths, and bolts and studs go in different locations. Label them so they can be installed in the correct holes.

6   Pull the cover straight off the engine (see illustration). If it's stuck, tap it lightly with a soft-face hammer or pry it carefully to break the gasket seal. Don't use excessive force or you'll crack the cover. If it's difficult to remove, check to make sure you've removed all the bolts.

7   Remove the oil pan (see Section 15).

INSTALLATION

8   Thoroughly clean and inspect all the parts. Use a gasket scraper to remove all traces of gasket material. Remove oil film with a solvent such as lacquer thinner or acetone.

9   Install the guide sleeves (if removed). Install the front cover, using a new gasket, and start the bolts two or three turns by hand. Note that the bolts are different lengths; be sure to install them in the correct holes.

10 Tighten the cover bolts evenly to the torque listed in this Chapter's Specifications.

11 Install the crankshaft position sensor (see Chapter 6).

12 Install the oil pan (see Section 15).

13 Install the crankshaft pulley (see Section 10, Step 4).

11.6 Remove the cover from the engine - if it's stuck, recheck to make sure all bolts and studs have been removed

14 Install the engine.

15 The remainder of installation is the reverse of the removal steps.

16 Run the engine and check for oil or coolant leaks.

12   Timing chain and sprockets - inspection, removal and installation

➡Note: This procedure requires the engine be removed from the vehicle to properly reseal the timing chain cover-to-oil pan joint.

CAMSHAFT ENDPLAY CHECK

1   Remove the timing chain cover (see Section 11).

2   Remove the rocker arm shafts (see Section 5).

3   Push the camshaft to the rear as far as it will go.

4   Install a dial indicator with its pointer on the camshaft sprocket bolt. Set the indicator to zero.

5   Pry the camshaft forward with a large screwdriver or prybar between the camshaft sprocket and the block. Note the dial indicator reading and compare with the endplay listed in this Chapter's Specifications. Replace the camshaft thrust plate (see Section 14) if endplay is excessive.

TIMING CHAIN AND TENSIONER INSPECTION

6   Remove the timing chain cover (see Section 11).

7   Align the crankshaft and camshaft timing marks.

8   Mark a reference point on the top chain link and position a ruler over the top of the chain.

9   Attach a torque wrench to the camshaft sprocket bolt and apply 15 ft-lbs of torque in the counterclockwise direction. Don't allow the crankshaft to rotate.

10 Note the point where your mark aligns on the ruler.

11 Apply 15 ft-lbs of torque in the clockwise direction and note the amount of movement.

12 The measurement is the timing chain deflection. If deflection is more than 1/8-inch, replace the timing chain (see below).

13 Check the tensioner for wear and damage. If tensioner face wear is excessive, replace the tensioner. Before reinstalling the tensioner,

it must be retracted (see Step 28). Tighten the tensioner bolts to the torque listed in this Chapter's Specifications.

CHAIN AND SPROCKET

Removal

▶ **Refer to illustrations 12.19 and 12.20**

14 Disconnect the cable from the negative battery terminal. Drain the cooling system and engine oil (see Chapter 1).

15 Remove the engine as described in Part F. Remove the oil pan (see Section 15).

16 Replace the oil filter (see Chapter 1).

17 Remove the drivebelt (see Chapter 1).

18 Remove the timing chain cover (see Section 11).

19 Turn the crankshaft until the timing marks are aligned (see illustration). Remove the camshaft sprocket Torx bolt and the crankshaft sprocket key. Also remove the timing chain tensioner.

12.19 Align the camshaft and crankshaft timing marks as shown (typical)

12.20 Remove the timing chain and sprockets together

20 Remove the sprockets together with the chain (see illustration). Do not disturb the crankshaft or camshaft while the timing chain and sprockets are removed.

21 If necessary, remove the Torx bolts that secure the chain guide and remove it from the block.

Installation

▶ **Refer to illustration 12.28**

22 Be sure the crankshaft and camshaft are positioned so the sprocket timing marks will align correctly after the sprockets are installed (see illustration 12.19).

23 If the chain guide was removed, install it. Be sure its pin is inserted into the block oil hole, then tighten the guide bolts to the torque listed in this Chapter's Specifications.

24 Place the sprockets in the chain with their timing marks aligned (see illustration 12.19). Install the sprockets and chain together on the crankshaft and camshaft.

12.28 To retract the timing chain tensioner so it can be installed, squeeze the tensioner pad and use a sharp-tipped probe to push the ratchet mechanism down, then in to release the latch, allowing the tensioner to retract

25 Install the crankshaft key.

26 Make sure the sprocket timing marks are still aligned (see illustration 12.19). The guide side of the chain must be straight, without any slack, for the marks to align accurately.

27 Install the camshaft sprocket and tighten the bolt to the torque listed in this Chapter's Specifications.

28 Squeeze the tensioner pad with your fingers. At the same time, use a sharp-tipped probe to push the ratchet mechanism down, then in. This will release the latch and let the tensioner retract (see illustration). Retain the tensioner pad in the retracted position by holding it or installing a clip or similar device.

29 Install the timing chain tensioner and allow the tensioner to press against the chain. Tighten the bolts to the torque listed in this Chapter's Specifications.

30 The remainder of installation is the reverse of the removal Steps.

31 Run the engine and check for oil or coolant leaks.

13 Valve lifters - removal, inspection and installation

▶ **Refer to illustrations 13.4, 13.8a and 13.8b**

REMOVAL

1 Remove the intake manifold (see Section 7).

2 Remove the cylinder heads (see Section 9).

3 The lifters protrude from their bores, so if there isn't a lot of varnish buildup, simply pull them out with your fingers. On engines with a lot of sludge and varnish, work the lifters up and down, using carburetor spray cleaner to loosen the deposits. If the lifters are particularly stubborn, special tools designed to grip and remove lifters are manufactured by many tool companies and are widely available.

4 Before removing the lifters, arrange to store them in a clearly labeled box to ensure that they're installed in their original locations (see illustration).

5 Remove the lifters and store them where they won't get dirty.

13.4 Store the lifters in a marked box so they can be returned to their original positions

13.8a Check the pushrod seat in the top of each lifter for wear

13.8b The roller on roller lifters must turn freely - check for wear and excessive play as well

INSPECTION

6   Parts for hydraulic valve lifters are not available separately. The work required to remove them from the engine again if cleaning is unsuccessful outweighs any potential savings from repairing them.

7   Clean the lifters with solvent and dry them thoroughly without mixing them up.

8   Check each lifter wall, pushrod seat and roller for scuffing, score marks and uneven wear. Replace any lifter that shows these conditions. If the lifter walls are worn (which isn't very likely), inspect the lifter bores in the engine block as well. If the pushrod seats are worn (see illustration), check the pushrod ends. Make sure each roller turns freely (see illustration).

9   The lifters and camshaft should be replaced as a set if any lifter needs replacement. Never install used lifters unless the original camshaft is used and the lifters can be installed in their original locations!

10 The original lifters, if they're being reinstalled, must be returned to their original locations.

INSTALLATION

11 Install the lifters in the bores. Coat them with moly-based grease or engine assembly lube. Note that when the lifters are installed, the alignment tab must fit in the groove in the lifter bore.

12 The remainder of installation is the reverse of the removal Steps.

14 Camshaft - removal, inspection and installation

ENDPLAY CHECK

1   Refer to Section 12 for this procedure.

LOBE LIFT CHECK

♦ **Refer to illustration 14.4**

2   In order to determine the extent of cam lobe wear, the lobe lift should be checked prior to camshaft removal. Refer to Section 4 and remove the valve covers. The rocker arm assembly must also be removed (see Section 5), but leave the pushrods in place.

3   Position the number one piston to TDC on the compression stroke (see Section 3).

4   Beginning with the number one cylinder, mount a dial indicator on the engine and position the plunger in-line with and resting on the first pushrod (see illustration).

5   Zero the dial indicator, then very slowly turn the crankshaft in the normal direction of rotation until the indicator needle stops and begins to move in the opposite direction. The point at which it stops indicates maximum cam lobe lift.

6   Record this figure for future reference, then reposition the piston at TDC on the compression stroke.

7   Move the dial indicator to the remaining number one cylinder pushrod and repeat the check. Be sure to record the results for each valve.

8   Repeat the check for the remaining valves. Since each piston must be at TDC on the compression stroke for this procedure, work from cylinder-to-cylinder, following the firing order sequence.

9   After the check is complete, compare the results to this Chapter's Specifications. If camshaft lobe lift is less than 0.005-inch for any of the lobes, cam lobe wear has occurred and a new camshaft should be installed.

14.4 Mount a dial indicator on the pushrod to check camshaft lobe lift (typical)

14.27 Remove the camshaft thrust plate bolts with a Torx bit and take the thrust plate off - note which end of the thrust plate is up so it can be installed correctly

14.28 As you're withdrawing the camshaft, support it near the block with both hands - be careful not to let the camshaft nick the bearings

REMOVAL

▶ **Refer to illustrations 14.27 and 14.28**

➡**Note: This procedure requires the engine be removed from the vehicle.**

10 Disconnect the negative cable from the battery.

11 Drain the cooling system and engine oil (see Chapter 1).

12 Remove the drivebelt (see Chapter 1).

13 Remove the engine (see Chapter 2F).

14 Remove the spark plug wires (see Chapter 1).

15 Remove the ignition coil pack and bracket (see Chapter 5).

16 Remove the alternator (see Chapter 5).

17 Position the number one piston to TDC on the compression stroke (see Section 3).

18 Mark the exact orientation of the camshaft position sensor in relation to the block.

19 The camshaft position sensor is installed in the same location as the oil pump drive gear on earlier models. Remove the camshaft position sensor and synchronizer assembly (see Chapter 6, Section 6).

20 Remove the valve covers (see Section 4).

21 Remove the intake manifold (see Section 7). The upper intake manifold can be left attached to the lower manifold.

22 Remove the rocker arms and pushrods (see Section 5).

23 Remove the valve lifters (see Section 13).

24 Remove the oil pan (see Section 15).

25 Remove the timing chain cover (see Section 11).

26 Remove the timing chain and sprockets (see Section 12).

27 Remove the camshaft thrust plate bolts with a Torx bit (see illustration) and remove the thrust plate from the block.

28 Carefully pull the camshaft out of the block, rotating it as you pull (see illustration). Don't let the camshaft lobes or journals nick the camshaft bearings.

INSPECTION

▶ **Refer to illustration 14.30**

29 After the camshaft has been removed from the engine, cleaned

14.30 The camshaft bearing journals are checked to pinpoint excessive wear and out-of-round conditions

with solvent and dried, inspect the bearing journals for uneven wear, pits and galling. If the journals are damaged, the bearing inserts in the engine are probably damaged as well. Both the camshaft and bearings will have to be replaced with new ones. Using a telescoping gauge, measure the inside diameter of each camshaft bearing and record the results (take two measurements, 90-degrees apart, at each bearing).

30 Measure the camshaft bearing journals with a micrometer to determine if they're excessively worn or out-of-round (see illustration). If they're out-of-round, the camshaft should be replaced with a new one. Subtract the bearing journal diameters from the corresponding bearing inside diameter measurements to obtain the oil clearance. If it's excessive, new bearings must be installed.

➡**Note: Camshaft bearing replacement requires special tools and expertise that place it outside the scope of the home mechanic. Take the block to an automotive machine shop to ensure that the job is done correctly.**

31 Check the camshaft lobes for heat discoloration, score marks, chopped areas, pitting, flaking and uneven wear. If the lobes are in good condition the camshaft can be reused.

32 Make sure the camshaft oil passages are clear and clean.

INSTALLATION

33 Lubricate the camshaft bearing journals and cam lobes with engine assembly lube.

34 Slide the camshaft into the engine. Support the cam near the block and be careful not to scrape or nick the bearings.

35 Coat both sides of the thrust plate with engine assembly lube, then install it so it covers the main oil gallery (see illustration 14.27). Tighten the bolts to the torque listed in this Chapter's Specifications.

36 The remainder of installation is the reverse of removal. On models with a camshaft position sensor, make sure to install it as described in Chapter 6, Section 6.

15 Oil pan and baffle - removal and installation

REMOVAL

◆ **Refer to illustrations 15.2 and 15.3**

→**Note: This procedure requires the engine be removed from the vehicle.**

1 Remove the engine from the vehicle (see Part F of this Chapter).

2 Remove the oil pan fasteners and remove the pan from the engine. Use a Torx bit to remove the bolt on each side of the crankshaft rear oil seal (see illustration).

3 If necessary, remove the baffle fasteners and remove the baffle (see illustration).

INSTALLATION

◆ **Refer to illustrations 15.9a, 15.9b, and 15.10**

✳✳ CAUTION:

Since two of the oil pan bolts are attached to the transmission, spacers are used between the oil pan and transmission. Failure to select the spacers correctly can cause oil pan damage or oil leaks when the pan is installed.

4 Using a gasket scraper, thoroughly clean all old gasket material from the oil pan and its mounting surface. Remove residue and oil film with a solvent such as acetone or lacquer thinner.

5 Temporarily place the pan on the engine and secure it with four nuts. Place a straightedge across the transmission mounting surface on the cylinder block and one of the mounting pads for the oil pan-to-transmission bolts.

6 Measure the gap between the mounting pad and straightedge with a feeler gauge.

7 Move the straightedge to the other mounting pad and measure its gap. Remove the nuts and detach the pan from the engine.

8 Select spacers for the mounting pads to compensate for the gap. Spacers are available in three thicknesses (see this Chapter's Specifications).

9 At the rear of the engine, apply a thin bead of RTV sealant to the

15.2 Use a Torx driver to remove the two bolts adjacent to the crankshaft rear oil seal

15.3 The oil baffle is secured to the main bearing caps

15.9a At the rear of the engine, apply thin beads of sealant to the outside edges of the gasket surface (A) and also to the crankshaft rear oil seal corners (B)

15.9b Apply beads of sealant to the corners of the front seal cover (arrows) and at the seams where the timing chain cover meets the engine block

outside edge of the gasket surface and another bead to the area around the crankshaft rear oil seal (see illustration). At the front of the engine, apply a bead of sealant to each of the engine block-to-timing-chain cover seams and to the corners of the front seal cover (see illustration).

10 Install a new pan gasket on the engine, followed by the oil pan. Install the pan fasteners and tighten them evenly to the torque listed in this Chapter's Specifications. The long screw next to the crankshaft rear oil seal passes through a boss on the pan, then through the pan flange and into the block (see illustration).

11 Install the spacers on the mounting pads before bolting the engine to the transmission.

15.10 The long Torx screw next to the crankshaft rear oil seal passes through a boss on the pan, then through the pan flange and into the block

16 Oil pump - removal and installation

REMOVAL

▶ **Refer to illustrations 16.3 and 16.4**

➡ **Note: This procedure requires the engine be removed from the vehicle.**

1   Remove the engine from the vehicle (see Part F of this Chapter).
2   Remove the oil pan (see Section 15).
3   Remove the oil pump mounting bolts and separate the pump from the engine (see illustration).
4   Withdraw the oil pump intermediate drive shaft (see illustration). If necessary, unbolt the inlet tube and screen from the pump.

16.3 Remove the oil pump mounting bolts and separate the pump from the engine

INSTALLATION

5   Fill one of the pump ports with clean engine oil and rotate the pump by hand to prime it.
6   If removed, install the oil pump pick-up tube on the pump, using a new gasket. Make sure the screen is clean and free of debris.
7   Insert the intermediate drive shaft into the engine, pointed end first.
8   Install the oil pump on the block. Install the oil pump bolts and tighten them to the torque listed in this Chapter's Specifications.
9   The remainder of installation is the reverse of removal.
10 Run the engine and make sure oil pressure comes up to normal quickly. If it doesn't, stop the engine and find out the cause. Severe engine damage can result from running an engine with insufficient oil pressure!

16.4 As you remove the intermediate driveshaft, note the different shapes of its ends and the location of the retainer ring on the shaft

17 Crankshaft oil seals replacement

FRONT SEAL - TIMING CHAIN COVER IN PLACE

1 Refer to Section 10 for this procedure.

FRONT SEAL - TIMING CHAIN COVER REMOVED

2 Support the timing chain cover on wooden blocks, then drive out the seal with a punch and hammer.

3 Check the seal bore in the timing chain cover for nicks or burrs.

4 Coat the seal lip and outer circumference with engine oil.

5 Position the new seal with its lip facing IN. Drive in the new seal with a seal driver. If a seal driver isn't available, use a large socket or piece of pipe the same diameter as the seal.

REAR SEAL

▶ **Refer to illustrations 17.10 and 17.15**

6 Remove the transmission (see Chapter 7).

7 Remove the clutch (if equipped) (see Chapter 8).

8 Remove the flywheel or driveplate (see Section 18).

9 Remove the engine rear plate.

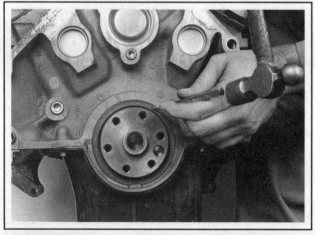

17.10 Be careful not to scratch the crankshaft when punching a hole in the seal

10 With a sharp awl or similar tool, punch two holes in the seal on opposite sides just above the point where the main bearing cap meets the cylinder block (see illustration).

11 Thread a sheet metal screw into each hole. Pry against the sheet metal screws with two large screwdrivers or small prybars to remove the seal.

➡**Note: If you need a fulcrum to pry against, use two small blocks of wood.**

❋❋ **CAUTION:**

Don't scratch or gouge the crankshaft seal surface.

12 Clean the oil seal bore in the block and main bearing cap. Check the seal bore and crankshaft sealing surface for nicks or burrs.

13 Apply a thin coat of clean engine oil to the outer diameter of the seal and to the contact surfaces of the seal and crankshaft.

14 Position the seal in the bore with its open end facing IN.

15 Drive the seal in with a seal installer until it is securely seated. Use a socket or piece of pipe the same diameter as the seal if a seal driver isn't available. As a last resort, you may be able to tap the seal into place with a hammer and drift, working around the circumference of the seal and driving it in a little at a time (see illustration).

16 After installation, the seal must be square with the crankshaft centerline and driven into the bore within the dimensions shown.

17.15 If a seal driver isn't available, carefully tap the seal into place with a hammer and drift

18 Flywheel/driveplate - removal and installation

18.3 Make alignment marks on the flywheel/driveplate and crankshaft

▶ **Refer to illustrations 18.3 and 18.4**

1 Raise the vehicle and support it securely on jackstands, then refer to Chapter 7 and remove the transmission. If it's leaking, now would be a very good time to replace the front pump seal/O-ring (automatic transmission only).

2 Remove the pressure plate and clutch disc (see Chapter 8) (manual transmission equipped vehicles). Now is a good time to check/replace the clutch components and pilot bearing.

3 Make alignment marks on the flywheel/driveplate and crankshaft to ensure correct alignment during reinstallation (see illustration).

4 Remove the bolts that secure the flywheel/driveplate to the crankshaft (see illustration). If the crankshaft turns, wedge a screwdriver

through the starter opening to jam the flywheel.

5   Remove the flywheel/driveplate from the crankshaft. Since the fly-wheel is fairly heavy, be sure to support it while removing the last bolt.

6   Clean the flywheel to remove grease and oil. Inspect the surface for cracks, rivet grooves, burned areas and score marks. Light scoring can be removed with emery cloth. Check for cracked and broken ring gear teeth. Lay the flywheel on a flat surface and use a straightedge to check for warpage.

7   Clean and inspect the mating surfaces of the flywheel/driveplate and the crankshaft. If the crankshaft rear seal is leaking, replace it before reinstalling the flywheel/driveplate.

8   Position the flywheel/driveplate against the crankshaft. Be sure to align the marks made during removal. Note that some engines have an alignment dowel or staggered bolt holes to ensure correct installa-tion. Before installing the bolts, apply thread locking compound to the threads.

9   Wedge a screwdriver through the starter motor opening to keep the flywheel/driveplate from turning as you tighten the bolts in a criss-cross pattern, to the torque listed in this Chapter's Specifications.

10 The remainder of installation is the reverse of the removal proce-dure.

18.4 Remove the mounting bolts and take the flywheel/ driveplate off the crankshaft - the manual transmission flywheel is heavy, so be sure to support it during removal

19 Engine mounts - check and replacement

Refer to Chapter 2A for theses procedures, but use the Specifica-tions listed in this Chapter.

Specifications

General

COIL PACK

Cylinder numbers (front-to-rear)
  Left (driver's) side   4-5-6
  Right side   1-2-3
Firing order   1-4-2-5-3-6

36071-2C-SPECS HAYNES

Cylinder numbering and coil terminal location

Camshaft

Lobe lift (intake and exhaust)	0.2720 inch
Endplay	
Standard	0.0008 to 0.004 inch
Service limit	0.009 inch
Journal diameter (standard)	
No. 1	1.951 to 1.952 inch
No. 2	1.937 to 1.938 inch
No. 3	1.922 to 1.923 inch
No. 4	1.907 to 1.908 inch
Bearing inside diameter (standard)	
No. 1	1.954 to 1.955 inch
No. 2	1.939 to 1.940 inch
No. 3	1.919 to 1.920 inch
No. 4	1.924 to 1.925 inch
Journal-to-bearing (oil) clearance	
Standard	0.001 to 0.0026 inch
Service limit	0.006 inch

Oil pan-to-transmission spacer thickness

Coded yellow	0.010 inch
Coded blue	0.020 inch
Coded pink	0.030 inch

Torque specifications   Ft-lbs (unless otherwise indicated)

➡**Note: One foot-pound (ft-lb) of torque is equivalent to 12 inch-pounds (in-lbs) of torque. Torque values below approximately 15 ft-lbs are expressed in inch-pounds, since most foot-pound torque wrenches are not accurate at these smaller values.**

Camshaft sprocket bolt	44 to 50
Camshaft thrust plate bolts	84 to 120 in-lbs
Crankshaft pulley bolt	
Step 1	30 to 37
Step 2	Tighten an additional 90-degrees
Cylinder head bolts (in sequence - see illustration 9.18)	
Step 1	22 to 26
Step 2	52 to 56
Step 3	Tighten an additional 90-degrees
Flywheel/driveplate bolts	
Step1	108 to 132 in-lbs
Step 2	50 to 55
Engine mount insulator-to-frame nuts	71 to 94
Engine mount insulator-to-bracket nuts	65 to 85
Engine mount bracket-to-block bolts	45 to 60
Exhaust manifold bolts	19
Exhaust pipe-to-manifold nuts	20
Lower intake manifold bolts/nuts	
Step 1	27 in-lbs
Step 2	89 in-lbs
Step 3	120 in-lbs
Step 4	144 in-lbs
Oil pump drive gear bolt	13 to 15
Oil pump pick-up tube-to-pump bolts	84 to 120 in-lbs
Oil pump-to-block bolts	13 to 15
Oil pan-to-block bolts	60 to 84 in-lbs
Timing chain cover bolts	13 to 15
Timing chain guide bolts	84 to 108 in-lbs
Timing chain tensioner bolts	84 to 108 in-lbs
Rocker arm shaft support bolts	
Step 1	24
Step 2	Tighten an additional 90-degrees
Valve cover bolts	60 to 72 in-lbs

Notes

2E

4.0L SOHC V6 ENGINE

Section

Reference to other Chapters

1 General information

This Part of Chapter 2 is devoted to in-vehicle repair procedures for the 4.0L SOHC (Single OverHead Camshaft) V6 engine as well as procedures such as timing chain(s) and sprocket(s) and oil pan (crankcase reinforcement section) removal which require removal of the engine from the vehicle. All information concerning engine removal and installation and engine block and cylinder head overhaul can be found in Part F of this Chapter.

This engine uses a jackshaft to drive the camshaft timing chains

and the oil pump. The left cylinder bank camshaft is driven by a chain at the front of the engine and the right cylinder bank camshaft is driven by a chain from the rear of the jackshaft. On four-wheel drive models, the balance shaft assembly is driven by a chain from the crankshaft sprocket.

The Specifications included in this Part of Chapter 2 apply only to the procedures contained in this Part. Part F of Chapter 2 contains the Specifications necessary for engine block rebuilding.

2 Repair operations possible with the engine in the vehicle

Many major repair operations can be accomplished without removing the engine from the vehicle.

Clean the engine compartment and the exterior of the engine with some type of degreaser before any work is done. It will make the job easier and help keep dirt out of the internal areas of the engine.

Depending on the components involved, it may be helpful to remove the hood to improve access to the engine as repairs are performed (refer to Chapter 11 if necessary). Cover the fenders to prevent damage to the paint. Special pads are available, but an old bedspread or blanket will also work.

If vacuum, exhaust, oil or coolant leaks develop, indicating a need for gasket or seal replacement, the repairs can generally be made with the engine in the vehicle. The intake and exhaust manifold gaskets and

cylinder head gaskets are all accessible with the engine in place.

Exterior engine components, such as the intake and exhaust manifolds, the water pump, the starter motor, the alternator and the fuel system components can be removed for repair with the engine in place.

The cylinder head(s) and the timing chain(s) removal procedures should be performed with the engine removed from the vehicle and bolted to an engine stand. Camshaft removal is also recommended with the engine out. Although professional mechanics perform these procedures in-vehicle, they are equipped with all the special tools and dealer tech information to make this possible. It is recommended for the home mechanic to remove the engine before attempting these repair procedures.

3 Top Dead Center (TDC) for number one piston - locating

▶ **Refer to illustration 3.5**

1 Top Dead Center (TDC) is the highest point in the cylinder that each piston reaches as it travels up-and-down during crankshaft rotation. Each piston reaches TDC on the compression stroke and again on the exhaust stroke, but TDC generally refers to piston position on the compression stroke.

2 Positioning the piston(s) at TDC is an essential part of many other repair procedures discussed in this manual.

3 Before beginning this procedure, be sure to place the transmission in Neutral and apply the parking brake or block the rear wheels. Remove the spark plugs (see Chapter 1). Disable the ignition system by disconnecting the wiring harness connector from the ignition coil pack (see Chapter 5).

4 In order to bring any piston to TDC, the crankshaft must be turned using one of the methods outlined below. When looking at the front of the engine, normal crankshaft rotation is clockwise.

   a) *The preferred method is to turn the crankshaft with a socket and ratchet attached to the bolt threaded into the front of the crankshaft.*

   b) *A remote starter switch, which may save some time, can also be used. Follow the instructions included with the switch. Once the piston is close to TDC, use a socket and ratchet as described in the previous paragraph.*

3.5 Timing marks - align the pointer on the crankshaft position sensor (A) with the mark in the crankshaft pulley (B)

   c) *If an assistant is available to turn the ignition switch to the Start position in short bursts, you can get the piston close to TDC without a remote starter switch. Make sure your assistant is out of the vehicle, away from the ignition switch, then use a socket and ratchet as described in Paragraph a) to complete the procedure.*

5   Install a compression gauge into the number one cylinder spark plug hole. Turn the crankshaft (see Step 4) until compression begins to register on the gauge, then turn it slowly until the TDC notch is aligned with the pointer on the crankshaft position sensor (see illustration).

➡Note: There are marks for TDC and for 10-degrees BTDC. Make sure you are on the TDC mark.

6   After the number one piston has been positioned at TDC on the compression stroke, TDC for any of the remaining pistons can be located by turning the crankshaft and following the firing order. Divide the crankshaft pulley into three equal sections with chalk marks at each point, each indicating 120-degrees of crankshaft rotation. Rotating the engine past TDC no. 1 to the next mark will place the engine at TDC for cylinder no. 4.

4   Valve covers - removal and installation

REMOVAL

1   Relieve the fuel system pressure (see Chapter 4), then disconnect the cable from the negative battery terminal (see Chapter 5).

2   Remove the upper intake manifold (see Section 6).

Right valve cover

▶ Refer to illustrations 4.3 and 4.10

3   Drain the cooling system (see Chapter 1), then disconnect the coolant hose brackets from the cylinder head and position the coolant hoses away from the valve cover (see illustration).

4   Disconnect the ignition wires from the valve cover (see Chapter 5).

5   Disconnect the DPF EGR electrical connector (see Chapter 6).

6   Remove the EGR pipe from the EGR valve and the exhaust manifold (see Chapter 6).

7   Disconnect the fuel line spring-lock coupling (see Chapter 4).

8   Remove the fuel line bracket bolt and separate the fuel supply line from the fuel rail (see Chapter 4).

9   Disconnect the fuel injector electrical connectors (see Chapter 4).

10 Remove the valve cover bolts (see illustration). Lift the valve cover off. Tap gently with a soft-face hammer if necessary to break the gasket seal.

Left valve cover

▶ Refer to illustration 4.17

11 Disconnect the electrical connector at the camshaft position sensor (see Chapter 6).

12 Disconnect the electrical connector from the ignition coil pack (see Chapter 5).

4.3 On the right side of the engine compartment, disconnect the coolant hose brackets from the cylinder head

13 Remove the cover from the main electrical connector at the valve cover, then push in the clip to detach the other side of the connector from the valve cover.

14 Disconnect the fuel injector electrical connectors (see Chapter 4).

15 Disconnect the accelerator cable (see Chapter 4).

16 Disconnect the ignition wires from the valve cover (see Chapter 5).

17 Remove the valve cover bolts (see illustration) and lift the valve cover off. Tap it gently with a soft-face hammer if necessary to break the gasket seal.

4.10 Location of the right-side valve cover mounting bolts

4.17 Location of the left-side valve cover mounting bolts

INSTALLATION

18 Clean the gasket surfaces on the intake manifold, cylinder head and valve cover. Use a shop rag and solvent to wipe off all residue and gasket material from the sealing surfaces.

19 Most valve cover gaskets are equipped with self-sticking sealant on the valve cover side. Pull the plastic film off the gasket and stick the gasket to the valve cover.

20 The remainder of installation is the reverse of the removal Steps. Tighten the valve cover bolts evenly, starting with the center bolts and working out, to the torque listed in this Chapter's Specifications.

5   Rocker arms and lash adjusters - removal, inspection and installation

➡Note: There are two methods of removing the rocker arms and lash adjusters on this model engine. The method recommended by the manufacturer accomplishes the removal of the rocker arms without the removal of the camshaft(s), using a special valve spring compressor made specifically for the SOHC engine. The valve spring compressor uses the camshaft as a pivot point and, with a ratchet or breaker bar attached, pushes down on the valve spring to release tension on the rocker arm. The alternative method requires the removal of the camshaft (see Section 11). Either method will achieve the same results, but it is much easier using the manufacturers special tool, if it can be located.

REMOVAL

▶ Refer to illustrations 5.2a, 5.2b and 5.3

1   Remove the valve cover(s) (see Section 4).
2   Install the special valve spring compressor and compress the spring just enough to remove the rocker arm (see illustrations).

✳ CAUTION:

Camshaft rocker arms and hydraulic lash adjusters MUST be reinstalled in the same location they were removed from. Label and store all components to avoid confusion during reassembly.

3   Remove the hydraulic lash adjuster (see illustration). If there are many miles on the vehicle, the adjusters may have become varnished and difficult to remove. Apply a little penetrating oil around the lash adjuster to help loosen the varnish.

5.2a The special valve spring compressor hooks under the camshaft at (A), pushes on the valve spring retainer at (B), and is operated by a ratchet or breaker bar placed at (C)

INSPECTION

▶ Refer to illustrations 5.4 and 5.6

4   Inspect each adjuster carefully for signs of wear or damage (see illustration). Since the lash adjusters can become clogged as mileage accumulates, we recommend replacing them if you're concerned about their condition or if the engine is exhibiting valve noise.

5.2b Compress the valve spring just enough to allow the rocker arm to be removed

5.3 Remove the lash adjuster and store it and the rocker arm in organized manner so the components will be returned to their original locations

5.4 Inspect the lash adjuster for signs of excessive wear or damage, such as pitting, scoring or signs of overheating (bluing or discoloration) - the areas of wear are the rocker arm pivot point (1) and the side surfaces where the lifter body contacts the cylinder head bore (2)

5.6 Check the rocker arm roller, the valve stem contact point and lash adjuster contact point (arrows)

5   A thin wire or paper clip can be placed in the oil hole to move the plunger and make sure it's not stuck.

➡**Note: The lash adjuster must have no more than 1.5 mm of total plunger travel. It's recommended that if replacement of any of the adjusters is necessary, that the entire set be replaced. This will avoid the need to repeat the repair procedure as the others require replacement in the future.**

6   Inspect the rocker arms for signs of wear or damage (see illustration).

INSTALLATION

7   Before installing the lash adjusters, bleed them of air. Stand the adjusters upright in a container of oil. Use a thin wire or paper clip to work the plunger up and down. This "primes" the adjuster and removes the air. Leave the adjusters in the oil until ready to install.

8   Lubricate the valve stem tip, rocker arm, and lash adjuster bore with clean engine oil.

9   Install the lash adjusters and, with the valve spring depressed as in Step 2, install each rocker arm.

10 The remainder of installation is the reverse of the removal procedure.

11 When starting the engine after replacing the adjusters, there will normally be some noise until all the air is bled from the lash adjusters. After the engine is warmed-up, raise the speed from idle to 3,000 rpm for one minute. Stop the engine and let it cool down. All of the noise should be gone when it is restarted.

6   Intake manifold - removal and installation

REMOVAL

▶ **Refer to illustrations 6.4 and 6.9**

1   Disconnect the cable from the negative battery terminal (see Chapter 5).

2   Remove the intake air duct from the air filter housing (see Chapter 4).

3   Disconnect the accelerator cable and the cruise control cable from the throttle valve (see Chapter 4). Remove the harness clips and position the cables off to the side. On 2006 and later models, remove the main electrical connector from the engine side of the PCM, remove the main harness support bolt, then set the harness aside. On 2011 models, this Step cannot be done until after Step 13 is completed.

4   Disconnect the vacuum hoses from the upper intake manifold (see illustration). Mark each hose with tape to insure correct reassembly.

5   Disconnect the IAC valve, the TPS and any other electrical connectors that may interfere with manifold removal.

6   Disconnect the EGR valve vacuum hose and the EVAP canister purge solenoid vacuum hose (see Chapter 6).

6.4 Disconnect the vacuum hoses from the intake manifold

7   Disconnect the EGR pipe from the intake manifold and the exhaust manifold (see Chapter 6).

6.9 Location of the intake manifold mounting bolts (two bolts hidden from view - 8 bolts total)

6.18 When replacing the intake manifold, install new O-ring gaskets around each runner

2010 and earlier models

8 Remove the ignition wires from the coil pack and the spark plugs (see Chapter 5).

9 Remove the intake manifold mounting bolts (see illustration).

10 Lift the intake manifold from the engine compartment.

2011 models

11 Remove the EGR vacuum regulator solenoid (see Chapter 6).

12 Disconnect the power brake booster vacuum hose at the intake manifold (see Chapter 9, if necessary).

13 Disconnect the spark plug wires and remove the ignition coil (see Chapter 5). Perform Step 3.

14 Disconnect the knock sensor electrical connector.

15 Remove the intake manifold mounting bolts. Lift up the manifold to access and remove the PCV fitting bolts from the manifold.

16 Remove the intake manifold from the engine.

INSTALLATION

▶ **Refer to illustration 6.18**

17 Clean away all traces of old gasket material. Remove oil and dirt with a cloth and solvent, such as lacquer thinner.

18 Install new O-ring gaskets around each of the six intake runners (see illustration).

➡**Note: No sealant is required.**

19 Install the manifold to the cylinder heads, making sure the bolt holes are aligned. Install the bolts and tighten them finger-tight.

➡**Note: Do not move the manifold back and forth, or the O-ring seals could move out of position, causing vacuum leaks.**

20 Tighten the bolts to the torque listed in this Chapter's Specifications, starting with the center bolts and working towards the ends.

21 The remainder of installation is the reverse of the removal steps.

22 Run the engine and check for oil, coolant and vacuum leaks.

7   Exhaust manifolds - removal and installation

REMOVAL

▶ **Refer to illustrations 7.5a, 7.5b and 7.5c**

1 Disconnect the cable from the negative battery terminal (see Chapter 5).

2 Disconnect the EGR pipe from the right manifold and the EGR valve (see Chapter 6).

3 Raise the vehicle and support it on jackstands.

4 Detach the exhaust pipe from the manifold(s). For access to the exhaust pipe nuts, it may be necessary to raise the vehicle and support it securely on jackstands.

5 Unbolt the exhaust manifold(s) from the cylinder head and remove it (see illustrations).

➡**Note: On the left side manifold, remove the nut holding the engine oil dipstick tube (see illustration).**

7.5a Location of the mounting nuts on the right side exhaust manifold

7.5b Location of the mounting nuts on the left side exhaust manifold

7.5c Remove the bolt and the engine oil dipstick tube

INSTALLATION

♦ Refer to illustration 7.7

6   Using a scraper, thoroughly clean the mating surfaces on the cylinder head, manifold and exhaust pipe. Remove residue with a solvent such as acetone or lacquer thinner.

7   Check that the mating surfaces are perfectly flat and not damaged in any way. Warped or damaged manifolds may require machining. Install the new gasket to the cylinder head studs and place the manifold on the cylinder head (see illustration). Tighten the bolts evenly to the torque listed in this Chapter's Specifications.

8   Connect the exhaust pipe to the manifold and tighten the nuts evenly to the torque listed in this Chapter's Specifications.

9   The remainder of installation is the reverse of the removal steps.

10 Run the engine and check for exhaust leaks.

7.7 Place the new gasket over the studs on the cylinder head

8   Cylinder heads - removal and installation

✳✳ CAUTION:

The engine must be completely cool when the heads are removed. Failure to allow the engine to cool off could result in head warpage.

➡Note 1: This is a difficult procedure and it is recommended the engine be removed from the vehicle and placed on an engine stand. However, it is possible to remove the cylinder heads in-vehicle but this method will require all the necessary special tools and an expert skill level in automotive repairs.

➡Note 2: The rocker arms and valve lash adjusters must be removed before any repair procedures on the cylinder heads, timing chains and jackshaft chains. Refer to Section 5 and remove all the rocker arms and valve lash adjusters.

REMOVAL

♦ Refer to illustration 8.7

1   Disconnect the cable from the negative battery terminal (see Chapter 5).

2   Drain the cooling system (see Chapter 1).

3   Remove the engine from the vehicle and mount it on an engine stand (see Chapter 2F).

4   Remove the intake manifold (see Section 6).

5   Label and disconnect the electrical connectors from the fuel injectors (see Chapter 4).

6   Remove the exhaust manifolds (see Section 7).

7   Remove the drivebelt (see Chapter 1) and the drivebelt tensioner (see illustration).

8   Remove the rocker arms and valve lash adjusters (see Section 5).

8.7 Remove the drivebelt tensioner mounting bolt

Right cylinder head

♦ **Refer to illustration 8.12**

9   Remove the alternator and the lower alternator mounting bracket (see Chapter 5).

10   Remove the upper radiator hose and the coolant bypass hose (see Chapter 3).

11   Disconnect the engine coolant temperature (ECT) sensor (see Chapter 6).

12   Remove the accessory bracket (see illustration).

13   Remove the thermostat housing (see Chapter 3).

14   Remove the bolts that retain the engine wiring harness to the engine brackets.

Left cylinder head

♦ **Refer to illustrations 8.17, 8.18, 8.19 and 8.20**

15   Disconnect the radio capacitor from the side of the ignition coil pack.

16   Remove the ignition coil assembly (see Chapter 5).

17   Remove the accessory bracket mounting bolts and position it off to the side (see illustration).

8.18   Remove the hydraulic chain tensioner - left side shown, right side is located at the rear of the cylinder head near the timing chain

8.12   Remove the bolts from the accessory bracket and set it aside

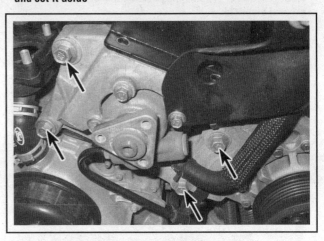

8.17   Location of the accessory bracket mounting bolts

➡Note: The accessory bracket must be removed and positioned off to the side with the power steering pump lines and air conditioning compressor lines attached. It will be necessary to remove the coil bracket bolts and carefully move the entire accessory bracket assembly toward the front of the vehicle.

8.19   The chain will hold the camshaft and sprocket in position while you remove the sprocket bolt (A) - then remove the upper cassette bolt (B)

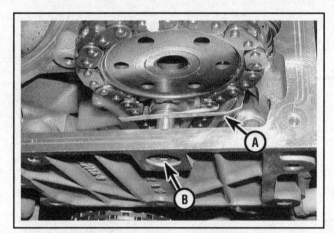

8.20 Slip a heavy-duty rubber band (A) over the chain, just below the sprocket, then remove the cassette bolt (B) - slip the sprocket out of the chain and the rubber band will prevent the slack from falling

18 Remove the hydraulic chain tensioner (see illustration).

19 Remove the bolt from the camshaft sprocket, then remove the Torx bolt below it in the head, which secures the camshaft chain "cassette" to the head (see illustration).

20 Remove the bolt holding the chain cassette to the head and pull up on the chain while slipping the sprocket out. Keep the slack out of the chain (to prevent dropping it below) and tie it to the cassette with a large rubber band (see illustration).

Both cylinder heads

21 Repeat Steps 17 through 20 for the right-hand cylinder head. If you are working in-vehicle, the sprocket is at the rear of the right cylinder head, and a special, offset tool is used to remove the sprocket bolt, but it is possible (though difficult) to remove it with a conventional wrench in-vehicle. Tie the chain for the rear sprocket up with a rubber band as in Step 20.

✳✳ CAUTION:

The sprocket bolt for the right cylinder head is a left-hand thread.

22 Remove the cylinder head bolts, following the reverse of the tightening sequence (see illustration 8.31). Loosen the bolts in sequence 1/4-turn at a time.

➡**Note: There are two 8 mm external Torx bolts (one on each side of the chain opening in the head) and eight 12 mm internal Torx bolts.**

If the head is to be completely overhauled, refer to Section 11 for removal of the camshafts.

23 Use a pry bar at the corners of the head-to-block mating surface to break the gasket seal. Do not pry between the cylinder head and engine block in the gasket sealing area.

24 Lift the cylinder head(s) off the engine. If resistance is felt, place a wood block against the end and strike the wood block with a hammer. Store the cylinder heads on wood blocks to prevent damage to the gasket sealing surfaces.

25 Remove the old cylinder head gasket(s). Before removing, note which gasket goes on which side, they are different and cannot be interchanged.

26 Cylinder head disassembly and inspection procedures are covered in detail in Chapter 2, Part F.

8.30 Make sure the cylinder head gaskets are installed in the correct location - they are not interchangeable

INSTALLATION

▶ **Refer to illustrations 8.30, 8.31, 8.35, 8.36 and 8.38**

27 The mating surfaces of the cylinder heads and block must be perfectly clean when the heads are installed. Use a gasket scraper to remove all traces of carbon and old gasket material, then clean the mating surfaces with lacquer thinner or acetone. If there's oil on the mating surfaces when the cylinder heads are installed, the gaskets may not seal correctly and leaks may develop. When working on the engine block, cover the open areas of the engine with shop rags to keep debris out during repair and reassembly. Use a vacuum cleaner to remove any debris that falls into the cylinders.

28 Check the engine block and cylinder head mating surfaces for nicks, deep scratches and other damage.

29 Use a tap of the correct size to chase the threads in the cylinder head bolt holes. Dirt, corrosion, sealant and damaged threads will affect torque readings.

30 Make sure the new gaskets are on the correct cylinder banks, and located on the dowels in the block. They are not interchangeable (see illustration).

31 Carefully position the cylinder heads on the engine block without disturbing the gaskets. Install new cylinder head bolts and following the recommended sequence (see illustration), tighten the bolts to the torque listed in this Chapter's Specifications. All bolts are tightened in

8.31 Cylinder head bolt tightening sequence - bolts (A) are 8 mm bolts, the rest are 12 mm bolts

8.35 Clamp the special crankshaft holding tool around the damper as shown, then tighten the bolt - this locks the crankshaft at TDC

8.36 Install the camshaft sprocket holding tool to the cylinder head inserting the pins on the aligning tool (A) into the holes in the sprocket - tighten the holder bolts (B), then tighten the sprocket bolt (C)

the first Step, then only the eight 12 mm bolts are tightened in Steps 2 and 3. Mark a stripe on each of the 12 mm head bolts to help keep track of the bolts that have been tightened the additional 90-degrees.

➡Note: The method used for the head bolt tightening procedure is referred to as "torque-angle" or "torque-to-yield" method. A special torque angle gauge (available at most auto parts stores) is available to attach to a breaker bar and socket for better accuracy during the tightening procedure.

32 Pull up the slack chain and insert the camshaft sprocket, align it with the camshaft and install the sprocket bolt.

❋❋ CAUTION:

Do not tighten the sprocket bolt at this time; the sprocket must rotate freely on the camshaft! Do this on both cylinder heads and install the bolts that hold the chain cassettes to the heads.

33 Install the camshaft chain tensioning tool into the chain tensioner location on the left cylinder head.

34 Make sure the engine is located at the correct position for cylinder number 1 at TDC (see Section 3). Rotate the engine clockwise to obtain number 1 TDC if necessary.

35 Clamp the special crankshaft holding tool over the crankshaft damper (flush with the rear edge of the damper) and with the straight end against the bottom of the block (see illustration). Tighten the bolt on the holding tool.

36 Install the camshaft holding tool on the rear of the left camshaft. Rotate the camshaft with a wrench to align the off-center slot on the rear of the camshaft with the tool. The slot is positioned down when aligned with the tool. Tighten the tool bolts securely. Install the camshaft sprocket holding tool on the left camshaft sprocket (see illustration). Tighten the holding tool bolts to hold the camshaft sprocket stationary, then tighten the camshaft sprocket bolt to the torque listed in this Chapter's Specifications.

37 Remove the tensioning tool from the left cylinder head and install the hydraulic tensioner. Install the tensioning tool into the right cylinder head tensioner location. Remove the camshaft and camshaft sprocket holding tools and the crankshaft holding tool.

38 Install the camshaft holding tool onto the front of the right cam-

8.38 Camshaft positioning tool at the front of the right camshaft - align the tool's projection with the slot in the end of the camshaft

shaft (see illustration). Rotate the camshaft to align the slots in the end of the camshaft with the tool. Tighten the holding tool bolts securely. Install the camshaft sprocket holding tool onto the rear of the camshaft (see illustration 8.35) and tighten the sprocket bolt to the torque listed in this Chapter's Specifications.

❋❋ CAUTION:

The right camshaft sprocket bolt is left-hand thread.

39 Remove the chain tensioning tool and install the hydraulic tensioner. Remove the camshaft and crankshaft holding tools.

40 Install the rocker arms and hydraulic valve lash adjusters (see Section 5).

41 The remaining installation steps are the reverse of removal.

42 Change the engine oil and filter (Chapter 1), then start the engine and check carefully for oil and coolant leaks.

9 Crankshaft pulley and front oil seal - removal and installation

REMOVAL

▶ **Refer to illustrations 9.7, 9.8 and 9.9**

1 Disconnect the cable from the negative battery terminal (see Chapter 5).

2 Remove the drivebelt (see Chapter 1).

3 Remove the engine cooling fan/shroud assembly (see Chapter 3).

4 Raise the vehicle and secure it on jackstands.

5 Remove the power steering fluid cooler mounting bolts and position the assembly to the side without disconnecting the fluid lines.

6 Remove the crankshaft pulley bolt.

7 Use a breaker bar and socket to remove the crankshaft pulley center bolt (see illustration). Discard the bolt and obtain a new one for installation.

➡**Note: It will be necessary to lock the pulley in position using a strap or chain wrench. Be sure to wrap a shop rag or a section of old drive belt around the pulley before installing the special tool.**

8 Using a bolt-type puller, pull the pulley from the crankshaft (see illustration).

➡**Note: Because the pulley is recessed, an adapter may be needed between the puller bolt and the crankshaft.**

9 Use a seal puller to remove the crankshaft front oil seal (see illustration). A screwdriver may be used instead, if the tip is wrapped with tape to avoid scratching the crankshaft.

10 Clean the seal bore and check it for nicks or gouges. Also examine the area of the hub that rides in the seal for signs of abnormal wear or scoring. For many popular engines, a repair sleeve is available to restore a smooth finish to the sealing surface. Check with your auto parts store.

INSTALLATION

▶ **Refer to illustration 9.11**

11 Coat the lip of the new seal with clean engine oil and drive it into the bore with a socket or section of pipe slightly smaller in diameter than the seal (see illustration). The open side of the seal faces into the engine.

9.8 Remove the pulley with a puller that bolts to the pulley hub; an adapter may be needed between the puller bolt and the crankshaft snout to prevent damaging the threads in the end of the crankshaft

9.7 To remove the crankshaft pulley, remove the center bolt

9.9 Use a seal puller to remove the old crankshaft seal, taking care not to damage the crankshaft or the seal bore in the cover

9.11 Drive the new seal in with a large socket or short section of appropriate-size pipe

12 Using clean engine oil, lubricate the sealing surface of the hub. Install the crankshaft pulley/damper with a special installation tool, available at most auto parts stores. Do not use a hammer to install the pulley/damper. Install a new center bolt and tighten it to the torque listed in this Chapter's Specifications.

➡Note: You must use a new pulley bolt (and washer, on 2011 models).

13 Apply silicone sealant to the Woodruff key slot.
14 The remainder of the installation is the reverse of the removal procedure.

10 Timing chain and sprockets - inspection, removal and installation

➡Note 1: This is a difficult procedure, involving special tools and the removal of the engine from the vehicle. Read through the entire Section and obtain the necessary tools before beginning the procedure.

➡Note 2: The rocker arms and valve lash adjusters must be removed before any repair procedures on the cylinder heads, timing chains and jackshaft chains. Refer to Section 5 and remove all the rocker arms and valve lash adjusters.

REMOVAL

▶ Refer to illustrations 10.4, 10.5, 10.6, 10.7, 10.8, 10.9, 10.10a and 10.10b

❊❊ CAUTION:

The timing system is complex. Severe engine damage will occur if you make any mistakes. Do not attempt this procedure unless you are highly experienced with this type of repair. If you are at all unsure of your abilities, consult an expert. Double-check all your work and be sure everything is correct before you attempt to start the engine.

1 Refer to Chapter 2 Part F and remove the engine from the vehicle. The balance of this procedure is written assuming you have the engine out and mounted on an engine stand.

2 Remove the rocker arms and the valve lash adjusters (see Section 5).
3 Refer to Section 12 and remove the lower oil pan cover, oil pump pickup tube and the crankcase reinforcement section.
4 Remove the bolts/nuts and the front cover from the engine block (see illustration).
5 This engine uses a jackshaft (in place of a camshaft on a conventional pushrod engine) to drive the camshaft timing chains and the oil pump (see illustration). The left cylinder bank camshaft is driven by a chain at the front of the engine and the right cylinder bank camshaft is driven by a chain from the rear of the jackshaft. On four-wheel drive models, the balance shaft assembly is driven by a chain from the crankshaft sprocket.
6 Remove the bolts retaining the jackshaft chain tensioner and the jackshaft chain guide (see illustration).

10.4 Remove the engine front cover bolts - the water pump may remain attached to the cover, if desired

10.5 Timing chain components - 2WD model show (4WD models are equipped with a balance shaft chain driven by the crankshaft sprocket)

1 Jackshaft sprocket
2 Jackshaft chain
3 Chain/cassette for left camshaft
4 Crankshaft sprocket

10.6 Remove the bolts retaining the jackshaft chain tensioner (A) and the chain guide (B)

10.7 Remove the jackshaft sprocket bolt, then remove the sprocket and chain

10.8 Remove the bolt and remove the left camshaft chain cassette and chain

10.9 Remove the rear jackshaft plug by tapping it sideways, then use pliers to extract it

7 Remove the bolt in the center of the jackshaft sprocket, then remove the sprocket with the jackshaft chain (see illustration).

8 If not previously removed, remove the top cassette bolt (see illustration 8.19), the camshaft sprocket (see Section 8), and the lower cassette-to-block bolt. Then remove the cassette, chain and jackshaft sprocket (see illustration).

9 To remove the right camshaft chain, remove the large plug covering the rear of the jackshaft (see illustration).

➡Note: Obtain a new plug for reassembly, the plug is not reusable.

10 Remove the Torx bolt and spacer through the opening, then remove the cassette bolt and the chain and cassette (see illustrations).

INSTALLATION

⬧ **Refer to illustration 10.16**

✳✳ CAUTION:

Before starting the engine, carefully rotate the crankshaft by hand through at least two full revolutions (use a socket and breaker bar on the crankshaft pulley center bolt). If you feel any resistance, STOP! There is something wrong - most likely, valves are contacting the pistons. You must find the problem before proceeding. Check your work and see if any updated repair information is available.

11 If the crankshaft has been rotated during this procedure, make sure the number one piston is at the top of its stroke (TDC) (see Section 3). The crankshaft keyway should point straight up.

12 Install the right camshaft timing chain cassette to the block. Secure the excess chain at the top of the cassette with a rubber band (see illustration 8.20). Install the rear jackshaft sprocket bolt and tighten it to the torque listed in this Chapter's Specifications. Install the rear jackshaft plug.

13 Install the left camshaft chain and cassette and tighten the lower bolt to the torque listed in this Chapter's Specifications.

14 Drape the jackshaft chain over the jackshaft sprocket and engage the chain onto the crankshaft sprocket. Install the jackshaft sprocket onto the jackshaft and tighten the jackshaft sprocket bolt to the torque listed in this Chapter's Specifications.

15 Install the jackshaft chain guide and tensioner (see illustration 10.6). Tighten the bolts to the torque listed in this Chapter's Specifications.

16 Clean the front surface of the engine block and front cover with lacquer thinner and install a new gasket (see illustration). Install the front cover, tightening the bolts to the torque listed in this Chapter's Specifications.

17 The remainder of installation is the reverse of the removal Steps. The timing procedure for each individual camshaft, using the special tools is described in Section 9.

18 Run the engine and check for oil or coolant leaks.

10.10a Remove this bolt and spacer . . .

10.10b . . . then remove this bolt and the chain and cassette

10.16 Install the new front cover gasket

11 Camshafts - removal, inspection and installation

11.7a Inspect the bearing surfaces and camshaft lobes for excessive wear or damage

11.7b Also inspect the bearing surface of each camshaft cap

11.9a Lay a strip of Plastigage on each camshaft journal

REMOVAL

→Note: This is a difficult procedure, involving special tools and the removal of the engine from the vehicle. This procedure covers the removal of the camshafts and the camshaft bearing caps. It will be necessary to refer to Section 8 for the camshaft timing procedure and the photos of the special tools and their placement on the cylinder heads. Read the entire Section and obtain the necessary tools before beginning the procedure.

1   Remove the valve covers (see Section 4).

2   Follow the procedure in Section 5 for removing the rocker arms and valve lash adjusters and see Section 8 for the procedure to disconnect the camshaft sprockets and timing chains from the camshafts.

3   Mount a dial indicator to the front of the cylinder head and measure the camshaft endplay of each camshaft. If the clearance is greater than the value listed in this Chapter's Specifications, replace the camshaft and/or the cylinder head.

4   Loosen the bearing cap bolts in 1/4-turn increments, following the reverse sequence of the tightening procedure (see illustration 11.13), until they can be removed by hand.

5   Remove the bearing caps and lift the camshaft off the cylinder head. Don't mix up the camshafts or any of the components. They must all go back to their original locations, and on the same cylinder head they were removed from.

6   Repeat this procedure for removal of the other camshaft.

INSPECTION

♦ **Refer to illustrations 11.7a, 11.7b, 11.9a and 11.9b**

7   Visually examine the cam lobes and bearing journals for score marks, pitting, galling and evidence of overheating (blue, discolored areas). Look for flaking of the hardened surface of each lobe (see illustrations).

8   Using a micrometer, measure the diameter of each camshaft journal and the lift of each camshaft lobe (see Chapter 2, Part F). Compare your measurements with the Specifications listed at the front of this Chapter, and if the diameter of any one of these is less than specified, replace the camshaft.

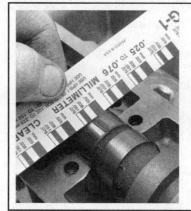

11.9b Compare the width of the crushed Plastigage to the scale on the envelope to determine the oil clearance

11.13 Camshaft bearing cap tightening sequence

9   Check the oil clearance for each camshaft bearing as follows:

a) Clean the bearing surfaces and the camshaft journals with lacquer thinner or acetone.

b) Carefully lay the camshaft(s) in place in the cylinder head. Don't install the rocker arms or lash adjusters and don't use any lubrication.

c) *Lay a strip of Plastigage on each journal (see illustration).*
d) *Install the camshaft caps.*
e) *Tighten the caps, a little at a time, to the torque listed in this Chapter's Specifications.*

➡**Note: Don't turn the camshaft while the Plastigage is in place.**

f) *Remove the bolts and detach the caps.*
g) *Compare the width of the crushed Plastigage (at its widest point) to the scale on the Plastigage envelope (see illustration).*
h) *If the clearance is greater than specified, and the diameter of any journal is less than specified, replace the camshaft. If the journal diameters are within specifications but the oil clearance is too great, the cylinder head is worn and must be replaced.*

10 Scrape off the Plastigage with your fingernail or the edge of a credit card - don't scratch or nick the journals or bearing surfaces.

INSTALLATION

▶ **Refer to illustration 11.13**

11 If the lash adjusters and/or rocker arms have been removed, install them in their original locations (see Section 5).
12 Apply moly-based engine assembly lubricant to the camshaft lobes and bearing journals, then install the camshaft(s).
13 Install the camshaft caps in the correct locations, and following the correct bolt tightening sequence (see illustration), tighten the bolts to the torque listed in this Chapter's Specifications.
14 Refer to Section 8 for the timing procedure for each camshaft, using the special tools.
15 The remainder of installation is the reverse of the removal procedure.

12 Oil pan - removal and installation

➡**Note: The complete oil pan assembly is comprised of two sections. The lower section is a sheet metal oil pan, while the upper section is a large aluminum casting that serves as a structural reinforcement for the lower part of the crankcase. The lower oil pan and the oil pump pick-up/screen may be removed with the engine in-vehicle, but the engine must be removed from the vehicle to remove the reinforcement section for access to the oil pump and crankshaft.**

REMOVAL

▶ **Refer to illustrations 12.2 and 12.5**

1 Remove the engine from the vehicle (see Part F of this Chapter).
2 Remove the lower oil pan fasteners (see illustration) and remove the sheet metal oil pan.
3 Remove the two bolts and the oil pump screen cover and tube.
4 To remove the reinforcement section, begin by removing the eight bolts in the center of the section (see illustration 12.16).
5 Remove the two rear reinforcement section-to-block bolts (see illustration), then the outside bolts on each side.
6 Carefully remove the reinforcement section from the block.

✳✳ **CAUTION:**

Do not pry between the reinforcement section and the block on any gasket sealing surface.

INSTALLATION

▶ **Refer to illustrations 12.8, 12.9a, 12.9b and 12.16**

✳✳ **CAUTION:**

Since two of the oil pan bolts are attached to the transmission, spacers are used between the oil pan and transmission. Failure to check the clearance and select the shims correctly can cause oil pan damage or oil leaks when the pan is installed. The engine must be removed from the engine stand for this check.

7 Using a gasket scraper, thoroughly clean all old gasket material from the engine block, reinforcement section and oil pan. Remove residue and oil film with a solvent such as acetone or lacquer thinner.
8 The eight center bolts of the reinforcement section are threaded

12.2 Lower oil pan bolts

12.5 Remove the two rearmost bolts

12.8 Turn the threaded reinforcement section inserts out (counterclockwise) several turns each with an Allen wrench to ensure they do not contact the main cap bolt head when the section is initially installed

12.9a Apply RTV sealant to the four places indicated on the front cover . . .

into the main cap bolt heads. Threaded inserts are installed in the reinforcement section to create support for the bolts without stressing the reinforcement section. Use an Allen wrench to back the inserts out until they are in the "index" position before installing the reinforcement section to the engine block (see illustration).

9   Apply RTV sealant to the rear main cap and the bottom of the front cover (see illustrations). On the front cover, there are four spots to seal, where the cover meets the block, and on either side of the front crankshaft seal, where the rubber end gasket will meet the side gaskets.

10 Position the new gaskets on the engine block. Install the two side gaskets, then the rubber end seals, making sure that the ends of the side gaskets fit into the notches on the rubber end seals. Add a small amount of RTV sealant over the joints between the side gaskets and end seals. Install the reinforcement section.

11 Install, but do not tighten, the reinforcement section side rail bolts, including the two rear bolts.

12 Place a straightedge across the transmission mounting surface on the cylinder block and one of the mounting pads for the reinforcement section-to-transmission bolts. Measure the clearance between the mounting pad and straightedge with a feeler gauge.

13 Move the straightedge to the other mounting pad and measure the clearance. The clearance should not exceed 0.010-inch (0.25 mm). If the reinforcement section protrudes over the rear edge of the engine block, tap it toward the front of the engine with a soft-faced hammer until it's flush (it may protrude a maximum of 0.002-inch [0.05 mm]). If the clearance is excessive, tap it to the rear of the engine.

14 Tighten the perimeter bolts/nuts, including the two rear lower block cradle-to-transmission bolts and the two rear lower block cradle-to-engine block bolts, to the torque listed in this Chapter's Specifications.

15 Tighten the reinforcement section threaded inserts to the torque listed in this Chapter's Specifications.

16 Install the interior reinforcement section bolts (lower cradle block bolts), using new seals on the two front bolts (the front two bolts are distinguished by their silver color). Tighten them in sequence to the torque listed in this Chapter's Specifications (see illustration).

17 Repeat the reinforcement section-to-engine block clearance check (see Step 13).

18 Install the oil pump pickup tube, place a new oil pan gasket in position and install the oil pan and bolts. Tighten the bolts to the torque listed in this Chapter's Specifications.

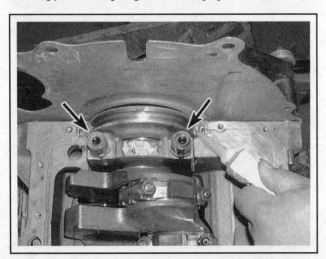

12.9b . . . and the two places indicated on the rear main cap

12.16 Crankcase reinforcement section bolt tightening sequence

13 Oil pump - removal and installation

REMOVAL

▶ **Refer to illustration 13.2**

1 Remove the lower and upper oil pan sections (see Section 12).

➡**Note: This involves removing the engine from the vehicle (see Part F of this Chapter).**

2 Remove the oil pump bolts and take the pump off the engine (see illustration).

3 Pull the oil pump intermediate driveshaft out of the engine.

INSTALLATION

▶ **Refer to illustration 13.5**

4 Fill one of the pump ports with clean engine oil and rotate the

13.2 Remove the two oil pump bolts

pump by hand to prime it.

5 Insert the intermediate drive shaft into the engine, pointed end first, until it engages the oil pump drive (see illustration). Make sure the travel limit clip is in place, and closer to the camshaft position sensor end. It fits tightly on a non-machined section of the driveshaft.

6 Install the oil pump on the block, using a new gasket. Make sure the pump engages the driveshaft. Install the oil pump bolts and tighten to the torque listed in this Chapter's Specifications.

7 The remainder of installation is the reverse of removal.

8 Run the engine and make sure oil pressure comes up to normal quickly. If it doesn't, stop the engine and find out the cause. Severe engine damage can result from running an engine with insufficient oil pressure!

13.5 Insert the oil pump driveshaft into the pump, then guide the driveshaft into the engine, making sure the travel limit clip is in place

14 Flywheel/driveplate - removal and installation

REMOVAL

1 Raise the vehicle and support it securely on jackstands, then refer to Chapter 7 and remove the transmission. If it's leaking, now would be a very good time to replace the front pump seal/O-ring (automatic transmission only).

2 Remove the pressure plate and clutch disc (see Chapter 8) (manual transmission equipped vehicles). Now is a good time to check/replace the clutch components and pilot bearing.

3 Use a center punch or paint to make alignment marks on the flywheel/driveplate and crankshaft to ensure correct alignment during reinstallation.

4 Remove the bolts that secure the flywheel/driveplate to the crankshaft. If the crankshaft turns, wedge a screwdriver in the ring gear teeth to jam the flywheel.

5 Remove the flywheel/driveplate from the crankshaft. Since the flywheel is fairly heavy, be sure to support it while removing the last

bolt. Automatic transmission equipped vehicles have a spacer between the crankshaft and the driveplate.

INSTALLATION

▶ **Refer to illustration 14.9a and 14.9b**

6 Clean the flywheel to remove grease and oil. Inspect the surface for cracks, rivet grooves, burned areas and score marks. Light scoring can be removed with emery cloth. Check for cracked and broken ring gear teeth. Lay the flywheel on a flat surface and use a straightedge to check for warpage.

7 Clean and inspect the mating surfaces of the flywheel/driveplate and the crankshaft. If the crankshaft rear seal is leaking, replace it before reinstalling the flywheel/driveplate.

8 Position the flywheel/driveplate against the crankshaft. Be sure to align the marks made during removal. Note that some engines have an alignment dowel or staggered bolt holes to ensure correct installa-

14.9a Flywheel bolt tightening sequence (2010 and earlier models)

14.9b Flywheel bolt tightening sequence (2011 modles)

tion. Before installing the bolts, apply thread locking compound to the threads.

9 Wedge a screwdriver in the ring gear teeth to keep the flywheel/driveplate from turning and tighten the bolts, in the correct sequence

(see illustrations), to the torque listed in this Chapter's Specifications.

10 The remainder of installation is the reverse of the removal procedure.

15 Rear main oil seal - replacement

1 The one-piece rear main oil seal is pressed into the engine block and the crankcase reinforcement section. Remove the transmission (see Chapter 7), the clutch components, if equipped (see Chapter 8) and the flywheel (see Section 14).

2 Pry out the old seal with a special seal removal tool or a flat blade screwdriver.

❋❋ CAUTION:

To prevent an oil leak after the new seal is installed, be very careful not to scratch or otherwise damage the crankshaft sealing surface or the bore in the engine block.

3 Clean the crankshaft and seal bore in the block thoroughly and de-grease these areas by wiping them with a rag soaked in lacquer thinner or acetone. Lubricate the lip of the new seal and the outer diameter of the crankshaft with engine oil. Make sure the edges of the new oil seal are not rolled over.

4 Position the new seal onto the crankshaft.

➡Note: **When installing the new seal, if so marked, the words THIS SIDE OUT on the seal must face out, toward the rear of the engine. Use a special rear main oil seal installation tool or a socket with the exact diameter of the seal to drive the seal in place. Make sure the seal is not off-set; it must be flush along the entire circumference of the seal carrier.**

5 The remainder of installation is the reverse of removal.

16 Engine mounts - check and replacement

CHECK

1 Engine mounts seldom require attention, but broken or deteriorated mounts should be replaced immediately or the added strain placed on the driveline components may cause damage or wear.

2 During the check, the engine must be raised slightly to remove the weight from the mounts.

3 Raise the vehicle and support it securely on jackstands, then position a jack under the engine oil pan. Place a large block of wood between the jack head and the oil pan, then carefully raise the engine just enough to take the weight off the mounts.

❋❋ WARNING:

DO NOT place any part of your body under the engine when it's supported only by a jack!

4 Check the mounts to see if the rubber is cracked, hardened or separated from the metal plates. Sometimes the rubber will split right down the center.

5 Check for relative movement between the mount plates and the engine or frame (use a large screwdriver or prybar to attempt to move

16.9a Location of the right engine mount upper mounting nuts

16.9b Location of the right engine mount lower mounting nut

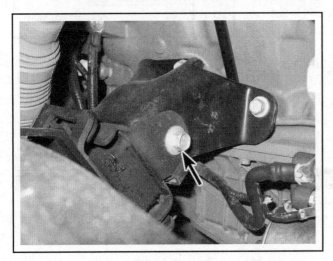

16.9c Location of the through-bolt on the left engine mount

16.9d Location of the lower mounting nut on the left engine mount

the mounts). If movement is noted, lower the engine and tighten the mount fasteners.

6   Rubber preservative should be applied to the mounts to slow deterioration.

REPLACEMENT

◆ Refer to illustrations 16.9a, 16.9b, 16.9c and 16.9d

7   Disconnect the negative battery cable from the battery (see Chapter 5), then raise the vehicle and support it securely on jackstands.

8   Remove the engine cooling fan/shroud assembly (see Chapter 3).

9   Remove the fasteners holding the mount to the engine bracket and the chassis (see illustrations).

10 Raise the engine slightly with a jack or hoist. Detach the mount from the chassis bracket.

11 Installation is the reverse of removal. Use thread-locking compound on the mount fasteners and be sure to tighten them securely.

Specifications

General

Displacement	4.0 liters (244 cubic inches)
Bore and stroke	
2010 and earlier	3.953 x 3.310 inches
2011	3.953 x 3.320 inches
Cylinder numbers (front-to-rear)	
Left (driver's) side	4-5-6
Right side	1-2-3
Firing order	1-4-2-5-3-6

Cylinder and coil terminal locations

Camshafts

Lobe lift (intake and exhaust)	0.259 inch
Allowable lobe lift loss	0.005 inch
Endplay	0.0003 to 0.007 inch
Journal diameter (all)	1.099 to 1.101 inches
Bearing inside diameter (all)	1.102 to 1.104 inches
Journal-to-bearing (oil) clearance	
Standard	0.002 to 0.004 inch
Service limit	0.006 inch

Torque specifications   Ft-lbs (unless otherwise indicated)

➡Note: One foot-pound (ft-lb) of torque is equivalent to 12 inch-pounds (in-lbs) of torque. Torque values below approximately 15 ft-lbs are expressed in inch-pounds, since most foot-pound torque wrenches are not accurate at these smaller values.

Accessory bracket bolts	31
Camshaft sprocket bolt*	63
Camshaft bearing cap bolts	
Step 1	53 in-lbs
Step 2	144 in-lbs
Crankshaft pulley bolt**	
2005 and earlier models	
Step 1	33
Step 2	Tighten additional 85-degrees
2006 and later models	
Step 1	41
Step 2	Tighten additional 85-degrees
Cylinder head bolts**	
All models except 2011 4.0L V6	
8 mm bolts	24
12 mm bolts	
Step 1	25
Step 2	Tighten an additional 90-degrees
Step 3	Tighten an additional 90-degrees

*The right camshaft uses a left-hand threaded bolt
** Bolt(s) must be replaced.

Torque specifications	Ft-lbs (unless otherwise indicated)

2011 4.0L V6 models
  Step 1, 12 mm bolts
    Stage 1 — 106 in-lbs
    Stage 2 — 18
  Step 2, 8 mm bolts — 24
  Step 3, retorque the 12 mm bolts
    Stage 1 — Tighten an additional 90-degrees
    Stage 2 — Tighten an additional 90-degrees
Drivebelt tensioner bolt — 35
Flywheel/driveplate bolts
  2010 and earlier
    Step 1 — 120 in-lbs
    Step 2 — 52
  2011
    Step 1 — 115 in-lbs
    Step 2 — 37
    Step 3 — Tighten an additional 90-degrees
Exhaust manifold nuts — 16
Exhaust manifold-to-EGR valve bolts (2011) — 25
Exhaust pipe-to-manifold nuts — 30
Engine front cover bolts
  2005 and earlier, and 2011 — 168 in-lbs
  2006 through 2010 — 18
Ignition coil bracket bolts (2011)
  Lower right bolts — 21
  Lower front bolts — 17
  Upper bolts — 71 in-lbs
Intake manifold bolts — 89 in-lbs
Jackshaft sprocket bolts
  Front
    Step 1 — 33
    Step 2 — Tighten an additional 90-degrees
  Rear (2010 and earlier)
    Step 1 — 15
    Step 2 — Tighten an additional 90-degrees
Jackshaft chain tensioner bolts — 80 in-lbs
Jackshaft chain guide bolts — 168 in-lbs
Jackshaft thrust plate bolts — 96 in-lbs
Oil pump screen cover and tube bolt — 89 in-lbs
Oil pump-to-block bolts — 168 in-lbs
Oil pan (sheet metal)-to-crankcase reinforcement section bolts
  2001 through 2006 — 80 in-lbs
  2007 and later — 97 in-lbs
Crankcase reinforcement section-to-block
  Perimeter bolts
    2010 and earlier — 120 in-lbs
    2011 — 124 in-lbs
  Perimeter nuts — 89 in-lbs
  Two Torx® bolts — 89 in-lbs

Torque specifications   Ft-lbs (unless otherwise indicated)

→Note: One foot-pound (ft-lb) of torque is equivalent to 12 inch-pounds (in-lbs) of torque. Torque values below approximately 15 ft-lbs are expressed in inch-pounds, since most foot-pound torque wrenches are not accurate at these smaller values.

Crankcase reinforcement section-to-block (continued)
    Threaded inserts   27 in-lbs
    Rear lower block cradle-to-transmission bolts
        2010 and earlier   32
        2011   35
    Rear lower block cradle-to-engine block
        (rear main oil seal)   71 in-lbs
    Lower block cradle bolts
        Step 1   132 in-lbs
        Step 2   25
Timing chain tensioner
    2010 and earlier   32
    2011   35
Timing chain cassette bolts
    Right side
        Upper bolt   89 lbs
    Left side
        Upper bolt
            2010 and earlier   108 in-lbs
            2011   106 in-lbs
        Lower bolt   168 in-lbs
Valve cover bolts   89 in-lbs

Section

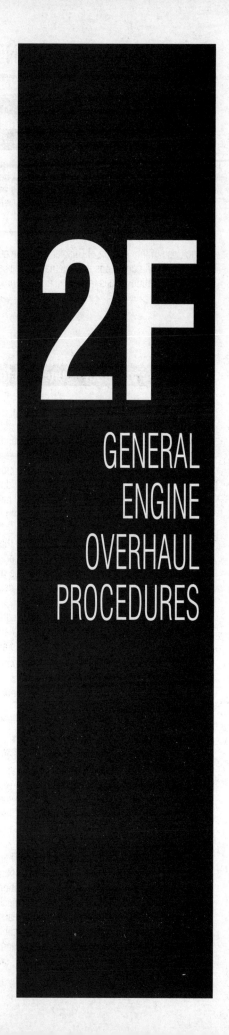

Reference to other Chapters

1 General information

✳✳ WARNING:

Some models covered by this manual are equipped with airbags. Always disable the airbag system before working in the vicinity of any airbag system component to avoid the possibility of accidental deployment of the airbag(s), which could cause personal injury (see Chapter 12).

Included in this portion of Chapter 2 are the general overhaul procedures for the cylinder heads and internal engine components.

The information ranges from advice concerning preparation for an overhaul and the purchase of replacement parts to detailed, step-by-step procedures covering removal and installation of internal engine components and the inspection of parts.

The following Sections have been written based on the assumption that the engine has been removed from the vehicle. For information concerning in-vehicle engine repair, as well as removal and installation of the external components necessary for the overhaul, see Parts A through E of this Chapter and Section 7 of this Part.

The Specifications included in this Part are only those necessary for the inspection and overhaul procedures which follow. Refer to Parts A through E for additional Specifications.

2 Engine overhaul - general information

It's not always easy to determine when, or if, an engine should be completely overhauled, as a number of factors must be considered.

High mileage is not necessarily an indication that an overhaul is needed, while low mileage doesn't preclude the need for an overhaul. Frequency of servicing is probably the most important consideration. An engine that's had regular and frequent oil and filter changes, as well as other required maintenance, will most likely give many thousands of miles of reliable service. Conversely, a neglected engine may require an overhaul very early in its life.

Excessive oil consumption is an indication that piston rings, valve seals and/or valve guides are in need of attention. Make sure that oil leaks aren't responsible before deciding that the rings and/or guides are bad. Perform a cylinder compression check to determine the extent of the work required (see Section 3).

Check the oil pressure with a gauge installed in place of the oil pressure sending unit and compare it to this Chapter's Specifications. If it's extremely low, the bearings and/or oil pump are probably worn out.

a) On four-cylinder engines, the oil pressure sender is located at the left rear of the block or near the oil filter.
b) On 3.0L V6 engines, the oil pressure sender is located at the right rear corner of the block.
c) On 4.0L V6 engines, the oil pressure sender is located on the driver's side of the block next to the water pump inlet - do not confuse the oil pressure sender with the oil level sensor located in the side of the oil pan.

Loss of power, rough running, knocking or metallic engine noises, excessive valve train noise and high fuel consumption rates may also point to the need for an overhaul, especially if they're all present at the same time. If a complete tune-up doesn't remedy the situation, major mechanical work is the only solution.

An engine overhaul involves restoring the internal parts to the specifications of a new engine. During an overhaul, the piston rings are replaced and the cylinder walls are reconditioned (rebored and/or honed). If a rebore is done by an automotive machine shop, new oversize pistons will also be installed. The main bearings, connecting rod bearings and camshaft bearings are generally replaced with new ones and, if necessary, the crankshaft may be reground to restore the journals. Generally, the valves are serviced as well, since they're usually in less-than-perfect condition at this point.

While the engine is being overhauled, other components, such as the starter and alternator, can be rebuilt as well. The end result should be a like-new engine that will give many trouble-free miles.

➡**Note: Critical cooling system components such as the hoses, drivebelts, thermostat and water pump MUST be replaced with new parts when an engine is overhauled.**

The radiator should be checked carefully to ensure that it isn't clogged or leaking (see Chapter 3). Also, we don't recommend overhauling the oil pump - always install a new one when an engine is rebuilt.

Before beginning the engine overhaul, read through the entire procedure to familiarize yourself with the scope and requirements of the job. Overhauling an engine isn't difficult if you follow all of the instructions carefully, have the necessary tools and equipment and pay close attention to all specifications; however, it is time consuming. Plan on the vehicle being tied up for a minimum of two weeks, especially if parts must be taken to an automotive machine shop for repair or reconditioning. Check on availability of parts and make sure that any necessary special tools and equipment are obtained in advance. Most work can be done with typical hand tools, although a number of precision measuring tools are required for inspecting parts to determine if they must be replaced. Often an automotive machine shop will handle the inspection of parts and offer advice concerning reconditioning and replacement.

➡**Note: Always wait until the engine has been completely disassembled and all components, especially the engine block, have been inspected before deciding what service and repair operations must be performed by an automotive machine shop.**

Since the block's condition will be the major factor to consider when determining whether to overhaul the original engine or buy a rebuilt one, never purchase parts or have machine work done on other components until the block has been thoroughly inspected. As a general rule, time is the primary cost of an overhaul, so it doesn't pay to install worn or substandard parts.

As a final note, to ensure maximum life and minimum trouble from a rebuilt engine, everything must be assembled with care in a spotlessly clean environment.

3 Cylinder compression check

♦ **Refer to illustration 3.8**

1   A compression check will tell you what mechanical condition the upper end (pistons, rings, valves, head gaskets) of your engine is in. Specifically, it can tell you if the compression is down due to leakage caused by worn piston rings, defective valves and seats or a blown head gasket.

➡**Note: The engine must be at normal operating temperature and the battery must be fully charged for this check.**

2   Begin by cleaning the area around the spark plugs before you remove them (compressed air should be used, if available, otherwise a small brush or even a bicycle tire pump will work). The idea is to prevent dirt from getting into the cylinders as the compression check is being done.

3   On V6 engines, remove all of the spark plugs from the engine (see Chapter 1).

4   On 2.3L four-cylinder engines with twin plug ignition, remove all four spark plugs from one side only. If you remove all eight plugs, compression will escape out the open spark plug hole.

5   Block the throttle wide open.

6   Disable the ignition system. On distributor ignitions, detach the coil secondary wire. On distributorless ignitions, detach the electrical connector from the coil pack (see Chapter 5).

7   Disable the fuel pump circuit (see Chapter 4, Section 2).

8   Install the compression gauge in the number one spark plug hole (see illustration).

9   Crank the engine over at least seven compression strokes and watch the gauge. The compression should build up quickly in a healthy engine. Low compression on the first stroke, followed by gradually increasing pressure on successive strokes, indicates worn piston rings. A low compression reading on the first stroke, which doesn't build up during successive strokes, indicates leaking valves or a blown head gasket (a cracked head could also be the cause). Deposits on the undersides of the valve heads can also cause low compression. Record the highest gauge reading obtained.

10 Repeat the procedure for the remaining cylinders and compare the results to this Chapter's Specifications.

11 Add some engine oil (about three squirts from a plunger-type oil can) to each cylinder, through the spark plug hole, and repeat the test.

3.8 A gauge with a threaded fitting for the spark plug hole is preferred over the type that requires hand pressure to maintain the seal during the compression check

12 If the compression increases after the oil is added, the piston rings are definitely worn. If the compression doesn't increase significantly, the leakage is occurring at the valves or head gasket. Leakage past the valves may be caused by burned valve seats and/or faces or warped, cracked or bent valves.

13 If two adjacent cylinders have equally low compression, there's a strong possibility that the head gasket between them is blown. The appearance of coolant in the combustion chambers or the crankcase would verify this condition.

14 If one cylinder is 20-percent lower than the others, and the engine has a slightly rough idle, a worn exhaust lobe on the camshaft could be the cause.

15 If the compression is unusually high, the combustion chambers are probably coated with carbon deposits. If that's the case, the cylinder head(s) should be removed and decarbonized.

16 If compression is way down or varies greatly between cylinders, it would be a good idea to have a leak-down test performed by an automotive repair shop. This test will pinpoint exactly where the leakage is occurring and how severe it is.

4 Engine rebuilding alternatives

The do-it-yourselfer is faced with a number of options when performing an engine overhaul. The decision to replace the engine block, piston/connecting rod assemblies and crankshaft depends on a number of factors, with the number one consideration being the condition of the block. Other considerations are cost, access to machine shop facilities, parts availability, time required to complete the project and the extent of prior mechanical experience on the part of the do-it-yourselfer.

Some of the rebuilding alternatives include:

Individual parts - If the inspection procedures reveal that the engine block and most engine components are in reusable condition, purchasing individual parts may be the most economical alternative. The block, crankshaft and piston/connecting rod assemblies should all be inspected carefully. Even if the block shows little wear, the cylinder bores should be surface honed.

Short block - A short block consists of an engine block with a crankshaft, camshaft, timing chain and sprockets and piston/connecting rod assemblies already installed. All new bearings are incorporated and all clearances will be correct. The existing valve train components, cylinder head(s) and external parts can be bolted to the short block with little or no machine shop work necessary.

Long block - A long block consists of a short block plus an oil pump, oil pan, cylinder heads, valve covers, valve train components and timing chain cover. All components are installed with new bearings, seals and gaskets incorporated throughout. The installation of manifolds and external parts is all that's necessary.

Give careful thought to which alternative is best for you and discuss the situation with local automotive machine shops, auto parts dealers and experienced rebuilders before ordering or purchasing replacement parts.

5 Engine removal - methods and precautions

If you've decided that an engine must be removed for overhaul or major repair work, several preliminary steps should be taken.

Locating a suitable place to work is extremely important. Adequate work space, along with storage space for the vehicle, will be needed. If a shop or garage isn't available, at the very least a flat, level, clean work surface made of concrete or asphalt is required.

Cleaning the engine compartment and engine before beginning the removal procedure will help keep tools clean and organized.

An engine hoist or A-frame will also be necessary. Make sure the equipment is rated in excess of the combined weight of the engine and accessories. Safety is of primary importance, considering the potential hazards involved in lifting the engine out of the vehicle.

If the engine is being removed by a novice, a helper should be available. Advice and aid from someone more experienced would also be helpful. There are many instances when one person cannot simultaneously perform all of the operations required when lifting the engine out of the vehicle.

Plan the operation ahead of time. Arrange for or obtain all of the tools and equipment you'll need prior to beginning the job. Some of the equipment necessary to perform engine removal and installation safely and with relative ease are (in addition to an engine hoist) a heavy duty floor jack, complete sets of wrenches and sockets as described in the front of this manual, wooden blocks and plenty of rags and cleaning solvent for mopping up spilled oil, coolant and gasoline. If the hoist must be rented, make sure that you arrange for it in advance and perform all of the operations possible without it beforehand. This will save you money and time.

Plan for the vehicle to be out of use for quite a while. A machine shop will be required to perform some of the work which the do-it-yourselfer can't accomplish without special equipment. These shops often have a busy schedule, so it would be a good idea to consult them before removing the engine in order to accurately estimate the amount of time required to rebuild or repair components that may need work.

Always be extremely careful when removing and installing the engine. Serious injury can result from careless actions. Plan ahead, take your time and a job of this nature, although major, can be accomplished successfully.

6 Engine - removal and installation

REMOVAL

▶ **Refer to illustrations 6.5a, 6.5b, 6.5c, 6.15 and 6.24**

❋❋ WARNING:

Some models covered by this manual are equipped with airbags. Always disable the airbag system before working in the vicinity of any airbag system component to avoid the possibility of accidental deployment of the airbag(s), which could cause personal injury (see Chapter 12).

❋❋ WARNING:

The air conditioning system is under high pressure. Do not loosen any hose fittings or remove any components until after the system has been discharged. Air conditioning refrigerant should be properly discharged into an EPA-approved recovery/recycling unit at a dealer service department or an automotive air conditioning repair facility. Always wear eye protection when disconnecting air conditioning system fittings.

❋❋ WARNING:

Gasoline is extremely flammable, so take extra precautions when you work on any part of the fuel system. Don't smoke or allow open flames or bare light bulbs near the work area, and don't work in a garage where a gas-type appliance (such as a water heater or a clothes dryer) is present. Since gasoline is carcinogenic, wear latex gloves when there's a possibility of being exposed to fuel, and, if you spill any fuel on your skin, rinse it off immediately with soap and water. Mop up any spills immediately and do not store fuel-soaked rags where they could ignite. The fuel system is under constant pressure, so, if any fuel lines are to be disconnected, the fuel pressure in the system must be relieved first (see Chapter 4 for more information). When you perform any kind of work on the fuel system, wear safety glasses and have a Class B type fire extinguisher on hand.

1 Refer to Chapter 4 and relieve the fuel system pressure, then disconnect the negative cable from the battery.

2 Cover the fenders and cowl and remove the hood (see Chapter 11). Special pads are available to protect the fenders, but an old bedspread or blanket will also work.

3 Remove the air cleaner assembly.

4 Drain the cooling system (see Chapter 1).

5 Label the vacuum lines, emissions system hoses, wiring connectors, ground straps and fuel lines to ensure correct reinstallation, then detach them. Pieces of masking tape with numbers or letters written on them work well (see illustration). If there's any possibility of confusion, make a sketch of the engine compartment and clearly label the lines, hoses and wires. Don't forget the following:

   a) *Oil level sensor connector, if equipped (in the oil pan on the driver's side of the vehicle) (see illustration).*
   b) *Wiring harness at the rear of the driver's side cylinder head (V6 engines).*
   c) *Hose bracket at the lower front corner of the engine on the passenger's side (V6 engines).*

6.5a Label each wire before unplugging the connector

6.5b The oil level sensor is mountedin the oil pan, forward of the starter (4.0L V6 engine)

6.5c The electrical connector for the crankshaft position sensor is located near the crankshaft pulley (arrow)

    d) Crankshaft position sensor connector near the crankshaft pulley, if equipped (see illustration).

6   Label and detach all coolant hoses from the engine.

7   Remove the drivebelt (see Chapter 1).

8   Remove the cooling fan, shroud and radiator (see Chapter 3).

9   Disconnect the fuel lines running from the engine to the chassis (see Chapter 4). Plug or cap all open fittings/lines.

10 Disconnect the throttle linkage (and TV linkage/speed control cable, if equipped) from the engine (see Chapter 4).

11 Unbolt the power steering pump (see Chapter 10). Leave the lines/hoses attached and make sure the pump is kept in an upright position in the engine compartment (use wire or rope to restrain it out of the way).

12 On air conditioned models, unbolt the compressor (see Chapter 3) and set it aside. DO NOT disconnect the hoses! On later models, the compressor and power steering pump can be set aside from the engine with the brackets.

13 Drain the engine oil (see Chapter 1) and remove the filter.

14 Remove the starter motor (see Chapter 5).

15 Remove the alternator (see Chapter 5). Remove the alternator bracket (see illustration). Remove the several bolts, nuts and clips securing the main engine harness and set the harness aside. Mark the bolts with tape for later reference. Unbolt the main connector at the PCM on the firewall and set the connector aside with a plastic bag over it for protection. Also cover the main connection on the PCM to prevent entry of dirt.

16 Disconnect the exhaust system from the engine (see Chapter 4).

17 If you're working on a vehicle with an automatic transmission, refer to Chapter 7, Part B and remove the torque converter-to-driveplate fasteners. Tag and disconnect all electrical connectors from the transmission.

18 Support the transmission with a jack. Position a block of wood between the jack head and transmission to prevent damage to the transmission. Special transmission jacks with safety chains are available - use one if possible.

19 Attach an engine sling or a length of chain to the lifting brackets on the engine.

20 Roll the hoist into position and connect the sling to it. Take up the slack in the sling or chain, but don't lift the engine.

✳✳ WARNING:

DO NOT place any part of your body under the engine when it's supported only by a hoist or other lifting device.

21 Remove the transmission-to-engine block bolts. Be sure to remove the two bolts that secure the engine oil pan to the transmission.

22 Remove the engine mount-to-frame bolts.

23 Recheck to be sure nothing is still connecting the engine to the transmission or vehicle. Disconnect anything still remaining.

24 Raise the engine slightly. It should move easily if it's completely disconnected. If it doesn't, it's stuck - DO NOT try to pry it loose or force it loose with the hoist, since it could shift suddenly and cause injury or damage. Find out why it won't move and fix the problem before continuing. Carefully work the engine forward to separate it from the transmission. If you're working on a vehicle with an automatic transmission, be sure the torque converter stays in the transmission (clamp a pair of vise-grips to the housing to keep the converter from sliding out). If you're working on a vehicle with a manual transmission, the input shaft must be completely disengaged from the clutch. Slowly

6.15 To remove the alternator bracket, remove the lower idler pulley bolt and pulley (A), but don't remove the drivebelt adjustment pulley (B) - then remove the three bracket bolts (arrows); one bolt is hidden behind the adjustment pulley (V6 engine shown)

raise the engine out of the engine compartment (see illustration). Check carefully to make sure nothing is hanging up.

25 Remove the clutch (if equipped - see Chapter 8) and flywheel/driveplate and mount the engine on an engine stand.

INSTALLATION

26 Check the engine and transmission mounts. If they're worn or damaged, replace them.

27 If you're working on a manual transmission equipped vehicle, install the clutch and pressure plate (see Chapter 8). Now is a good time to install a new clutch.

28 Carefully lower the engine into the engine compartment - make sure the engine mounts line up.

29 If you're working on an automatic transmission equipped vehicle, remove the vise grips and guide the torque converter into the crankshaft following the procedure outlined in Chapter 7, Part B.

30 If you're working on a manual transmission equipped vehicle, apply a dab of high-temperature grease to the input shaft and guide it into the crankshaft pilot bearing until the bellhousing is flush with the engine block.

31 Install the transmission-to-engine bolts and tighten them securely.

❊❊ CAUTION:

DO NOT use the bolts to force the transmission and engine together!

6.24 Carefully raise the engine from the engine compartment

32 Reinstall the remaining components in the reverse order of removal.

33 Add coolant, oil, power steering and transmission fluid as needed.

34 Run the engine and check for leaks and proper operation of all accessories, then install the hood and test drive the vehicle.

7 Engine overhaul - disassembly sequence

1 It's much easier to disassemble and work on the engine if it's mounted on a portable engine stand. A stand can often be rented quite cheaply from an equipment rental yard. Before the engine is mounted on a stand, the flywheel/driveplate should be removed from the engine.

2 If a stand isn't available, it's possible to disassemble the engine with it blocked up on the floor. Be extra careful not to tip or drop the engine when working without a stand.

3 If you're going to obtain a rebuilt engine, all external components must come off first, to be transferred to the replacement engine, just as they will if you're doing a complete engine overhaul yourself. These include:

> Alternator and brackets (if not removed during engine removal)
> Emissions control components
> Coil pack, spark plug wires and spark plugs
> Thermostat and housing cover
> Water pump
> EFI components
> Intake/exhaust manifolds
> Oil filter
> Engine mounts
> Engine rear plate
> Clutch and flywheel/driveplate

➡**Note:** When removing the external components from the engine, pay close attention to details that may be helpful or important during installation. Note the installed position of gaskets, seals, spacers, pins, brackets, washers, bolts and other small items.

4 If you're obtaining a short block, which consists of the engine block, crankshaft, pistons and connecting rods all assembled, then the cylinder head, oil pan and oil pump will have to be removed as well. See Engine rebuilding alternatives for additional information regarding the different possibilities to be considered.

5 If you're planning a complete overhaul, the engine must be disassembled and the internal components removed in the following order:

FOUR-CYLINDER ENGINE

> Clutch and flywheel or driveplate
> Valve cover
> Intake and exhaust manifolds
> Timing belt or chain, sprockets and covers
> Cylinder head
> Camshaft and related components
> Oil pan
> Front cover
> Oil pump
> Piston/connecting rod assemblies
> Crankshaft and main bearings

V6 ENGINES

Clutch and flywheel or driveplate
Valve covers
Rocker assemblies and pushrods
Intake and exhaust manifolds
Cylinder heads
Oil pan
Oil pump
Timing chain cover and cover plate
Timing chain and sprockets
Valve lifters
Camshaft
Piston/connecting rod assemblies
Crankshaft and main bearings

6   Before beginning the disassembly and overhaul procedures,

make sure the following items are available.

Common hand tools
Small cardboard boxes or plastic bags for storing parts
Gasket scraper
Ridge reamer
Vibration damper puller
Micrometers
Telescoping gauges
Dial indicator set
Valve spring compressor
Cylinder surfacing hone
Piston ring groove cleaning tool
Electric drill motor
Tap and die set
Wire brushes
Oil gallery brushes
Cleaning solvent

8   Jackshaft and balance shaft (4.0L SOHC V6 engine) - removal, inspection and installation

➡**Note: All 4.0L SOHC V6 engines are equipped with a jackshaft. 4WD models with the V6 engine are equipped with a jackshaft and a balance shaft.**

REMOVAL

▶ **Refer to illustrations 8.3 and 8.5**

1   Disconnect the cable from the negative battery terminal (see Chapter 5).

2   The camshafts, timing chains and sprockets and the jackshaft chain and sprocket must be removed before extracting the jackshaft (see Part E of this Chapter).

3   From above, at the top-rear of the block, remove the bolt holding the oil pump drive and pull out the drive assembly (see illustration).

4   Remove the two jackshaft thrust plate bolts, and any spacer that

may be in place. Installing a long bolt in the front of the jackshaft to use as a handle, guide the jackshaft gently out of the block, without nicking the journals on the jackshaft bearings in the block.

5   Compress the balance shaft tensioner by hand and insert a drill bit or pin to hold it in place, then remove the tensioner bolts and the tensioner (see illustration).

6   Slide the balance shaft chain and crankshaft sprocket from the crankshaft and balance shaft sprocket.

➡**Note: Do not remove the bolt from the balance shaft sprocket.**

7   Rotate the engine on the engine stand so that the bottom of the block is up. Remove the two rear bolts and the balance shaft assembly.

➡**Note: Two of the balance shaft assembly mounting bolts are the ones removed to take off the tensioner.**

8.3 Remove the oil pump drive assembly retaining bolt and clamp (A) and pull the drive assembly (B) straight up and out of the engine block

8.5 Press the balance shaft tensioner in and insert a pin (A) - remove the balance shaft tensioner bolts (B) and remove the tensioner assembly (C)

INSPECTION

8 The jackshaft rides in a bearing at the front of the block and a bushing at the rear. Check the jackshaft bearings in the block for wear and damage. Look for galling, pitting and discolored areas.

9 Jackshaft bearing replacement requires special tools and expertise that place it outside the scope of the home mechanic. Take the block to an automotive machine shop to ensure the job is done correctly.

INSTALLATION

Jackshaft

10 Lubricate the jackshaft bearing journals with engine assembly lubricant.

11 Slide the jackshaft into the engine, using a long bolt screwed into the front of the jackshaft as a handle. Support the shaft near the block and be careful not to scrape or nick the bearings. Install the jackshaft thrust plate and tighten the bolts to the torque listed in this Chapter's Specifications.

Balance shaft

▸ **Refer to illustration 8.14**

12 Lubricate the front bearing and rear journal of the balance shaft with engine oil and insert the balance shaft assembly carefully onto the block. The block should be turned bottom-end up on the engine stand, and the crankshaft should be positioned with cylinder number 1 at TDC.

13 Install and tighten the balance shaft bolts to the torque listed in this Chapter's Specifications.

14 Turn the balance shaft sprocket until the two dots on the sprocket align over the hole in the front of the assembly, and the timing mark on the front of the lower shaft aligns with the balance shaft-to-block mat-

8.14 To align the balance shaft for chain installation, turn the sprocket until the marks on the sprocket (A) align with the hole in the assembly (B) and the lower shaft mark (C) aligns with the mating line of the assembly and engine block

ing line (see illustration). Install a 4 mm pin or drill bit into the hole to hold it in this position.

➡**Note: It may take quite a few turns of the balance shaft sprocket to get the shaft and sprocket timing marks sets to align, because of the reduction gearing in the assembly.**

15 Install the balance shaft chain and the crankshaft sprocket. Install the balance shaft chain guide and tensioner (with the tensioner pinned) (see illustration 8.5). Tighten the chain guide and tensioner bolts to the torque listed in this Chapter's Specifications. Remove the pin from the tensioner and remove the alignment pin from the balance shaft sprocket.

16 Refer to Chapter 2A and install the camshaft timing chain cassettes, jackshaft chain and jackshaft sprocket.

9 Cylinder head - disassembly, cleaning and inspection

▸ **Refer to illustrations 9.2, 9.3 and 9.4**

➡**Note: New and rebuilt cylinder heads are commonly available for most engines at dealerships and auto parts stores. Due to the fact that some specialized tools are necessary for the disassembly and inspection procedures, and replacement parts may not be readily available, it may be more practical and economical for the home mechanic to purchase replacement heads rather than taking the time to disassemble, inspect and recondition the originals.**

1 Cylinder head disassembly involves removal of the intake and exhaust valves and related components. On V6 engines, remove the rocker arm shaft assemblies. On four-cylinder engines, remove the camshaft, followers and lash adjusters. Label the parts or store them separately so they can be reinstalled in their original locations.

2 Before the valves are removed, arrange to label and store them, along with their related components, so they can be kept separate and reinstalled in the same valve guides they are removed from (see illustration).

3 Compress the springs on the first valve with a spring compressor and remove the keepers (see illustration). Carefully release the valve

spring compressor and remove the retainer and spring.

4 Pull the valve out of the head, then remove the oil seal from the guide. If the valve binds in the guide won't pull through, push it back into the head and deburr the area around the keeper groove with a fine file or whetstone (see illustration).

5 Repeat the procedure for the remaining valves. Remember to keep all the parts for each valve together so they can be reinstalled in the same locations.

6 Once the valves and related components have been removed and stored in an organized manner, the head should be thoroughly cleaned and inspected. If a complete engine overhaul is being done, finish the engine disassembly procedures before beginning the cylinder head cleaning and inspection process.

7 Thorough cleaning of the cylinder head(s) and related valve train components, followed by a detailed inspection, will enable you to decide how much valve service work must be done during the engine overhaul.

➡**Note: If the engine was severely overheated, the cylinder head is probably warped (see Step 12).**

9.2 A small plastic bag, with an appropriate label, can be used to store the valve train components so they can be kept together and reinstalled in the original location

9.3 Use a valve spring compressor to compress the spring, then remove the keepers from the valve stem

9.4 If the valve won't pull through the guide, deburr the edge of the stem end and the area around the top of the keeper groove with a file or whetstone

CLEANING

8   Scrape all traces of old gasket material and sealing compound off the head gasket, intake manifold and exhaust manifold sealing surfaces. Be very careful not to gouge the cylinder head. Special gasket removal solvents that soften gaskets and make removal much easier are available at auto parts stores.

9   Remove all built up scale from the coolant passages.

10 Run a stiff wire brush through the various holes to remove deposits that may have formed in them.

11 Run an appropriate size tap into each of the threaded holes to remove corrosion and thread sealant that may be present. If compressed air is available, use it to clear the holes of debris produced by this operation.

✳✳ WARNING:

Wear eye protection when using compressed air!

9.18 Check the cylinder head gasket surface for warpage by trying to slip a feeler gauge under the straightedge (see this Chapter's Specifications for the maximum warpage)

12 Clean the rocker arm pivot stud threads with a wire brush.

13 Clean the cylinder head with solvent and dry it thoroughly. Compressed air will speed the drying process and ensure that all holes and recessed areas are clean.

➡Note: **Decarbonizing chemicals are available and may prove very useful when cleaning cylinder heads and valve train components. They are very caustic and should be used with caution. Be sure to follow the instructions on the container.**

14 Clean the rocker arms, fulcrums or shafts, bolts and pushrods with solvent and dry them thoroughly (don't mix them up during the cleaning process). Compressed air will speed the drying process and can be used to clean out the oil passages.

15 Clean all the valve springs, spring seats, keepers and retainers with solvent and dry them thoroughly. Do the components from one valve at a time to avoid mixing up the parts.

16 Scrape off any heavy deposits that may have formed on the valves, then use a motorized wire brush to remove deposits from the valve heads and stems. Again, make sure the valves don't get mixed up.

INSPECTION

♦ **Refer to illustration 9.18, 9.20, 9.21, 9.22, 9.23 and 9.24**

➡Note: **Be sure to perform all of the following inspection procedures before concluding that machine shop work is required. Make a list of the items that need attention.**

Cylinder head

17 Inspect the head very carefully for cracks, evidence of coolant leakage and other damage. If cracks are found, check with an automotive machine shop concerning repair. If repair isn't possible, a new cylinder head should be obtained.

18 Using a straightedge and feeler gauge, check the head gasket mating surface for warpage (see illustration). If the warpage exceeds the limit listed in this Chapter's Specifications, it can be resurfaced at an automotive machine shop.

➡Note: **If the heads are resurfaced, the intake manifold flanges will also require machining.**

19 Examine the valve seats in each of the combustion chambers.

9.20 A dial indicator can be used to determine the valve stem-to-guide clearance (move the valve stem as indicated by the arrows)

9.21 Check for valve wear at the points shown here

If they're pitted, cracked or burned, the head will require valve service that's beyond the scope of the home mechanic.

20 Check the valve stem-to-guide clearance by measuring the lateral movement of the valve stem with a dial indicator attached securely to the head (see illustration). The valve must be in the guide and approximately 1/16-inch off the seat. The total valve stem movement indicated by the gauge needle must be divided by two to obtain the actual clearance. After this is done, if there's still some doubt regarding the condition of the valve guides they should be checked by an automotive machine shop (the cost should be minimal).

Valves

21 Carefully inspect each valve face for uneven wear, deformation, cracks, pits and burned areas (see illustration). Check the valve stem for scuffing and galling and the neck for cracks. Rotate the valve and check for any obvious indication that it's bent. Look for pits and excessive wear on the end of the stem. The presence of any of these conditions indicates the need for valve service by an automotive machine shop.

22 Measure the margin width on each valve (see illustration). Any valve with a margin narrower than 1/32-inch will have to be replaced with a new one.

Valve components

23 Check each valve spring for wear (on the ends) and pits. Measure the free length and compare it to the Specifications (see illustration). Any springs that are shorter than specified have sagged and should not be reused. The tension of all springs should be checked with a special fixture before deciding that they're suitable for use in a rebuilt engine (take the springs to an automotive machine shop for this check).

24 Stand each spring on a flat surface and check it for squareness (see illustration). If any of the springs are distorted or sagged, replace all of them with new parts.

25 Check the spring retainers and keepers for obvious wear and cracks. Any questionable parts should be replaced with new ones, as extensive damage will occur if they fail during engine operation.

Cam followers (four-cylinder engine)

26 Clean all the parts thoroughly. Make sure that all oil passages are open.

27 Inspect the pad at the valve end of the follower and the camshaft

9.22 The margin width on each valve must be as specified - if no margin exists, the valve cannot be reused

9.23 Measure the free length of each valve spring with a dial or vernier caliper

9.24 Check each valve spring for squareness

end pad for indications of scuffing or abnormal wear. If the pad is grooved, replace the follower. Do not attempt to true the surface by grinding.

Rocker arm components (V6 engines)

28 Check the rocker arm faces (the areas that contact the pushrod ends and valve stems) for pits, wear, galling, score marks and rough spots. Check the rocker arm shafts as well. Look for cracks in each rocker arm and shaft.

29 Inspect the pushrod ends for scuffing and excessive wear. Roll each pushrod on a flat surface, like a piece of plate glass, to determine if it's bent.

30 Any damaged or excessively worn parts must be replaced with new ones.

31 If the inspection process indicates that the valve components are in generally poor condition and worn beyond the limits specified, which is usually the case in an engine that's being overhauled, reassemble the valves in the cylinder head and refer to Section 10 for valve servicing recommendations.

10 Valves - servicing

1 Because of the complex nature of the job and the special tools and equipment needed, servicing of the valves, the valve seats and the valve guides, commonly known as a valve job, should be done by a professional.

2 The home mechanic can remove and disassemble the heads, do the initial cleaning and inspection, then reassemble and deliver them to a dealer service department or an automotive machine shop for the actual service work. Doing the inspection will enable you to see what condition the head and valvetrain components are in and will ensure that you know what work and new parts are required when dealing with an automotive machine shop.

3 The dealer service department, or automotive machine shop, will remove the valves and springs, recondition or replace the valves and valve seats, recondition the valve guides, check and replace the valve springs, spring retainers and keepers (as necessary), replace the valve seals with new ones, reassemble the valve components and make sure the installed spring height is correct. The cylinder head gasket surface will also be resurfaced if it's warped.

4 After the valve job has been performed by a professional, the head will be in like-new condition. When the head is returned, be sure to clean it again before installation on the engine to remove any metal particles and abrasive grit that may still be present from the valve service or head resurfacing operations. Use compressed air, if available, to blow out all the oil holes and passages

11 Cylinder head - reassembly

▶ **Refer to illustration 11.7**

1 Regardless of whether or not the head was sent to an automotive repair shop for valve servicing, make sure it's clean before beginning reassembly.

11.7 Be sure to check the valve spring installed height for each valve (the distance from the top of the seat/shims to the underside of the retainer)

2 If the head was sent out for valve servicing, the valves and related components will already be in place. Go to Step 7.

3 Lubricate and install each valve, then install new seals on each of the valve stems. Don't twist or cock the seals during installation or they won't seat properly on the valve stems.

4 Drop the spring seat or shim(s) over the valve guide and set the valve spring and retainer in place.

5 Compress the springs with a valve spring compressor and carefully install the keepers in the upper groove, then slowly release the compressor and make sure the keepers seat properly. Apply a small dab of grease to each keeper to hold it in place if necessary.

6 Repeat the procedure for the remaining valves. Be sure to return the components to their original locations - don't mix them up!

7 Check the installed valve spring height with a ruler graduated in 1/32-inch increments or a dial caliper. If the head was sent out for service work, the installed height should be correct (but don't automatically assume that it is). The measurement is taken from the top of each spring seat or shim(s) to the bottom of the retainer (see illustration). If the height is greater than the figure listed in this Chapter's Specifications, shims can be added under the springs to correct it.

❋❋ CAUTION:

Don't, under any circumstances, shim the springs to the point where the installed height is less than specified.

12 Pistons/connecting rods - removal

◆ **Refer to illustrations 12.1, 12.3, 12.4 and 12.6**

➡**Note: Prior to removing the piston/connecting rod assemblies, remove the cylinder head(s), the oil pan and the oil pump by referring to the appropriate Sections in Chapter 2.**

1   Use your fingernail to feel if a ridge has formed at the upper limit of ring travel (about 1/4-inch down from the top of each cylinder). If carbon deposits or cylinder wear have produced ridges, they must be completely removed with a special tool (see illustration). Follow the manufacturer's instructions provided with the tool. Failure to remove the ridges before attempting to remove the piston/connecting rod assemblies may result in piston breakage.

2   After the cylinder ridges have been removed, turn the engine upside-down so the crankshaft is facing up.

3   Before the connecting rods are removed, check the endplay with feeler gauges. Slide them between the first connecting rod and the crankshaft throw until the play is removed (see illustration). The endplay is equal to the thickness of the feeler gauge(s). If the endplay exceeds the service limit, new connecting rods will be required. If new rods (or a new crankshaft) are installed, the endplay may fall under the specified minimum (if it does, the rods will have to be machined to restore it - consult an automotive machine shop for advice if necessary). Repeat the procedure for the remaining connecting rods.

4   Check the connecting rods and caps for identification marks (see illustration). If they aren't plainly marked, use a small center-punch to make the appropriate number of indentations on each rod and cap (1, 2, 3, etc.).

5   Loosen each of the connecting rod cap nuts 1/2-turn at a time until they can be removed by hand. Remove the number one connecting rod cap and bearing insert. Don't drop the bearing insert out of the cap.

6   Slip a short length of plastic or rubber hose over each connecting rod cap bolt to protect the crankshaft journal and cylinder wall as the piston is removed (see illustration).

7   Remove the bearing insert and push the connecting rod/piston assembly out through the top of the engine. Use a wooden hammer

12.1 A ridge reamer is required to remove the ridge from the top of each cylinder - do this before removing the pistons!

12.4 Check the connecting rod and cap for identification marks - if they aren't visible, mark the rods and caps with a hammer and punch to indicate which cylinder they came from (be sure to mark the rod and cap on the same side so they can be reassembled correctly)

12.3 Connecting rod side clearance is measured with feeler gauges inserted between the rod cap and crankshaft

12.6 Place short pieces of hose over the connecting rod studs to protect the crankshaft and cylinder walls

handle to push on the upper bearing surface in the connecting rod. If resistance is felt, double-check to make sure that all of the ridge was removed from the cylinder.

8   Repeat the procedure for the remaining cylinders.

9   After removal, reassemble the connecting rod caps and bearing inserts in their respective connecting rods and install the cap nuts fin-ger tight. Leaving the old bearing inserts in place until reassembly will help prevent the connecting rod bearing surfaces from being accidentally nicked or gouged.

10   Don't separate the pistons from the connecting rods (see Section 17 for additional information).

13 Crankshaft - removal

♦ **Refer to illustrations 13.1, 13.3 and 13.4**

➡**Note: The crankshaft can be removed only after the engine has been removed from the vehicle. It's assumed that the flywheel or driveplate, vibration damper, timing chain, oil pan, oil pump and piston/connecting rod assemblies have already been removed.**

1   Before the crankshaft is removed, check the endplay. Mount a dial indicator with the stem in line with the crankshaft and just touching one of the crank throws (see illustration).

2   Push the crankshaft all the way to the rear and zero the dial indicator. Next, pry the crankshaft to the front as far as possible and check the reading on the dial indicator. The distance that it moves is the end-play. If it's greater than the limit listed in this Chapter's Specifications, check the crankshaft thrust surfaces for wear. If no wear is evident, new main bearings should correct the endplay.

3   If a dial indicator isn't available, feeler gauges can be used. Gently pry or push the crankshaft all the way to the front of the engine. Slip feeler gauges between the crankshaft and the front face of the thrust main bearing (number 3 bearing) to determine the clearance (see illustration).

4   Check the main bearing caps to see if they're marked to indicate their locations. They should be numbered consecutively from the front of the engine to the rear (see illustration). If they aren't, mark them with number stamping dies or a center-punch. Main bearing caps generally have a cast-in arrow, which points to the front of the engine. Loosen the main bearing cap bolts 1/4-turn at a time each, until they can be removed by hand. Note if any stud bolts are used and make sure they're returned to their original locations when the crankshaft is reinstalled.

5   Gently tap the caps with a soft-face hammer, then separate them from the engine block. If necessary, use the bolts as levers to remove the caps. Try not to drop the bearing inserts if they come out with the caps.

6   Carefully lift the crankshaft out of the engine. It may be a good idea to have an assistant available, since the crankshaft is quite heavy. With the bearing inserts in place in the engine block and main bearing caps, return the caps to their respective locations on the engine block and tighten the bolts finger tight.

13.1 Checking crankshaft endplay with a dial indicator

13.3 Checking crankshaft endplay with a feeler gauge

13.4 The main bearing caps are numbered from the front to the rear of the engine and have cast-in arrow that point to the front of the engine when the caps are installed

14 Engine block - cleaning

▸ Refer to illustrations 14.1, 14.8 and 14.10

✳✳ CAUTION:

The core plugs (also known as freeze plugs or soft plugs) may be difficult or impossible to retrieve if they're driven into the block coolant passages.

1   Remove all the core plugs from the engine block. To do this, knock one side of the plug into the block with a hammer and punch, then grasp it with large pliers and pull it out (see illustrations).

2   Using a gasket scraper, remove all traces of gasket material from the engine block. Be very careful not to nick or gouge the gasket sealing surfaces.

3   Remove the main bearing caps and separate the bearing inserts from the caps and the engine block. Tag the bearings, indicating which cylinder they were removed from and whether they were in the cap or the block, then set them aside.

4   Remove all of the threaded oil gallery plugs from the block. The plugs are usually very tight - they may have to be drilled out and the holes retapped. Use new plugs when the engine is reassembled.

5   If the engine is extremely dirty it should be taken to an automotive machine shop to be steam cleaned or hot tanked.

6   After the block is returned, clean all oil holes and oil galleries one more time. Brushes specifically designed for this purpose are available at most auto parts stores. Flush the passages with warm water until the water runs clear, dry the block thoroughly and wipe all machined surfaces with a light, rust preventive oil. If you have access to compressed air, use it to speed the drying process and to blow out all the oil holes and galleries.

✳✳ WARNING:

Wear eye protection when using compressed air!

7   If the block isn't extremely dirty or sludged up, you can do an adequate cleaning job with hot soapy water and a stiff brush. Take plenty of time and do a thorough job. Regardless of the cleaning

14.1a A hammer and large punch can be used to knock the core plugs sideways in their bores

14.1b Pull the core plugs from the block with pliers

14.8 All bolt holes in the block - particularly the main bearing cap and head bolt holes - should be cleaned and restored with a tap (be sure to remove debris from the holes after this is done)

14.10 A large socket on an extension can be used to drive the new core plugs into the bores

method used, be sure to clean all oil holes and galleries very thoroughly, dry the block completely and coat all machined surfaces with light oil.

8   The threaded holes in the block must be clean to ensure accurate torque readings during reassembly. Run the proper size tap into each of the holes to remove rust, corrosion, thread sealant or sludge and restore damaged threads (see illustration). If possible, use compressed air to clear the holes of debris produced by this operation. Now is a good time to clean the threads on the head bolts and the main bearing cap bolts as well.

9   Reinstall the main bearing caps and tighten the bolts finger tight.

10 After coating the sealing surfaces of the new core plugs with Permatex no. 2 sealant, install them in the engine block (see illustration). Make sure they're driven in straight and seated properly or leakage could result. Special tools are available for this purpose, but a large socket, with an outside diameter that will just slip into the core plug, a 1/2-inch drive extension and a hammer will work just as well.

11 Apply non-hardening sealant (such as Permatex no. 2 or Teflon pipe sealant) to the new oil gallery plugs and thread them into the holes in the block. Make sure they're tightened securely.

12 If the engine isn't going to be reassembled right away, cover it with a large plastic trash bag to keep it clean.

15 Engine block - inspection

▶ **Refer to illustrations 15.4a, 15.4b and 15.4c**

1   Before the block is inspected, it should be cleaned as described in Section 14.

2   Visually check the block for cracks, rust and corrosion. Look for stripped threads in the threaded holes. It's also a good idea to have the block checked for hidden cracks by an automotive machine shop that has the special equipment to do this type of work. If defects are found, have the block repaired, if possible, or replaced.

3   Check the cylinder bores for scuffing and scoring.

4   Measure the diameter of each cylinder at the top (just under the ridge area), center and bottom of the cylinder bore, parallel to the crankshaft axis (see illustrations).

5   Next, measure each cylinder's diameter at the same three locations across the crankshaft axis. Compare the results to this Chapter's Specifications.

6   If the required precision measuring tools aren't available, the piston-to-cylinder clearances can be obtained, though not quite as accurately, using feeler gauge stock. Feeler gauge stock comes in 12-inch lengths and various thickness and is generally available at auto parts stores.

7   To check the clearance, select a feeler gauge and slip it into the cylinder along with the matching piston. The piston must be positioned exactly as it normally would be. The feeler gauge must be between the piston and cylinder on one of the thrust faces (90-degrees to the piston

15.4a Measure the diameter of each cylinder at a right angle to the engine centerline (A), and parallel to the engine centerline (B) - out-of-round is the difference between A and B; taper is the difference between A and B at the top of the cylinder and A and B at the bottom of the cylinder

15.4b The ability to "feel" when the telescoping gauge is at the correct point will be developed over time, so work slowly and repeat the check until you're satisfied the bore measurementis accurate

15.4c The gauge is then measured with a micrometer to determine the bore size

pin bore).

8   The piston should slip through the cylinder (with the feeler gauge in place) with moderate pressure.

9   If it falls through or slides through easily, the clearance is excessive and a new piston will be required. If the piston binds at the lower end of the cylinder and is loose toward the top, the cylinder is tapered. If tight spots are encountered as the piston/feeler gauge is rotated in the cylinder, the cylinder is out-of-round.

10 Repeat the procedure for the remaining pistons and cylinders.

11 If the cylinder walls are badly scuffed or scored, or if they're out-of-round or tapered beyond the limits given in this Chapter's Specifications, have the engine block rebored and honed at an automotive machine shop. If a rebore is done, oversize pistons and rings will be required.

12 If the cylinders are in reasonably good condition and not worn to the outside of the limits, and if the piston-to-cylinder clearances can be maintained properly, then they don't have to be rebored. Honing is all that's necessary (see Section 16).

16 Cylinder honing

◗ Refer to illustrations 16.3a and 16.3b

1   Prior to engine reassembly, the cylinder bores must be honed so the new piston rings will seat correctly and provide the best possible combustion chamber seal.

➡Note: If you don't have the tools or don't want to tackle the honing operation, most automotive machine shops will do it for a reasonable fee.

2   Before honing the cylinders, install the main bearing caps and tighten the bolts to the torque listed in this Chapter's Specifications.

3   Two types of cylinder hones are commonly available - the flex hone or "bottle brush" type and the more traditional surfacing hone with spring-loaded stones. Both will do the job, but for the less experienced mechanic the "bottle brush" hone will probably be easier to use. You'll also need some kerosene or honing oil, rags and an electric drill motor. Proceed as follows:

a) Mount the hone in the drill motor, compress the stones and slip it into the first cylinder (see illustration). Be sure to wear safety goggles or a face shield!

b) Lubricate the cylinder with plenty of honing oil, turn on the drill and move the hone up-and-down in the cylinder at a pace that will produce a fine crosshatch pattern on the cylinder walls. Ideally, the crosshatch lines should intersect at approximately a 60-degree angle (see illustration). Be sure to use plenty of lubricant and don't take off any more material than is absolutely necessary to produce the desired finish.

➡Note: Piston ring manufacturers may specify a smaller crosshatch angle than the traditional 60-degrees - read and follow any instructions included with the new rings.

c) Don't withdraw the hone from the cylinder while it's running. Instead, shut off the drill and continue moving the hone up-and-down in the cylinder until it comes to a complete stop, then compress the stones and withdraw the hone. If you're using a "bottle brush" type hone, stop the drill motor, then turn the chuck in the normal direction of rotation while withdrawing the hone from the cylinder.

d) Wipe the oil out of the cylinder and repeat the procedure for the remaining cylinders.

4   After the honing job is complete, chamfer the top edges of the cylinder bores with a small file so the rings won't catch when the pistons are installed. Be very careful not to nick the cylinder walls with the end of the file.

5   The entire engine block must be washed again very thoroughly with warm, soapy water to remove all traces of the abrasive grit produced during the honing operation.

➡Note: The bores can be considered clean when a lint-free white cloth - dampened with clean engine oil - used to wipe them out doesn't pick-up any more honing residue, which will show up as gray areas on the cloth. Be sure to run a brush through all oil holes and galleries and flush them with running water.

6   After rinsing, dry the block and apply a coat of light rust preventive oil to all machined surfaces. Wrap the block in a plastic trash bag to keep it clean and set it aside until reassembly.

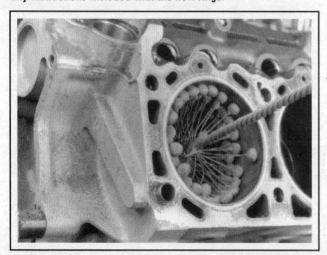

16.3a A "bottle brush" hone is the easiest type of hone to use

16.3b The cylinder hone should leave a smooth, crosshatch pattern with the lines intersecting at approximately a 60-degree angle

17 Pistons/connecting rods - inspection

♦ Refer to illustrations 17.4a, 17.4b, 17.10 and 17.11

1   Before the inspection process can be carried out, the piston/connecting rod assemblies must be cleaned and the original piston rings removed from the pistons.

➡**Note: Always use new piston rings when the engine is reassembled.**

2   Using a piston ring installation tool, carefully remove the rings from the pistons. Be careful not to nick or gouge the pistons in the process.

3   Scrape all traces of carbon from the top of the piston. A hand-held wire brush or a piece of fine emery cloth can be used once the majority of the deposits have been scraped away. Do not, under any circumstances, use a wire brush mounted in a drill motor to remove deposits from the pistons. The piston material is soft and may be eroded away by the wire brush.

4   Use a piston ring groove cleaning tool to remove carbon deposits from the ring grooves. If a tool isn't available, a piece broken off the old ring will do the job. Be very careful to remove only the carbon deposits - don't remove any metal and do not nick or scratch the sides of the ring grooves (see illustrations).

5   Once the deposits have been removed, clean the piston/rod assemblies with solvent and dry them with compressed air (if available). Make sure the oil return holes in the back sides of the ring grooves are clear.

6   If the pistons and cylinder walls aren't damaged or worn excessively and if the engine block is not rebored, new pistons won't be necessary. Normal piston wear appears as even vertical wear on the piston thrust surfaces and slight looseness of the top ring in its groove. New piston rings, however, should always be used when an engine is rebuilt.

7   Carefully inspect each piston for cracks around the skirt, at the pin bosses and at the ring lands.

8   Look for scoring and scuffing on the thrust faces of the skirt, holes in the piston crown and burned areas at the edge of the crown. If the skirt is scored or scuffed, the engine may have been suffering from overheating and/or abnormal combustion, which caused excessively high operating temperatures. The cooling and lubrication systems should be checked thoroughly. A hole in the piston crown is an indication that abnormal combustion (preignition) was occurring. Burned areas at the edge of the piston crown are usually evidence of spark knock (detonation). If any of the above problems exist, the causes must

17.4a The piston ring grooves can be cleaned with a special tool, as shown here . . .

be corrected or the damage will occur again. The causes may include intake air leaks, incorrect fuel/air mixture, incorrect ignition timing and EGR system malfunctions.

9   Corrosion of the piston, in the form of small pits, indicates that coolant is leaking into the combustion chamber and/or the crankcase. Again, the cause must be corrected or the problem may persist in the rebuilt engine.

10 Measure the piston ring side clearance by laying a new piston ring in each ring groove and slipping a feeler gauge in beside it (see illustration). Check the clearance at three or four locations around each groove. Be sure to use the correct ring for each groove - they are different. If the side clearance is greater than the figure listed in this Chapter's Specifications, new pistons will have to be used.

11 Check the piston-to-bore clearance by measuring the bore (see Section 15) and the piston diameter. Make sure the pistons and bores are correctly matched. Measure the piston across the skirt, at a 90-degree angle to and in line with the piston pin (see illustration). Subtract the piston diameter from the bore diameter to obtain the clearance. If it's greater than specified, the block will have to be rebored and new pistons and rings installed.

17.4b . . . or a section of a broken ring

17.10 Check the ring side clearance with a feeler gauge at several points

12 Check the piston-to-rod clearance by twisting the piston and rod in opposite directions. Any noticeable play indicates excessive wear, which must be corrected. The piston/connecting rod assemblies should be taken to an automotive machine shop to have the pistons and rods resized and new pins installed.

13 If the pistons must be removed from the connecting rods for any reason, they should be taken to an automotive machine shop. While they are there have the connecting rods checked for bend and twist, since automotive machine shops have special equipment for this purpose.

➡**Note: Unless new pistons and/or connecting rods must be installed, do not disassemble the pistons and connecting rods.**

14 Check the connecting rods for cracks and other damage. Temporarily remove the rod caps, lift out the old bearing inserts, wipe the rod and cap bearing surfaces clean and inspect them for nicks, gouges and scratches. After checking the rods, replace the old bearings, slip the caps into place and tighten the nuts finger tight.

➡**Note: If the engine is being rebuilt because of a connecting rod knock, be sure to install new rods.**

17.11 Measure the piston diameter at a 90-degree angle to the piston pin and in line with it

18 Crankshaft - inspection

▶ **Refer to illustrations 18.1, 18.2, 18.4, 18.6 and 18.8**

1 Remove all burrs from the crankshaft oil holes with a stone, file or scraper (see illustration).

2 Clean the crankshaft with solvent and dry it with compressed air (if available). Be sure to clean the oil holes with a stiff brush (see illustration) and flush them with solvent.

3 Check the main and connecting rod bearing journals for uneven wear, scoring, pits and cracks.

4 Rub a penny across each journal several times (see illustration). If a journal picks up copper from the penny, it's too rough and must be reground.

5 Check the rest of the crankshaft for cracks and other damage. It should be magnafluxed to reveal hidden cracks - an automotive machine shop will handle the procedure.

6 Using a micrometer, measure the diameter of the main and connecting rod journals and compare the results to this Chapter's Speci-

fications (see illustration). By measuring the diameter at a number of points around each journal's circumference, you'll be able to determine whether or not the journal is out-of-round. Take the measurement at each end of the journal, near the crank throws, to determine if the journal is tapered.

7 If the crankshaft journals are damaged, tapered, out-of-round or worn beyond the limits given in the Specifications, have the crankshaft re-ground by an automotive machine shop. Be sure to use the correct size bearing inserts if the crankshaft is reconditioned.

8 Check the oil seal journals at each end of the crankshaft for wear and damage. If the seal has worn a groove in the journal, or if it's nicked or scratched (see illustration), the new seal may leak when the engine is reassembled. In some cases, an automotive machine shop may be able to repair the journal by pressing on a thin sleeve. If repair isn't feasible, a new or different crankshaft should be installed.

9 Refer to Section 19 and examine the main and rod bearing inserts.

18.1 The oil holes should be chamfered so sharp edges don't gouge or scratch the new bearings

18.2 Use a wire or stiff plastic bristle brush to clean the oil passages in the crankshaft

18.4 Rubbing a penny lengthwise on each journal will reveal its condition - if copper rubs off and is embedded in the crankshaft, the journals should be reground

18.6 Measure the diameter of each crankshaft journal at several points to detect taper and out-of-round conditions

18.8 If the seals have worn grooves in the crankshaft journals, or if the seal contact surfaces are nicked or scratched, the new seals will leak

19 Main and connecting rod bearings - inspection

◆ **Refer to illustration 19.1**

1   Even though the main and connecting rod bearings should be replaced with new ones during the engine overhaul, the old bearings should be retained for close examination, as they may reveal valuable information about the condition of the engine (see illustration).

2   Bearing failure occurs because of lack of lubrication, the presence of dirt or other foreign particles, overloading the engine and corrosion. Regardless of the cause of bearing failure, it must be corrected before the engine is reassembled to prevent it from happening again.

3   When examining the bearings, remove them from the engine block, the main bearing caps, the connecting rods and the rod caps and lay them out on a clean surface in the same general position as their location in the engine. This will enable you to match any bearing problems with the corresponding crankshaft journal.

4   Dirt and other foreign particles get into the engine in a variety of ways. It may be left in the engine during assembly, or it may pass through filters or the PCV system. It may get into the oil, and from there into the bearings. Metal chips from machining operations and normal engine wear are often present. Abrasives are sometimes left in engine components after reconditioning, especially when parts are not thoroughly cleaned using the proper cleaning methods. Whatever the source, these foreign objects often end up embedded in the soft bearing material and are easily recognized. Large particles will not embed in the bearing and will score or gouge the bearing and journal. The best prevention for this cause of bearing failure is to clean all parts thoroughly and keep everything spotlessly clean during engine assembly. Frequent and regular engine oil and filter changes are also recommended.

5   Lack of lubrication (or lubrication breakdown) has a number of interrelated causes. Excessive heat (which thins the oil), overloading (which squeezes the oil from the bearing face) and oil leakage or throw off (from excessive bearing clearances, worn oil pump or high engine speeds) all contribute to lubrication breakdown. Blocked oil passages, which usually are the result of misaligned oil holes in a bearing shell, will also oil starve a bearing and destroy it. When lack of lubrication is the cause of bearing failure, the bearing material is wiped or extruded from the steel backing of the bearing. Temperatures may increase to the point where the steel backing turns blue from overheating.

6   Driving habits can have a definite effect on bearing life. Full throttle, low speed operation (lugging the engine) puts very high loads on bearings, which tends to squeeze out the oil film. These loads cause the bearings to flex, which produces fine cracks in the bearing face (fatigue failure). Eventually the bearing material will loosen in pieces and tear away from the steel backing. Short trip driving leads to corrosion of bearings because insufficient engine heat is produced to drive

19.1 Typical bearing failures

off the condensed water and corrosive gases. These products collect in the engine oil, forming acid and sludge. As the oil is carried to the engine bearings, the acid attacks and corrodes the bearing material.

7   Incorrect bearing installation during engine assembly will lead to bearing failure as well. Tight fitting bearings leave insufficient bearing oil clearance and will result in oil starvation. Dirt or foreign particles trapped behind a bearing insert result in high spots on the bearing which lead to failure.

20 Camshaft, lifters and bearings - inspection and replacement

CAMSHAFT INSPECTION

▸ **Refer to illustration 20.1 and 20.5**

1   Measure the major (A) and minor (B) diameters of each cam lobe (see illustration). The difference between the readings is the lobe lift. Compare your measurement to the lobe lift in this Chapter's Specifications.

2   If the lobe lift is 0.005-inch less than specified, replace the camshaft and all the lifters or followers.

3   After the camshaft is removed from the engine, cleaned with solvent and dried, inspect the bearing journals for uneven wear, pitting and evidence of seizure. If the journals are damaged, the bearing inserts are probably damaged as well. Both the camshaft and bearings will have to be replaced with new ones.

4   Inspect the bearing journals for uneven wear, pitting or evidence of seizure. If the journals are damaged, the bearing inserts are probably damaged as well. Both the camshaft and bearings will have to be replaced with new ones.

5   Measure the camshaft bearing journals with a micrometer (see illustration) to determine if they are excessively worn or out-of-round. If they are more than 0.001-inch out-of-round, the camshaft should be replaced with a new one.

6   Check the camshaft lobes for heat discoloration, score marks, chipped areas, pitting and uneven wear.

7   If the lobes are in good condition and if the lobe lift measurements are as specified, the camshaft can be reused.

LIFTER INSPECTION

▸ **Refer to illustration 20.9**

8   Clean the lifters with solvent and dry them thoroughly without mixing them up.

9   Check that the roller on each lifter turns freely and shows no signs of pitting, scoring or other wear (see illustration). Check the pushrod seat in each lifter for wear. Also make sure each lifter fits in its original bore without excessive looseness. Wear is only normally encountered at very high mileage or in cases of neglected engine lubrication.

10 Press down on the plunger using a Phillips screwdriver to make sure it operates freely without binding.

11 If the lifters show signs of wear or binding they must be replaced as a complete set and the camshaft must be replaced as well.

12 If new lifters are being installed, a new camshaft must also be installed. If a new camshaft is installed, then use new lifters as well. Never install used lifters unless the original camshaft is used and the lifters can be installed in their original locations.

BEARING REPLACEMENT

13 Camshaft bearing replacement requires special tools and expertise that place it outside the scope of the do-it-yourselfer. Take the block (V6) or head (four-cylinder) to an automotive machine shop to ensure that the job is done correctly.

20.1 To verify camshaft lobe lift, measure the major (A) and minor (B) diameters of each lobe with a micrometer or vernier caliper - subtract each minor diameter from the major diameter to arrive at lobe lift

20.5 Use a micrometer to check the camshaft journals for wear, taper and out-of-round conditions

20.9 The roller on roller lifters must turn freely - check for wear and excessive play as well

21 Engine overhaul - reassembly sequence

1   Before beginning engine reassembly, make sure you have all the necessary new parts, gaskets and seals as well as the following items on hand:

    Common hand tools
    A 1/2-inch drive torque wrench
    Piston ring installation tool
    Piston ring compressor
    Vibration damper installation tool
    Short lengths of rubber or plastic hose
      to fit over connecting rod bolts
    Plastigage
    Feeler gauges
    A fine-tooth file
    New engine oil
    Engine assembly lube or moly-base grease
    Gasket sealant
    Thread locking compound

2   In order to save time and avoid problems, engine reassembly must be done in the following general order:

FOUR-CYLINDER ENGINE

    New camshaft bearings (must be done by an automotive machine
      shop)
    Piston rings
    Crankshaft and main bearings
    Piston/connecting rod assemblies
    Oil pump

    Front engine cover
    Oil pan
    Camshaft and related components
    Cylinder heads
    Timing belt, sprockets and covers
    Intake and exhaust manifolds
    Valve cover
    Clutch and flywheel or driveplate

V6 ENGINES

    New camshaft bearings (must be done by an automotive machine
      shop)
    Piston rings
    Crankshaft and main bearings
    Piston/connecting rod assemblies
    Camshaft
    Valve lifters
    Timing chain and sprockets
    Timing chain cover
    Oil pump
    Oil pan
    Cylinder heads
    Intake and exhaust manifolds
    Rocker arms and pushrods
    Valve covers
    Clutch and flywheel or driveplate

22 Piston rings - installation

▶ **Refer to illustrations 22.3, 22.4, 22.5, 22.9a, 22.9b and 22.12**

1   Before installing the new piston rings, the ring end gaps must be checked. It's assumed that the piston ring side clearance has been checked and verified correct (see Section 17).

2   Lay out the piston/connecting rod assemblies and the new ring sets so the ring sets will be matched with the same piston and cylinder during the end gap measurement and engine assembly.

3   Insert the top (number one) ring into the first cylinder and square it up with the cylinder walls by pushing it in with the top of the piston (see illustration). The ring should be near the bottom of the cylinder, at the lower limit of ring travel.

4   To measure the end gap, slip feeler gauges between the ends of the ring until a gauge equal to the gap width is found (see illustration). The feeler gauge should slide between the ring ends with a slight amount of drag. Compare the measurement to this Chapter's Specifications. If the gap is larger or smaller than specified, double-check to make sure you have the correct rings before proceeding.

5   If the gap is too small, it must be enlarged or the ring ends may come in contact with each other during engine operation, which can cause serious damage to the engine. The end gap can be increased by filing the ring ends very carefully with a fine file. Mount the file in a vise equipped with soft jaws, slip the ring over the file with the ends contacting the file face and slowly move the ring to remove material from the ends. When performing this operation, file only from the outside in (see illustration).

22.3 When checking piston ring end gap, the ring must be square in the cylinder bore (this is done by pushing the ring down with the top of a piston as shown)

6   Excess end gap isn't critical unless it's greater than 0.040-inch. Again, double-check to make sure you have the correct rings for your engine.

7   Repeat the procedure for each ring that will be installed in the

ENGINE BEARING ANALYSIS

Debris

Babbitt bearing embedded with debris from machinings

Microscopic detail of debris

Microscopic detail of gouges

Overplated copper alloy bearing gouged by cast iron debris

Aluminum bearing embedded with glass beads

Microscopic detail of glass beads

Damaged lining caused by dirt left on the bearing back

Misassembly

Result of a lower half assembled as an upper - blocking the oil flow

Excessive oil clearance is indicated by a short contact arc

Polished and oil-stained backs are a result of a poor fit in the housing bore

Result of a wrong, reversed, or shifted cap

Overloading

Damage from excessive idling which resulted in an oil film unable to support the load imposed

Damaged upper connecting rod bearings caused by engine lugging; the lower main bearings (not shown) were similarly affected

The damage shown in these upper and lower connecting rod bearings was caused by engine operation at a higher-than-rated speed under load

Misalignment

A warped crankshaft caused this pattern of severe wear in the center, diminishing toward the ends

A poorly finished crankshaft caused the equally spaced scoring shown

A tapered housing bore caused the damage along one edge of this pair

A bent connecting rod led to the damage in the "V" pattern

Lubrication

Result of dry start: The bearings on the left, farthest from the oil pump, show more damage

Result of a low oil supply or oil starvation

Severe wear as a result of inadequate oil clearance

Corrosion

Microscopic detail of corrosion

Corrosion is an acid attack on the bearing lining generally caused by inadequate maintenance, extremely hot or cold operation, or inferior oils or fuels

Microscopic detail of cavitation

Example of cavitation - a surface erosion caused by pressure changes in the oil film

Damage from excessive thrust or insufficient axial clearance

Bearing affected by oil dilution caused by excessive blow-by or a rich mixture

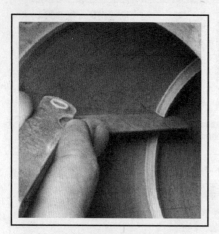

22.4 With the ring square in the cylinder, measure the end gap with a feeler gauge

22.5 If the end gap is too small, clamp a file in a vise and file the ring ends (from the outside in only) to enlarge the gap slightly

22.9a Installing the spacer/expander in the oil control ring groove

first cylinder and for each ring in the remaining cylinders. Remember to keep rings, pistons and cylinders matched up.

8   Once the ring end gaps have been checked/corrected, the rings can be installed on the pistons.

9   The oil control ring (lowest one on the piston) is usually installed first. It's composed of three separate components. Slip the spacer/expander into the groove (see illustration). If an anti-rotation tang is used, make sure it's inserted into the drilled hole in the ring groove. Next, install the lower side rail. Don't use a piston ring installation tool on the oil ring side rails, as they may be damaged. Instead, place one end of the side rail into the groove between the spacer/expander and the ring land, hold it firmly in place and slide a finger around the piston while pushing the rail into the groove (see illustration). Next, install the upper side rail in the same manner.

10   After the three oil ring components have been installed, check to make sure that both the upper and lower side rails can be turned

smoothly in the ring groove.

11   The number two (middle) ring is installed next. It's usually stamped with a mark which must face up, toward the top of the piston.

➡**Note: Always follow the instructions printed on the ring package or box - different manufacturers may require different approaches. Do not mix up the top and middle rings, as they have different cross-sections.**

12   Use a piston ring installation tool and make sure the identification mark is facing the top of the piston, then slip the ring into the middle groove on the piston (see illustration). Don't expand the ring any more than necessary to slide it over the piston.

13   Install the number one (top) ring in the same manner. Make sure the mark is facing up. Be careful not to confuse the number one and number two rings.

14   Repeat the procedure for the remaining pistons and rings.

22.9b DO NOT use a piston ring installation tool when installing the oil ring side rails

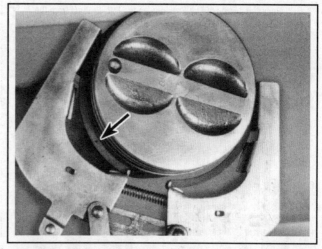

22.12 Installing the compression rings with a ring expander - the mark (arrow) must face up

23 Crankshaft - installation and main bearing oil clearance check

◆ **Refer to illustrations 23.5, 23.11, 23.15, and 23.22**

1 Crankshaft installation is the first step in engine reassembly. It's assumed at this point that the engine block and crankshaft have been cleaned, inspected and repaired or reconditioned.

2 Position the engine with the bottom facing up.

3 Remove the main bearing cap bolts and lift out the caps. Lay them out in the proper order to ensure correct installation.

4 If they're still in place, remove the original bearing inserts from the block and the main bearing caps. Wipe the bearing surfaces of the block and caps with a clean, lint-free cloth. They must be kept spotlessly clean.

MAIN BEARING OIL CLEARANCE CHECK

5 Clean the back sides of the new main bearing inserts and lay one in each main bearing saddle in the block. If one of the bearing inserts from each set has a large groove in it, make sure the grooved insert is installed in the block. Lay the other bearing from each set in the corresponding main bearing cap. Make sure the tab on the bearing insert fits into the recess in the block or cap.

23.5 The upper main bearing in position (flanged thrust bearing shown) - the oil hole in the bearing must align with the oil hole(s) in the block

23.11 Lay the Plastigage strips (arrow) on the main bearing journals, parallel to the crankshaft centerline

❈❈ CAUTION:

The oil holes in the block must line up with the oil holes in the bearing insert (see illustration). Do not hammer the bearing into place and don't nick or gouge the bearing faces. No lubrication should be used at this time.

6 The flanged thrust bearing must be installed in the third cap and saddle (counting from the front of the engine).

7 Clean the faces of the bearings in the block and the crankshaft main bearing journals with a clean, lint-free cloth.

8 Check or clean the oil holes in the crankshaft, as any dirt here can go only one way - straight through the new bearings.

9 Once you're certain the crankshaft is clean, carefully lay it in position in the main bearings.

10 Before the crankshaft can be permanently installed, the main bearing oil clearance must be checked.

11 Cut several pieces of the appropriate size Plastigage (they must be slightly shorter than the width of the main bearings) and place one piece on each crankshaft main bearing journal, parallel with the journal axis (see illustration).

12 Clean the faces of the bearings in the caps and install the caps in their respective positions (don't mix them up) with the arrows pointing toward the front of the engine. Don't disturb the Plastigage.

13 Starting with the center main and working out toward the ends, tighten the main bearing cap bolts, in three steps, to the torque listed in this Chapter's Specifications. Don't rotate the crankshaft at any time during this operation.

14 Remove the bolts and carefully lift off the main bearing caps. Keep them in order. Don't disturb the Plastigage or rotate the crankshaft. If any of the main bearing caps are difficult to remove, tap them gently from side-to-side with a soft-face hammer to loosen them.

15 Compare the width of the crushed Plastigage on each journal to the scale printed on the Plastigage envelope to obtain the main bearing oil clearance (see illustration). Check the Specifications to make sure it's correct.

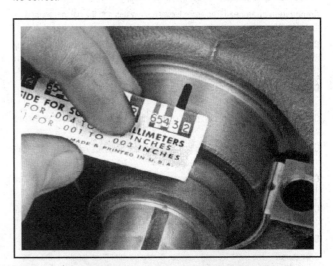

23.15 Compare the width of the crushed Plastigage to the scale on the envelope to determine the main bearing oil clearance (always take the measurement at the widest point of the Plastigage); be sure to use the correct scale - standard and metric ones are included

GLOSSARY

B

Backlash - The amount of play between two parts. Usually refers to how much one gear can be moved back and forth without moving the gear with which it's meshed.

Bearing Caps - The caps held in place by nuts or bolts which, in turn, hold the bearing surface. This space is for lubricating oil to enter.

Bearing clearance - The amount of space left between shaft and bearing surface. This space is for lubricating oil to enter.

Bearing crush - The additional height which is purposely manufactured into each bearing half to ensure complete contact of the bearing back with the housing bore when the engine is assembled.

Bearing knock - The noise created by movement of a part in a loose or worn bearing.

Blueprinting - Dismantling an engine and reassembling it to EXACT specifications.

Bore - An engine cylinder, or any cylindrical hole; also used to describe the process of enlarging or accurately refinishing a hole with a cutting tool, as to bore an engine cylinder. The bore size is the diameter of the hole.

Boring - Renewing the cylinders by cutting them out to a specified size. A boring bar is used to make the cut.

Bottom end - A term which refers collectively to the engine block, crankshaft, main bearings and the big ends of the connecting rods.

Break-in - The period of operation between installation of new or rebuilt parts and time in which parts are worn to the correct fit. Driving at reduced and varying speed for a specified mileage to permit parts to wear to the correct fit.

Bushing - A one-piece sleeve placed in a bore to serve as a bearing surface for shaft, piston pin, etc. Usually replaceable.

C

Camshaft - The shaft in the engine, on which a series of lobes are located for operating the valve mechanisms. The camshaft is driven by gears or sprockets and a timing chain. Usually referred to simply as the cam.

Carbon - Hard, or soft, black deposits found in combustion chamber, on plugs, under rings, on and under valve heads.

Cast iron - An alloy of iron and more than two percent carbon, used for engine blocks and heads because it's relatively inexpensive and easy to mold into complex shapes.

Chamfer - To bevel across (or a bevel on) the sharp edge of an object.

Chase - To repair damaged threads with a tap or die.

Combustion chamber - The space between the piston and the cylinder head, with the piston at top dead center, in which air-fuel mixture is burned.

Compression ratio - The relationship between cylinder volume (clearance volume) when the piston is at top dead center and cylinder volume when the piston is at bottom dead center.

Connecting rod - The rod that connects the crank on the crankshaft with the piston. Sometimes called a con rod.

Connecting rod cap - The part of the connecting rod assembly that attaches the rod to the crankpin.

Core plug - Soft metal plug used to plug the casting holes for the coolant passages in the block.

Crankcase - The lower part of the engine in which the crankshaft rotates; includes the lower section of the cylinder block and the oil pan.

Crank kit - A reground or reconditioned crankshaft and new main and connecting rod bearings.

Crankpin - The part of a crankshaft to which a connecting rod is attached.

Crankshaft - The main rotating member, or shaft, running the length of the crankcase, with offset throws to which the connecting rods are attached; changes the reciprocating motion of the pistons into rotating motion.

Cylinder sleeve - A replaceable sleeve, or liner, pressed into the cylinder block to form the cylinder bore.

D

Deburring - Removing the burrs (rough edges or areas) from a bearing.

Deglazer - A tool, rotated by an electric motor, used to remove glaze from cylinder walls so a new set of rings will seat.

E

Endplay - The amount of lengthwise movement between two parts. As applied to a crankshaft, the distance that the crankshaft can move forward and back in the cylinder block.

F

Face - A machinist's term that refers to removing metal from the end of a shaft or the face of a larger part, such as a flywheel.

Fatigue - A breakdown of material through a large number of loading and unloading cycles. The first signs are cracks followed shortly by breaks.

Feeler gauge - A thin strip of hardened steel, ground to an exact thickness, used to check clearances between parts.

Free height - The unloaded length or height of a spring.

Freeplay - The looseness in a linkage, or an assembly of parts, between the initial application of force and actual movement. Usually perceived as slop or slight delay.

Freeze plug - See Core plug.

G

Gallery - A large passage in the block that forms a reservoir for engine oil pressure.

Glaze - The very smooth, glassy finish that develops on cylinder walls while an engine is in service.

H

Heli-Coil - A rethreading device used when threads are worn or damaged. The device is installed in a retapped hole to reduce the thread size to the original size.

I

Installed height - The spring's measured length or height, as installed on the cylinder head. Installed height is measured from the spring seat to the underside of the spring retainer.

J

Journal - The surface of a rotating shaft which turns in a bearing.

K

Keeper - The split lock that holds the valve spring retainer in position on the valve stem.

Key - A small piece of metal inserted into matching grooves machined into two parts fitted together - such as a gear pressed onto a shaft - which prevents slippage between the two parts.

Knock - The heavy metallic engine sound, produced in the combustion chamber as a result of abnormal combustion - usually detonation. Knock is usually caused by a loose or worn bearing. Also referred to as detonation, pinging and spark knock. Connecting rod or main bearing knocks are created by too much oil clearance or insufficient lubrication.

L

Lands - The portions of metal between the piston ring grooves.

Lapping the valves - Grinding a valve face and its seat together with lapping compound.

Lash - The amount of free motion in a gear train, between gears, or in a mechanical assembly, that occurs before movement can begin. Usually refers to the lash in a valve train.

Lifter - The part that rides against the cam to transfer motion to the rest of the valve train.

M

Machining - The process of using a machine to remove metal from a metal part.

Main bearings - The plain, or babbitt, bearings that support the crankshaft.

Main bearing caps - The cast iron caps, bolted to the bottom of the block, that support the main bearings.

O

O.D. - Outside diameter.

Oil gallery - A pipe or drilled passageway in the engine used to carry engine oil from one area to another.

Oil ring - The lower ring, or rings, of a piston; designed to prevent excessive amounts of oil from working up the cylinder walls and into the combustion chamber. Also called an oil-control ring.

Oil seal - A seal which keeps oil from leaking out of a compartment. Usually refers to a dynamic seal around a rotating shaft or other moving part.

O-ring - A type of sealing ring made of a special rubberlike material; in use, the O-ring is compressed into a groove to provide the sealing action.

Overhaul - To completely disassemble a unit, clean and inspect all parts, reassemble it with the original or new parts and make all adjustments necessary for proper operation.

P

Pilot bearing - A small bearing installed in the center of the flywheel (or the rear end of the crankshaft) to support the front end of the input shaft of the transmission.

Pip mark - A little dot or indentation which indicates the top side of a compression ring.

Piston - The cylindrical part, attached to the connecting rod, that moves up and down in the cylinder as the crankshaft rotates. When the fuel charge is fired, the piston transfers the force of the explosion to the connecting rod, then to the crankshaft.

Piston pin (or wrist pin) - The cylindrical and usually hollow steel pin that passes through the piston. The piston pin fastens the piston to the upper end of the connecting rod.

Piston ring - The split ring fitted to the groove in a piston. The ring contacts the sides of the ring groove and also rubs against the cylinder wall, thus sealing space between piston and wall. There are two types of rings: Compression rings seal the compression pressure in the combustion chamber; oil rings scrape excessive oil off the cylinder wall.

Piston ring groove - The slots or grooves cut in piston heads to hold piston rings in position.

Piston skirt - The portion of the piston below the rings and the piston pin hole.

Plastigage - A thin strip of plastic thread, available in different sizes, used for measuring clearances. For example, a strip of plastigage is laid across a bearing journal and mashed as parts are assembled. Then parts are disassembled and the width of the strip is measured to determine clearance between journal and bearing. Commonly used to measure crankshaft main-bearing and connecting rod bearing clearances.

Press-fit - A tight fit between two parts that requires pressure to force the parts together. Also referred to as drive, or force, fit.

Prussian blue - A blue pigment; in solution, useful in determining the area of contact between two surfaces. Prussian blue is commonly used to determine the width and location of the contact area between the valve face and the valve seat.

R

Race (bearing) - The inner or outer ring that provides a contact surface for balls or rollers in bearing.

Ream - To size, enlarge or smooth a hole by using a round cutting tool with fluted edges.

Ring job - The process of reconditioning the cylinders and installing new rings.

Runout - Wobble. The amount a shaft rotates out-of-true.

S

Saddle - The upper main bearing seat.

Scored - Scratched or grooved, as a cylinder wall may be scored by abrasive particles moved up and down by the piston rings.

Scuffing - A type of wear in which there's a transfer of material between parts moving against each other; shows up as pits or grooves in the mating surfaces.

Seat - The surface upon which another part rests or seats. For example, the valve seat is the matched surface upon which the valve face rests. Also used to refer to wearing into a good fit; for example, piston rings seat after a few miles of driving.

Short block - An engine block complete with crankshaft and piston and, usually, camshaft assemblies.

Static balance - The balance of an object while it's stationary.

Step - The wear on the lower portion of a ring land caused by excessive side and back-clearance. The height of the step indicates the ring's extra side clearance and the length of the step projecting from the back wall of the groove represents the ring's back clearance.

Stroke - The distance the piston moves when traveling from top dead center to bottom dead center, or from bottom dead center to top dead center.

Stud - A metal rod with threads on both ends.

T

Tang - A lip on the end of a plain bearing used to align the bearing during assembly.

Tap - To cut threads in a hole. Also refers to the fluted tool used to cut threads.

Taper - A gradual reduction in the width of a shaft or hole; in an engine cylinder, taper usually takes the form of uneven wear, more pronounced at the top than at the bottom.

Throws - The offset portions of the crankshaft to which the connecting rods are affixed.

Thrust bearing - The main bearing that has thrust faces to prevent excessive endplay, or forward and backward movement of the crankshaft.

Thrust washer - A bronze or hardened steel washer placed between two moving parts. The washer prevents longitudinal movement and provides a bearing surface for thrust surfaces of parts.

Tolerance - The amount of variation permitted from an exact size of measurement. Actual amount from smallest acceptable dimension to largest acceptable dimension.

U

Umbrella - An oil deflector placed near the valve tip to throw oil from the valve stem area.

Undercut - A machined groove below the normal surface.

Undersize bearings - Smaller diameter bearings used with re-ground crankshaft journals.

V

Valve grinding - Refacing a valve in a valve-refacing machine.

Valve train - The valve-operating mechanism of an engine; includes all components from the camshaft to the valve.

Vibration damper - A cylindrical weight attached to the front of the crankshaft to minimize torsional vibration (the twist-untwist actions of the crankshaft caused by the cylinder firing impulses). Also called a harmonic balancer.

W

Water jacket - The spaces around the cylinders, between the inner and outer shells of the cylinder block or head, through which coolant circulates.

Web - A supporting structure across a cavity.

Woodruff key - A key with a radiused backside (viewed from the side).

16 If the clearance is not as specified, the bearing inserts may be the wrong size - oversize or undersize (which means different ones will be required). Before deciding that different inserts are needed, make sure that no dirt or oil was between the bearing inserts and the caps or block when the clearance was measured. If the Plastigage was wider at one end than the other, the journal may be tapered (refer to Section 18).

17 Carefully scrape all traces of the Plastigage material off the main bearing journals and/or the bearing faces. Use your fingernail or the edge of a credit card - don't nick or scratch the bearing faces.

FINAL CRANKSHAFT INSTALLATION

18 Carefully lift the crankshaft out of the engine.

19 Clean the bearing faces in the block, then apply a thin, uniform layer of moly-base grease or engine assembly lube to each of the bearing surfaces. Be sure to coat the thrust faces as well as the journal face of the thrust bearing.

20 Make sure the crankshaft journals are clean, then lay the crankshaft back in place in the block.

21 Clean the faces of the bearings in the caps, then apply lubricant to them.

22 Install the caps in their respective positions with the arrows pointing toward the front of the engine. Apply sealant into the corners and on the mating surfaces where the rear main cap meets the cylinder block (see illustration).

23 Install the bolts.

24 Tighten all except the thrust bearing cap bolts to the specified torque (work from the center out and approach the final torque in three steps).

25 Tighten the thrust bearing cap bolts to 10-to-12 ft-lbs.

26 Tap the ends of the crankshaft forward and backward with a lead or brass hammer to line up the main bearing and crankshaft thrust surfaces.

23.22 Before installing the rear main cap, apply sealant to the cap mating surfaces and in the corners where the cap meets the block

27 Retighten all main bearing cap bolts to the specified torque, starting with the center main and working out toward the ends. Also, install the rear main bearing oil seal over the end of the crankshaft. Be sure it is installed to the correct depth (see Chapter 2 Part A, B, C, D or E).

28 On manual transmission-equipped models, install a new pilot bearing in the end of the crankshaft (see Chapter 8).

29 Rotate the crankshaft a number of times by hand to check for any obvious binding.

30 The final step is to check the crankshaft endplay with a feeler gauge or a dial indicator as described in Section 13. The endplay should be correct if the crankshaft thrust faces aren't worn or damaged and new bearings have been installed.

24 Rear main oil seal - installation

See Chapter 2A, 2B, 2C, 2D or 2E.

25 Pistons/connecting rods - installation and rod bearing oil clearance check

▶ **Refer to illustrations 25.5, 25.9, 25.11, 25.13 and 25.17**

1 Before installing the piston/connecting rod assemblies, the cylinder walls must be perfectly clean, the top edge of each cylinder must be chamfered, and the crankshaft must be in place.

2 Remove the cap from the end of the number one connecting rod (refer to the marks made during removal). Remove the original bearing inserts and wipe the bearing surfaces of the connecting rod and cap with a clean, lint-free cloth. They must be kept spotlessly clean.

CONNECTING ROD BEARING OIL CLEARANCE CHECK

3 Clean the back side of the new upper bearing insert, then lay it in place in the connecting rod. Make sure the tab on the bearing fits into the recess in the rod. Don't hammer the bearing insert into place and be very careful not to nick or gouge the bearing face. Don't lubricate the

bearing at this time.

4 Clean the back side of the other bearing insert and install it in the rod cap. Again, make sure the tab on the bearing fits into the recess in the cap, and don't apply any lubricant. It's critically important that the mating surfaces of the bearing and connecting rod are perfectly clean and oil free when they're assembled.

5 Position the piston ring gaps at intervals around the piston (see illustration).

6 Slip a section of plastic or rubber hose over each connecting rod cap bolt.

7 Lubricate the piston and rings with clean engine oil and attach a piston ring compressor to the piston. Leave the skirt protruding about 1/4-inch to guide the piston into the cylinder. The rings must be compressed until they're flush with the piston.

8 Rotate the crankshaft until the number one connecting rod journal is at BDC (bottom dead center) and apply a coat of engine oil to the

25.5 Ring end gap positions: Align the oil ring spacer gap at D, the oil ring side rails at C (one inch either side of the pin centerline), and the compression rings at A and B, one inch either side of the pin centerline

25.9 The arrow in the top of each piston must face the FRONT of the engine as the pistons are installed

cylinder walls.

9   With the arrow on top of the piston (see illustration) facing the front of the engine, gently insert the piston/connecting rod assembly into the number one cylinder bore and rest the bottom edge of the ring compressor on the engine block. Be sure the oil squirt hole in each connecting rod faces towards the center of the engine when the rod is installed.

> ✳✳ **CAUTION:**
>
> **If the oil squirt hole faces the wrong way when the arrow on the piston points toward the front, the rod and piston have been assembled incorrectly. Correct the problem before assembling further.**

10   Tap the top edge of the ring compressor to make sure it's contacting the block around its entire circumference.

11   Gently tap on the top of the piston with the end of a wooden hammer handle (see illustration) while guiding the end of the connecting rod into place on the crankshaft journal. The piston rings may try to pop out of the ring compressor just before entering the cylinder bore,

so keep some down pressure on the ring compressor. Work slowly, and if any resistance is felt as the piston enters the cylinder, stop immediately. Find out what's hanging up and fix it before proceeding. Do not, for any reason, force the piston into the cylinder - you might break a ring and/or the piston.

12   Once the piston/connecting rod assembly is installed, the connecting rod bearing oil clearance must be checked before the rod cap is permanently bolted in place.

13   Cut a piece of the appropriate size Plastigage slightly shorter than the width of the connecting rod bearing and lay it in place on the number one connecting rod journal, parallel with the journal axis (see illustration).

14   Clean the connecting rod cap bearing face, remove the protective hoses from the connecting rod bolts and install the rod cap. Make sure the mating mark on the cap is on the same side as the mark on the connecting rod.

15   Install the nuts and tighten them to the torque listed in this Chapter's Specifications, working up to it in three steps.

➡**Note: Use a thin-wall socket to avoid erroneous torque readings that can result if the socket is wedged between the rod cap and nut. If the socket tends to wedge itself between the nut and the cap, lift up on it slightly until it no longer contacts the cap. Do not rotate the crankshaft at any time during this operation.**

25.11 Drive the piston gently into the cylinder bore with the end of a wooden or plastic hammer handle

25.13 Lay the Plastigage strips (arrow) on the main bearing journals, parallel to the crankshaft centerline

16 Remove the nuts and detach the rod cap, being very careful not to disturb the Plastigage.

17 Compare the width of the crushed Plastigage to the scale printed on the Plastigage envelope to obtain the oil clearance (see illustration). Compare it to the Specifications to make sure the clearance is correct.

18 If the clearance is not as specified, the bearing inserts may be the wrong size (which means different ones will be required). Before deciding that different inserts are needed, make sure that no dirt or oil was between the bearing inserts and the connecting rod or cap when the clearance was measured. Also, recheck the journal diameter. If the Plastigage was wider at one end than the other, the journal may be tapered (refer to Section 18).

FINAL CONNECTING ROD INSTALLATION

19 Carefully scrape all traces of the Plastigage material off the rod journal and/or bearing face. Be very careful not to scratch the bearing - use your fingernail or the edge of a credit card.

20 Make sure the bearing faces are perfectly clean, then apply a uniform layer of clean moly-base grease or engine assembly lube to both of them. You'll have to push the piston into the cylinder to expose the face of the bearing insert in the connecting rod - be sure to slip the protective hoses over the rod bolts first.

21 Slide the connecting rod back into place on the journal, remove the protective hoses from the rod cap bolts, install the rod cap and tighten the nuts to the specified torque. Again, work up to the torque in three steps.

22 Repeat the entire procedure for the remaining pistons/connecting rods.

23 The important points to remember are:

a) *Keep the back sides of the bearing inserts and the insides of the connecting rods and caps perfectly clean when assembling them.*

b) *Make sure you have the correct piston/rod assembly for each cylinder.*

c) *The notch or mark on the piston must face the front of the engine.*

25.17 Measuring the width of the crushed Plastigage to determine the rod bearing oil clearance (be sure to use the correct scale - standard and metric ones are included)

d) *Lubricate the cylinder walls with clean oil.*

e) *Lubricate the bearing faces when installing the rod caps after the oil clearance has been checked.*

24 After all the piston/connecting rod assemblies have been properly installed, rotate the crankshaft a number of times by hand to check for any obvious binding.

25 As a final step, the connecting rod endplay must be checked. Refer to Section 12 for this procedure.

26 Compare the measured endplay to the Specifications to make sure it's correct. If it was correct before disassembly and the original crankshaft and rods were reinstalled, it should still be right. If new rods or a new crankshaft were installed, the endplay may be inadequate. If so, the rods will have to be removed and taken to an automotive machine shop for resizing.

26 Initial start-up and break-in after overhaul

✳✳ WARNING:

Have a fire extinguisher handy when starting the engine for the first time.

1 Once the engine has been installed in the vehicle, double-check the engine oil and coolant levels.

2 With the spark plugs out of the engine and the ignition system disabled (see Section 3), crank the engine until oil pressure registers on the gauge or the light goes out.

3 Install the spark plugs, hook up the plug wires and restore the ignition system functions (see Section 3).

4 Start the engine. It may take a few moments for the fuel system to build up pressure, but the engine should start without a great deal of effort.

➥**Note: If backfiring occurs through the carburetor or throttle body, recheck the valve timing and ignition timing.**

5 After the engine starts, it should be allowed to warm up to normal operating temperature. While the engine is warming up, make a thorough check for fuel, oil and coolant leaks.

6 Shut the engine off and recheck the engine oil and coolant levels.

7 Drive the vehicle to an area with minimum traffic, accelerate from 30 to 50 mph, then allow the vehicle to slow to 30 mph with the throttle closed. Repeat the procedure 10 or 12 times. This will load the piston rings and cause them to seat properly against the cylinder walls. Check again for oil and coolant leaks.

8 Drive the vehicle gently for the first 500 miles (no sustained high speeds) and keep a constant check on the oil level. It is not unusual for an engine to use oil during the break-in period.

9 At approximately 500 to 600 miles, change the oil and filter.

10 For the next few hundred miles, drive the vehicle normally. Do not pamper it or abuse it.

11 After 2000 miles, change the oil and filter again and consider the engine broken in.

Specifications

Four-cylinder SOHC engines

General

Oil pressure	40 to 60 psi @ 2000 rpm
Compression pressure	Lowest reading cylinder must be within 15 psi of highest reading cylinder (100 psi minimum)

Engine block

Cylinder bore	
Diameter	3.7795 to 3.7810 inch
Out-of-round limit	0.0015 inch
Taper limit	0.005 inch

Cylinder head and valves

Cylinder head warpage limit	0.006 inch (overall)
Valve face angle	
2005 and earlier models	44-degrees
2006 and later models	45-degrees
Valve seat angle, all models	45-degrees
Valve margin width	1/32-inch
Valve stem diameter	
2005 and earlier models	
Intake	0.2746 to 0.2754 inch
Exhaust	0.2736 to 0.2744 inch
2006 and later models	
Intake	0.2153 to 0.2159 inch
Exhaust	0.2151 to 0.2157 inch

Maximum PSI	Minimum PSI	Maximum PSI	Minimum PSI	Maximum PSI	Minimum PSI	Maximum PSI	Minimum PSI
134	101	164	123	194	145	224	168
136	102	166	124	196	147	226	169
138	104	168	126	198	148	228	171
140	105	170	127	200	150	230	172
142	107	172	129	202	151	232	174
144	108	174	131	204	153	234	175
146	110	176	132	206	154	236	177
148	111	178	133	208	156	238	178
150	113	180	135	210	157	240	180
152	114	182	136	212	158	242	181
154	115	184	138	214	160	244	183
156	117	186	140	216	162	246	184
158	118	188	141	218	163	248	186
160	120	190	142	220	165	250	187
162	121	192	144	222	166		

Cylinder compression variation chart - locate your maximum compression reading on the chart and look to the right to find the minimum acceptable compression (then compare it to your lowest reading)

Cylinder head and valves (continued)

Valve stem-to-guide clearance
    2.3L engine
        2005 and earlier
            Intake   0.0010 to 0.0027 inch
            Exhaust   0.0015 to 0.0032 inch
        2006 and later
            Intake   0.0009 inch
            Exhaust   0.0011 inch
    2.5L engine
            Intake   0.0008 to 0.0027 inch
            Exhaust   0.0018 to 0.0037 inch
Valve spring free length
    2005 and earlier models   2.020 inches
    2006 and later models   1.768 inches
Valve spring installed height
    2005 and earlier models   1.54 to 1.58 inches
    2006 and later models   1.492 inches

Crankshaft and connecting rods

Crankshaft endplay
    2005 and earlier   0.004 to 0.008 inch
    2006 and later   0.008 to 0.016 inch
Connecting rod side clearance   0.0035 to 0.0115 inch
Main bearing journal diameter
    2005 and earlier   2.2059 to 2.2051 inches
    2006 and later   2.0460 to 2.0470 inches
Out-of-round limit   0.0006 inch
Taper limit   0.0006 inch
Main bearing oil clearance
    Nominal
        2005 and earlier   0.0008 to 0.0015 inch
        2006 and later   0.0007 to 0.0018 inch
    Allowable   0.0008 to 0.0026 inch
Connecting rod bearing journal
    Diameter
        2005 and earlier   2.0464 to 2.0472 inches
        2006 and later   1.9570 to 1.9680 inches
    Out-of-round limit   0.0006 inch
    Taper limit
        2.3L   0.0006 inch
        2.5L   0.0005 inch
Connecting rod bearing oil clearance
    Nominal   0.0008 to 0.0015 inch
    Allowable   0.0008 to 0.0026 inch

Pistons and rings

2.3L engine
    Piston diameter
        2005 and earlier   3.7883 to 3.7793 inches
        2006 and later
            Marked "1"   3.4452 to 3.4456 inches
            Marked "2"   3.4440 to 3.4450 inches
            Marked "3"   3.4443 to 3.4453 inches

Piston-to-bore clearance	0.010 to 0.020 inch
Piston ring side clearance	
Compression rings	0.0016 to 0.0033 inch
Oil ring	Snug fit
Piston ring end gap	
2005 and earlier	
Compression ring (top)	0.008 to 0.012 inch
Compression ring (second)	0.013 to 0.019 inch
Oil ring	0.010 to 0.030 inch
2006 and later	
Compression ring (top)	0.006 to 0.012 inch
Compression ring (second)	0.012 to 0.018 inch
Oil ring	0.010 to 0.030 inch
2.5L engine	
Piston diameter	
Code red	3.7780 to 3.7785 inches
Code blue	3.7785 to 3.7790 inches
Code Yellow	3.7790 to 3.7795 inches
Piston-to-bore clearance	0.001 to 0.002 inch
Piston selection in relation to bore size	
Code red	3.7795 to 3.7800 inches
Code blue	3.7800 to 3.7805 inches
Code yellow	3.7805 to 3.7810 inches
Piston ring side clearance	
Compression rings	0.0014 to 0.0030 inch
Oil ring	Snug fit
Piston ring end gap	
Upper compression ring	0.008 to 0.018 inch
Lower compression ring	0.013 to 0.023 inch
Oil ring	0.010 to 0.035 inch

Camshaft

Lobe lift (intake and exhaust)	0.2163 inch
Bearing journal diameter	1.7713 to 1.7720 inches
Bearing oil clearance	
Standard	0.001 to 0.003 inch
Service limit	0.006 inch
Endplay	
Standard	0.001 to 0.007 inch
Service limit	0.009 inch

Torque specifications*

	Ft-lbs
Main bearing cap bolts	
Step 1	51 to 59
Step 2	76 to 84
Connecting rod nuts	
Step 1	26 to 30
Step 2	31 to 36

Refer to Part A for additional torque specifications.

2.3L DOHC engine

➡Note: At the time of writing, this engine was largely considered "un-rebuildable." Check with an automotive machine shop to see if aftermarket components and service techniques have been developed if your engine requires repair. New short blocks can be purchased through a dealership.

3.0L V6 engine

General

Oil pressure	40 to 60 psi @ 2500 rpm
Compression pressure	Lowest reading cylinder must be within 15 psi of highest reading cylinder (100 psi minimum)

Engine block

Cylinder bore	
Diameter	3.504 inches
Out-of-round limit	0.002 inch
Taper limit	0.002 inch

Cylinder head and valves

Cylinder head warpage limit	0.006 inch (overall)
Valve face angle	44-degrees
Valve seat angle	45-degrees
Valve margin width	1/32-inch
Valve stem-to-guide clearance	
Intake	0.0010 to 0.0027 inch
Exhaust	0.0015 to 0.0032 inch
Valve spring installed height	1.736 to 1.650 inches
Valve spring free length	1.84 inches

Crankshaft and connecting rods

Crankshaft endplay	0.004 to 0.008 inch
Connecting rod side clearance	0.006 to 0.014 inch
Main bearing journal	
Diameter	2.5190 to 2.5198 inches
Out-of-round limit	0.0003 inch
Taper limit	0.0006 inch
Main bearing oil clearance	
Nominal	0.001 to 0.0014 inch
Allowable	0.0005 to 0.0023 inch
Connecting rod journal	
Diameter	2.1253 to 2.1261 inches
Out-of-round limit	0.0003 inch
Taper limit	0.0003 inch
Connecting rod bearing oil clearance	
Nominal	0.001 to 0.0014 inch
Allowable	0.00086 to 0.0027 inch

Pistons and rings

Piston diameter	
Coded red	3.5024 to 3.5031 inches
Coded blue	3.5035 to 3.5041 inches
Coded yellow	3.5045 to 3.5051 inches

Piston-to-bore clearance	0.0012 to 0.0022 inch
Piston ring side clearance	
Compression rings	0.0016 to 0.0037 inch
Oil ring	Snug fit
Piston ring end gap	
Compression rings	0.010 to 0.020 inch
Oil ring	0.010 to 0.049 inch

Camshaft

Lobe lift	0.260 inch
Bearing journal diameter	2.0074 to 2.0084 inches
Bearing oil clearance	0.001 to 0.003 inch
Endplay	0.007 inch

Torque specifications*	**Ft-lbs**
Connecting rod nuts	26
Main bearing cap bolts	59

Refer to Part C for additional torque specifications.

4.0L pushrod V6 engine

General

Oil pressure	40 to 60 psi @ 2000 rpm
Cylinder compression pressure	Lowest reading cylinder must be within 15 psi of highest reading cylinder (100 psi minimum)

Engine block

Cylinder bore	
Diameter	3.9527 to 3.9543 inches
Out-of-round limit	0.005 inch
Taper limit	0.005 inch

Cylinder head and valves

Cylinder head warpage limit	0.006 inch (overall)
Valve face angle	44-degrees
Valve seat angle	45-degrees
Valve margin width	1/32 inch
Valve stem diameter	
Intake	0.3159 to 0.3167 inch
Exhaust	0.3149 to 0.3156 inch
Valve stem-to-guide clearance	
Intake	0.0008 to 0.0025 inch
Exhaust	0.0018 to 0.0035 inch
Valve spring free length	1.91 inches
Valve spring installed height	1-37/64 to 1-39/64 inch

Crankshaft and connecting rods

Crankshaft endplay	0.002 to 0.0125 inch
Connecting rod side clearance	
Standard	0.0002 to 0.0025 inch
Service limit	0.014 inch

4.0L pushrod V6 engine (continued)

Crankshaft and connecting rods (continued)

Main bearing journal	
Diameter	2.2433 to 2.2441 inches
Out-of-round limit	0.0006 inch
Taper limit	0.0006 inch
Main bearing oil clearance	
Nominal	0.0008 to 0.0015 inch
Allowable	0.0005 to 0.0019 inch
Connecting rod journal	
Diameter (standard)	2.1252 to 2.1260 inches
Out-of-round limit	0.0006 inch
Taper limit	0.0006 inch
Connecting rod bearing oil clearance	
Nominal	0.0003 to 0.0022 inch
Allowable	0.0005 to 0.0024 inch

Pistons and rings

Piston diameter	3.9524 to 3.9531 inches
Piston-to-bore clearance	0.0008 to 0.0019 inch
Piston ring side clearance	
Compression rings	0.0020 to 0.0033 inch
Oil ring	Snug fit
Piston ring end gap	
Compression rings	0.015 to 0.023 inch
Oil ring rails	0.015 to 0.055 inch

Camshaft

Lobe lift	0.272 inch
Bearing journal diameter	
No. 1	1.951 to 1.952 inches
No. 2	1.937 to 1.938 inches
No. 3	1.922 to 1.923 inches
No. 4	1.907 to 1.908 inches
Bearing oil clearance	0.001 to 0.003 inch
Endplay	0.002 to 0.006

Torque specifications*

	Ft-lbs
Main bearing cap bolts	
Step 1	25
Step 2	72
Connecting rod cap nuts	
Step 1	15
Step 2	Tighten an additional 90-degrees

Refer to Part D for additional torque specifications.

4.0L SOHC V6 engine

Cylinder bore

Diameter	3.953 inches
Out-of-round limit	0.001 inch
Taper	0.001 inch maximum

Valves and related components

Intake valve

Seat angle	45 degrees
Seat width	0.06 to 0.094 inch
Seat runout limit	0.002 inch maximum
Stem diameter (standard)	0.274 to 0.275 inch
Valve stem-to-guide clearance	0.001 to 0.002 inch
Valve face angle	45 degrees
Valve face runout limit	0.001 inch maximum

Exhaust valve

Seat angle	45 degrees
Seat width	0.050 to 0.083 inch
Seat runout limit	0.002 inch maximum
Stem diameter (standard)	
2010 and earlier	0.0275 inch
2011	0.0274 inch
Valve stem-to-guide clearance	0.001 to 0.003 inch
Valve face angle	45 degrees
Valve face runout limit	0.001 inch maximum

Valve spring

Free length, intake and exhaust	1.70 inches
Out-of-square limit	
2010 and earlier	2 degrees maximum
2011	1.5 degrees maximum
Installed height, intake and exhaust	
2010 and earlier	1.569 to 1.601 inches
2011	1.569 to 1.608 inches

Crankshaft and connecting rods

Crankshaft endplay	0.002 to 0.0126 inch
Connecting rods	
Connecting rod journal	
Diameter	2.125 to 2.126 inches
Out-of-round and taper limits	0.0003 inch
Bearing oil clearance	
Desired	0.0003 to 0.0024 inch
Allowable	0.0005 to 0.002 inch
Connecting rod side clearance (endplay)	0.0036 to 0.0106 inch
Main bearing journal	
Diameter	2.243 to 2.244 inches
Out-of-round and taper limits	0.0003 inch
Bearing oil clearance	
Desired	
2010 and earlier	0.0008 to 0.0015 inch
2011	0.0003 to 0.0024 inch
Allowable	0.0005 to 0.002 inch

4.0L SOHC V6 engine (continued)

Pistons and rings

Piston diameter	
Standard	3.9520 to 3.9528 inches
Coded 0.5 mm	3.9716 to 3.9724 inches
Coded 1.0 mm	3.990 to 3.991 inches
Piston-to-bore clearance limit	
2010 and earlier	0.0012 to 0.0020 inch
2011	0.0012 to 0.0023 inch
Piston ring end gap	
Compression ring (top)	0.008 to 0.018 inch
Compression ring (bottom)	0.018 to 0.028 inch
Oil ring	Snug fit
Piston ring side clearance	
Compression rings	0.002 to 0.003 inch
Oil ring	Snug fit

Torque specifications*   Ft-lbs (unless otherwise indicated)

➡ Note: One foot-pound (ft-lb) of torque is equivalent to 12 inch-pounds (in-lbs) of torque. Torque values below approximately 15 ft-lbs are expressed in inch-pounds, since most foot-pound torque wrenches are not accurate at these smaller values.

Main bearing cap bolts	
2010 and earlier	72
2011	
Step 1	26
Step 2	Tighten an additional 57-degrees
Connecting rod cap nuts/bolts**	
Step 1	
2010 and earlier	162 in-lbs
2011	177 in-lbs
Step 2	Tighten an additional 90-degrees
Jackshaft retainer plate bolts	
2010 and earlier	80 to 115 in-lbs
2011	97 in-lbs
Balance shaft assembly bolts	19 to 21
Balance shaft chain guide bolts	80 to 97 in-lbs
Balance shaft tensioner bolts	21 to 22

  * Refer to Chapter 2, Part E for additional torque specifications.
  ** Use new nuts and bolts.

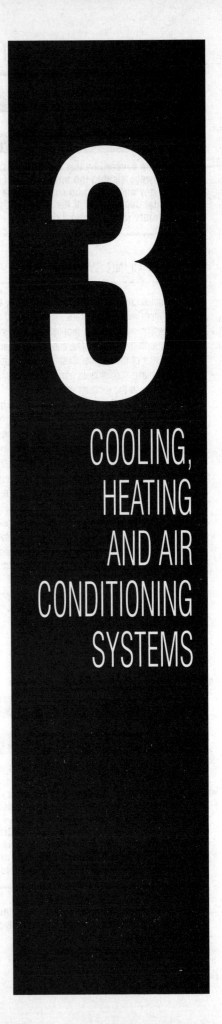

3

COOLING, HEATING AND AIR CONDITIONING SYSTEMS

1 General information

ENGINE COOLING SYSTEM

All vehicles covered by this manual employ a pressurized engine cooling system with thermostatically controlled coolant circulation. An impeller type water pump mounted on the front of the block pumps coolant through the engine. The coolant flows around each cylinder and toward the rear of the engine. Cast-in coolant passages direct coolant around the intake and exhaust ports, near the spark plug areas and in close proximity to the exhaust valve guides.

A wax pellet type thermostat is located in a housing near the front of the engine. During warm up, the closed thermostat prevents coolant from circulating through the radiator. As the engine nears normal operating temperature, the thermostat opens and allows hot coolant to travel through the radiator, where it's cooled before returning to the engine.

The cooling system is sealed by a pressure type cap, which raises the boiling point of the coolant and increases the cooling efficiency of the radiator.

On early models, the coolant reservoir serves as both the point at which fresh coolant is added to the cooling system to maintain the proper fluid level and as a holding tank for overheated coolant. On this type of system, coolant that escapes past the pressure cap is saved and reused.

On later models, the coolant reservoir is a pressurized part of the cooling system and is called an expansion tank.

HEATING SYSTEM

The heating system consists of a blower fan and heater core located in the heater box, the hoses connecting the heater core to the engine cooling system and the heater/air conditioning control head on the dashboard. Hot engine coolant is circulated through the heater core. When the heater mode is activated, a flap door opens to expose the heater box to the passenger compartment. A fan switch on the control head activates the blower motor, which forces air through the core, heating the air.

AIR CONDITIONING SYSTEM

The air conditioning system consists of a condenser mounted in front of the radiator, an evaporator mounted adjacent to the heater core, a compressor mounted on the engine, a filter-drier (accumulator) which contains a high pressure relief valve and the plumbing connecting all of the above components.

A blower fan forces the warmer air of the passenger compartment through the evaporator core (sort of a radiator-in-reverse), transferring the heat from the air to the refrigerant. The liquid refrigerant boils off into low pressure vapor, taking the heat with it when it leaves the evaporator.

2 Antifreeze/coolant - general information

➡Note: Non-toxic antifreeze is now manufactured and available at local auto parts stores, but even these types should be disposed of properly.

The cooling system should be filled with a water/ethylene glycol based antifreeze solution which will prevent freezing down to at least -20-degrees F (even lower in cold climates). It also provides protection against corrosion and increases the coolant boiling point.

The cooling system should be drained, flushed and refilled at least every other year (see Chapter 1). The use of antifreeze solutions for periods of longer than two years is likely to cause damage and encourage the formation of rust and scale in the system.

Before adding antifreeze to the system, check all hose connections. Antifreeze can leak through very minute openings.

The exact mixture of antifreeze to water which you should use depends on the relative weather conditions. The mixture should contain at least 50-percent antifreeze, but should never contain more than 70-percent anti-freeze. Consult the mixture ratio chart on the antifreeze container before adding coolant.

3 Thermostat - check and replacement

Do not remove the radiator or expansion cap, drain the coolant or replace the thermostat until the engine has cooled completely.

CHECK

1 Before assuming the thermostat is to blame for a cooling system problem, check the coolant level, drivebelt tension (see Chapter 1) and temperature gauge (or light) operation.

2 If the engine seems to be taking a long time to warm up (based on heater output or temperature gauge operation), the thermostat is probably stuck open. Replace the thermostat with a new one.

3 If the engine runs hot, use your hand to check the temperature of the upper radiator hose. If the hose isn't hot, but the engine is, the thermostat is probably stuck closed, preventing the coolant inside the engine from escaping to the radiator. Replace the thermostat.

✳✳ **CAUTION:**

Don't drive the vehicle without a thermostat. The computer may stay in open loop and emissions and fuel economy will suffer.

4 If the upper radiator hose is hot, it means that the coolant is flowing and the thermostat is open. Consult the Troubleshooting Section at the front of this manual for cooling system diagnosis.

REPLACEMENT

▶ **Refer to illustrations 3.8a and 3.8b**

5 Disconnect the negative battery cable from the battery.

6 Remove the air cleaner air duct from the throttle body and air cleaner, if necessary.

7 Drain the cooling system (see Chapter 1). If the coolant is relatively new or in good condition (see Chapter 1), save it and reuse it.

8 Follow the upper radiator hose to the engine to locate the thermostat housing (see illustrations). On 2001 and later 2.3L four-cylinder engines, follow the lower radiator hose to the thermostat housing. Disconnect the electrical connectors on the housing as well. On this engine the thermostat and housing are serviced as an assembly. The housing is located as follows:

a) Four-cylinder engines: on the front of the engine.
b) V6 engine: near the front of the intake manifold.

9 Loosen the hose clamp, then detach the hose from the fitting. If it's stuck, grasp it near the end with a pair of adjustable pliers and twist it to break the seal, then pull it off. If the hose is old or deteriorated, cut it off and install a new one. On 2.5L engines, also cut the heater hose at the thermostat housing.

✳✳ **CAUTION:**

Do not cut through to the hose fitting. A deep score may cause a leak.

10 If the outer surface of the large fitting that mates with the hose is deteriorated (corroded, pitted, etc.), it may be damaged further by hose removal. If it is, the thermostat housing cover will have to be replaced.

11 Remove the bolts and detach the housing cover. If the cover is stuck, tap it with a soft-face hammer to jar it loose. Be prepared for some coolant to spill out as the gasket seal is broken.

12 Note how it's installed (which end is facing toward the engine), then remove the thermostat. It may be necessary to rotate the thermostat to free it. On 2.5L engines, there are two tabs on the thermostat that fit into notches in the thermostat housing.

13 Stuff a rag into the engine opening, then remove all traces of corrosion from the housing and cover with a gasket scraper. Remove the rag from the opening and clean the mating surfaces with lacquer thinner or acetone.

14 On 4.0L engines, make sure the sealing ring is positioned correctly on the thermostat.

15 Install the new thermostat in the housing with the bridge section toward the outlet housing cover (the spring end is normally directed towards the engine). On 4.0L engines, make sure the air release valve is in the up position.

16 Install the housing cover and bolts. Tighten the bolts to the torque listed in this Chapter's Specifications.

17 Reattach the hose to the fitting and tighten the hose clamp securely.

18 Refill the cooling system (see Chapter 1).

19 Install the air cleaner air duct (if removed).

20 Start the engine and allow it to reach normal operating temperature. Keep the system topped up as necessary. As air is purged from the cooling system, more coolant may be needed. Check for leaks and proper thermostat operation (as described in Steps 2 through 4).

3.8a Location of the thermostat housing on four-cylinder engines (arrow) (upper radiator hose removed for clarity)

3.8b Location of the thermostat housing on 4.0L V6 engines

4 Radiator - removal and installation

▶ **Refer to illustrations 4.3a, 4.3b, 4.5 and 4.6**

✳✳ WARNING:

If vehicle is equipped with airbags, refer to Chapter 12 to disarm the airbag system prior to performing any work described below.

✳✳ WARNING:

Wait until the engine is completely cool before beginning this procedure.

1 Disconnect the negative battery cable from the battery.
2 Drain the cooling system (see Chapter 1). If the coolant is clean, you may save it and reuse it.
3 Loosen the hose clamps and slide them back on the hoses, then detach the radiator hoses from the fittings (see illustrations). If they're stuck, grasp each hose near the end with a pair of adjustable pliers and twist it to break the seal, then pull it off - be careful not to distort the radiator fittings! If the hoses are old or deteriorated, cut them off and install new ones.

✳✳ CAUTION:

Do not cut through to the hose fitting. A deep score may cause a leak.

4 Disconnect the reservoir hose from the radiator filler neck.
5 Remove the screws that attach the fan shroud to the radiator and slide the shroud toward the engine (see illustration). Let the shroud rest on the fan.

➡**Note: On most 2001 and later 2.3L four-cylinder engines, the fan shroud incorporates an electric cooling fan that can be removed as a single unit. Disconnect the fan's electrical connector and remove the power steering reservoir fasteners and move it aside to remove the shroud.**

4.3a Use a socket or screwdriver to loosen the hose clamp (arrow)

6 If the vehicle is equipped with an automatic transmission, hold the cooler fittings with a backup wrench and disconnect the lines from the radiator (see illustration). Use a drip pan to catch spilled fluid.
7 Plug the lines and fittings to avoid spillage and contamination. Automatic transmission internal parts require very clean conditions.
8 Remove the radiator mounting bolts.
9 Carefully lift the radiator up and out of its lower mounting pads or grommets. Remove the radiator and be careful not to spill coolant on the vehicle or scratch the paint.
10 With the radiator removed, it can be inspected for leaks and damage. If it needs repair, have a radiator shop or dealer service department perform the work as special techniques are required.
11 Bugs and dirt can be removed from the radiator with compressed air and a soft brush. Don't bend the cooling fins while doing this. If you are careful, you can straighten out the fins to permit better flow, but in most cases this is not necessary.
12 Check the radiator mounts for deterioration and make sure there's

4.3b On spring-type hose clamps, squeeze the clamp with pliers and slide it back along the hose

4.5 Remove the shroud mounting bolts and place the shroud over the fan

4.6 On automatic transmission models, hold the cooler line fittings with a backup wrench and unscrew the fittings

nothing in them when the radiator is installed.

13 Installation is the reverse of the removal procedure with the following additions:

a) *After installation, fill the cooling system with the proper mixture of antifreeze and water (see Chapter 1).*

➡**Note: On later models, the system must be bled after filling.**

b) *Start the engine and check for leaks. Allow the engine to reach normal operating temperature, indicated by the upper radiator hose becoming hot. Recheck the coolant level and add more if required.*

c) *If you're working on an automatic transmission equipped vehicle, check and add transmission fluid as needed (see Chapter 1).*

5   Cooling fan and viscous clutch - inspection, removal and installation

❊❊ WARNING:

To avoid possible injury or damage, DO NOT operate the engine with a damaged fan. Plastic fans crack and can fly apart when the engine is revved. Do not attempt to repair fan blades - replace a damaged fan with a new one.

VISCOUS CLUTCH INSPECTION

1   Disconnect the negative cable from the battery.

2   Rock the fan fore and aft by hand to check for excessive bearing play.

3   With the engine cold, turn the fan by hand. The fan should turn freely.

4   Visually inspect for substantial fluid leakage from the clutch assembly. If problems are noted, replace the clutch assembly.

5   Reconnect the battery cable and warm up the engine. With the engine completely warmed up, turn off the ignition switch and disconnect the negative battery cable from the battery. Turn the fan by hand. Some drag should be evident. If the fan turns easily, the viscous clutch is not working. Replace the fan clutch.

REMOVAL

Four-cylinder engines

➡**Note: Some 2001 and later 2.3L engines have an electric cooling fan that is integral with the fan shroud.**

6   Disconnect the negative cable from the battery.

2010 and earlier models

7   Disconnect the reservoir hose from the radiator filler neck.

8   Remove the screws securing the shroud to the radiator and slide the shroud toward the engine (see Section 4).

9   Remove the four screws and washers attaching the fan/clutch assembly to the water pump drivebelt hub (if equipped). On 2001 through 2010 2.3L engines, remove the drivebelt (see Chapter 1), then hold the cooling fan pulley with strap wrench (or equivalent) while removing the fan nut.

10   Lift the fan/clutch assembly out of the engine compartment. On 2.5L engines, remove the fan bolts and set the fan/clutch assembly forward into the shroud, the remove the shroud mounting bolts and remove the fan/clutch and shroud from the vehicle together.

2011 models

11   Remove the air filter housing duct (see Chapter 4).

12   Remove the drivebelt (see Chapter 1), then hold the cooling fan pulley with a strap wrench while removing the fan nut.

13   Remove the fan/clutch assembly. Remove the bolts to separate the fan from the fan clutch.

V6 engines

14   Disconnect the negative cable from the battery.

2010 and earlier models

◗ **Refer to illustrations 5.17a and 5.17b**

15   Disconnect the reservoir hose from the radiator filler neck.

16   Remove the screws securing the shroud to the radiator and slide the shroud toward the engine (see Section 4).

17   Remove the large nut securing the clutch hub assembly to the water pump drivebelt hub.

❊❊ CAUTION:

On 2.9L and 3.0L V6 engines, the nut has a left-hand thread; turn the nut clockwise to loosen it. On later 4.0L V6 engines, the nut has standard right-hand threads, but on some earlier

5.17a Two special wrenches are used to remove the fan clutch on V6 models - the shorter one is used with a breaker bar and holds the water pump pulley; the longer one loosens the clutch hub nut

models, the nut has left-hand threads, and you'll have to look at the exposed threads of the pulley hub to determine which way to turn the nut to loosen it. Two special tools are necessary, a fan clutch pulley holder and a fan clutch nut wrench, available at most auto parts stores that carry tools (see illustrations). If the special tools are not available, use a strap wrench to hold the assembly from rotating and use a large adjustable wrench to unscrew the large nut.

18 Lift the fan/clutch assembly out of the engine compartment.

2011 models

19 Remove the air filter housing duct (see Chapter 4).
20 Remove the drivebelt (see Chapter 1). Remove the cooling fan nut using special tools (see Step 17).
21 Remove the fan bolts, and set the fan/clutch assembly in the shroud.

5.17b Hold the pulley from turning (A) and turn the nut counterclockwise to loosen it (B)

22 Remove the fan shroud, fan and fan clutch as an assembly. Remove the bolts to separate the fan from the fan clutch.

INSTALLATION

23 Inspect the fan blades for damage and defects. Replace it if necessary by removing the fasteners securing the fan to the clutch assembly.

✳✳ CAUTION:

If the fan clutch is stored, position it with the radiator side facing down.

24 Installation is the reverse of the removal steps. Tighten the fan and clutch nut evenly and to the torque listed in this Chapter's Specifications.

---

6   Coolant reservoir/expansion tank removal and installation

▶ **Refer to illustration 6.5**

✳✳ WARNING:

Wait until the engine is completely cool before beginning this procedure.

1   On 2011 4.0L V6 models, remove the air filter housing (see Chapter 4). On 2011 2.3L models, clamp off the EGR valve heater hose.
2   On models with an expansion tank, drain the cooling system (see Chapter 1).
3   If equipped, loosen the cruise control servo mounting bolt at the fender and move the servo aside.
4   Disconnect all hoses to the tank/reservoir. Remove any electrical connectors.
5   Remove any tank/reservoir mounting bolts or fasteners and lift the tank/reservoir out of the engine compartment (see illustration).
6   Clean out the tank with soapy water and a brush to remove any

6.5 The coolant reservoir is secured to the inner fender panel by screws (early models)

deposits inside. Inspect the tank carefully for cracks. If they exist, replace the unit.
7   Installation is the reverse of removal.

7 Coolant temperature sending unit - replacement

GENERAL INFORMATION

▶ **Refer to illustration 7.3**

1 There are two engine coolant temperature senders. One drives the temperature gauge or warning light on the instrument panel; this is generally referred to as the sending unit. The other is used by the computer to determine engine coolant temperature and adjust fuel/air mixture accordingly; this is generally referred to as a sensor. The two are easily distinguished, since the sending unit for the temperature gauge has only one wire going to it, while the unit that provides information to the computer has two or three wires to it.

2 On SOHC four-cylinder engines, the sending unit for the gauge or light is threaded into the driver's side of the engine block, at the rear, just below the cylinder head. On 2001 and later 2.3L engines the sending unit is located at the rear of the engine mounted into the coolant outlet pipe.

✳✳ CAUTION:

Do not mistake the temperature sending unit for the oil pressure sending unit, which is just above the coolant temperature sending unit, threaded into the cylinder head.

3 On V6 engines, the sending unit for the gauge is located on the front lower part of the intake manifold, near the thermostat housing (see illustration).

REPLACEMENT

4 Allow the cooling system to completely cool down, then open the

7.3 A typical temperature sending unit (arrow)

cooling system pressure cap to relieve any pressure in the cooling system. Install the cap. This will minimize coolant loss during this procedure.

5 Disconnect the electrical connector from the sending unit.

6 Wrap the threads of the new sending unit with Teflon tape.

7 Remove the old sending unit from the engine. Place your finger over the hole in the engine to minimize coolant loss.

8 Immediately install the new sending unit and tighten it securely.

9 Connect the sending unit electrical connector.

10 Check coolant level and top up if necessary (see Chapter 1).

11 Start the engine and check for leaks.

8 Water pump - check and replacement

CHECK

▶ **Refer to illustration 8.4**

1 The water pump is driven by the accessory drivebelt on all models.

2 A failure in the water pump can cause serious engine damage

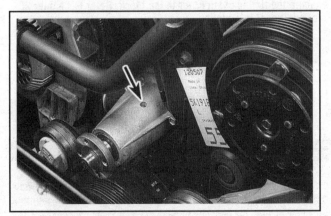

8.4 A typical water pump weep hole (arrow) - on some models the hole is on the bottom of the pump

due to overheating.

3 There are two ways to check the operation of the water pump while it's installed on the engine. If the pump is defective, it should be replaced with a new or rebuilt unit.

4 Water pumps are equipped with weep or vent holes. If a failure occurs in the pump seal, coolant will leak from the hole (see illustration). In most cases you'll need a flashlight to find the hole on the water pump to check for leaks.

5 If the water pump shaft bearings fail there may be a howling sound at the front of the engine while it's running. Shaft wear can be felt if the water pump pulley is rocked up and down. Don't mistake drivebelt slippage, which causes a squealing sound, for water pump bearing failure.

REPLACEMENT

✳✳ WARNING 1:

Wait until the engine is completely cool before beginning this procedure.

✳✳ WARNING 2:

The air conditioning system is under high pressure. Do not

loosen any hose fittings or remove any components until after the system has been discharged by a dealer service department or service station. Always wear eye protection when disconnecting air conditioning system fittings.

2001 and later 2.3L engines

6 Disconnect the cable from the negative terminal of the battery. On 2011 models, remove the air filter housing duct (see Chapter 4).

7 Drain the cooling system (see Chapter 1). If the coolant is clean, you may reuse it.

✳✳ WARNING:

Most coolant is toxic. Keep stored coolant away from pets and small children. Spilled coolant must be removed quickly and safely.

8 Remove the drive belt (see Chapter 1).

9 Remove the bolts that hold the water pump pulley onto the water pump.

10 Remove the bolts that secure the water pump to the engine block.

11 Carefully pull the water pump directly straight out from the block.

12 Lubricate the O-ring seal on the replacement water pump with Merpol® or equivalent.

13 Installation is the reverse of removal. Be sure to tighten the fasteners to the torque listed in this Chapter's Specifications. Refill the cooling system as described in Chapter 1.

All other models

♦ Refer to illustration 8.21

14 Disconnect the negative battery cable from the battery.

15 Drain the cooling system (see Chapter 1). If the coolant is clean, you may save it and reuse it.

16 Remove the cooling fan and shroud (see Sections 4 and 5).

17 Remove the drivebelt (see Chapter 1) and the pulley at the end of the water pump shaft.

18 Loosen the clamps and detach the hoses from the water pump. If they're stuck, grasp each hose near the end with a pair of adjustable pliers and twist it to break the seal, then pull it off. If the hoses are deteriorated, cut them off and install new ones.

19 On four-cylinder SOHC engines, remove the outer timing belt cover (see Chapter 2A).

20 On 2010 and earlier V6 engines, if necessary, remove the alternator and its mounting bracket from the water pump (see Chapter 5). Without disconnecting the air-conditioning lines, remove the air-conditioning compressor mounting bracket with the compressor and power steering pump still attached. Set the assembly aside without disconnecting any lines.

8.21 Locations of the water pump bolts on the 4.0L pushrod V6 engine

21 Remove the bolts and detach the water pump from the engine (see illustration). Note the locations of the various lengths and different types of bolts as they're removed to ensure correct installation.

22 Clean the bolt threads and the threaded holes in the engine to remove corrosion and sealant.

23 Compare the new pump to the old one to make sure they're identical.

24 Remove all traces of old gasket material from the engine gasket surface with a gasket scraper.

25 Clean the engine and new water pump gasket mating surfaces with lacquer thinner or acetone.

26 Apply a thin coat of RTV sealant to the engine side of the new gasket.

27 Apply a thin layer of RTV sealant to the gasket mating surface of the new pump, then carefully mate the gasket and the pump. Slip a couple of bolts through the pump mounting holes to hold the gasket in place.

28 Carefully attach the pump and gasket to the engine and thread the bolts into the holes finger tight.

29 Install the remaining bolts (if they also hold the alternator bracket in place, be sure to reposition the bracket at this time). Tighten them evenly to the torque listed in this Chapter's Specifications in 1/4-turn increments. Don't overtighten them or the pump may be distorted.

➡Note: On 3.0L engines, some of the water pump bolts also secure the timing chain cover to the block. Refer to Chapter 2C for additional information.

30 Reinstall all parts removed for access to the pump.

31 Refill the cooling system and check the drivebelt tension (see Chapter 1). Run the engine and check for leaks.

9 Heater - general information

The heater circulates engine coolant through a small radiator (heater core) in the passenger compartment. Air is drawn in through an opening in the cowl, then blown (by the blower motor) through the heater core to pick up heat. The heated air is blended with varying amounts of unheated air to regulate the temperature. The heated air is then blown into the passenger compartment. Various doors in the heater control the flow of air to the floor and through the instrument panel louvers and defroster outlets.

10 Heater and air conditioning control assembly - removal and installation

1   On 2001 and later models, turn the temperature control knob to the full cool position.

2   Disconnect the negative cable from the battery. Remove the radio (see Chapter 12).

3   On 2001 and later models, remove the two screws that are located just above the climate control knobs that secure the cluster trim. For all years (with or without screws) pull the trim carefully as this will release the spring clips holding the trim on. Once the trim is released, disconnect any electrical connectors.

4   Remove the four screws securing the control panel to the instrument panel.

5   Pull the control assembly through the opening in the instrument panel far enough to allow removal of electrical and vacuum connections. On 2000 models, the assembly can now be removed from the vehicle. On 2001 and later models, pull the temperature control knob from the front. From behind, remove the screw that holds the switch

with the cable then separate it as a unit from the control assembly. Remove the control assembly away from the instrument panel.

6   Use a small screwdriver and remove the vacuum harness from the vacuum switch on the side of the control assembly.

7   At the back of the control assembly, use a screwdriver or needle-nose pliers and disconnect the temperature and function cable from the white control bracket, if equipped.

8   At the bottom of the control assembly, disconnect the temperature control cable from the control, if equipped.

9   Pull enough cable through the instrument opening until the function cable can be held vertical to the control assembly, then remove the cable end from the function lever.

10 Remove the control assembly from the instrument panel.

11 Installation is the reverse of removal.

→**Note: If a new control unit is installed, the original blower switch and function switch must be transferred to the new unit.**

11 Heater control cables - check and adjustment

CHECK

1   Move the control lever or turn the control knob all the way from left to right.

2   If the control lever or control knob stops before the end and bounces back, the cables are out of adjustment.

ADJUSTMENT

3   Squeeze the tabs on either side of the glove box door to disengage it, then let the door hang down to provide access to the control cables.

4   Working through the glove box opening, remove the cable jacket from its metal attaching clip on top of the heater assembly. The cable ends should remain attached to the door cams and/or crank arms at this time.

5   To adjust the temperature control cable, set the temperature lever or knob to the Cool position and hold it there.

6   Push gently on the black cable jacket to seat the blend door (push until you feel resistance).

7   Reinstall the cable to the clip by pushing the jacket into the clip from the top until it snaps in.

8   To adjust the function control cable, set the function control lever or knob to Defrost and hold it there.

9   Pull on the white cam jacket until the cam travel stops.

10 Reinstall the cable to the clip by pushing the jacket into the clip from the top until it snaps in.

11 Run the system on High and actuate the levers, checking for proper operation. Readjust if necessary.

12 Install the glove box door.

12 Heater blower motor and circuit - check and replacement

☀ WARNING:

Some models covered by this manual are equipped with airbags. Always disable the airbag system before working in the vicinity of any airbag system component to avoid the possibility of accidental deployment of the airbag(s), which could cause personal injury (see Chapter 12).

CIRCUIT CHECKS

Basic circuit check

▶ **Refer to illustration 12.2**

1   Check the fuse and all connections in the circuit for looseness and corrosion. Make sure the battery is fully charged.

2   Backprobe the blower motor connector with two large straight-pins (leave the connector plugged in). The blower motor is located in the engine compartment on the passenger side of the firewall (see illustration).

12.2 The electrical connector is on the right side of the blower motor

12.16 Push down on the electrical connector locking tab and disconnect the connector

12.17 Remove the screws securing the heater blower motor (arrows)

3   Connect a voltmeter across the two pins on the connector.

4   With the transmission in Park, the parking brake securely applied, turn the ignition switch to the On position (engine not running).

5   Have an assistant turn the blower switch through each position and note the voltage readings. Changes in voltage indicates that the blower switch should be able to vary the motor speed at different positions.

6   If there is voltage at the connector, but the motor does not operate, you can test the motor separately. With the connector disconnected, connect one terminal on the motor to a good ground. Connect the other terminal to the battery positive terminal through a fused jumper. The motor should operate at its highest speed. If it does, check the condition of the connectors and connecting wires. If the motor still does not operate, the motor is probably faulty.

Blower motor resistor assembly check

7   The blower resistor assembly is located on the heater case to the right of the blower motor. There are several resistance elements mounted on the resistor board to provide four blower speeds.

8   Remove the blower resistor from its mounting location and visually check for damage. Check the resistor block for continuity between all terminals. If the thermal limiter circuit has been opened as a result of excessive heat, it should be replaced with the identical part.

Blower switch check

9   Turn the ignition switch to the Off position.

10   Disconnect the blower resistor electrical connector.

11   Using an ohmmeter, check for continuity to ground at each wire terminal with the blower switch in its corresponding position (see the wiring diagrams at the end of Chapter 12).

✱✱ CAUTION:

Make sure the ignition switch is OFF before probing the Hi speed circuit or damage to your meter may result.

12   If there's an open (no continuity) in any one of the circuits, either the switch is defective or the wiring harness is open. Remove the control panel (see Section 10) and check the switch for continuity. If there's no continuity in all of the switch positions, check for continuity in the ground circuit.

13   If the switch is defective, replace the control panel assembly.

➡**Note: On most later models, the blower switch and/or function switch can be replaced separately by releasing the three clips on the back of the unit.**

BLOWER MOTOR REPLACEMENT

▶ **Refer to illustrations 12.16 and 12.17**

✱✱ WARNING:

If vehicle is equipped with airbags, refer to Chapter 12 to disarm the airbag system prior to performing any work described below.

14   Disconnect the negative battery cable.

15   On 2001 and later models, move the cruise control servo aside by disconnecting the electrical connector and removing the mounting screw.

16   Disconnect the blower motor connector (see illustration). Remove the vent tube, if equipped.

17   Remove the blower motor mounting screws and remove the motor (see illustration).

18   Remove the blower motor wheel hub pushnut and the clamp from the shaft. Pull the blower motor wheel from the shaft.

19   Installation is the reverse of these steps.

13 Heater core - replacement

✳✳ WARNING:

Some models covered by this manual are equipped with airbags. Always disable the airbag system before working in the vicinity of any airbag system component to avoid the possibility of accidental deployment of the airbag(s), which could cause personal injury (see Chapter 12).

REMOVAL

▸ **Refer to illustration 13.5**

1 Allow the cooling system to completely cool down.
2 Using a thick cloth for protection, turn the radiator filler cap to the first stop.
3 Step back and let the pressure release.
4 Once the pressure has been released, completely drain the cooling system (see Chapter 1).
5 Working within the engine compartment, loosen the clamps on the heater hoses at the engine compartment side of the firewall (see illustration). Twist the hoses and carefully separate them from the heater core tubes.
6 Plug or cap the heater core tubes to prevent coolant from spilling into the passenger compartment when the heater core is removed.
7 Place a plastic sheet on the floor of the vehicle to prevent stains if the coolant spills.
8 On 2011 models, remove the air conditioning evaporator (see Section 18).
9 Remove the instrument panel (see Chapter 11).
10 On 2001 and later models, remove the PCM, the PCM heat sink

13.5 Disconnect the heater hoses from the fittings at the firewall (arrow)

and ground strap (see Chapter 6).
11 Remove the heater plenum chamber. Remove the heater core cover, if equipped.
12 Separate the heater core from the heater plenum chamber.

INSTALLATION

13 Installation is the reverse of the removal procedure, with the following additions:

   a) *Fill the cooling system (see Chapter 1).*
   b) *Run the engine, check for leaks and test the heater.*

14 Air conditioning system - check and maintenance

▸ **Refer to illustration 14.5**

✳✳ WARNING:

The air conditioning system is under high pressure. Do not loosen any hose fittings or remove any components until after the system has been discharged by a dealer service department or service station. Always wear eye protection when disconnecting air conditioning system fittings.

1 The following maintenance checks should be performed on a regular basis to ensure that the air conditioner continues to operate at peak efficiency.

   a) *Check the compressor drivebelt. If it's worn or deteriorated, replace it (see Chapter 1).*
   b) *Check the system hoses. Look for cracks, bubbles, hard spots and deterioration. Inspect the hoses and all fittings for oil bubbles and seepage. If there's any evidence of wear, damage or leaks, replace the hose(s).*
   c) *Inspect the condenser fins for leaves, bugs and other debris. Use a "fin comb" or compressed air to clean the condenser.*
   d) *Make sure the system has the correct refrigerant charge.*

2 It's a good idea to operate the system for about 10 minutes at least once a month, particularly during the winter. Long term non-use can cause hardening, and subsequent failure, of the seals.
3 Leaks in the air conditioning system are best spotted when the system is brought up to temperature and pressure, by running the engine with the air conditioning ON for five minutes. Shut the engine off and inspect the air conditioning hoses and connections. Traces of oil usually indicate refrigerant leaks.
4 Because of the complexity of the air conditioning system and the special equipment necessary to service it, in-depth troubleshooting and repairs are not included in this manual. However, simple checks and component replacement procedures are provided in this Chapter.
5 If the air conditioning system doesn't operate at all, check the fuse panel and the Wide Open Throttle (WOT) relay, located in the relay

14.5 The WOT relay (arrow) disengages the air conditioning clutch to reduce the engine load during wide open throttle conditions

box in the engine compartment (see illustration) or the connector to the air conditioning compressor clutch.

6   The most common cause of poor cooling is simply a low system refrigerant charge. If a noticeable drop in cool air output occurs, the following quick check will help you determine if the refrigerant level is low.

CHECKING THE REFRIGERANT CHARGE

7   Warm the engine up to normal operating temperature.

8   Place the air conditioning temperature selector at the coldest setting and put the blower at the highest setting. Open the doors (to make sure the air conditioning system doesn't cycle off as soon as it cools the passenger compartment).

9   With the compressor engaged - the clutch will make an audible click and the center of the clutch will rotate - feel the evaporator inlet pipe between the fixed orifice tube and the evaporator with one hand while placing your other hand on the metal portion of the hose between the evaporator and the accumulator.

10   The pipe leading from the fixed orifice to the evaporator should be cold, and the outlet hose should be slightly colder (3 to 10-degrees F). If the outlet is considerably warmer than the inlet, the system charge

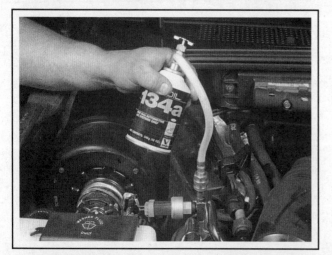

14.15 Connect the refrigerant recharging hose to the low-pressure charging port

14.12 A basic charging kit for R-134a systems is available at most auto parts stores - it must say R-134a (not R-12) and so should the 12-ounce can of refrigerant

is low. The earliest warning that a system is low on refrigerant is the air coming out of the ducts inside the vehicle. If the air isn't as cold as it used to be, the system probably needs a charge. Further inspection or testing of the system requires special tools and techniques and is beyond the scope of this manual.

11   If the inlet pipe has frost accumulation or feels cooler than the accumulator surface, the refrigerant charge is low.

ADDING REFRIGERANT

▶ **Refer to illustrations 14.12 and 14.15**

12   Buy an automotive charging kit at an auto parts store. A charging kit includes a 12-ounce can of refrigerant, a tap valve and a short section of hose that can be attached between the tap valve and the system low side service valve (see illustration).

✳✳ WARNING:

Never add more than one can of refrigerant to the system. If more than one can needs to be added, the system should be discharged, evacuated, leak tested and recharged by a licensed automotive air conditioning technician.

13   Hook up the charging kit by following the manufacturer's instructions.

✳✳ WARNING:

DO NOT hook the charging kit hose to the system high side! The fittings on the charging kit are designed to fit only on the low side of the system.

14   Back off the valve handle on the charging kit and screw the kit onto the refrigerant can, making sure first that the O-ring or rubber seal inside the threaded portion of the kit is in place.

✳✳ WARNING:

Wear protective eye wear when dealing with pressurized refrigerant cans.

15 Remove the dust cap from the low-side charging port (just above the coolant recovery tank) and attach the quick-connect fitting on the kit hose (see illustration).

16 Warm up the engine and turn on the air conditioner. Keep the charging kit hose away from the fan and other moving parts. The charging process requires the compressor to be running. Open the vehicle doors to keep the clutch from cycling off. This will keep the compressor engaged.

17 Turn the valve handle on the kit until the stem pierces the can, then back the handle out to release the refrigerant. You should be able to hear the rush of gas. Add refrigerant to the low side of the system until both the accumulator surface and the evaporator inlet pipe feel about the same temperature. Allow stabilization time between each addition.

18 If you have an accurate thermometer, you can place it in the center air conditioning duct inside the vehicle and keep track of the outlet air temperature. A charged system that is working properly should cool to 40-degrees F. If the ambient (outside) air temperature is very high, say 110-degrees F, the duct air temperature may be as high as 60-degrees F, but generally the air conditioning is 30 to 50-degrees F cooler than the ambient air.

19 When the can is empty, turn the valve handle to the closed position and release the connection from the low-side port. Replace the dust cap.

20 Remove the charging kit from the can and store the kit for future use with the piercing valve in the UP position, to prevent inadvertently piercing the can on the next use.

15 Air conditioning compressor - removal and installation

▶ Refer to illustrations 15.3 and 15.5

✳✳ WARNING:

The air conditioning system is under high pressure. DO NOT disassemble any part of the system (hoses, compressor, line fittings, etc.) until after the system has been depressurized by a dealer service department or service station, and the refrigerant recovered.

➥Note: The accumulator (see Section 17) should be replaced whenever the compressor is replaced.

➥Note: On 2011 models, the drivebelt does not need to be completely removed; it can be removed from the air conditioning compressor pulley only.

1 Have the air conditioning system discharged (see **Warning** above).

2 Disconnect the negative cable from the battery. On 4.0L engines, unbolt and set aside the power steering reservoir, then remove the four bolts and the power steering bracket.

3 Disconnect the electrical connector from the compressor (see illustration).

4 Remove the drivebelt (see Chapter 1).

5 Remove the bolt that secures the refrigerant lines to the rear of the compressor. Plug the open fittings to prevent entry of dirt and moisture (see illustration). On 2011 models, remove the compressor manifold bolts and remove the manifold and tube from the compressor. On 2011 4.0L V6 models, remove the inner fenderwell liner.

6 Unbolt the compressor from the mounting brackets and lift it out of the vehicle.

7 If a new compressor is being installed, follow the directions with the compressor regarding the draining of excess oil prior to installation.

8 The clutch may have to be transferred from the original to the new compressor.

9 Installation is the reverse of removal with the following additions:

   a) *Replace all O-rings with new ones specifically made for air conditioning system use. Lubricate them with special PAG refrigerant oil designed for use in R-134a systems. Use mineral oil on R-12 systems.*

✳✳ CAUTION:

Do not use the wrong lubricant or you may contaminate the system!

   b) *Have the system evacuated, recharged and leak tested by the shop that discharged it.*

15.3 Disconnect the electrical connector from the front end of the compressor (arrow)

15.5 The refrigerant lines are secured to the rear of the compressor by one bolt (arrow)

16 Air conditioning condenser - removal and installation

⁂ WARNING:

Some models covered by this manual are equipped with airbags. Always disable the airbag system before working in the vicinity of any airbag system component to avoid the possibility of accidental deployment of the airbag(s), which could cause personal injury (see Chapter 12).

⁂ WARNING:

The air conditioning system is under high pressure. DO NOT disassemble any part of the system (hoses, compressor, line fittings, etc.) until after the system has been depressurized by a dealer service department or service station, and the refrigerant recovered.

1   Have the air conditioning system discharged (see **Warning** above).

2   On all 4.0L engines, remove the air cleaner duct.

3   Disconnect the refrigerant lines from the condenser. On some models, this requires a spring lock coupling tool similar to that used for fuel injection lines (see Chapter 4).

4   Remove the mounting fasteners for the radiator and tilt it back for clearance to remove the condenser.

➡Note: Be careful not to damage the radiator with the cooling fan when tilting or moving the radiator back. Radiator removal is recommended if clearance to remove the condenser cannot be achieved without damage to either component.

5   Remove the top seal by removing the push-pin fasteners.

6   Remove the mounting fasteners for the condenser.

7   Lift the condenser out of the vehicle and plug the lines to keep dirt and moisture out.

8   If the original condenser will be reinstalled, store it with the line fittings on top to prevent oil from draining out.

9   If a new condenser is being installed, pour one ounce of refrigerant oil into it prior to installation.

⁂ CAUTION:

Use PAG oil for R-134a systems and mineral refrigerant oil for R-12 systems.

10 Reinstall the components in the reverse order of removal. Be sure the rubber pads are in place under the condenser (if equipped). Be sure the seals are in place around the condenser (if equipped).

11 Have the system evacuated, recharged and leak tested by the shop that discharged it.

17 Air conditioning accumulator - removal and installation

⁂ WARNING:

The air conditioning system is under high pressure. DO NOT disassemble any part of the system (hoses, compressor, line fittings, etc.) until after the system has been depressurized by a dealer service department or service station, and the refrigerant recovered.

REMOVAL

▶ **Refer to illustration 17.4**

1   Have the air conditioning system discharged (see **Warning** above).

2   Disconnect the negative cable from the battery.

3   Unplug the electrical connector from the pressure switch near the top of the accumulator. Unscrew the pressure switch.

4   Disconnect the refrigerant line from the accumulator (see illustration). This requires a spring lock coupling tool of the type used for fuel injection system lines (see Chapter 4).

5   Use a backup wrench to hold the fitting that connects the accumulator to the evaporator core, then disconnect the fitting. Plug the open fittings to prevent entry of dirt and moisture.

6   Remove all mounting bracket fasteners, then lift the accumulator out.

7   If a new accumulator is being installed, remove the Schrader valve and pour the oil out into a measuring cup, noting the amount. Add fresh refrigerant oil to the new accumulator equal to the amount removed from the old unit, plus one ounce.

⁂ CAUTION:

Use PAG oil for R-134a systems and mineral refrigerant oil for R-12 systems.

INSTALLATION

8   Loosely position the new accumulator in place.

9   Connect the accumulator to the evaporator core, using a new

17.4 The accumulator is mounted on the evaporator case in the engine compartment - disconnect this quick-disconnect fitting (arrow)

O-ring lubricated with clean refrigerant oil. At the same time, align the bracket with the slot between the evaporator case flanges.

10 Using a backup wrench, tighten the fitting securely.

11 Fully install the accumulator mounting bracket and tighten all fasteners.

12 Install the clip that holds the evaporator inlet tube to the bracket (if equipped).

13 Place a new O-ring, lubricated with clean refrigerant oil of the correct type, on the pressure switch nipple on the accumulator.

14 Install the pressure switch. If it has a metal base, tighten it to the torque listed in this Chapter's Specifications. If it has a plastic base, tighten it by hand only. Connect the pressure switch electrical connector.

15 Reconnect the negative cable to the battery.

16 Take the vehicle to the shop that discharged the air conditioning system. Have the system evacuated, recharged and tested for leaks.

18 Air conditioning evaporator - replacement

✳✳ WARNING:

The air conditioning system is under high pressure. DO NOT disassemble any part of the system (hoses, compressor, line fittings, etc.) until after the system has been depressurized by a dealer service department or service station, and the refrigerant recovered.

➡**Note 1: On 2001 and later models, the evaporator is serviced as an assembly with the evaporator housing. It isn't available individually.**

➡**Note 2: The accumulator (see Section 17) should be replaced whenever the evaporator is replaced.**

1   Have the air conditioning system discharged (see **Warning** above).

2   Disconnect the cable from the negative terminal of the battery. On 2011 models, remove the air filter housing duct (see Chapter 4).

3   Remove the accumulator as described in Section 17.

4   Remove the fasteners to the vacuum reservoir tank and bracket and set aside (if equipped).

5   Move the cruise control servo aside by disconnecting the electrical connector and removing the mounting screw (if equipped).

6   On 2001 and later 2.3L engines, remove the air conditioning compressor (see Section 15)

7   On 3.0L and 4.0L V6 engines, remove the coolant and windshield washer reservoirs mounted together.

8   Disconnect the blower motor and blower motor resistor electrical connectors (see Section 12).

9   On 2001 and later engines, disconnect the heater hoses from the heater core tubes (see Section 13)

10 Move the window washer hose and small hose retainer aside.

11 Disconnect the heater control vacuum hose from the vacuum control valve (in-line with one of the heater hoses).

12 Disconnect the refrigerant line from the evaporator to the condenser using a spring lock coupling tool. Cap the lines to prevent entry of dirt and moisture.

13 On 3.0L and 4.0L V6 engines, remove the hose bracket from the top of the A/C evaporator housing.

14 On 4.0L V6 engines, remove the hose bracket mounted on the rear of the engine.

15 Remove all fasteners to the evaporator housing noting that some may exist inside the passenger compartment at the firewall.

16 On 2001 and later, disconnect the vacuum hose connector from inside the passenger compartment.

17 Remove the evaporator housing.

18 On 2000 models, remove the core.

19 Installation is the reverse of removal with the following additions:

a) *Replace all O-rings with new ones specifically made for air conditioning system use. Lubricate them with special PAG refrigerant oil designed for use in R-134a systems. Use mineral oil on R-12 systems.*

✳✳ CAUTION:

Do not use the wrong lubricant or you may contaminate the system.

b) *Have the system evacuated, recharged and leak tested by the shop that discharged it.*

Specifications

General

Expansion tank cap pressure rating (if equipped)	13 to 18 psi
Thermostat rating temperature range (opening to fully open)	
2010 and earlier	192-199 degrees F to 210-226 degrees F
2011	
2.3L four-cylinder engine	194 degrees F to 207-223 degrees F
4.0L V6 engine	194-201 degrees F to 223 degrees F
Cooling system capacity	See Chapter 1
Refrigerant type and capacity	Refer to HVAC specification label
Coolant temperature sending unit (if equipped)	
switch close	249 degrees F

Torque specifications   Ft-lbs (unless otherwise indicated)

→Note: One foot-pound (ft-lb) of torque is equivalent to 12 inch-pounds (in-lbs) of torque. Torque values below approximately 15 ft-lbs are expressed in inch-pounds, since most foot-pound torque wrenches are not accurate at these smaller values.

Cooling fan-to-clutch bolts	
2010 and earlier	50 to 70 in-lbs
2011	
2.3L four-cylinder engine	80 in-lbs
4.0L V6 engine	62 in-lbs
Fan clutch-to-water pump, nut or bolt	
Four-cylinder engines	
2005 and earlier	13 to 17
2006 and later	41
V6 engines	
2005 and earlier	30 to 100
2006 and later	41
Thermostat housing bolts	
Four-cylinder engines	
2000 models	15 to 22
2001 models	
2.5L	15 to 22
2.3L	89 in-lbs
2002 and later models	89 in-lbs
V6 engines	
3.0L	14 to 21
4.0L	80 to 106 in-lbs
Water pump bolts	
Four-cylinder engines	
1993 through 2000	15 to 22
2001 models	
2.5L	15 to 22
2.3L	89 in-lbs
2002 and later models	89 in-lbs
V6 engines	
3.0L	
Short bolts (6 mm)	75 to 106 in-lbs
Long bolts (8 mm) (if equipped)	18
4.0L	
Short bolts (6 mm)	89 in-lbs
Long bolts (8 mm) (if equipped)	18
Water pump pulley bolts	
Four-cylinder engines	177 in-lbs
V6 engines	18
Accumulator pressure switch	
Metal base	60 to 120 in-lbs
Plastic base	Hand tighten only

Section

Reference to other Chapters

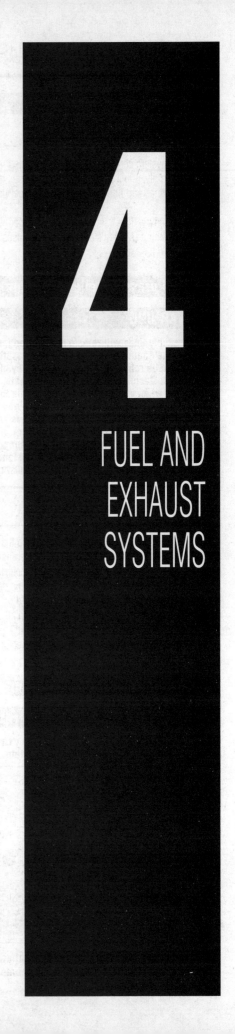

4

FUEL AND EXHAUST SYSTEMS

1 General information

FUEL SYSTEM

The fuel system consists of the fuel tank, the fuel pump, an air cleaner assembly, a fuel injection system and the various Teflon hoses, steel lines and fittings connecting the fuel delivery components together.

Vehicles covered by this manual are equipped with the Ford Multiport Fuel Injection (MFI) system. This system uses one fuel injector per cylinder.

The fuel pump is a single high pressure electric pump located within the fuel tank.

EXHAUST SYSTEM

All vehicles are equipped with exhaust manifold(s), a catalytic converter, an exhaust pipe and a muffler. Any component of the exhaust system can be replaced. See Chapter 6 for further details regarding the catalytic converter.

2 Fuel pressure relief procedure

❋❋ WARNING:

The fuel supply lines will remain pressurized for a long period of time after the engine is shut down. The pressure within the fuel system must be relieved before servicing any of the fuel delivery components. Gasoline is extremely flammable, so take extra precautions when you work on any part of the fuel system. Don't smoke or allow open flames or bare light bulbs near the work area, and don't work in a garage where a gas-type appliance (such as a water heater or clothes dryer) is present. If you spill any fuel on your skin, rinse it off immediately with soap and water. When you perform any kind of work on the fuel system, wear safety glasses and have a Class B type fire extinguisher on hand.

2010 AND EARLIER MODELS

1 The fuel pump switch - sometimes called the "inertia switch" - shuts off fuel to the engine in the event of a collision. This switch provides an easy way to relieve fuel pressure before servicing any fuel injection component. The switch is located in the passenger compartment. On B-series models, the switch is located on the passenger's side of the transmission hump, under the carpet. On all other models, the switch is located behind the passenger's side kick panel.

2 Unplug the inertia switch electrical connector.

3 Crank the engine with the starter for 15 to 20 seconds.

4 The fuel system pressure is now relieved. When you're finished working on the fuel system, reconnect the electrical connector back onto the switch and push the reset button on the top of the switch (just in case it may have "popped").

5 Even though the pressure has been relieved, it's a good idea to wrap a rag around fuel fittings when they are disconnected.

2011 MODELS

➡**Note: This procedure requires a fuel pressure test kit (available at your local auto parts store).**

6 Disconnect the cable from the negative battery terminal

7 Locate the fuel pressure relief valve on the fuel rail and remove it.

8 Place a drain pan under the vehicle to catch any fuel that may drain during the procedure. Install the test kit in accordance with the manufacturer's instructions.

9 To relieve the pressure, slowly turn the valve on the test kit. Refer to the instructions that come with the kit.

10 The fuel system pressure has now been relieved; it's a good idea to wrap a rag around fuel fittings when they are disconnected.

11 Before repressurizing the system, turn the ignition key through all positions, and wait three seconds before proceeding.

3 Fuel lines and fittings - general information

❋❋ WARNING:

Gasoline is extremely flammable, so take extra precautions when you work on any part of the fuel system. Don't smoke or

3.1 Some fuel lines use spring lock couplings (these are the fuel inlet and return lines in the engine compartment, viewed through the wheel well)

allow open flames or bare light bulbs near the work area, and don't work in a garage where a gas-type appliance (such as a water heater or clothes dryer) is present. Since gasoline is carcinogenic, wear latex gloves when there's a possibility of being exposed to fuel, and, if you spill any fuel on your skin, rinse it off immediately with soap and water. Mop up any spills immediately and do not store fuel-soaked rags where they could ignite. The fuel system is under constant pressure, so, if any fuel lines are to be disconnected, the fuel pressure in the system must be relieved first (see Section 2). When you perform any kind of work on the fuel system, wear safety glasses and have a Class B type fire extinguisher on hand.

SPRING LOCK COUPLINGS - DISASSEMBLY AND REASSEMBLY

▶ **Refer to illustrations 3.1, 3.2 and 3.4a through 3.4e**

1 The fuel supply and return lines used on these engines have spring lock couplings at some connections (see illustration). The male

3.2 These special tools are required to connect and disconnect engine compartment fuel lines

3.4a Open the tool and place it over the line . . .

3.4b . . . then slide the tool against the fuel line fitting so the lip inside the tool (arrows) . . .

3.4c . . . pushes against the garter spring (arrow)

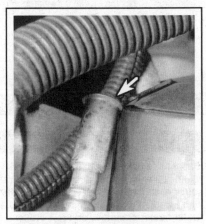

3.4d Push the tool against the spring until the spring slides off the flared female end of the line (arrow)

end of the spring lock coupling, which is girded by two O-rings, is inserted into a female flared end fitting. The coupling is secured by a garter spring which prevents disengagement by gripping the flared end of the female fitting. A clip and tether assembly provides additional security (see illustration).

2 To disconnect the spring lock coupling supply fitting, you'll need to obtain a special spring lock coupling tool or its equivalent (see illustration), available at most auto parts stores, designed for:

    a) 3/8-inch return fitting
    b) 1/2-inch supply fitting
    c) 5/8-inch return fitting

3 Before disconnecting the line, unclip the safety clip (see illustration 3.1b).

4 To disconnect and reconnect the line, refer to the accompanying illustrations and follow the information in the captions.

STAINLESS STEEL FITTING - DISASSEMBLY AND REASSEMBLY

5 All fuel lines outside the engine compartment are either Teflon hose and stainless steel (fuel supply and return lines) or carbon steel

3.4e To reconnect the line, place the flared female end (A) over the O-ring on the male end and push the ends together until the flared end slips under the garter spring (B) - tug on the ends to make sure they're locked, then install the safety clip

(vapor line). These lines are fastened to the frame rails with integral clips and connect with stainless steel fittings. This type of fitting consists of a female tube end with internal retaining "fingers" that grasp a formed male tube end. A safety clip holds the two ends of the fitting together.

6   To disconnect the stainless steel fitting, you'll need to obtain a quick-disconnect tool kit, available at most auto parts stores that carry tools.

7   Release the safety clip from the fitting and install the proper quick-disconnect tool on the fitting body.

8   Align the quick-disconnect tool on the fitting and push the tool into the fitting body to release the retaining fingers holding the male tube end. Once the fingers are released, pull the male tube end from the female fitting end and remove the tool.

9   On 4.0L engines, study the connector carefully before detaching the fuel return line fitting from the pressure regulator.

10   After disassembly, inspect and clean the tube end sealing surfaces. Also inspect the inside of the fitting for any internal damage. If damage is noted, replace the fuel tube.

11   Before reconnecting the fitting, wipe the male tube end with a clean cloth. Check the inside of the fitting to make sure that it's free of dirt and/or obstructions.

12   To reconnect the fitting, align it with the male tube end and push the tube into the fitting. When the fitting is engaged, a definite click will be heard. Pull on the fitting to ensure that it's fully engaged.

FUEL LINES - TEFLON-STAINLESS STEEL AND CARBON STEEL

❋❋ WARNING:

Use only the recommended tubing materials. Other types of tubing could fail in service.

13   Teflon-stainless steel fuel lines must not be repaired using hose and hose clamps. Should the fittings or steel tubing ends become damaged, approved service parts must be used to replace the lines. Splicing such lines with seamless steel tubing or rubber hose is not recommended.

14   If a length of Teflon hose is damaged, it should be replaced only with an approved service part.

4   Fuel pump/fuel pressure - check

❋❋ WARNING:

Gasoline is extremely flammable, so take extra precautions when you work on any part of the fuel system. Don't smoke or allow open flames or bare light bulbs near the work area, and don't work in a garage where a gas-type appliance (such as a water heater or clothes dryer) is present. Since gasoline is carcinogenic, wear latex gloves when there's a possibility of being exposed to fuel, and, if you spill any fuel on your skin, rinse it off immediately with soap and water. Mop up any spills immediately and do not store fuel-soaked rags where they could ignite. The fuel system is under constant pressure, so, if any fuel lines are to be disconnected, the fuel pressure in the system must be relieved first (see Section 2). When you perform any kind of work on the fuel system, wear safety glasses and have a Class B type fire extinguisher on hand.

➡Note: Always make sure there is fuel in the tank before assuming the fuel pump is defective.

GENERAL CHECK

1   An electric fuel pump malfunction will usually result in a loss of fuel flow and/or pressure that is often reflected by a corresponding drop in performance (or a no-run condition).

2   Verify the pump actually runs. Remove the fuel filler cap and have an assistant turn the ignition switch to On - you should hear a brief whirring noise as the pump comes on and pressurizes the system. Have the assistant start the engine (if possible). This time you should hear a constant whirring sound from the pump (but it's more difficult to hear with the engine running).

3   If the pump doesn't run (makes no sound), check the fuel pump fuse and relay (see Chapter 12). If the fuse and relay located in the power distribution box are okay, check the continuity of the inertia switch with an ohmmeter (see Section 2 for the location of the switch). If the inertia switch is good, proceed to the next Step. If the fuse is blown, replace it and see if the pump works (if it blows again, trace the fuel pump circuit for a short to ground). If the fuse doesn't blow but the fuel pump still doesn't work, proceed to the next Step.

4   With the ignition off, unplug the electrical connector from the fuel pump. Using a jumper wire, ground the negative terminal of the fuel pump. Using a fused jumper wire, apply 12-volts to the fuel pump feed terminal.

5   If the fuel pump doesn't run, replace it (see Section 7). If it does run, the problem lies somewhere in the electrical circuit to the fuel pump (refer to the wiring diagrams at the back of this manual).

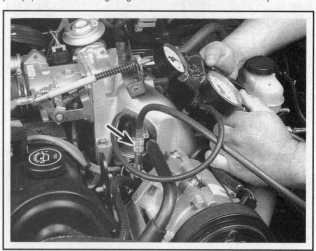

4.7 Connect the fuel pressure gauge to the Schrader valve on the fuel rail (arrow) (four-cylinder engine shown)

PRESSURE CHECK

♦ Refer to illustration 4.7

→Note: **The fuel pressure regulator is located in the fuel tank along with the fuel pump. The system is equipped with a fuel pressure damper on the fuel rail. The damper is similar in appearance to a fuel pressure regulator, but the damper's only purpose is to reduce fuel pulsations in the fuel rail.**

6   Relieve the fuel pressure (see Section 2).

7   Connect a fuel pressure gauge to the Schrader valve on the fuel rail (see illustration).

8   Turn the ignition switch to the On position. The fuel pump should run for about two seconds, then the pressure should hold steady. Note the reading on the gauge and compare it to the pressure listed in this Chapter's Specifications.

9   If the pressure is higher than specified, check for a faulty regulator.

10 If the pressure is lower than specified:

a) *Replace the fuel filter (it may be clogged*

b) *Look for a pinched or clogged fuel hose or line between the fuel tank and the fuel rail*

c) *Look for leaks in the fuel feed line.*

d) *Check for leaking injectors.*

11 Turn the ignition switch to OFF, wait one minute and recheck the pressure on the gauge. Compare the reading with the hold pressure listed in this Chapter's Specifications. If the hold pressure is less than specified:

a) *The fuel delivery line or a quick-connect fitting might be leaking.*

b) *A fuel injector (or injectors) may be leaking.*

c) *The fuel pump might be defective.*

12 After the testing is done, relieve the fuel system pressure (see Section 2) and remove the fuel pressure gauge.

---

5   Fuel tank - removal and installation

✳✳ WARNING:

Gasoline is extremely flammable, so take extra precautions when you work on any part of the fuel system. Don't smoke or allow open flames or bare light bulbs near the work area, and don't work in a garage where a gas-type appliance (such as a water heater or clothes dryer) is present. Since gasoline is carcinogenic, wear latex gloves when there's a possibility of being exposed to fuel, and, if you spill any fuel on your skin, rinse it off immediately with soap and water. Mop up any spills immediately and do not store fuel-soaked rags where they could ignite. The fuel system is under constant pressure, so, if any fuel lines are to be disconnected, the fuel pressure in the system must be relieved first (see Section 2). When you perform any kind of work on the fuel system, wear safety glasses and have a Class B type fire extinguisher on hand.

→Note: **The following procedure is much easier to perform if the fuel tank is empty. Some tanks have a drain plug for this purpose. If the tank does not have a drain plug, siphon the gasoline into an approved gasoline container.**

1   Remove the fuel tank filler cap to relieve fuel tank pressure.

2   Relieve the fuel system pressure (see Section 2).

3   Detach the negative cable from the battery.

4   If the tank still has fuel in it, siphon it into an approved gasoline container.

✳✳ WARNING:

Don't start the siphoning action by mouth! Use a siphoning kit, available at most auto parts stores.

5   Raise the vehicle and place it securely on jackstands.

6   Remove the heat shield, skid plate (if equipped) and the front retaining strap.

7   Support the fuel tank with a floor jack or jackstands. Position a piece of wood between the jack head and the fuel tank to protect the tank.

8   On 2010 and earlier models, remove the bolt from the rear retaining strap and pivot the strap down until it is hanging out of the way.

9   Loosen the screw clamps at the fill pipe and the vent pipe. Disconnect the pipes at the tank.

10 Lower the tank enough to disconnect all the vapor valve, fuel line and electrical connectors from the sender unit, vapor valve and fuel pump module (as equipped).

→Note: **To simplify installation, clearly label the hoses/lines and fittings. Plug the hoses/lines to prevent leakage and contamination of the fuel system.**

→Note: **On 2011 models, the fuel pump module cover must be removed to access some of the connectors.**

11 Disconnect any remaining fuel pump, fuel gauge sending unit, or Fuel Tank Pressure (FTP) sensor connectors (as equipped) at the rear of the fuel tank.

12 Remove the tank from the vehicle.

✳✳ WARNING:

Store the tank in a safe place, away from sparks and open flames (read the Warning at the beginning of this Section).

13 Installation is the reverse of removal. The manufacturer recommends that new tank retaining strap bolts be used. On 2011 models, tighten the fuel pump module cover nuts to 80 in-lbs.

6 Fuel tank - cleaning and repair

1 The polyethylene fuel tank cannot be repaired. No reliable repair procedures are available to correct leaks or damage. Fuel tank replacement is the only approved service.

✳✳ WARNING:

Even after cleaning and flushing of the fuel tank, explosive fumes can remain and ignite.

2 If the fuel tank is removed from the vehicle, it should not be placed in an area where sparks or open flames could ignite the fumes coming out of the tank. Be especially careful inside garages where a natural gas-type appliance is located, because the pilot light could cause an explosion.

3 Whenever the fuel tank is steam-cleaned or otherwise serviced, the vapor valve assembly should be replaced. All grommets and seals must be replaced to prevent possible leakage.

7 Fuel pump - removal and installation

✳✳ WARNING:

Gasoline is extremely flammable, so take extra precautions when you work on any part of the fuel system. Don't smoke or allow open flames or bare light bulbs near the work area, and don't work in a garage where a gas-type appliance (such as a water heater or clothes dryer) is present. Since gasoline is carcinogenic, wear latex gloves when there's a possibility of being exposed to fuel, and, if you spill any fuel on your skin, rinse it off immediately with soap and water. Mop up any spills immediately and do not store fuel-soaked rags where they could ignite. The fuel system is under constant pressure, so, if any fuel lines are to be disconnected, the fuel pressure in the system must be relieved first (see Section 2). When you perform any kind of work on the fuel system, wear safety glasses and have a Class B type fire extinguisher on hand.

1 Remove the fuel tank (refer to Section 5).

2 Remove any dirt that has accumulated where the fuel sender/pump is attached to the fuel tank. Don't allow dirt to enter the fuel tank.

3 Turn the lock ring counterclockwise with lock ring wrench (or

other suitable tool) until it's loose. Remove the lock ring.

4 Carefully pull the fuel pump/sending unit assembly from the tank. Don't bend the arm for the sending unit float.

5 Remove the old lock ring seal and discard it.

6 Clean the fuel pump mounting flange, the tank mounting surface and seal ring groove.

7 Installation is the reverse of the removal procedure with the following additions:

   a) *Apply a thin coat of heavy grease to the new lock ring seal to hold it in place during assembly. Install the seal in the lock ring groove.*

   b) *Install the fuel sender/pump unit into the fuel tank so that the tabs of the unit are positioned into the slots in the fuel tank. Make sure to keep the seal in place during installation until the lock ring has been tightened properly.*

   c) *Hold the fuel sender/pump unit in place, install and tighten the locking ring clockwise with the lock ring wrench, or equivalent, until the stop is against the retainer ring tab.*

8 Fuel level sending unit - replacement

✳✳ WARNING:

Gasoline is extremely flammable, so take extra precautions when you work on any part of the fuel system. Don't smoke or allow open flames or bare light bulbs near the work area, and don't work in a garage where a gas-type appliance (such as a water heater or clothes dryer) is present. Since gasoline is carcinogenic, wear latex gloves when there's a possibility of being exposed to fuel, and, if you spill any fuel on your skin, rinse it off immediately with soap and water. Mop up any spills immediately and do not store fuel-soaked rags where they could ignite.

The fuel system is under constant pressure, so, if any fuel lines are to be disconnected, the fuel pressure in the system must be relieved first (see Section 2). When you perform any kind of work on the fuel system, wear safety glasses and have a Class B type fire extinguisher on hand.

The fuel sender is an integral part of the fuel pump assembly. Remove and replace the fuel pump and sending unit as described in Section 7.

9 Air cleaner housing - removal and installation

▶ **Refer to illustrations 9.3 and 9.4**

1 Disconnect the negative cable from the battery.

2 Disconnect the crankcase ventilation hose on V6 models.

3 Disconnect the electrical connector at the Mass Air Flow (MAF) sensor (see illustration).

4 Disconnect the electrical connector at the Intake Air Temperature (IAT) sensor (if equipped) (see illustration).

5 Loosen the air cleaner housing clamps at the engine air cleaner and the throttle body and remove the housing. On later models, to remove the air filter housing duct, loosen and remove the clamps at both ends of the duct. Disconnect all electrical connectors and hoses, and lift the duct from the vehicle.

6 Installation is the reverse of the removal procedure. Tighten all clamps and fittings securely.

9.3 Detach the electrical connector from the Mass Air Flow sensor (arrow) . . .

9.4 . . . and the Intake Air Temperature sensor (arrow)

10 Accelerator cable - removal and installation

▶ **Refer to illustrations 10.1 and 10.2**

1   Remove the accelerator linkage shield (see illustration).
2   Disconnect the accelerator cable from the throttle lever ball stud at the throttle body (see illustration).
3   Detach the accelerator cable from its bracket on the intake manifold.

➡**Note: Bracket location may differ on later models.**

4   From inside the vehicle, remove the cable end from the top of the accelerator pedal.
5   Release the retaining clips at the dash panel and push the cable through the dash panel into the engine compartment.

6   Installation is the reverse of the removal procedure, except for the following points:

   a) Make sure that no wiring or hoses contact any moving portion of the accelerator controls.
   b) Before starting the engine, make sure that the throttle operates smoothly without any sticking or binding from the accelerator pedal.
   c) With the engine running, make sure that the throttle operates normally and the engine returns to idle when you remove your foot from the accelerator pedal.

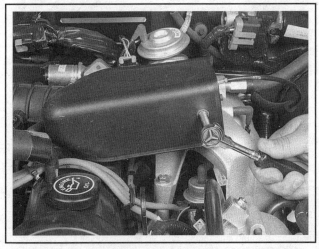

10.1 Remove the shield over the accelerator cable linkage

10.2 Pry the end of the accelerator cable from the throttle lever

11 Electronic fuel injection system - general checks

⁂ WARNING:

Gasoline is extremely flammable, so take extra precautions when you work on any part of the fuel system. Don't smoke or allow open flames or bare light bulbs near the work area, and don't work in a garage where a gas-type appliance (such as a water heater or clothes dryer) is present. Since gasoline is carcinogenic, wear latex gloves when there's a possibility of being exposed to fuel, and, if you spill any fuel on your skin, rinse it off immediately with soap and water. Mop up any spills immediately and do not store fuel-soaked rags where they could ignite. The fuel system is under constant pressure, so, if any fuel lines are to be disconnected, the fuel pressure in the system must be relieved first (see Section 2). When you perform any kind of work on the fuel system, wear safety glasses and have a Class B type fire extinguisher on hand.

→Note: The following procedure assumes that the fuel pump works and fuel pressure is adequate (see Section 4).

PRELIMINARY CHECKS

1 Check all electrical connectors that are related to the system. Loose electrical connectors and poor grounds can cause many problems that resemble more serious malfunctions.

2 Check to see that the battery is fully charged, as the control unit and sensors depend on an accurate supply voltage in order to properly meter the fuel.

3 Check the air filter element. A dirty or partially blocked filter will severely impede performance and economy (see Chapter 1).

4 If you find a blown fuse, replace it and see if it blows again. If it does, search for a grounded wire in the harness to the fuel pump (see Chapter 12).

SYSTEM CHECKS

5 Check the condition of the vacuum hoses connected to the intake manifold.

6 Remove the air intake duct from the throttle body (see Section 9) and check for dirt, carbon or other residue build-up in the throttle body, particularly around the throttle plate. If it is dirty, clean it with carburetor cleaner and a toothbrush.

7 With the engine running, place an automotive stethoscope against each injector, and listen for a clicking sound indicating that it is working. If you don't have a stethoscope, you can use a long screwdriver - place the tip of the screwdriver against the injector body and listen through the handle.

8 If you came across an injector that doesn't make any sound, install a "noid" light in line with the wiring harness of each suspected injector, start the engine and check to see if the noid light flashes. If it does, the injector is receiving proper voltage. If it doesn't flash, further diagnosis is necessary by the dealer or other experienced repair shop.

9 With the engine OFF and the fuel injector electrical connectors disconnected, measure the resistance of each injector. Compare the resistance readings with the values listed in this Chapter's Specifications.

12 Electronic fuel injection system - component check and replacement

→Note: To replace the CMP, TPS, IAC, IAT and MAF sensors, refer to Chapter 6.

UPPER INTAKE MANIFOLD AND THROTTLE BODY

→Note: Some later engines do not have a two-piece intake manifold.

SOHC four-cylinder engines

▶ Refer to illustrations 12.5 and 12.9

1 Remove the air cleaner housing (see Section 9).

2 Remove the splash shield from the accelerator linkage (see illustration 10.1). Remove the accelerator cable bracket and disconnect the accelerator cable from the throttle body (see Section 10).

3 Disconnect the electrical connections to the throttle position sensor, idle air control valve and EGR vacuum regulator control. On 2.5L engines, remove the engine ground wire (if equipped) from the manifold stud.

4 Disconnect the PCV hose from the intake manifold.

5 Label and disconnect the vacuum hoses from the manifold vacuum tee (see illustration).

6 Disconnect the EGR transducer hoses from the EGR valve, and remove EGR valve (see Chapter 6).

7 Remove the bolts and studs that secure the upper intake manifold.

12.5 Disconnect the vacuum hoses from the intake manifold

8 Thoroughly clean all old gasket material from the mating surfaces of the upper intake manifold and the lower intake manifold.

9 Install a new gasket on the lower intake manifold, then install the upper manifold and tighten the fasteners in sequence to the torque listed in this Chapter's Specifications (see illustration).

10 The remainder of installation is the reverse of the removal steps.

12.9 Upper intake manifold bolt tightening sequence (SOHC four-cylinder engine)

3.0L V6 engine

♦ Refer to illustration 12.19

11 Label and disconnect the electrical connectors and vacuum lines between the upper intake manifold and the engine and body.

12 Remove the splash shield from the accelerator linkage. Remove the accelerator cable bracket and disconnect the accelerator cable from the throttle body (see Section 10).

13 Remove the air inlet tube that connects the air cleaner to the throttle body.

14 Label and disconnect the vacuum lines from the upper intake manifold.

15 Detach the PCV valve from the right valve cover and disconnect the hose from the throttle body.

16 Detach the spark plug wires from the ignition coil and move them out of the way.

17 Remove the ignition coil with bracket, the EGR vacuum regulator control and the radio ignition interference capacitor.

18 Disconnect the hoses from the EGR valve, then remove the EGR valve.

19 Remove bolts and studs that secure the upper intake manifold (see illustration), and remove the manifold.

20 Thoroughly clean all old gasket material from the mating surfaces of the upper intake manifold and the lower intake manifold.

21 Install a new gasket on the lower intake manifold, then install the upper manifold and tighten the fasteners evenly to the torque listed in this Chapter's Specifications.

22 The remainder of installation is the reverse of the removal steps.

12.19 On the 3.0L engine, remove the bolts and studs securing the upper intake manifold to the lower intake manifold

4.0L V6 engine

♦ Refer to illustrations 12.30, 12.31a and 12.31b

23 Label and disconnect the electrical connectors and vacuum lines between the upper intake manifold, engine and body.

24 Remove the splash shield from the accelerator linkage. Remove the accelerator cable bracket and disconnect the accelerator cable from the throttle body (see Section 10).

25 Remove the air inlet tube that connects the air cleaner to the throttle body.

26 Label and disconnect the vacuum lines from the upper intake manifold.

27 Detach the PCV valve from the right valve cover (see Chapter 6).

28 Detach the spark plug wires from the back of the upper intake manifold.

29 Disconnect the canister purge line at the throttle body fitting.

30 Remove the bolt that secures the air conditioning refrigerant line at the upper rear part of the manifold (see illustration). DO NOT disconnect any refrigerant lines!

31 Remove the six nuts that secure the upper intake manifold (see illustrations). Note the cap over the front stud. Lift the upper manifold and throttle body together off the fuel rail and lower intake manifold.

32 Thoroughly clean all old gasket material from the mating surfaces of upper intake manifold and the fuel rail.

12.30 Unbolt the air conditioning hose bracket from the upper intake manifold and move it aside DO NOT disconnect any refrigerant lines

12.31a Remove the upper intake manifold nuts with a socket and extension

12.31b Note the cap over the front stud (arrow) - remove it before unscrewing the nut

12.39 Disconnect the electrical connector and remove the throttle body mounting bolts

33 Install a new gasket on the fuel rail, then install the upper manifold and tighten the fasteners evenly to the torque listed in this Chapter's Specifications.

34 The remainder of installation is the reverse of the removal steps.

THROTTLE BODY

▶ **Refer to illustration 12.39**

35 Remove the splash shield from the accelerator linkage and disconnect the accelerator cable (see Section 10).

36 Disconnect the electrical connector from the throttle position sensor.

37 Unclamp and disconnect the air inlet duct at the throttle body.

38 Disconnect the canister purge hose from underneath the throttle body (if equipped).

39 Remove the four throttle body mounting bolts (see illustration). Remove the throttle body and gasket from the upper intake manifold.

2011 models

40 Remove the air filter housing duct (see Chapter 4).

41 Remove the throttle body cover bolts and remove the cover.

42 On 2.3L models, disconnect the accelerator cable and cruise control cable (if equipped).

43 Disconnect the electrical connector from the Throttle Position Sensor (TPS).

44 Remove the four throttle body mounting bolts and remove the throttle body.

All models

45 Carefully clean all old gasket material from the mating surface of throttle body and upper intake manifold.

✳✳ CAUTION:

Don't let gasket material fall into the manifold.

46 Place a new gasket on the manifold, then install the throttle body and tighten the screws to the torque listed in this Chapter's Specifications. The remainder of installation is the reverse of the removal steps.

FUEL RAIL AND INJECTORS

Removal

▶ **Refer to illustrations 12.52, 12.53a, 12.53b, 12.53c and 12.54**

47 If the engine is very dirty, it may be a good idea to steam clean the engine first to prevent dirt from contaminating exposed fittings and fuel metering orifices.

48 Relieve the fuel system pressure (see Section 2). Disconnect the negative cable from the battery.

49 Remove the air inlet tube that runs between the air cleaner and throttle body.

50 Remove the upper intake manifold (if equipped) as described previously in this Section.

51 Disconnect the fuel supply and return lines (see Section 3).

52 Disconnect the electrical connectors from the fuel injectors (see illustration).

53 Remove the bolts that secure the fuel rail (see illustrations). Carefully lift the fuel rail and injectors out with a rocking, pulling motion.

54 The injectors may come out with the fuel rail or remain attached to the lower intake manifold. Detach the injectors as follows:

 a) Remove the injector retaining clip(s), if equipped.
 b) Carefully pull the injector out with a rocking motion (see illustration).

12.52 Use a small screwdriver to disengage the locking tang or retaining clip on the fuel injector electrical connectors

12.53a To remove the fuel rail on a 3.0L V6 engine, remove the two bolts from each side of the fuel rail . . .

12.53b . . . then gently lift and rock the fuel rail to disengage the injectors from their ports in the intake manifold

12.53c Remove the bolts that secure the fuel rail to the lower intake manifold (4.0L pushrod V6 engine)

12.53d Fuel rail bolts on the 4.0L V6 SOHC engine

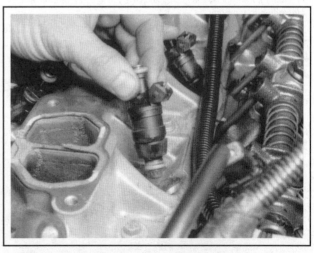

12.54 Detach the fuel injectors with a rocking, pulling motion and take them out

Installation

▶ **Refer to illustration 12.55**

55 On 2010 and earlier models, check the injector O-rings for damage or deterioration and replace as needed (see illustration). On 2011 models, new, fuel-resistant O-rings must be used to prevent fuel leaks - replace the O-rings now.

56 Inspect the plastic hat that covers the end of each injector (if it's not on the injector, it may be in the intake manifold). Replace the hat if damaged or deteriorated.

57 Lubricate the injector O-rings with a light film of engine oil. Each injector uses two O-rings.

✳✳ CAUTION:

Don't lubricate the injector O-rings with silicone grease. It will clog them.

58 Install the injectors in the fuel rail with a light rocking motion.

59 The remainder of installation is the reverse of the removal steps.

60 Turn the ignition key On and Off several times (without starting

12.55 Use a small screwdriver to peel off the old O-rings from either end of the injectors

the engine) to pressurize the fuel system. Check all fuel system connections for leaks.

13 Exhaust system service - general information

✳✳ WARNING:

Inspection and repair of exhaust system components should be done only after enough time has elapsed after driving the vehicle to allow the system components to cool completely. Also, when working under the vehicle, make sure it is securely supported on jackstands.

1 The exhaust system consists of the exhaust manifolds, the catalytic converter, the mufflers, the tailpipe and all connecting pipes, brackets, hangers and clamps. The exhaust system is attached to the body with mounting brackets and rubber hangers. If any of these components are improperly installed, excessive noise and vibration will be transmitted to the body.

2 Conduct regular inspections of the exhaust system to keep it safe and quiet. Look for any damaged or bent parts, open seams, holes, loose connections, excessive corrosion or other defects which could allow exhaust fumes to enter the vehicle. Deteriorated exhaust system components should not be repaired; they should be replaced with new parts.

3 If the exhaust system components are extremely corroded or rusted together, welding equipment will probably be required to remove them. The convenient way to accomplish this is to have a muffler repair

shop remove the corroded sections with a cutting torch. If, however, you want to save money by doing it yourself (and you don't have a welding outfit with a cutting torch), simply cut off the old components with a hacksaw. If you have compressed air, special pneumatic cutting chisels can also be used. If you do decide to tackle the job at home, be sure to wear safety goggles to protect your eyes from metal chips and work gloves to protect your hands.

4 Here are some simple guidelines to follow when repairing the exhaust system:

a) *Work from the back to the front when removing exhaust system components.*

b) *Apply penetrating oil to the exhaust system component fasteners to make them easier to remove.*

c) *Use new gaskets, hangers and clamps when installing exhaust systems components.*

d) *Apply anti-seize compound to the threads of all exhaust system fasteners during reassembly.*

e) *Be sure to allow sufficient clearance between newly installed parts and all points on the underbody to avoid overheating the floor pan and possibly damaging the interior carpet and insulation. Pay particularly close attention to the catalytic converter and heat shield.*

Specifications

Fuel system pressure (key on, engine off)

2000 models	55 to 65 psi
2001 models	
2.3L four-cylinder engine	35 to 55 psi
2.5L four-cylinder engine	30 to 65 psi
3.0L V6 engine	30 to 65 psi
4.0L V6 engine	40 to 65 psi
2002 models	
2.3L four-cylinder engine	30 to 55 psi
3.0L V6 engine	40 to 65 psi
4.0L V6 engine	30 to 65 psi
2003 through 2007 models	48 to 70 psi
2008 and later models	60 to 65 psi
System hold pressure (after 1 minute)	No more than 5 psi drop from recorded pressure

Fuel injector resistance

All models	12 to 16 ohms

Torque specifications   Ft-lbs (unless otherwise indicated)

➡**Note: One foot-pound (ft-lb) of torque is equivalent to 12 inch-pounds (in-lbs) of torque. Torque values below approximately 15 ft-lbs are expressed in inch-pounds, since most foot-pound torque wrenches are not accurate at these smaller values.**

Intake manifold* fasteners	
2000 2.3L and 2.5L SOHC engines	
Step 1	84 to 120 in-lbs
Step 2	19 to 28
2.3L DOHC engines (2001 and later)	
2010 and earlier	156 in-lbs
2011	159 in-lbs
3.0L V6 engines	89 in-lbs
4.0L V6 engines	
2005 and earlier	15 to 18
2006 and later	89 in-lbs
Lower intake manifold bolts	See Chapter 2
Throttle body bolts	
SOHC engines	15 to 22
DOHC engines	89 in-lbs
3.0L V6 engines	19
4.0L V6 engines	
2010 and earlier	76 to 106 in-lbs
2011	80 in-lbs
Fuel rail mounting bolts/studs	
2010 and earlier	
Four-cylinder engines	15 to 22
3.0L V6 engine	72 to 96 in-lbs
4.0L V6 engines	84 to 120 in-lbs
2011	
2.3L four-cylinder engine	18
4.0L V6 engine	17

*On some models, this is referred to as the upper intake manifold.

Notes

Section

Reference to other Chapters

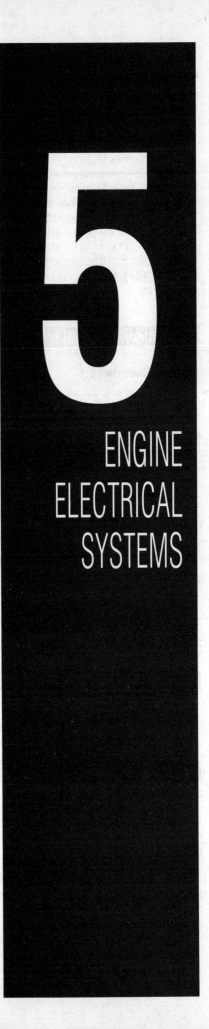

5

ENGINE
ELECTRICAL
SYSTEMS

1 General information

The engine electrical systems include all ignition, charging and starting components. Because of their engine-related functions, these components are considered separately from chassis electrical devices like the lights, instruments, etc.

Be very careful when working on the engine electrical components. They are easily damaged if checked, connected or handled improperly. The alternator is driven by an engine drivebelt which could cause serious injury if your hands, hair or clothes become entangled in it with the engine running. Both the starter and alternator are connected directly to the battery and could arc or even cause a fire if mishandled, overloaded or shorted out.

Never leave the ignition switch on for long periods of time with the engine off. Don't disconnect the battery cables while the engine is running. Correct polarity must be maintained when connecting battery cables from another source, such as another vehicle, during jump starting. Always disconnect the negative cable first and hook it up last or the battery may be shorted by the tool being used to loosen the cable clamps.

Additional safety related information on the engine electrical systems can be found in Safety first near the front of this manual. It should be referred to before beginning any operation included in this Chapter.

2 Battery - removal and installation

▶ **Refer to illustration 2.1**

1   Disconnect both cables from the battery terminals (see illustration).

✳✳ CAUTION:

Always disconnect the negative cable first and hook it up last or sparks may occur that can cause the battery to explode.

2   Remove the battery heat shield (if equipped).
3   Locate the battery hold-down clamp at the base of the battery. Remove the bolt and the hold-down clamp.
4   Lift out the battery. Special straps or clamps that attach to the battery are available - lifting and moving the battery is much easier if you use one.
5   Installation is the reverse of removal. Make sure the battery cables and battery posts are free of corrosion. Clean them if necessary (see Section 4).

2.1 Disconnect the negative cable first, then the positive cable

3 Battery - emergency jump starting

Refer to the *Booster battery (jump) starting* procedure at the front of this manual.

4 Battery cables - check and replacement

1   Periodically inspect the entire length of each battery cable for damage, cracked or burned insulation and corrosion. Poor battery cable connections can cause starting problems and decreased engine performance.
2   Check the cable-to-terminal connections at the ends of the cables for cracks, loose wire strands and corrosion. The presence of white, fluffy deposits under the insulation at the cable terminal connection is a sign that the cable is corroded and should be replaced. Check the terminals for distortion, missing mounting bolts and corrosion.
3   When replacing the cables, always disconnect the negative cable first and hook it up last or the battery may be shorted by the tool used to loosen the cable clamps. Even if only the positive cable is being replaced, be sure to disconnect the negative cable from the battery first.

4   Disconnect and remove the cable. Make sure the replacement cable is the same length and wire size (diameter).
5   Clean the threads of the starter relay or ground connection with a wire brush to remove rust and corrosion. Apply a light coat of petroleum jelly to the threads to prevent future corrosion.
6   Attach the cable to the starter relay or ground connection and tighten the mounting nut/bolt securely.
7   Before connecting the new cable to the battery, make sure that it reaches the battery post without having to be stretched. Clean the battery posts and cable ends thoroughly and apply a light coat of petroleum jelly to prevent corrosion (see Chapter 1).
8   Connect the positive cable first, followed by the negative cable.

5   Ignition system - general information

All engines covered in this manual are equipped with electronic distributorless ignition systems that have no moving parts. This system includes a Crankshaft Position (CKP) sensor which provides base timing information and cylinder identification to the Powertrain Control Module (PCM). The PCM determines when to fire the spark plugs based on the CKP information, engine speed, load, temperature and other sensor data. The Ignition Control Module, controlled by the PCM, fires spark plugs for two cylinders at the same time. One cylinder is fired on its compression stroke while the other is fired on its exhaust stroke.

There are some variations within this basic design. Most four-cylinder engines, 3.0L engines and all 4.0L engines use a 36 tooth pulley on the crankshaft. A missing tooth on this pulley provides information about basic timing and cylinder identification. Another important difference is that many four-cylinder engines have twin spark plugs (two spark plugs per cylinder), and it has two ignition coil packs.

2000 2.5L four-cylinder engines have an unusual ignition arrangement. Each cylinder has two spark plugs and two plug wires leading to two separate coilpacks. The PCM controls the timing of ignition and which plugs to fire. Each coilpack fires two plugs at the same time, one for a cylinder on its compression stroke and another waste spark on a cylinder that is on its exhaust stroke. When the engine is being started, the PCM allows the system to fire only one plug per cylinder. The two-plug firing commences once the engine is started. When testing for spark on a 2.5L engine, you will not get a signal from the spark plugs on the left side of the engine during cranking, while you should get a signal from the plugs on the right.

6   Ignition system - check

▶ Refer to illustrations 6.2 and 6.4

✳✳ WARNING:

Because of the high voltage generated by the ignition system, extreme care should be taken whenever an operation is performed involving ignition components. This not only includes the igniter (electronic ignition), coil, distributor and spark plug wires, but related components such as spark plug connectors, tachometer and other test equipment.

1   If the engine turns over but won't start, disconnect the spark plug lead from any spark plug and attach it to a calibrated ignition tester (available at most auto parts stores). Make sure the tester is designed for Ford ignition systems if a universal tester isn't available.

2   Connect the clip on the tester to a bolt or metal bracket on the engine (see illustration), crank the engine and watch the end of the tester to see if bright blue, well-defined sparks occur.

3   If sparks occur, sufficient voltage is reaching the spark plug to fire it (repeat the check at the remaining plug wires to verify that all the ignition coils and wires are functioning). However, the plugs themselves may be fouled, so remove and check them as described in Chapter 1 or install new ones.

4   If no spark occurs or the spark is intermittent, check for battery voltage to the ignition coil (see illustration). Check for a bad spark plug wire by swapping wires. Check the coils and EDIS ignition module. If the checks fail to identify the problem, have the system diagnosed at a dealer service department or other properly equipped repair facility.

ALTERNATIVE METHOD

➡**Note: If you're unable to obtain a calibrated ignition tester, the following method will allow you to determine if the ignition system has spark, but it won't tell you if there's enough voltage produced to actually initiate combustion in the cylinders.**

5   Remove the wire from one of the spark plugs. Using an insulated tool, hold the wire about 1/4-inch from a good ground and have an assistant crank the engine.

6   If bright blue, well-defined sparks occur, sufficient voltage is reaching the plug to fire it. However, the plug(s) may be fouled, so remove and check them as described in Chapter 1 or install new ones.

7   If there's no spark, check the remaining wires in the same manner. A few sparks followed by no spark is the same condition as no spark at all.

8   If no sparks occur, remove the distributor cap and check the cap and rotor as described in Chapter 1. If moisture is present, dry out the cap and rotor, then reinstall the cap and repeat the spark test.

6.2 To use a calibrated ignition tester (available at most auto parts stores), simply disconnect a spark plug wire, attach the wire to the tester, clip the tester to a convenient ground and operate the starter. If there is enough power to fire the plug, sparks will be visible in the tester

6.4 Primary wiring to the ignition coil on an electronic distributorless ignition system

9   If there's still no spark, disconnect the secondary coil wire from the distributor cap, hold it about 1/4-inch from a good engine ground with an insulated tool and crank the engine again.

➡ **Note: On 2.5L four-cylinder engines, which have two plugs per cylinder, a spark tester will only work on the right-side plugs during cranking.**

10 If no sparks occur, check the primary (small) wire connections at the coil to make sure they're clean and tight.

11 If sparks now occur, the distributor cap and rotor (3.0L engines only), plug wire(s) and spark plug(s) may be defective.

12 If there's still no spark, the coil-to-cap wire may be bad (check the resistance with an ohmmeter and compare it to the Specifications). If a known good wire doesn't make any difference in the test results, the ignition coil, module or other internal components may be defective. Refer further testing to a Ford dealer or qualified electrical specialist.

7   Ignition coil - check, removal and installation

CHECK

▶ **Refer to illustrations 7.1 and 7.2**

1   With the ignition off, disconnect the electrical connector from the coil. Connect an ohmmeter across the coil primary (center terminal) terminal and the outer terminal (see illustration). The manufacturer does not specify a resistance, but it should be less than 5.0 ohms. If the resistance is very high or open circuit, the coil may be defective. Take it to your dealer or other competent repair shop for testing before replacing it. They can bench test it for you, often for nothing.

2   Connect an ohmmeter between the secondary terminals of the coil (see illustration). The resistance should be as listed in this Chapter's Specifications. Remember that cylinders are paired - two will fire at the same time. On four-cylinder engines 1/4 and 2/3 are paired. On V6 engines, 1/5, 2/6 and 3/4 are paired.

REPLACEMENT

▶ **Refer to illustrations 7.4 and 7.5**

3   Disconnect the negative cable from the battery.

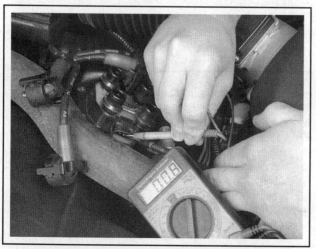

7.1 To check the primary resistance of a distributorless coil, connect the probes to the center terminal and outer terminal of the coil. Check all coil packs this way

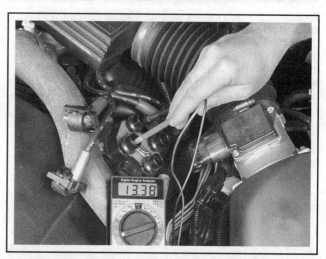

7.2 Check the coil secondary resistance by probing the paired cylinders

7.4 Disconnect the electrical connector from the coil pack

7.5 Squeeze the locking tabs to release the spark plug wires

4 Disconnect the ignition coil electrical connector(s) from the coil/coil pack (see illustration).

5 Disconnect the spark plug wires by squeezing the locking tabs (if equipped) and twisting while pulling (see illustration). DO NOT just pull on the wires to disconnect them.

6 Remove the bolts securing the ignition coil to the mounting bracket on the engine.

7 Installation is the reverse of the removal procedure with the following additions:

a) Prior to installing the spark plug lead into the ignition coil, coat the entire interior of the rubber boot with Silicone Dielectric Compound.
b) Insert each spark plug wire into the proper terminal of the ignition coil. Push the wire into the terminal and make sure the boots are fully seated and both locking tabs are engaged properly.
c) If equipped, make sure the radio ignition interference capacitor is reinstalled on the same coil from which it was removed.

8 Crankshaft position sensor - removal and installation

Refer to Chapter 6, Section 5 for information on the crankshaft position sensor.

9 Camshaft position sensor - removal and installation

Refer to Chapter 6, Section 5 for information on the camshaft position sensor.

10 Charging system - general information and precautions

The charging system includes the alternator with integral voltage regulator, an ammeter or charge indicator light, the battery, a fusible link and the wiring between all the components. The charging system supplies electrical power for the ignition system, the lights, the radio, etc. The alternator is driven by a drivebelt at the front of the engine.

The purpose of the integral solid-state voltage regulator is to limit the alternator's voltage to a preset value. This prevents power surges, circuit overloads, etc., during peak voltage output.

The charging system doesn't ordinarily require periodic maintenance. However, the drivebelt, battery, wires and connections should be inspected at the intervals outlined in Chapter 1.

Be very careful when making electrical circuit connections to the vehicle and note the following:

a) When reconnecting wires to the alternator from the battery, be sure to note the polarity.
b) Before using arc welding equipment to repair any part of the vehicle, disconnect the wires from the alternator and the battery terminals.
c) Never start the engine with a battery charger connected.
d) Always disconnect both battery leads before using a battery charger.
e) Never disconnect the battery when the engine is running.
f) The alternator is turned by the engine drivebelt which could cause serious injury if your hands or clothes become entangled in it with the engine running.
g) Because the alternator is connected directly to the battery, it could arc or cause a fire if overloaded or shorted out.
h) Wrap a plastic bag over the alternator and secure it with rubber bands before steam cleaning the engine.

11 Charging system - check

➡Note 1: If the alternator requires service it must be replaced as an assembly. Both new and rebuilt units are readily available. Replacement parts are not available individually.

➡Note 2: The alternators on later models have an internal voltage regulator. Testing these units requires advanced techniques and testing equipment. We recommend having the removed unit tested at a qualified service location (some parts retailers will provide this service as a courtesy). If the unit tests OK, then it is advised to have the charging system checked by a qualified service technician. If your vehicle has an alternator/generator like the one that is shown in illustration 11.8 (with an external voltage regulator), then you can use the following procedures for testing.

1 If a malfunction occurs in the charging circuit, don't automatically assume that the alternator is causing the problem. First check the following items:

a) The battery cables where they connect to the battery. Make sure the connections are clean and tight (see Chapter 1).
b) Check the external alternator wiring harness and the connectors at the alternator. They must be in good condition, clean, free of corrosion and tight.
c) Check the drivebelt condition and tension (see Chapter 1).
d) Make sure the alternator mounting and adjustment bolts are tight.
e) Check the fusible link located between the starter relay and the alternator. If it's burned out, determine the cause, repair the circuit and replace the link (see Chapter 12).
f) Run the engine and check the alternator for abnormal noise.

2   Turn the headlights on for 10 to 15 seconds to remove any surface charge from the battery. Wait three to five minutes for the battery voltage to stabilize before continuing with Step 3.

3   Connect a voltmeter between the battery terminals and check the battery voltage with the engine off. It should be approximately 12.6-volts.

4   Run the engine at a fast idle (approximately 1500 rpm) and check the battery voltage again after the voltage stops rising. This may take a few minutes. It should now be higher than battery voltage, but not more than 3-volts higher.

5   If the voltage reading is less than the specified charging voltage, perform the Under-voltage test in this Section. If it is higher, perform the Over-voltage test.

6   Turn on the high beam headlights and turn the heater or air conditioner blower to its highest setting. Run the engine at 2,000 rpm and check the voltage reading. It should now be at least 0.5-volt higher than battery voltage. If not, perform the Under-voltage test.

7   If the voltage readings are correct in the preceding Steps, the charging system is working properly. Use a 12-volt test light and the wiring diagrams (see Chapter 12) to check for a battery drain.

UNDER-VOLTAGE TEST

▶ **Refer to illustrations 11.8, 11.9, 11.11 and 11.13**

8   Unplug the electrical connector from the voltage regulator. Connect an ohmmeter between the A and F terminal screws (see illustration). The ohmmeter should indicate at least 2.4 ohms.

   a) *If the ohmmeter reading is too low, the regulator is defective.*
   b) *If the ohmmeter reading is within specifications, reconnect the electrical connector to the regulator and perform Step 9.*

9   Connect the voltmeter negative lead to the alternator rear housing and the positive lead to the regulator A terminal screw (see illustration). The voltmeter should indicate battery voltage. If not, check the A circuit for breaks or bad connections.

10 Repeat the load test (see Step 6).

11 If the voltmeter indicates battery voltage in Step 9, place the ignition key in the Off position. Connect the voltmeter negative lead to the alternator frame and the positive lead to the F terminal screw (see illustration).

   a) *If the voltmeter indicates no voltage, replace the alternator.*
   b) *If the voltmeter indicates battery voltage, proceed to Step 12.*

11.8 Connect an ohmmeter between the A and F terminal screws

12 Turn the ignition key to the Run position, but don't start the engine. Touch the voltmeter negative lead to the rear of the alternator and the positive lead to the F terminal screw on the regulator.

   a) *If the voltmeter indicates more than two volts, perform the I circuit test in this Section.*
   b) *If the voltmeter indicates two volts or less, proceed to Step 13.*

13 Perform the load test (see Step 6) with the voltmeter positive terminal connected to the alternator output stud (see illustration).

   a) *If voltage increases to more than 0.5-volt above battery voltage, check the wiring from alternator to starter relay for breaks or bad connections.*
   b) *If the voltage does not increase to more than 0.5 volt above battery voltage, perform Step 14.*

14 Connect a jumper wire between the alternator rear housing and the regulator F terminal screw. Repeat the load test (see Step 6) with the voltmeter positive lead connected to one of the B+ jumper wire terminals.

   a) *If voltage increases by more than 0.5-volt, replace the regulator (see Section 13).*
   b) *If voltage doesn't increase by more than 0.5-volt, replace the alternator.*

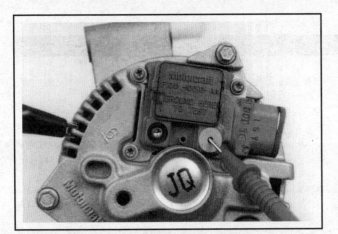

11.9 Connect the voltmeter negative lead to the alternator housing and the positive lead to the regulator A terminal screw

11.11 Connect the voltmeter negative lead to the alternator housing and the positive lead to the F terminal screw

11.13 Perform the load test with the voltmeter positive lead connected to the alternator output stud

OVER-VOLTAGE TEST

15 Turn the key to the On position but leave the engine off.

16 Connect the voltmeter negative lead to the alternator rear housing and connect the positive lead to the alternator output connection at the starter relay, then to the regulator A terminal. If the voltage readings differ by more than 0.5-volt, check the A circuit for breaks or bad connections.

17 If Step 16 doesn't correct the problem, check for loose regulator grounding screws and tighten as needed.

18 If the voltage reading is still too high, place the ignition key in the Off position. Connect the voltmeter negative lead to the alternator frame. Connect the voltmeter positive lead to the A terminal screw, then to the F terminal screw.

 a) *If the voltage readings at the two screw heads are different, replace the alternator.*

 b) *If the voltage readings at the two screw heads are the same, the regulator is defective and the alternator must be replaced.*

S AND/OR I CIRCUIT TEST

19 Disconnect the alternator electrical connector.

20 Connect one jumper wire from the alternator A terminal to its corresponding terminal in the electrical connector. Connect another jumper wire from the regulator F screw to the alternator housing.

21 Start the engine and let it idle.

22 Connect the voltmeter negative lead to the alternator housing. Connect the positive lead to the connector S terminal and A terminal in turn. Voltage at the A terminal should be approximately double the reading at the S terminal.

 a) *If the readings are as specified, the regulator is defective and the alternator must be replaced.*

 b) *If there is no voltage, check the wiring for breaks or bad connections. If the wiring is good, replace the alternator.*

12 Alternator - removal and installation

♦ **Refer to illustration 12.6**

1 Disconnect the negative cable from the battery.

2 Remove the air cleaner assembly (see Chapter 4)

3 Unplug the electrical connectors from the alternator.

4 Remove the electrical connector bracket (if equipped).

5 Remove the drivebelt (see Chapter 1). On 2011 models, disconnect the alternator B+ terminal wire(s).

6 Remove the mounting bolts holding the alternator to its mounting bracket (see illustration), and remove the alternator.

7 Installation is the reverse of removal.

12.6 Location of the alternator mounting bolts (arrows)

13 Voltage regulator/alternator brushes - replacement

▶ **Refer to illustrations 13.3, 13.4, 13.5 and 13.9**

1   Remove the alternator (see Section 12).

2   Set the alternator on a clean workbench.

3   Remove the four voltage regulator mounting screws (see illustration).

4   Detach the voltage regulator/brush holder assembly (see illustration).

5   Detach the rubber plugs and remove the brush lead retaining screws and nuts to separate the brush leads from the holder (see illustration). Note that the screws have Torx heads and require a special screwdriver.

6   After noting the relationship of the brushes to the brush holder assembly, remove both brushes. Don't lose the springs.

7   Install the brushes into the regulator. Make sure the springs are properly compressed and the brushes are properly inserted into the recesses in the brush holder.

8   Install the brush lead retaining screws and nuts.

9   Insert a short section of wire, like a paper clip, through the hole in the voltage regulator (see illustration) to hold the brushes in the retracted position during regulator installation.

10   Carefully install the regulator. Make sure the brushes don't hang up on the rotor.

11   Install the voltage regulator screws and tighten them securely.

12   Remove the wire or paper clip.

13   Install the alternator (see Section 12).

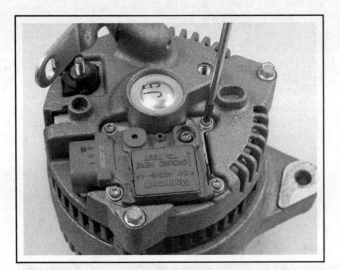

13.3 To remove the voltage regulator/brush assembly, remove the four screws

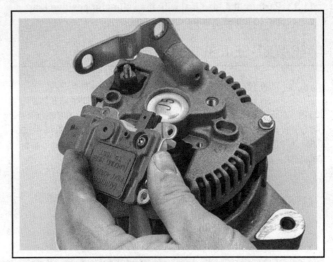

13.4 Lift the assembly from the alternator

13.5 To remove the brushes from the voltage regulator/brush holder assembly, remove the rubber plugs from the two brush lead screws and remove both screws

13.9 Before installing the voltage regulator/brush holder assembly, insert a paper clip as shown to hold the brushes in place during installation. After installation, remove the paper clip

14 Starting system - general information

The system is composed of the starter motor, starter relay, battery, ignition switch, safety switch and connecting wires.

Turning the ignition key to the Start position actuates the starter relay through the starter control circuit. The starter relay then connects the battery to the starter. The battery supplies the electrical energy to the starter motor, which does the actual work of cranking the engine.

Vehicles equipped with an automatic transmission have a Neutral start switch in the starter control circuit, which prevents operation of the starter unless the shift lever is in Neutral or Park. The circuit on vehicles with a manual transmission prevents operation of the starter motor unless the clutch pedal is depressed.

Never operate the starter motor for more than 15 seconds at a time without pausing to allow it to cool for at least two minutes. Excessive cranking can cause overheating, which can seriously damage the starter.

15 Starter motor and circuit - in-vehicle check

1   If a malfunction occurs in the starting circuit, do not immediately assume that the starter is causing the problem. First, check the following items:

   a) *Make sure the battery cable clamps, where they connect to the battery, are clean and tight.*
   b) *Check the condition of the battery cables (see Section 4). Replace any defective battery cables with new ones.*
   c) *Test the condition of the battery (see Chapter 1). If it does not pass all the tests, replace it with a new battery.*
   d) *Check the starter mounting bolts for tightness.*
   e) *Check the adjustment of the Digital Transmission Range sensor (automatic transmission) or Clutch Pedal Position (CPP) switch (manual transmission). Make sure the shift lever is in PARK or NEUTRAL (automatic transmission) or the clutch pedal is pressed (manual transmission). Refer to Chapter 7B for the DTR sensor adjustment procedure. Refer to Chapter 12 wiring diagrams, if necessary, when performing circuit checks. These systems must operate correctly to provide battery voltage to the ignition switch.*
   f) *Check the operation of the starter relay. On later models, the starter relay is located in the engine compartment fuse and relay box.*

2   If the starter motor spins but the engine doesn't turn over, then the drive assembly in the starter motor is slipping and the starter motor must be replaced (see Section 16).

3   If, when the switch is actuated, the starter motor doesn't operate at all but the starter relay operates (clicks), then the problem lies with either the battery, the starter relay contacts, the starter solenoid or the starter motor electrical connections.

4   If the starter relay doesn't click when the ignition switch is actuated, a discharged battery is the most likely cause. If the battery is fully charged, the starter relay circuit may be open or the relay itself could be defective. Check the starter relay circuit or replace the relay (see Section 17).

EARLY MODELS

➡**Note: These checking procedures apply only to early models. The starter relays on later models are mounted in the engine compartment fuse/relay box (see Step 1f).**

5   To check the starter relay circuit, remove the push-on electrical connector from the relay (red with blue stripe). Make sure that the connection is clean and secure and the relay bracket is grounded. If the connections are good, check the operation of the relay with a jumper wire. To do this, place the transmission in Park (automatic) or Neutral (manual). Remove the push-on connector from the relay. Connect a jumper wire between the battery positive terminal and the relay main terminal (BAT side) on the starter relay. If the starter motor now operates, the starter relay is okay. The problem is in the ignition switch, Neutral start switch, starter/clutch switch, or in the starting circuit wiring (look for open or loose connections). Reconnect the push-on electrical connector.

6   If the starter motor still doesn't operate, check the starter relay contacts. To do this, momentarily jumper across the two large terminals with red wires at the starter relay.

✳✳ CAUTION:

Use a jumper with the same size wire or larger. If the starter operates, the starter relay is good, and the trouble must be with the starter solenoid; replace the starter. If the starter still does not operate, replace the starter relay (see Section 17).

7   If the starter motor cranks the engine at an abnormally slow speed, first make sure the battery is fully charged and all terminal connections are clean and tight. Also check the connections at the starter relay and battery ground. Eyelet terminals should not be easily rotated by hand. Also check for a short to ground. If the engine is partially seized, or has the wrong (too heavy) viscosity oil in it, it will crank slowly.

16 Starter motor - removal and installation

◗ **Refer to illustrations 16.4, 16.5a and 16.5b**

➡**Note: On 2001 and later models with 2.3L engines, remove the left front inner splash shield to gain access to the starter motor.**

1   Disconnect the cable from the negative terminal of the battery.

2   Raise the vehicle and support it securely on jackstands.

3   If equipped, remove and discard the protective covers from the starter motor terminals.

16.4 The starter wires are connected to the terminals at the top of the starter

16.5a Remove the lower mounting nut

16.5b Remove the upper mounting bolt and remove the starter

4   Disconnect the wiring from the terminals on the starter motor (see illustration).

5   While supporting the starter, remove the starter motor mounting bolts (see illustrations) and detach the starter from the engine.

6   Installation is the reverse of removal. Tighten the starter bolts to the torque listed in this Chapter's Specifications. Replace the starter solenoid terminal protective caps with new ones, if equipped.

17 Starter relay - removal and installation

▶ **Refer to illustration 17.1**

➡**Note: The following procedure applies only to those vehicles with externally mounted starter relays like the one shown in illustration 17.1.**

1   The starter relay is located in the engine compartment, mounted between the battery and the power distribution box (see illustration).

2   Disconnect the negative cable from the battery.

3   Label the wires and the terminals on the relay to prevent mix-up during installation.

4   Disconnect the small wire from the starter relay.

5   Disconnect the positive battery cable and the feed cable from the starter relay.

6   Disconnect the starter feed cable from the other terminal on the starter relay.

7   Remove the mounting bolts and remove the relay.

8   Installation is the reverse of the removal procedure with the following additions:

   a) *Prior to installing the relay, clean the mounting surface with a wire brush or sandpaper to provide a good ground.*

   b) *Attach the relay to the inner fender panel and tighten the bolts securely.*

✳✳ CAUTION:

Do not overtighten the bolts - they are self-threading and can easily strip out the holes in the sheet metal.

   c) *Be sure to connect the cables to the correct terminals on the relay. Refer to the labels made in Step 3.*

17.1 The starter relay is located between the battery and the power distribution box in the engine compartment

Specifications

Ignition system
EDIS coil secondary resistance   13 to 15 K-ohms

Battery voltage
Engine off	12-volts
Engine running	14 to 15-volts

Alternator brush length
New	1/2-inch
Minimum	1/4-inch

Torque specifications

	Ft-lbs
Alternator mounting bolts	
2001 and later 2.3L engines	18
2011 4.0L engine	35
All other engines	30 to 40
Distributor hold-down bolt	17 to 25
Starter mounting bolts	15 to 20

Notes

Section

Reference to other Chapters

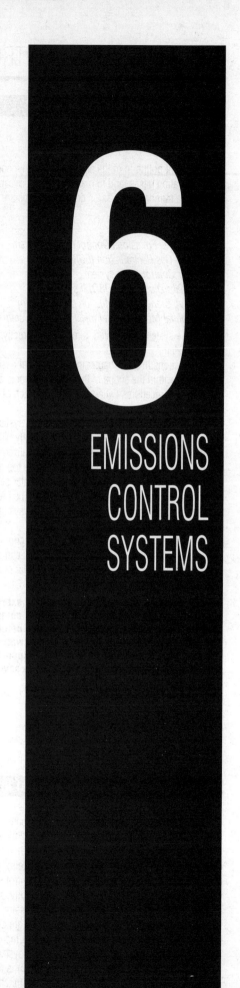

6

EMISSIONS
CONTROL
SYSTEMS

1   General information

▶ **Refer to illustration 1.6**

To prevent pollution of the atmosphere from incompletely-burned and evaporating gases, and to maintain good driveability and fuel economy, a number of emission control systems are incorporated. They include the:

Catalytic converters
Evaporative Emissions Control (EVAP) system
Exhaust Gas Recirculation (EGR) system
Idle Air Control (IAC) system
On-Board Diagnostic (OBD) II system
Positive Crankcase Ventilation (PCV) system
Sequential Multiport Fuel Injection (SFI) system

All of these systems are linked, directly or indirectly, to the emission control system.

The Sections in this Chapter include general descriptions, checking procedures within the scope of the home mechanic and component replacement procedures (when possible) for each of the systems listed above.

Before assuming that an emissions control system is malfunctioning, check the fuel and ignition systems carefully. The diagnosis of some emission-control devices requires specialized tools, equipment and training. If checking and servicing become too difficult or if a procedure is beyond your ability, consult a dealer service department. Remember, the most frequent cause of emissions problems is simply a loose or broken vacuum hose or wire, so always check the hose and wiring connections first.

This doesn't mean, however, that emission control systems are particularly difficult to maintain and repair. You can quickly and easily perform many checks and do most of the regular maintenance at home with common tune-up and hand tools.

➡**Note: Because of a Federally mandated extended warranty which covers the emission control system components, check with your dealer about warranty coverage before working on any emissions-related systems. Once the warranty has expired, you may wish to perform some of the component checks and/or replacement procedures in this Chapter to save money.**

1.6 The Vehicle Emissions Control Information (VECI) label is located in the engine compartment on the radiator support. It contains important emissions specifications and adjustment information specific to your vehicle

Pay close attention to any special precautions outlined in this Chapter. It should be noted that the illustrations of the various systems may not exactly match the system installed on the vehicle you're working on because of changes made by the manufacturer during production or from year-to-year.

A Vehicle Emissions Control Information (VECI) label is located in the engine compartment (see illustration). This label contains important emissions specifications and adjustment information, as well as a vacuum hose schematic with emissions components identified. When servicing the engine or emissions systems, the VECI label in your particular vehicle should always be checked for up-to-date information.

2   Diagnostic systems - general information

One of the first automotive applications of computers was self-diagnosis of system and component failures. While early on-board diagnostic computers simply lit a "CHECK ENGINE" light on the dash ("SERVICE ENGINE SOON" light on some models), present systems must monitor complex interactive emission control systems, and provide enough data to the technician to successfully isolate a malfunction.

The computer's role in self-diagnosing emission control problems has become so important that such computers are now required by Federal law. OBD II, a second generation system is incorporated in 2000 and later models with EEC-V emission control systems.

The purpose of On Board Diagnostics (OBD) is to ensure that emission related components and systems are functioning properly to reduce emission levels of several pollutants emitted by auto and truck engines. The first step is to detect that a malfunction has occurred which may cause increased emissions. The next step is for the system to notify the driver so that the vehicle can be serviced. The final step is to store enough information about the malfunction so that it can be identified and repaired.

Many of the self-diagnostic tests performed by early OBD systems are retained in OBD II systems, however, they are more sensitive in detecting malfunctions. OBD II systems perform many additional tests not required under the earlier OBD. These include monitoring for engine misfires and detecting deterioration of the catalytic converter.

3 On-Board Diagnostic (OBD-II) system

SCAN TOOL INFORMATION

▶ **Refer to illustrations 3.1 and 3.2**

1   Hand-held scanners are the most powerful and versatile tools for analyzing engine management systems used on later model vehicles (see illustration). Early model scanners handle codes and some diagnostics for many systems. Each brand scan tool must be examined carefully to match the year, make and model of the vehicle you are working on. Often, interchangeable cartridges are available to access the particular manufacturer (Ford, GM, Chrysler, Toyota etc.). Some manufacturers will specify by continent (Asia, Europe, USA, etc.).

➡**Note: An aftermarket generic scanner should work with any model covered by this manual. However, some early OBD-II models, although technically classified as OBD-II compliant by the manufacturer and by the federal government, might not be fully compliant with all SAE standards for OBD-II. Some generic scanners are unable to extract all the codes from these early OBD-II models. Before purchasing a generic scan tool, contact the manufacturer of the scanner you're planning to buy and verify that it will work properly with the OBD-II system you want to scan. If necessary, of course, you can always have the codes extracted by a dealer service department or an independent repair shop with a professional scan tool.**

2   With the arrival of the Federally mandated emission control system (OBD-II), a specially designed scanner has been developed. Several tool manufacturers have released OBD-II scan tools for the home mechanic (see illustration).

OBD-II SYSTEM GENERAL DESCRIPTION

3   All models are equipped with the second generation OBD-II system. This system consists of an on-board computer known as the Powertrain Control Module (PCM), and information sensors, which monitor various functions of the engine and send data to the PCM. This system incorporates a series of diagnostic monitors that detect and identify fuel injection and emissions control systems faults and store the information in the computer memory. This updated system also tests sensors and output actuators, diagnoses drive cycles, freezes data and clears codes.

4   This powerful diagnostic computer must be accessed using an OBD-II scan tool and 16-pin Data Link Connector (DLC) located under the driver's dash area. The PCM is mounted at the right end of the firewall, in the engine compartment. The PCM is the brain of the electronically-controlled fuel and emissions system. It receives data from a number of sensors and other electronic components (switches, relays, etc.). Based on the information it receives, the PCM generates output signals to control various relays, solenoids (fuel injectors) and other actuators. The PCM is specifically calibrated to optimize the emissions, fuel economy and driveability of the vehicle.

5   It isn't a good idea to attempt diagnosis or replacement of the PCM or emission control components at home while the vehicle is under warranty. Because of a Federally mandated warranty that covers the emissions system components, and because any owner-induced damage to the PCM, sensors and/or control devices may void this warranty, take the vehicle to a dealer service department if the PCM or a system component malfunctions.

INFORMATION SENSORS (OBD-II)

6   **Brake Pedal Position (BPP) switch** - The BPP switch is located at the top of the brake pedal. It's a normally open switch that closes when the brake pedal is applied and sends a signal to the PCM, which interprets this signal as its cue to disengage the torque converter clutch. The BPP switch is also used to disengage the brake shift interlock.

7   **Camshaft Position (CMP) sensor** - The CMP sensor produces a signal that the PCM uses to identify the number 1 cylinder and to time the firing sequence of the fuel injectors.

8   **Crankshaft Position (CKP) sensor** - The CKP sensor produces a signal that the PCM uses to determine the position of the crankshaft. The CKP sensor is located on the front of the engine, to the side of the crankshaft pulley.

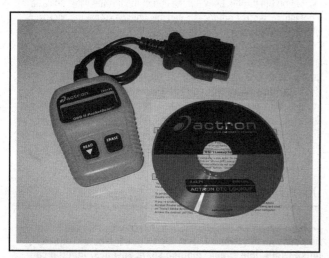

3.1 Simple code readers are an economical way to extract trouble codes when the CHECK ENGINE light comes on

3.2 Scanners like these from Actron and AutoXray are powerful diagnostic aids - they can tell you just about anything that you want to know about your engine management system

9 **Cylinder Head Temperature (CHT) sensor** (4-cylinder models) - The CHT sensor is located in the cylinder head. The CHT sensor is a thermistor, a type of variable resistor in which the resistance changes in accordance with the change in temperature. The CHT is known as a negative temperature coefficient (NTC) thermistor because as the temperature increases, the resistance decreases, and vice versa. The PCM uses the CHT sensor to monitor the operating temperature of the engine. These sensors must be replaced with new ones whenever they are removed.

10 **Differential pressure feedback EGR system sensor** - On SOHC V6 engines, the differential pressure feedback EGR system sensor is located near the EGR valve. This sensor is a pressure transducer that monitors the pressure differential across a metering orifice located in the sensor. A transducer is a device that receives a signal from one system and transfers that signal to another system, often in a different form. The differential pressure feedback EGR system sensor outputs a voltage signal that's proportional to the pressure drop across its metering orifice. The PCM uses this data to calculate the EGR flow rate.

11 **Digital Transmission Range (DTR) sensor** - The DTR sensor is located at the manual lever of the 5R44E and 5R55S automatic transmissions. The DTR sensor functions like a conventional Park/Neutral Position (PNP) switch: it prevents the engine from starting in any gear other than Park or Neutral, and it closes the circuit for the back-up lights when the shift lever is moved to Reverse. The PCM also sends a voltage signal to the TR sensor, which uses a series of step-down resistors that act as a voltage divider. The PCM monitors the TR sensor's voltage output, which corresponds to the position of the manual lever. Thus the PCM is able to determine the gear selected and is able to determine the correct pressure for the electronic pressure control system of the transaxle.

12 **Engine Coolant Temperature (ECT) sensor** (V6 models) - The ECT sensor is a thermistor (temperature-sensitive variable resistor) that sends a voltage signal to the PCM, which uses this data to determine the temperature of the engine coolant. The ECT sensor helps the PCM control the air/fuel mixture ratio and ignition timing, and it also helps the PCM determine when to turn the Exhaust Gas Recirculation (EGR) system on and off.

13 **Fuel Tank Pressure (FTP) sensor** - The fuel tank pressure sensor can be located in the fuel tank, near the fuel pump/fuel level sending unit module, or in-line with the fuel lines. It measures the fuel tank pressure when the PCM tests the EVAP system, and it's also used to control fuel tank pressure by signaling the EVAP system to purge the tank when the pressure becomes excessive.

14 **Intake Air Temperature (IAT) sensor** - The IAT sensor, which is an integral component of the Mass Air Flow (MAF) sensor, monitors the temperature of the air entering the engine and sends a signal to the PCM. The IAT sensor cannot be replaced by itself. If it's defective, you'll have to replace the MAF sensor.

15 **Intermediate Shaft Speed (ISS) sensor** - The ISS sensor is a magnetic pick-up found on 5R44E and 5R55E automatic transmissions. The ISS sensor sends data on planetary sun gear speed to the PCM, which uses this information to determine the correct operating pressure for the transmission.

16 **Knock sensor** - The knock sensor is a piezoelectric crystal that oscillates in proportion to engine vibration. The term piezoelectric refers to the property of certain crystals that produce a voltage when subjected to a mechanical stress. The oscillation of the piezoelectric crystal produces a voltage output that is monitored by the PCM, which retards the ignition timing when the oscillation exceeds a certain threshold. When the engine is operating normally, the knock sensor oscillates

consistently and its voltage signal is steady. When detonation occurs, engine vibration increases, and the oscillation of the knock sensor exceeds a design threshold. Detonation is an uncontrolled explosion, after the spark occurs at the spark plug, which spontaneously combusts the remaining air/fuel mixture, resulting in a pinging or slapping sound. If allowed to continue, engine performance is diminished and damage to the pistons can result. The knock sensor is located below the intake manifold, in the valley between the cylinder heads on V6 engines. On 4-cylinder engines, the knock sensor is bolted to the left side of the block, just below the intake manifold.

17 **Mass Air Flow (MAF) sensor** - The MAF sensor is secured by screws to an opening in the air filter housing just before the intake duct. The MAF sensor is the principal means by which the Powertrain Control Module (PCM) monitors intake airflow. It uses a hot-wire sensing element to measure the amount of air entering the engine. The wire is maintained at a temperature of 392 degrees F (200 degrees C) above the ambient temperature by electrical current. As intake air passes through the MAF sensor and over the hot wire, it cools the wire, and the control system immediately corrects the temperature back to its constant value. The current required to maintain the constant value is used by the PCM as an indicator of airflow. The MAF sensor also incorporates an integral Intake Air Temperature (IAT) sensor. The two components cannot be serviced separately; if either sensor is defective, replace the MAF sensor.

18 **Output Shaft Speed (OSS) sensor** - The OSS sensor is a magnetic pick-up coil. The OSS sensor provides the Powertrain Control Module (PCM) with information about the rotational speed of the output shaft in the transmission. The PCM uses this information to control the torque converter and to calculate speed scheduling and the correct pressure for the Electronic Pressure Control system.

19 **Oxygen sensors** - An oxygen sensor is a galvanic battery that generates a small variable voltage signal in proportion to the difference between the oxygen content in the exhaust stream and the oxygen content in the ambient air. The PCM uses the voltage signal from the upstream oxygen sensor to maintain a stoichiometric air/fuel ratio of 14.7:1 by constantly adjusting the on-time of the fuel injectors. There are four oxygen sensors, one upstream and one downstream sensor for each cylinder head.

20 **Throttle Position (TP) sensor** - The TP sensor, which is located on the throttle body, on the end of the throttle valve shaft, is a potentiometer that produces a variable voltage signal in accordance with the opening angle of the throttle valve. This voltage signal tells the PCM when the throttle is closed, in a cruise position, or wide open, or anywhere in between. The PCM uses this information, along with data from a number of other sensors, to calculate injector on-time.

21 **Turbine Shaft Speed (TSS) sensor** - The TSS sensor is a magnetic pick-up coil. The TSS sensor provides the PCM with information about the rotational speed of the turbine (input) shaft. The PCM uses this information to determine control strategies for the Torque Converter Clutch (TCC) and to determine the static Electronic Pressure Control (EPC) pressure setting during shifts.

OUTPUT ACTUATORS

➡**Note: Based on the information it receives from the information sensors described above, the PCM adjusts fuel injector pulse width, idle speed, ignition spark advance, ignition coil dwell and EVAP canister purge operation. It does so by controlling the output actuators. The following list provides a brief description of the function, location and operation of each of the important output actuators.**

22 **EVAP canister purge valve** - The EVAP canister purge valve is normally closed. But when ordered to do so by the PCM, under certain operating conditions, it allows fuel vapors from the EVAP canister to be drawn into the intake manifold for combustion. See Section 8 for more information.

23 **EVAP canister vent solenoid or vent valve** - The canister vent valve is normally open, but it closes and seals off the EVAP system for inspection and maintenance tests and for OBD-II leak and pressure tests. See Section 8 for more information.

24 **Exhaust Gas Recirculation (EGR) vacuum regulator solenoid and valve** - When the engine is put under a load (hard acceleration, passing, going up a steep hill, pulling a trailer, etc.), combustion chamber temperature increases. When combustion chamber temperature exceeds 2500 degrees, excessive amounts of oxides of nitrogen (NOx) are produced. NOx is a precursor of photochemical smog. When combined with hydrocarbons (HC), other reactive organic compounds (ROCs) and sun light, it forms ozone, nitrogen dioxide, nitrogen nitrate and other nasty stuff. The vacuum-controlled EGR valve allows exhaust gases to be recirculated back to the intake manifold, where they dilute the incoming air/fuel mixture, which lowers the combustion chamber temperature and decreases the amount of NOx produced during high-load conditions. The amount of exhaust gases recirculated to the intake is determined by the strength of the vacuum signal delivered to the EGR valve. The PCM-controlled EGR vacuum regulator solenoid is the electromagnetic device that regulates the supply of vacuum to the EGR valve.

25 **Fuel injectors** - The fuel injectors, which spray a fine mist of fuel into the intake ports, where it is mixed with incoming air, are inductive coils under PCM control. For more information about the injectors, see Chapter 4.

26 **Idle Air Control (IAC) valve** - The IAC valve controls the amount of air allowed to bypass the throttle valve when the throttle valve is at its (nearly closed) idle position. The IAC valve is controlled by the PCM. When the engine is placed under an additional load at idle (low-speed maneuvers or the air conditioning compressor, for example), the engine can run roughly, stumble and even stall. To prevent this from happening, the PCM opens the IAC valve, to increase the idle speed enough to overcome the extra load imposed on the engine. See Section 6 for more information.

27 **Ignition coil(s)** - The ignition coil(s) is/are under the control of the Powertrain Control Module (PCM). There is no ignition control module. Instead, coil drivers inside the PCM turn the primary side of the coil(s) on and off. For more information about the ignition coil(s), see Chapter 5.

4   Obtaining and clearing OBD-II Diagnostic Trouble Codes (DTCs)

1   When the PCM recognizes a malfunction in a monitored emission control system, component or circuit, it turns on the SERVICE ENGINE SOON light, also known as the Malfunction Indicator Light (MIL), on the dash. The PCM will continue to display the MIL until the problem is fixed and the Diagnostic Trouble Code (DTC) is cleared from the PCM's memory.

2   To test the critical emission control components, circuit and systems on an OBD-II vehicle, the PCM runs a series of monitors during each vehicle trip. The monitors are a series of testing protocols used by the PCM to determine whether each monitored component, circuit or system is functioning satisfactorily. The monitors must be run in a certain order. For example, the oxygen sensor monitor cannot run until the engine, the catalytic converter and the oxygen sensors are all warmed up. Another example, the misfire monitor cannot run until the engine is in closed-loop operation. An OBD-II trip consists of operating the vehicle (after an engine-off period) and driving it in such a manner that the PCM's monitors test all of the monitored components, circuits and systems at least once.

3   If the PCM recognizes a fault in some component, circuit or system while it's running the monitors, it stores a Diagnostic Trouble Code (DTC) and turns on the Malfunction Indicator Light (MIL) on the instrument cluster. A DTC can self-erase, but only after the MIL has been extinguished. For example, the MIL might be extinguished for a misfire or fuel system malfunction if the fault doesn't recur when monitored during the next three subsequent sequential driving cycles in which the conditions are similar to those under which the malfunction was first identified. For other types of malfunctions, the criteria for extinguishing the MIL can vary.

4   Once the MIL has been extinguished, the PCM must pass the diagnostic test for the most recent DTC for 40 warm-up cycles (80 warm-up cycles for the fuel system monitor and the misfire monitor). A warm-up cycle consists of the following chain of events:

The engine has been started and is running
The engine temperature rises by at least 40-degrees above its temperature when it was started
The engine coolant temperature crosses the 160-degree F mark
The engine is turned off after meeting the above criteria

OBTAINING DTCS

5   Before outputting any DTCs stored in the PCM, thoroughly inspect ALL electrical connectors and hoses. Make sure that all electrical connections are tight, clean and free of corrosion. And make sure that all hoses are correctly connected, fit tightly and are in good condition (no cracks or tears). Also, make sure that the engine is tuned up. A poorly running engine is probably one of the biggest causes of emission-related malfunctions. Often, simply giving the engine a good tune-up will correct the problem.

6   Of course, if the MIL does NOT go out after several driving cycles, it's probably an indication that something must be repaired or

replaced before the DTC can be erased and the MIL extinguished. This means that you will need to extract the DTC(s) from the PCM, make the necessary repair or replace a component, then erase the DTC yourself.

7   All models are equipped with On-Board Diagnostic II (OBD-II) systems, the Diagnostic Trouble Codes (DTCs) can only be accessed with a scan tool. Professional scan tools are expensive, but relatively inexpensive generic scan tools (see illustrations 3.1 and 3.2) are available at most automotive parts stores. Simply plug the connector of the scan tool into the diagnostic connector, which is located under the left side of the dash, and then follow the instructions included with the scan tool to extract the DTCs.

8   Once you have outputted all of the stored DTCs, look them up on the accompanying DTC chart.

9   After troubleshooting the source of each DTC, make any necessary repairs or replace the defective component(s).

CLEARING THE DTCS

10   Clear the DTCs with the scan tool in accordance with the instructions provided by the scan tool's manufacturer.

DIAGNOSTIC TROUBLE CODES

11   The accompanying tables are a list of the Diagnostic Trouble Codes (DTCs) that can be accessed by a do-it-yourselfer working at home (there are many more DTCs available to dealerships with proprietary scan tools and software, but those codes cannot be accessed by a generic scan tool). If, after you have checked and repaired the connectors, wire harness and vacuum hoses (if applicable) for an emission-related system, component or circuit, the problem persists, have the vehicle checked by an automotive service technician.

OBD-II TROUBLE CODES

➡**Note: Not all trouble codes apply to all models.**

Code	Probable cause
P0030	Upstream oxygen sensor, bank 1, heater circuit
P0040	Upstream oxygen sensors swapped (crossed wiring harnesses)
P0041	Downstream oxygen sensors swapped (crossed wiring harnesses)
P0050	Oxygen sensor heater control circuit open or short, Bank 2, sensor 1
P0054	Oxygen sensor heater control circuit resistance, Bank 1, sensor 2
P0060	Downstream oxygen sensor heater circuit open or short, Bank 2, sensor 2
P060A	Internal Powertrain Control Module (PCM) error
P060B	Internal Powertrain Control Module (PCM) analog to digital processing error
P060C	Internal Powertrain Control Module (PCM) main processor error
P061B	Internal Powertrain Control Module (PCM) torque calculation error
P061C	Internal Powertrain Control Module (PCM) engine rpm calculation error
P061D	Internal Powertrain Control Module (PCM) air mass error
P061F	Internal Powertrain Control Module (PCM) Throttle Actuator Controller (TAC) error
P0068	Throttle Position (TP) sensor inconsistent with Mass Air Flow sensor
P0098	Intake Air Temperature sensor circuit, open or short
P0102	Mass Air Flow (MAF) sensor circuit, low input
P0103	Mass Air Flow (MAF) sensor circuit, high input
P0104	Mass Air Flow (MAF) sensor circuit, intermittent failure
P0106	Barometric (BARO) pressure sensor circuit, performance problem
P0107	Barometric (BARO) pressure sensor/MAP sensor circuit, low voltage
P0108	Barometric (BARO) pressure sensor/MAP sensor circuit, high voltage

Code	Probable cause
P0109	BARO/MAP sensor circuit intermittent
P0111	Intake Air Temperature (IAT) sensor 1 circuit, range/performance problem
P0112	Intake Air Temperature (IAT) sensor 1 circuit, low input
P0113	Intake Air Temperature (IAT) sensor circuit, high input
P0114	Intake Air Temperature (IAT) sensor circuit, intermittent failure
P0116	Engine Coolant Temperature (ECT) circuit range/performance problem
P0117	Engine Coolant Temperature (ECT) sensor circuit, low input
P0118	Engine Coolant Temperature (ECT) sensor circuit, high input
P0119	Engine Coolant Temperature (ECT) sensor circuit, intermittent failure (4.0L V6)
P0121	Throttle Position (TP) circuit out of range or performance problem
P0123	Throttle Position (TP) sensor circuit, high input
P0125	Insufficient coolant temperature for closed loop fuel control (4.0L V6)
P0128	Coolant temperature below thermostat regulated temperature (4.0L V6)
P0130	Oxygen sensor heater control circuit resistance, Bank 1, sensor 1
P0131	Upstream oxygen sensor circuit problem (right cylinder bank)
P0132	Upstream oxygen sensor circuit, high voltage (right cylinder bank)
P0133	Upstream oxygen sensor circuit, slow response (right cylinder bank)
P0136	Downstream oxygen sensor circuit problem (right cylinder bank)
P0138	Downstream oxygen sensor circuit, high voltage (right cylinder bank)
P0139	Upstream oxygen sensor heater circuit, slow response, Bank 1, sensor 2
P0141	Downstream oxygen sensor heater circuit problem , Bank 1, sensor 2
P0148	Fuel delivery error
P0150	Oxygen sensor heater control circuit resistance, Bank 2, sensor 1
P0151	Upstream oxygen sensor circuit, low voltage (left cylinder bank)
P0152	Upstream oxygen sensor circuit, high voltage (left cylinder bank)
P0153	Heated oxygen sensor circuit, slow response (left cylinder bank)
P0154	Upstream oxygen sensor heater circuit problem, Bank 2, sensor 1
P0156	Downstream oxygen sensor circuit problem (left cylinder bank)
P0158	Downstream oxygen sensor circuit, high voltage (left cylinder bank)
P0159	Downstream oxygen sensor circuit, slow response, Bank 2, sensor 2
P0161	Downstream oxygen sensor heater circuit problem, Bank 2, sensor 2
P0171	System too lean (right cylinder bank)

OBD-II TROUBLE CODES

➡ **Note: Not all trouble codes apply to all models.**

Code	Probable cause
P0172	System too rich (right cylinder bank)
P0174	System too lean (left cylinder bank)
P0175	System too rich (left cylinder bank)
P0176	Flexible Fuel (FF) sensor circuit malfunction
P0180	Fuel Rail Temperature (FRT) sensor A circuit, open or short
P0181	Fuel Rail Temperature (FRT) sensor A circuit, range/performance
P0182	Fuel Rail Temperature (FRT) sensor circuit, low input
P0183	Fuel Rail Temperature (FRT) sensor circuit, high input
P0190	Fuel Rail Pressure (FRP) sensor A circuit, reference voltage
P0191	Fuel Rail Pressure (FRP) sensor circuit, range/ performance
P0192	Fuel Rail Pressure (FRP) sensor circuit, low input
P0193	Fuel Rail Pressure (FRP) sensor circuit, high input
P0196	Engine Oil Temperature sensor circuit range/performance problem
P0197	Engine Oil Temperature sensor circuit, low input
P0198	Engine Oil Temperature sensor circuit, high input
P0201	Injector no. 1 circuit malfunction
P0202	Injector no. 2 circuit malfunction
P0203	Injector no. 3 circuit malfunction
P0204	Injector no. 4 circuit malfunction
P0205	Injector no. 5 circuit malfunction
P0206	Injector no. 6 circuit malfunction
P0217	Engine coolant over-temperature
P0218	Transmission fluid over-temperature
P0219	Engine over speed condition
P0221	Throttle Position (TP) sensor B circuit range/performance problem
P0222	Throttle Position (TP) sensor B circuit, low input
P0223	Throttle Position (TP) sensor B circuit, high input
P0230	Fuel pump primary circuit malfunction
P0231	Fuel pump secondary circuit low
P0232	Fuel pump secondary circuit high

Code	Probable cause
P0261	Cylinder 1 injector circuit low
P0262	Cylinder 1 injector circuit high
P0264	Cylinder 2 injector circuit low
P0265	Cylinder 2 injector circuit high
P0267	Cylinder 3 injector circuit low
P0268	Cylinder 3 injector circuit high
P0270	Cylinder 4 injector circuit low
P0271	Cylinder 4 injector circuit high
P0273	Cylinder 5 injector circuit low
P0274	Cylinder 5 injector circuit high
P0276	Cylinder 6 injector circuit low
P0277	Cylinder 6 injector circuit high
P0297	Vehicle overspeed condition
P0298	Engine oil over temperature condition
P0300	Random misfire detected
P0301	Cylinder no. 1 misfire detected
P0302	Cylinder no. 2 misfire detected
P0303	Cylinder no. 3 misfire detected
P0304	Cylinder no. 4 misfire detected
P0305	Cylinder no. 5 misfire detected
P0306	Cylinder no. 6 misfire detected
P0310	Misfire detection monitor
P0315	PCM unable to learn crankshaft pulse wheel tooth spacing
P0316	Misfire occurred during first 1000 engine revolutions
P0320	Ignition engine speed input circuit malfunction
P0325	Knock sensor 1 circuit malfunction (right cylinder head)
P0326	Knock sensor 1 circuit range/performance (right cylinder bank)
P0330	Knock sensor 2 circuit malfunction (left cylinder bank)
P0331	Knock sensor 2 circuit range/performance (left cylinder bank)
P0340	Camshaft Position (CMP) sensor circuit malfunction (right cylinder head)
P0345	Camshaft Position (CMP) sensor circuit malfunction (left cylinder head)
P0350	Ignition coil primary or secondary circuit malfunction
P0400	EGR flow failure (outside the minimum or maximum limits)

OBD-II TROUBLE CODES

➡Note: Not all trouble codes apply to all models.

Code	Probable cause
P0401	Exhaust Gas Recirculation (EGR) valve, insufficient flow detected
P0402	Exhaust Gas Recirculation (EGR) valve, excessive flow detected
P0403	EEGR electric motor windings or circuits to PCM shorted or open (2.3L engine)
P0410	Secondary Air Injection (AIR) system, low flow
P0411	Secondary Air Injection (AIR) system, upstream flow
P0412	Secondary Air Injection (AIR) system, circuit malfunction
P0420	Catalyst system efficiency below threshold (right cylinder bank)
P0430	Catalyst system efficiency below threshold (left cylinder bank)
P0442	EVAP control system, small leak detected
P0443	EVAP control system, canister purge valve circuit malfunction
P0446	EVAP control system canister vent solenoid circuit malfunction
P0451	Fuel tank pressure sensor circuit out of range or performance problem
P0452	Fuel tank pressure sensor circuit, low input
P0453	Fuel tank pressure sensor circuit, high input
P0454	Fuel tank pressure sensor circuit, noisy
P0455	EVAP control system, big leak detected
P0456	EVAP control system, very small leak detected
P0457	EVAP control system, leak detected (fuel filler neck cap loose or off)
P0460	Fuel level sensor circuit malfunction
P0461	Fuel level sensor circuit range or performance problem
P0462	Fuel level sensor circuit, low input
P0463	Fuel level sensor circuit, high input
P0480	Fan 1, control primary circuit malfunction (2.3L engine)
P0481	Fan 2, control circuit, open or short
P0482	Medium Fan Control (MFC) primary circuit failure
P0491	Secondary Air Injection (AIR) system, Bank 1, low flow
P0500	Vehicle Speed Sensor (VSS), circuit malfunction
P0501	Vehicle Speed Sensor (VSS) range/performance problem
P0503	Vehicle Speed Sensor (VSS), intermittent malfunction
P0504	Brake switch circuit, correlation to brake position switch

Code	Probable cause
P0505	Idle Air Control (IAC) system malfunction
P0506	Idle Air Control (IAC) rpm lower than expected
P0507	Idle Air Control (IAC) rpm higher than expected
P0511	Idle Air Control (IAC) circuit malfunction
P0512	Starter relay circuit, short
P0528	Visctronic Drive Fan (VDF) speed sensor circuit malfunction
P0532	Air conditioning pressure sensor circuit, low voltage
P0533	Air conditioning pressure sensor circuit, high voltage
P0534	Low air conditioning cycling period
P0537	Air conditioning evaporator temperature circuit, low input
P0538	Air conditioning evaporator temperature circuit, high input
P0552	Power Steering Pressure (PSP) sensor circuit malfunction
P0553	Power Steering Pressure (PSP) sensor circuit malfunction
P0562	System voltage low
P0563	System voltage high
P0571	Brake switch, A circuit
P0572	Brake switch, A circuit, low voltage
P0573	Brake switch, A circuit, high voltage
P0579	Cruise control multifunction input A circuit range or performance problem
P0581	Cruise control multifunction input A circuit, high
P0600	Serial communication link (PCM) error
P0602	Control module programming error
P0603	Powertrain Control Module (PCM) Keep-Alive-Memory (KAM) test error
P0604	Powertrain Control Module (PCM) Random (RAM) memory corrupted
P0605	Powertrain Control Module (PCM) Read-Only-Memory (ROM) error
P0606	Powertrain Control Module (PCM), internal communication error
P0607	Powertrain Control Module (PCM), PCM needs reprogramming
P0610	Powertrain Control Module (PCM), vehicle options error
P0611	Fuel injector control module performance
P0620	Generator control circuit failure
P0622	Generator field terminal, circuit failure
P0625	Generator field terminal, circuit low
P0627	Fuel pump, A circuit, control/open

OBD-II TROUBLE CODES

➡ **Note: Not all trouble codes apply to all models.**

Code	Probable cause
P062F	Powertrain Control Module (PCM) EEPROM error
P0634	PCM/ECM/TCM internal temperature too high
P0641	Sensor reference voltage A circuit or open
P0642	Reference voltage circuit, low voltage
P0643	Reference voltage circuit, high voltage
P0645	Air conditioning clutch relay (wide open throttle a/c cutoff) primary circuit malfunction
P0657	Transmission solenoid actuator, supply voltage circuit open
P0660	Intake manifold tuning valve control circuit open (right cylinder bank) V6
P0663	Intake manifold tuning valve control circuit open (left cylinder bank) V6
P0689	Ignition switch or PATS circuits, open or short
P0703	Brake Pedal Position (BPP) switch circuit input malfunction
P0704	Clutch pedal position switch malfunction
P0705	Transmission range sensor, A circuit input
P0707	Transmission range sensor, A circuit, low
P0708	Transmission range sensor, A circuit, high
P0711	Transmission Fluid Temperature sensor A circuit range/performance problem
P0712	Transmission Fluid Temperature sensor A circuit low
P0713	Transmission Fluid Temperature sensor A circuit high
P0715	Input Shaft Speed (ISS) sensor A circuit
P0717	Input Shaft Speed (ISS) sensor A circuit, no signal
P0718	Input Shaft Speed (ISS) sensor A circuit, intermittent
P0720	Insufficient input from Output Shaft Speed (OSS) sensor
P0721	Noise interference on Output Shaft Speed (OSS) sensor signal
P0722	No signal from Output Shaft Speed (OSS) sensor
P0723	Output Shaft Speed (OSS) sensor circuit, intermittent failure
P0812	Reverse Switch (RS) input circuit malfunction
P0815	Automatic transmission, upshift switch circuit
P0830	Clutch pedal switch A circuit
P0833/P0840	Clutch pedal switch B circuit

5   Powertrain Control Module (PCM) - removal and installation

▶ Refer to illustration 5.1

➡Note: On 2008 and later models, the replacement of the PCM requires that the original programming be retrieved via a scan tool before PCM removal. The programming would then be downloaded to the new PCM and the original instrument cluster. This is a procedure best performed at a dealership.

1   The Powertrain Control Module (PCM) is located on the passenger's side of the engine compartment, along the upper edge of the firewall (see illustration).

2   Should it become necessary to remove or replace the PCM, disconnect the negative battery cable from the battery.

3   Loosen the bolt in the center of the connector and disconnect the PCM connector.

4   Remove the two nuts securing the PCM to the firewall and remove the PCM.

5   Installation is reversal of removal.

➡Note: The vehicle may have to be driven up to ten miles after PCM replacement to allow the PCM to relearn its adaptive strategy. During that time, the engine may run roughly.

5.1 The Powertrain Control Module is located along the upper edge of the firewall in the engine compartment

6   Information sensors

ENGINE COOLANT TEMPERATURE (ECT) SENSOR REPLACEMENT

▶ Refer to illustration 6.2

✳✳ WARNING:

Wait until the engine is completely cool before replacing the sensor.

➡Note: On 2001 and later 2.3L models, a Cylinder Head Temperature (CHT) sensor is used instead of an ECT sensor (see Steps 4 through 8).

➡Note: The ECT sensor can be found near the thermostat housing or close to where the upper radiator hose attaches to the intake manifold.

1   On 2011 models, drain the cooling system (see Chapter 1).

2   Before installing the new sensor, wrap the threads with Teflon sealing tape to prevent leakage and thread corrosion (see illustration). Remove the radiator cap to relieve any pressure that may still be present in the system, then reinstall it. Unplug the electrical connector. On 2011 models, remove the sensor retaining clip.

3   Unscrew and remove the ECT sensor.

✳✳ CAUTION:

Handle the coolant sensor with care. Damage to this sensor will affect the operation of the entire fuel injection system.

4   Install the sensor and tighten it securely. On 2011 models, use a new O-ring. Refill the cooling system on 2011 models (see Chapter 1);

on all other models, check the coolant level and add some, if necessary (see Chapter 1).

CYLINDER HEAD TEMPERATURE (CHT) SENSOR

✳✳ CAUTION:

Any time a CHT sensor is removed, it must be replaced with a new one.

➡Note: This sensor is only used on 2001 and later 2.3L engines. The CHT sensor is located either between the #2 and #3 spark plugs in the cylinder head and accessed through the valve cover, or just ahead of the ignition coil pack.

6.2 To prevent leakage, wrap the threads of the coolant temperature sensor with Teflon tape before installing it

6.9a Typical upstream oxygen sensor and electrical connector (upstream sensor for left cylinder bank on 4.0L SOHC model shown)

1　Electrical connector
2　Upstream oxygen sensor (left sensor shown, right sensor similar)

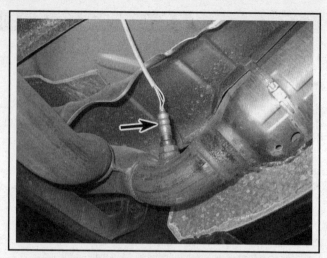

6.9b Typical downstream oxygen sensor (downstream sensor for left cylinder bank on 4.0L SOHC model shown)

6.12 The electrical connector for the right downstream oxygen sensor is located on the right side of the transmission (4.0L SOHC model shown)

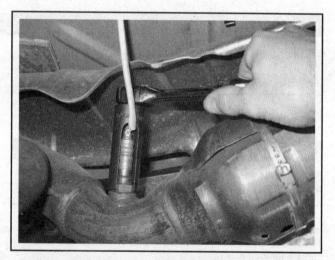

6.13 Use an oxygen sensor socket or an open-end wrench to remove the downstream oxygen sensor (4.0L SOHC model shown)

5　Disconnect the cable from the negative battery terminal (see Chapter 5).

6　Carefully pull back the CHT cover to expose the electrical connector, then disconnect it from the CHT sensor.

7　Unscrew the CHT sensor and remove it.

8　Installation is the reverse of removal. Do not over-tighten the new CHT sensor when installing it.

OXYGEN SENSORS

▶ **Refer to illustrations 6.9a and 6.9b**

9　Generally, there are two oxygen sensors for each cylinder head on all later model vehicles.

➡**Note: Some early models may only have one oxygen sensor.**

Each upstream oxygen sensor (see illustration) is located directly below the exhaust manifold flanges and above the upstream catalytic converter. Each downstream oxygen sensor (see illustration) is located in the exhaust pipe, directly behind the upstream catalyst, and ahead of the main catalyst.

➡**Note: Some very early models may only have one catalyst.**

10　Disconnect the cable from the negative battery terminal (see Chapter 5).

11　Raise the vehicle and place it securely on jackstands.

Replacement

▶ **Refer to illustrations 6.12 and 6.13**

12　Disconnect the oxygen sensor electrical connector (see illustration).

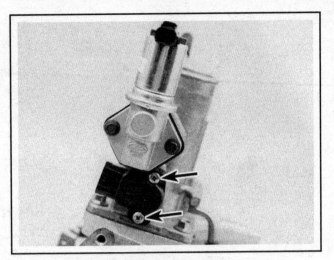

6.18 Remove the two screws from the TPS (arrows) and separate it from the throttle body

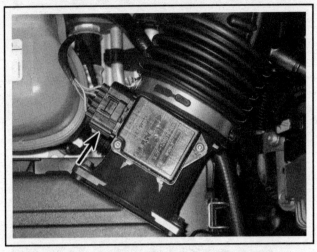

6.22 Disconnect the electrical connector from the MAF sensor (4.0L SOHC model shown)

13 Using an oxygen sensor socket or open-end wrench, remove the oxygen sensor (see illustration). If the sensor is difficult to loosen, spray some penetrant onto the sensor threads and allow it to soak in for the period of time specified by the penetrant manufacturer.

14 Apply a light coating of anti-seize compound to the threads of the new (or old) oxygen sensor to facilitate future removal.

15 Installation is otherwise the reverse of removal. Be sure to tighten the oxygen sensor securely.

THROTTLE POSITION SENSOR (TPS) REPLACEMENT

▶ **Refer to illustration 6.18**

16 The Throttle Position Sensor (TPS) is located on the throttle body. On most models, remove the cover on the throttle body to gain access to the TPS.

17 Disconnect the cable from the negative battery terminal (see Chapter 5).

18 The TPS is a non-adjustable unit. Remove the two retaining screws (see illustration) and separate the TPS from the throttle body.

➡**Note: The TPS is attached to the throttle body with adhesive on the screws. Loosen them with a hand-tool two turns, then use a power-driver to remove them the rest of the way. The friction heat will loosen the adhesive.**

19 Installation is the reverse of removal. Be sure to line up the slot in the TPS with the blade on the throttle shaft. On later models with adhesive screws, the TPS and the screws cannot be reused. They must be replaced.

MASS AIRFLOW SENSOR (MAF) REPLACEMENT

▶ **Refer to illustrations 6.22 and 6.24**

20 The Mass Air Flow (MAF) sensor is located between the air filter housing and the air intake duct (early models), or on the air filter housing duct (later models).

21 Disconnect the cable from the negative battery terminal (see Chapter 5).

22 Disconnect the electrical connector from the MAF sensor (see illustration).

6.24 To detach the MAF sensor from the air filter housing, remove these four bolts (4.0L SOHC model shown)

23 On early models, remove the air cleaner outlet tube assembly (see Chapter 4).

24 Remove the MAF sensor retaining bolts and lift the MAF sensor out (see illustration). On 2011 models, discard the gasket.

25 Installation is the reverse of removal. On 2011 models, use a new gasket.

AIR CONDITIONING CLUTCH CONTROL

General Information

➡**Note: Refer to Chapter 12 for additional information on the location of the relays.**

26 During air conditioning operation, the PCM controls the application of the air conditioning compressor clutch. The PCM controls the air conditioning clutch control relay to delay clutch engagement after the air conditioning is turned ON to allow the idle air control valve to adjust the idle speed of the engine to compensate for the additional load. The PCM also controls the relay to disengage the clutch in the

6.31 With the engine running, disconnect the IAC connector (arrow). The engine rpm should drop if the solenoid is working correctly

6.34 Remove the two screws securing the IAC valve to the throttle body

event of an excessively high or low pressure within the system or an overheating problem.

Inspection

27 In most cases, if the air conditioning does not function, the problem is probably related to the air conditioning system relays and switches and not the PCM.

28 Be sure to check all fuses before doing anything else. If a blown fuse is found, trace the circuit and find out why it failed. Other common causes of the compressor clutch not operating are a low refrigerant charge or a faulty pressure cycling switch.

29 If the air conditioning is operating properly and idle is too low when the air conditioning compressor turns on or is too high when the air conditioning compressor turns off, check for an open circuit between the air conditioning control relay and the PCM.

IDLE AIR CONTROL (IAC) VALVE

General Information

30 The Idle Air Control valve controls engine idle speed by allowing a small amount of air to bypass the throttle plate. The PCM controls operation of the IAC valve.

Replacement

▸ **Refer to illustrations 6.31 and 6.34**

➡**Note: On V6 engines and 2001 and later 2.3L engines, the IAC is mounted to the intake manifold.**

31 On most models, the Intake Air Control (IAC) valve is located on the throttle body (see illustration). Remove the cover (if equipped) on the throttle body to gain access to the IAC valve.

32 Disconnect the cable from the negative battery terminal (see Chapter 5).

33 Disconnect the electrical connector from the IAC valve.

34 Remove the two screws securing the IAC valve to the throttle body (see illustration).

➡**Note: If you're replacing the IAC valve on a four-cylinder engine, the job can be made easier by removing the throttle body from the upper intake manifold first.**

35 Clean off all traces of gasket from the IAC valve and throttle body. Be careful not to damage the gasket mating surfaces if you must scrape them.

✳✳ **CAUTION:**

Do not use solvent to clean the IAC valve.

36 Installation is the reverse of removal.

POWER STEERING PRESSURE SWITCH

General information

37 Turning the steering wheel increases power steering fluid pressure and engine load. The pressure switch will close before the load can cause an idle problem.

38 A pressure switch that will not open or an open circuit from the PCM will cause timing to retard at idle and this will affect idle quality.

39 A pressure switch that will not close or an open circuit may cause the engine to die when the power steering system is used heavily.

Replacement

40 Any problems with the power steering pressure switch or circuit should be repaired by a dealer service department or other qualified repair shop.

CAMSHAFT POSITION (CMP) SENSOR

General information

41 The Camshaft Position (CMP) sensor provides information that the PCM uses to determine Top Dead Center for cylinder number 1 so that it can sequence coil firing and fuel injection at the right time for all cylinders. Not all models require a CMP sensor. In many cases, only California models with manual transmissions are so equipped.

➡**Note: The CMP sensor is sometimes referred to as the Cylinder ID (CID) sensor.**

42 Camshaft Position (CMP) sensor location varies by model:

6.49 Camshaft Position sensor and synchronizer details - V6 engine

1	Synchro positioning tool	5	Synchronizer
2	Timing chain cover	6	Camshaft Position sensor
3	Clamp	7	Bolt
4	Oil pump intermediate shaft		

a) 2000 four-cylinder engines: oil pump body
b) 2001 and later four-cylinder engines: valve cover
c) 2000 3.0L V6 engines: cylinder block
d) 2000 4.0L pushrod V6 engines: cylinder block
e) 4.0L SOHC V6 engines: left valve cover

Replacement

43 On early models equipped with a CMP sensor, the sensor is mounted on a synchronizer assembly, which is essentially a drive unit for the sensor. If you are simply replacing the CMP sensor, it is not necessary to remove the synchronizer assembly from the engine - just remove the screws from the sensor, detach it from the synchronizer and install the new sensor.

44 However, many engine repair procedures require removal of the

6.51 With the housing seated against the engine block, the arrow on the tool (B) should point about 75-degrees (3.0L V6) or 60-degrees (4.0L V6) counterclockwise from the engine centerline (A)

synchronizer assembly, in which case it will be necessary to perform the removal procedure to time the synchronizer.

Four-cylinder engines

45 Disconnect the cable from the negative terminal of the battery. On 2011 models, disconnect the intake manifold vacuum hose.

46 Disconnect the CMP electrical connector, remove the sensor mounting bolts and detach the sensor from the oil pump body or valve cover.

47 Installation is the reverse of removal. Tighten the bolts securely.

3.0L V6 engine and 2000 4.0L (pushrod) V6 engines

▶ Refer to illustrations 6.49 and 6.51

➡Note: This procedure requires the use of a special tool, available at most auto parts stores.

48 Position the engine at Top Dead Center (TDC) compression for cylinder number 1 (see Chapter 2). The engine must remain in this position throughout the entire procedure. Disconnect the cable from the negative terminal of the battery.

49 Mark the relative position of the camshaft position sensor electrical connector so the assembly can be oriented properly upon installation (this is only necessary if the synchronizer assembly will be removed). Disconnect the electrical connector from the camshaft position sensor. Remove the screws and detach the sensor from the synchronizer assembly. If you will be removing the synchronizer assembly, remove the bolt and withdraw the synchronizer from the engine (see illustration).

50 Place a special positioning tool, available at most auto parts stores, onto the synchronizer assembly (see illustration 6.49). Align the vane of the synchronizer with the radial slot in the special tool. Turn the

6.57 To remove the CMP sensor from the valve cover on a V6 model, disconnect the electrical connector and remove the retaining bolt

tool on the synchronizer until the boss on the tool is engaged with the notch on the synchronizer.

51 Lubricate the gear, thrust washer and lower bearing of the synchronizer assembly with clean engine oil. Insert the assembly into the engine, with the tool pointing about 75-degrees (3.0L) or 60-degrees (4.0L) counterclockwise from the engine's centerline (see illustration).

52 Turn the tool clockwise a little so the synchronizer engages with the oil pump intermediate shaft. Push down on the synchronizer, turning the tool gently until the gear on the synchronizer engages with the gear on the camshaft.

53 On the 3.0L engine, the head of the tool should be pointing to the rear, approximately 33 to 45-degrees counterclockwise from the centerline of the engine when the synchronizer is fully inserted (see illustration 6.51).

→Note: No angle specification is available for the 4.0L engine.

54 Install the hold-down bolt and tighten it securely. Remove the positioning tool.

55 Install the camshaft position sensor and tighten the screws securely.

✳✳ CAUTION:

Check the position of the electrical connector on the sensor to make sure it is aligned with the mark you made in Step 47. If it isn't oriented correctly, DO NOT rotate the synchronizer to reposition it - doing so will result in the fuel system being out of time with the engine, will could damage the engine (and at the very least cause driveability problems). If the connector is not oriented properly, repeat the synchronizer installation procedure.

56 Plug in the electrical connector to the sensor and reconnect the cable to the negative terminal of the battery.

2001 and later 4.0L SOHC V6 engines

▸ Refer to illustration 6.57

57 The CMP sensor (see illustration) is located on the left valve cover.

58 Disconnect the cable from the negative battery terminal (see Chapter 5).

59 Disconnect the electrical connector from the CMP sensor.

60 Remove the CMP sensor retaining bolt and remove the sensor.

61 Installation is the reverse of removal.

CRANKSHAFT POSITION (CKP) SENSOR

General information

62 The Crankshaft Position (CKP) sensor is located at the front of the engine, in close proximity to the crankshaft damper. The sensor detects the passing of teeth on the crankshaft damper. This data is used by the computer to calculate ignition firing and fuel injection timing.

Replacement

2.5L engines

63 Disconnect the cable from the negative terminal of the battery.

64 Remove the accessory drivebelt. Remove the four bolts that retain the crankshaft pulley to the crankshaft pulley hub assembly and remove the crankshaft pulley.

65 Remove the timing belt outer cover and rotate the crankshaft so that the keyway is at the ten o'clock position.

66 Remove the two retaining bolts for the CKP sensor. Remove the plastic wire harness retainer which secures the sensor harness to the sensor mounting bracket.

67 Slide the sensor harness out from behind the inner timing belt cover and remove the CKP sensor assembly.

68 If a new sensor is being installed, remove the large electrical connector from it.

69 Slide the sensor wire harness behind the timing belt inner cover, install the CKP sensor into place and install the two bolts finger tight at this time.

70 Install the sensor's large electrical connector onto the harness.

✳✳ CAUTION:

Ensure the four wires are installed in the proper location within the connector. If installed incorrectly the sensor will NOT operate correctly.

71 Connect the CKP sensor connector to the engine wiring harness.

72 Rotate the crankshaft so the outer vane on the pulley hub assembly engages both sides of the Crankshaft Hall-Effect Sensor Positioner. Tighten the sensor mounting bolts.

73 Rotate the crankshaft so the outer vane on the crankshaft pulley hub no longer engages the positioner tool, then remove the tool.

74 Install the sensors wiring harness plastic retainer, install the bolt and tighten securely.

75 Install the timing belt outer cover, the crankshaft pulley and the accessory drive belt.

76 Attach the negative battery cable to the battery.

2001 and later 2.3L engines

→Note: The CKP sensor for this engine must be replaced with a new one whenever it is removed because there is a special alignment tool that must be used to install the sensor that can only be obtained with the purchase of a new sensor - the tool is not sold separately.

77 Disconnect the cable from the negative battery terminal (see Chapter 5).

78 The CKP sensor is mounted right next to the crankshaft pulley.

79 Disconnect the electrical connector to the CKP sensor.

80 Set the engine at TDC (see Chapter 2B).

81 With the special timing pin and crankshaft pulley alignment tool in place, remove the mounting bolts for the CKP sensor.

82 To install the CKP sensor, install the mounting bolts - but do not tighten them.

83 Adjust the CKP sensor by using the CKP sensor alignment tool, then tighten the mounting bolts securely.

V6 engines

84 Detach the cable from the negative terminal of the battery.

85 Unplug the electrical connector from the sensor. Unscrew the two sensor mounting bolts and detach the sensor from the front cover.

86 Installation is the reverse of the removal procedure.

BRAKE ON/OFF SWITCH OR BRAKE PEDAL POSITION (BPP) SENSOR

General information

▶ Refer to illustration 6.87

87 The brake On/Off switch or BPP sensor tells the PCM when the brakes are being applied. The switch/sensor closes when brakes are applied and opens when the brakes are released. The switch/sensor is located on the brake pedal assembly (see illustration).

88 The brake light circuit and bulbs are wired into the switch/sen-

6.87 The Brake Pedal Position (BPP) switch is located at the top of the brake pedal BOO switch

sor circuit so it is important in diagnosing any driveability problems to make sure all the brake light bulbs are working properly (not burned out) or the driver may experience poor idle quality.

Replacement

89 Refer to Chapter 9 for the replacement procedure.

7 Exhaust Gas Recirculation (EGR) system - general information and component replacement

GENERAL DESCRIPTION

1 The EGR system is used to lower NOx (oxides of nitrogen) emission levels caused by high combustion temperatures. The EGR recirculates a small amount of inert exhaust gases into the intake manifold. The additional mixture lowers the temperature of combustion thereby reducing the formation of NOx compounds.

COMPONENT REPLACEMENT

EGR valve

▶ Refer to illustrations 7.4 and 7.5

➡Note: 2002 and later 3.0L engines are not equipped with an EGR valve.

➡Note: When buying a new EGR valve, make sure that you get the correct one. Use the stamped code located on the top of the EGR valve when purchasing it.

2 Disconnect the negative battery cable from the battery.

3 Remove the air cleaner outlet tube (see Chapter 4).

4 Disconnect the EGR valve vacuum hose (if equipped) (see illustration).

7.4 The Exhaust Gas Recirculation (EGR) valve (1) is located at the right rear corner of the intake manifold, near the firewall (V6 SOHC model shown, others are similar); before unbolting the EGR valve, disconnect the vacuum line (2)

7.5 Unscrew the EGR pipe fitting (1) from the EGR valve, then remove the two EGR valve mounting bolts (2) (right bolt shown, left bolt not visible)

7.13 The EGR vacuum regulator valve (1) is located behind the intake manifold, near the other EGR components; before removing the vacuum regulator valve, disconnect the electrical connector (2)

7.17 Differential pressure feedback EGR system sensor removal details

1   Differential pressure feedback EGR system sensor
2   Electrical connector
3   Rubber hoses

5   Disconnect the EGR exhaust manifold tube (see illustration). On 2001 and later 2.3L engines, remove the coolant plumbing to the EGR valve; the EGR valve is mounted at the rear of the engine, close to the firewall. For access to the EGR valve from below, support the transmission and remove the transmission crossmember (see Chapter 7A or 7B).

6   Remove the EGR valve retainer bolts and EGR valve from intake manifold, or intake manifold EGR tube (see illustration 7.5).

7   Remove the EGR gasket, clean the manifold of any remaining gasket material and clean the EGR valve gasket surface if valve is to be reused.

8   Installation is the reverse of removal.

EGR tube

9   On 2010 and earlier models, remove the EGR valve (see Steps 2 through 7). On 2011 2.3L models, remove the intake manifold (see Chapter 2B). On 2011 4.0L models, remove the DPFE sensor (see Steps 16 through 19).

10   Disconnect the EGR tube fittings and remove the tube; on some models, it is necessary to remove the EGR tube-to-manifold connector.

11   Installation is the reverse of removal.

EGR Vacuum Regulator Solenoid (if equipped)

▶ **Refer to illustration 7.13**

12   Disconnect the negative battery cable.

13   Disconnect the electrical connector and vacuum hoses from the EGR vacuum regulator solenoid (see illustration).

14   Remove the nuts securing the solenoid and remove the solenoid.

15   Installation is the reverse of removal

Differential Pressure Feedback Sensor (if equipped)

▶ **Refer to illustration 7.17**

16   Disconnect the negative battery cable.

17   Disconnect any pushpin retainers at the sensor, then disconnect the electrical connector from the DPFE sensor (see illustration).

18   Disconnect the vacuum hoses from the sensor.

19   Remove the bolts securing the sensor and remove it.

20   Installation is the reverse of removal.

8   Evaporative Emissions Control (EVAP) system - general information and component replacement

GENERAL DESCRIPTION

1   The Evaporative Emissions Control (EVAP) system prevents fuel system vapors (which contain unburned hydrocarbons) from escaping into the atmosphere. On warm days, vapors trapped inside the fuel tank expand until the pressure reaches a certain threshold. Then the fuel vapors are routed from the fuel tank through the fuel vapor vent valve and the fuel vapor control valve to the EVAP canister, where they're stored temporarily until the next time the vehicle is operated. When the conditions are right (engine warmed up, vehicle up to speed, moderate or heavy load on the engine, etc.) the Powertrain Control Module (PCM) opens the canister purge valve, which allows the fuel vapors to be drawn from the canister into the intake manifold, from which they're drawn into the engine with the air/fuel mixture. This system is complex and virtually impossible to troubleshoot without the right tools and training. However, the following description should give you a good idea of how it works:

2   The EVAP canister(s) is/are located under the vehicle, on top of the fuel tank on 2002 and 2003 models. On later models, the canister is mounted to the underside of the body, rearward of the rear axle. Each EVAP canister, which contains activated charcoal, is a repository for storing fuel vapors. You'll have to raise the vehicle to inspect or replace the canister(s), or any other part of the EVAP system, except for the canister purge valve (which is located in the engine compartment). The canisters are designed to be maintenance-free and should last the life of the vehicle. There are several other important components located on top of the fuel tank: the fuel tank pressure sensor and the fuel vapor vent valve (an integral part of the fuel tank on 2002 models, a separate component located behind the fuel tank on 2003 models). A couple of other components are located behind the fuel tank: the dust separator and, on 2003 models, the fuel vapor vent valve.

3   The fuel tank pressure sensor, which is located near the in-tank fuel pump/fuel level sending unit module on top of the fuel tank, monitors the pressure inside the tank, and transmits its measurement to the PCM during an OBD-II leak test. It also forces the EVAP system to purge when the fuel tank pressure becomes too high.

4   The Fuel Vapor Vent (FVV) valve (if equipped) controls the flow of fuel vapors entering the EVAP system, prevents the fuel tank from overfilling during refueling and prevents liquid fuel from entering the vapor delivery system if the vehicle rolls over. The FVV valve is mounted on top of the fuel tank and is an integral component of the tank. It cannot be removed or repaired. If the FVV valve is defective, you must replace the fuel tank.

5   The canister vent solenoid is mounted behind the fuel tank, inline between the dust separator and the rear EVAP canister. The canister vent solenoid is normally open, but it seals off the EVAP system for inspection and maintenance (I/M 240) testing and for OBD-II leak and pressure tests.

6   The fuel filler pipe check valve is an integral component of either the fuel tank or the filler neck pipe. It prevents liquid fuel from escaping from the fuel tank into the fuel filler neck pipe during refueling or in the event of a vehicle rollover. The fuel filler pipe check valve is not serviceable separately. Depending on its location on your vehicle, you will have to replace either the fuel filler neck pipe or the fuel tank.

7   The evaporative emission (EVAP) canister purge valve, which is under the control of the Powertrain Control Module (PCM), regulates the flow of vapors being purged from the EVAP canister into the intake manifold. The canister purge valve is normally closed. It opens only when directed to do so by the PCM, which uses the availability of intake manifold vacuum and data from various information sensor inputs to determine when and how long to open the valve. The interval of time during which the purge valve is opened by the PCM is known as its "duty cycle." The purge valve is located in the engine compartment, on a bracket near the brake master cylinder.

8   The evaporative emission (EVAP) dust separator, which is located behind the canister vent solenoid, prevents dust and dirt particles suspended in the atmosphere from entering the EVAP system.

General system checks

9   The most common symptom of a faulty EVAP system is a strong fuel odor (particularly during hot weather). If you smell fuel while driving or (more likely) right after you park the vehicle and turn off the engine, check the fuel filler cap first. Make sure that it's screwed onto the fuel filler neck all the way. If the odor persists, inspect all EVAP hose connections, both in the engine compartment and under the vehicle. You'll have to raise the vehicle and place it securely on jackstands to inspect most of the EVAP system, since it's located under the vehicle. Be sure to inspect each hose attached to the canister for damage and leakage along its entire length. Repair or replace as necessary. Inspect the canister for damage and look for fuel leaking from the bottom. If fuel is leaking or the canister is otherwise damaged, replace it.

10   Poor idle, stalling, and poor driveability can be caused by a defective fuel vapor vent valve or canister purge valve, a damaged canister, cracked hoses, or hoses connected to the wrong tubes. Fuel loss or fuel odor can be caused by fuel leaking from fuel lines or hoses, a cracked or damaged canister, or a defective vapor valve.

11   To check for excessive fuel vapor pressure in the fuel tank, remove the gas cap and listen for the sound of pressure release. If the fuel tank emits a whooshing sound when you open the filler cap, fuel tank vapor pressure is excessive. Inspect the canister vapor hoses and the canister inlet port for blockage or collapsed hoses. Also inspect the vapor vent valve. A complete test can only be done with a proprietary OBD-II scan tool (see Section 3), which will run a series of checks using the fuel tank pressure sensor and other output actuators to detect excessive pressure. You'll have to take the vehicle to a dealer service department or other qualified repair shop to have the EVAP system professionally diagnosed.

COMPONENT REPLACEMENT

➠**Note: On early models, it may be necessary to remove the spare tire to access the EVAP components. On later models, the canister and other EVAP components are mounted to the underside of the body, rearward of the rear axle.**

12   Clearly label, then detach, all vacuum lines from the canister.

13   Loosen the canister mounting clamp bolt and pull the canister out.

14   Installation is the reverse of removal.

9   Positive Crankcase Ventilation (PCV) system

▶ Refer to illustration 9.1

1   The Positive Crankcase Ventilation (PCV) system reduces hydro-carbon emissions by scavenging crankcase vapors. It does this by circulating fresh air from the air cleaner through the crankcase, where it mixes with blow-by gases and is then rerouted through a PCV valve to the intake manifold (see illustration).

2   The main components of the PCV system are the PCV valve, a fresh-air filtered inlet and the vacuum hoses connecting these two components with the engine and the EECS system.

3   To maintain idle quality, the PCV valve restricts the flow when the intake manifold vacuum is high. If abnormal operating conditions arise, the system is designed to allow excessive amounts of blow-by gases to flow back through the crankcase vent tube into the air cleaner to be consumed by normal combustion.

4   Checking and replacement of the PCV valve and filter is covered in Chapter 1.

9.1 Gas flow in a typical PCV system

10 Catalytic converter - general information, check and replacement

GENERAL DESCRIPTION

1   The catalytic converter is an emission-control device added to the exhaust system to reduce pollutants from the exhaust gas stream. A single-bed converter design is used in combination with a three-way (reduction) catalyst. The catalytic coating on the three-way catalyst contains platinum and rhodium, which lowers the levels of oxides of nitrogen (NOx) as well as hydrocarbons (HC) and carbon monoxide (CO).

PHYSICAL CHECKS

2   The catalytic converter requires little if any maintenance or servicing at regular intervals. However, the system should be inspected whenever the vehicle is raised on a lift or if the exhaust system is checked or serviced.

3   Check all connections in the exhaust pipe assembly for looseness or damage. Also check all the clamps for damage, cracks, or missing fasteners. Check the rubber hangers for cracks.

4   The converter itself should be checked for damage or dents which could affect its performance and/or be hazardous to your health. At the same time the converter is inspected, check the metal protector plate under it and the heat insulator above it for damage or loose fasteners.

FUNCTIONAL CHECKS

5   Potential converter problems can be associated with two situations: vehicle fails state smog certification check or exhibits low power. Both situations can be caused by a converter that has been overheated and is either non-functional or restrictive.

6   A non-functional converter is difficult to diagnose. If all other engine systems are operating properly, and the converter is relatively cold (this is a judgment call, no specifications exist, do not check by feeling converter) the converter is probably bad.

7   A restricted converter can be checked. If a performance issue is in question, proceed to backpressure check.

BACKPRESSURE CHECK

8   Attach a vacuum gauge to a source of manifold vacuum and attach a tachometer to the engine.

9   Set the parking brake and put the transmission in Park.

10   Start the engine and warm it to operating temperature. Turn the engine off and wait for a few minutes (this allows any backpressure to escape).

11   Start the engine and observe the vacuum gauge. Vacuum should be 16 in-Hg or greater on an engine in a good state of tune.

12   Let the engine idle for a few minutes while watching the gauge. Vacuum should hold fairly steady.

13   Increase the engine speed and hold it for one minute at 2000 rpm while observing the vacuum gauge. The vacuum gauge should read continuously high vacuum at the end of one minute with no additional throttle required to maintain rpm. If the vacuum gauge dropped significantly or if more throttle was required to maintain rpm, converter restriction can be suspected. Turn the engine off and proceed to the next operation to isolate the problem further.

14   Let the exhaust system cool, then remove the exhaust pipe at the exhaust manifold(s).

15   Repeat the test. If vacuum is now steady and high in the engine-running test, the converter is restricted. Replace the converter.

✳✳ CAUTION:

Although rare, if a restricted muffler is suspected, reconnect the converter, disconnect the muffler and repeat the test to determine if the muffler is the cause.

REPLACEMENT

16 Do not attempt to remove the catalytic converter until the complete exhaust system is cool. Raise the vehicle and support it securely on jackstands. Apply some penetrating oil to the clamp bolts and allow it to soak in.

17 Remove the bolts and the rubber hangers, then separate the converter from the exhaust pipes. Remove the old gaskets if they are stuck to the pipes.

18 Installation of the converter is the reverse of removal. Use new exhaust pipe gaskets and tighten the clamp bolts securely. Replace the rubber hangers with new ones if the originals are deteriorated. Start the engine and check carefully for exhaust leaks.

EXHAUST Y-PIPE REPLACEMENT

➡**Note: This procedure applies to later model 4.0L V6 engines only.**

19 Disconnect the O2 sensor electrical connector (see Section 6, if necessary). While supporting the exhaust Y-pipe with a jack, remove the two right pipe-to-muffler bolts and two flag nuts. Discard the flag nuts; new ones must be used on installation.

20 Remove the transmission mount and isolator-to-transmission bolt. Remove and discard the two left pipe-to-right pipe nuts; new ones must be used on installation.

21 Loosen, but don't remove the two right pipe-to-exhaust manifold nuts.

22 Remove and discard the two left pipe-to-exhaust manifold nuts; new ones must be used on installation.

23 Remove the left Y-pipe and gasket. Discard the gasket; a new one must be used on installation.

24 Remove and discard the two right pipe-to-exhaust manifold nuts; new ones must be used on installation.

25 Remove the right Y-pipe and gasket. Discard the gasket; a new one must be used on installation.

26 Install the right Y-pipe, new gasket and new pipe-to-exhaust manifold bolts. Only install the bolts loosely at this time.

27 Install the left Y-pipe, new gasket and new pipe-to-exhaust manifold bolts. Only install the bolts loosely at this time.

28 Loosely install the two new left pipe-to-right pipe nuts. Install the transmission mount, then install the isolator bolt and tighten it to 66 ft-lbs.

29 Loosely install the two new right pipe-to-muffler bolts. Install the two new flag nuts, then tighten all Y-pipe bolts to 30 ft-lbs. Reconnect the O2 sensor electrical connector.

11 Digital Transmission Range (DTR) sensor - replacement and adjustment

➡ **Refer to illustrations 11.8, 11.10, 11.11a and 11.11b**

➡**Note: This procedure applies only to later model vehicles with an automatic transmission.**

➡**Note: The following procedure is intended for the home mechanic who does not possess or have access to the special DTR sensor alignment tool used by dealership service departments to align the DTR sensor, because it's difficult to obtain one of these special alignment tools. The method described here for aligning the DTR sensor should be adequate. If it isn't, drive the vehicle to a dealer or other repair shop after installing the DTR sensor and have it adjusted. Failure to do so might set a Diagnostic Trouble Code and cause driveability problems.**

1 Disconnect the cable from the negative battery terminal (see Chapter 5).

2 Place the shift lever inside the vehicle in the NEUTRAL ("N") position.

3 Raise the vehicle and place it securely on jackstands.

4 The DTR sensor is located at the manual lever, on the left side of the transmission.

5 Peel back the rubber boot that protects the DTR sensor electrical connector, then disconnect the electrical connector from the DTR sensor.

6 Disconnect the shift cable from the manual control lever by pulling it UP.

7 Remove the manual lever from the manual lever shaft.

8 Mark the relationship of the DTR sensor to the transmission (see illustration).

9 Remove the DTR sensor mounting bolts (see illustration 11.8) and remove the DTR sensor from the manual lever shaft.

10 Before installing the DTR sensor make sure that the transmission is still in Neutral. If you're not sure, take the manual lever and use it to rotate the manual lever shaft counterclockwise until it stops, then rotate

11.8 Mark the relationship of the DTR sensor to the transmission; to detach the DTR sensor from the transmission, remove these two bolts

11.10 The transmission should still be in Neutral, but if it's been accidentally shifted into another gear, put it back in Neutral by using the manual lever; move the manual lever counterclockwise until it stops, then clockwise two clicks

the manual lever shaft two clicks clockwise (see illustration). The transmission is now in Neutral.

11 If you look closely at the DTR sensor, you will see Neutral alignment marks on the sensor's rotating inner ring (the one that rotates with the manual lever shaft) and on the stationary ring around the periphery of the rotating ring (see illustration). Align the Neutral marks on these two rings and then slide the DTR sensor onto the manual lever shaft

(see illustration). Note the two keyways on the manual lever shaft; the two ridges, 180-degrees apart, on the rotating ring of the DTR sensor must be aligned with these two keyways in order to install the DTR sensor on the shaft. There are also a pair of notches, 180-degrees apart, in the circumference of the rotating ring, that are for seating the locator pins on the factory tool.

➡ **Note: On a conventional Park/Neutral Position (PNP) switch, this alignment method would be sufficiently accurate to realign the PNP switch for installation (since all you're really doing is ensuring that the vehicle will start only in Park or Neutral). On a DTR sensor (which is an information sensor for the PCM), aligning the Neutral mark of the rotating ring to its corresponding Neutral mark on the stationary ring might not be sufficiently accurate, because the range of movement of the DTR sensor is very small.**

12 When everything is correctly aligned tighten the DTR sensor mounting bolts. Recheck the alignment of the Neutral marks. If they're off, loosen the bolts, readjust the DTR sensor and re-tighten the bolts.

✳✳ CAUTION:

To prevent binding and consequent damage to the DTR, always loosen or tighten the two bolts evenly; turn one bolt one turn, then turn the other bolt one turn, and alternate until both bolts are either removed or installed.

13 The remainder of installation is otherwise the reverse of removal.

14 If necessary, drive the vehicle to a dealer and have the DTR sensor realigned.

11.11a Digital Transmission Range (DTR) sensor installation details:

1   *Make sure that the Neutral alignment mark on the inner rotating ring is aligned with the Neutral alignment mark on the stationary ring*
2   *The two ridges, 180-degrees apart, on the inside of the rotating ring must be aligned with the keyways on the manual lever shaft (see next illustration)*
3   *These notches in the rotating ring are for two of the locator pins on the special factory TR sensor alignment tool*

11.11b When installing the DTR sensor, make sure that the two ridges (1) on the inside of the rotating ring are aligned with the keyways (2) on the manual lever shaft (second ridge and keyway not shown)

12 Knock sensor - replacement

◗ **Refer to illustrations 12.5 and 12.7**

1   The knock sensor is located in the valley between the cylinder heads on V6 engines, and on the left side of the block on 2.3L engines, just below the intake manifold.

2   Disconnect the cable from the negative battery terminal (see Chapter 5).

3   On 2.3L engines, disconnect the knock sensor harness connector, the remove the sensor mounting bolt and the sensor.

➡**Note: Once the knock sensor is removed, it cannot be reused. A new sensor must be installed.**

4   On V6 engines, remove the intake manifold (see Chapter 2D or 2E).

5   On early V6 engines, remove the noise shield (see illustration)

6   Disconnect the knock sensor electrical connector.

➡**Note: The knock sensor connector location varies with the model year and date of manufacture. On some models, the knock sensor connector is located on the left end of the firewall, but on other models, the connector is located in the valley between the cylinder heads, closer to the knock sensor.**

7   Remove the knock sensor retaining bolt and remove the knock sensor (see illustration).

8   Installation is the reverse of removal. Be sure to tighten the knock sensor retaining bolt securely.

12.5 On early V6 models, carefully remove the noise shield packed between the intake runners of the lower intake manifold

12.7 Remove the knock sensor retaining bolt (V6 model shown, 4-cylinder sensor is on the side of the block)

13 Intermediate Shaft Speed (ISS) sensor - replacement

◗ **Refer to illustrations 13.4, 13.6a and 13.6b**

➡**Note: This procedure applies to models with a 4-speed (5R44E) or 5-speed (5R55E) automatic transmission.**

1   Disconnect the cable from the negative battery terminal (see Chapter 5).

2   Raise the vehicle and place it securely on jackstands.

3   The ISS sensor is located on the left side of the transmission, just above the DTR.

➡**Note: On some later models, there are three speed sensors on the upper left side of the transmission. The ISS sensor is the middle one. Don't confuse it with the front sensor, which is the Turbine Shaft Speed (TSS) sensor, or the rear sensor, which is the Output Shaft Speed (OSS) sensor.**

4   Disconnect the electrical connector from the ISS sensor (see illustration).

13.4 Disconnect the ISS sensor electrical connector; to detach the sensor from the transmission, remove this bolt

13.6a Remove and discard the old ISS sensor O-ring

13.6b Before installing the new ISS sensor O-ring, be sure to lubricate it with petroleum jelly

5   Remove the OSS sensor retaining bolt.
6   If you're planning to reuse the old ISS sensor, remove and discard the old O-ring (see illustration). Before installing the new O-ring, lubricate it with petroleum jelly (see illustration). If you're installing a

new ISS sensor, be sure to lubricate the new O-ring.
7   Installation is the reverse of removal. Be sure to tighten the ISS sensor bolt securely.

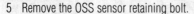

14   Output Shaft Speed (OSS) sensor - replacement

➡**Note: This procedure applies to models with a 4-speed (5R44E) or 5-speed (5R55E) automatic transmission.**

1   Disconnect the cable from the negative battery terminal (see Chapter 5).
2   Raise the vehicle and place it securely on jackstands.
3   On 4WD models, remove the front driveshaft (see Chapter 8).
4   The OSS sensor is located on the upper left side of the transmission, at the rear.
➡**Note: On some later models, there are three speed sensors on the upper left side of the transmission. The OSS sensor is**

the rear one. Don't confuse it with the front sensor, which is the Turbine Shaft Speed (TSS) sensor, or the middle sensor, which is the Intermediate Shaft Speed (ISS) sensor.

5   Disconnect the electrical connector from the OSS sensor.
6   Remove the OSS sensor retaining bolt.
7   If you're planning to reuse the old OSS sensor, remove and discard the old O-ring. Before installing the new O-ring, lubricate it with petroleum jelly.
8   Installation is the reverse of removal. Be sure to tighten the OSS sensor bolt securely.

15   Turbine Shaft Speed (TSS) sensor - replacement

➡**Note: This procedure applies to models with a 4-speed (5R44E) or 5-speed (5R55E) automatic transmission.**

1   Disconnect the cable from the negative battery terminal (see Chapter 5).
2   Raise the vehicle and place it securely on jackstands.
3   The TSS sensor is located on the left side of the transmission.
➡**Note: On some later models, there are three speed sensors on the upper left side of the transmission. The TSS sensor is the front one. Don't confuse it with the middle sensor, which is the Intermediate Shaft Speed (ISS) sensor, or the rear sensor, which is the Output Shaft Speed (OSS) sensor.**

4   Detach the shift cable from the cable bracket, then remove the bracket for access.
5   Disconnect the electrical connector from the TSS sensor.
6   Remove the TSS sensor retaining bolt.
7   If you're planning to reuse the old TSS sensor, remove and discard the old O-ring. Before installing the new O-ring, lubricate it with petroleum jelly.
8   Installation is the reverse of removal. Be sure to tighten the TSS sensor bolt securely.

Section

7A

MANUAL TRANSMISSION

1 General information

All vehicles covered in this manual come equipped with a 5-speed manual transmission or an automatic transmission. All information on the manual transmission is included in this Part of Chapter 7. Information on the automatic transmission can be found in Part B of this Chapter.

Due to the complexity, unavailability of replacement parts and the special tools necessary, internal transmission repair procedures are not recommended for the home mechanic.

Depending on the expense involved in having a faulty transmission overhauled, it may be an advantage to consider replacing the unit with either a new or rebuilt one. Your local dealer or transmission shop should be able to supply you with information concerning cost, availability and exchange policy. Regardless of how you decide to remedy a transmission problem, you can still save a lot of money by removing and installing the unit yourself.

2 Shift lever - removal and installation

▶ Refer to illustration 2.2

1   Place the transmission in Neutral.
2   Carefully pull back on the carpeting and remove the shifter boot retaining bolts (see illustration).

→Note: Later models have a plastic trim attached to the boot that is screwed to the floor. Remove the screws and pull the trim up to get to the bolt that secures the shift lever. The boot and trim are removed as an assembly after the shift lever is removed (next step).

3   Remove the bolt that secures the shift lever to the transmission. On 2001 and later models, the shift lever is attached to the transmission with a threaded stud and nut. To remove the lever, remove the nut from the right side of the lever and thread it onto the left side of the lever. Tighten the nut to draw out the threaded stud.
4   Pull the shift lever straight up and off the transmission.
5   Installation is the reverse of the removal Steps.

2.2 Hold back the carpet and remove the shifter boot retaining bolts or screws

3 Transmission mount - check and replacement

▶ Refer to illustrations 3.2 and 3.3

1   Insert a large screwdriver or pry bar into the space between the transmission extension housing and the frame crossmember and pry up.
2   The transmission should not move significantly away from the mount (see illustration). If it does, the mount should be replaced.
3   To replace the mount, remove the two nuts securing the mount to the frame crossmember and the two bolts securing the mount to the transmission extension housing (see illustration).
4   Place a jack under the transmission with a piece of wood on top of it to protect the transmission case. Apply a slight amount of jack pressure and raise the transmission. Remove mount and install a new one.
5   Installation is the reverse of the removal Steps.

3.2 Pry up on the transmission mount and check for excessive looseness

3.3 Remove the two bolts attaching the transmission mount to the frame crossmember and the two bolts securing the mount to the transmission extension housing

4   Manual transmission - removal and installation

▶ **Refer to illustration 4.8**

1   Disconnect the cable from the negative terminal of the battery.
2   Shift the transmission into neutral.
3   Remove the shift lever (see Section 2).
4   Raise the vehicle and support it securely on jackstands. On 2011 4WD models, remove the catalytic converter (see Chapter 6).
5   Drain the transmission lubricant (see Chapter 1).
6   Remove the driveshaft (see Chapter 8). On 2WD models, install a plug in the transmission rear extension housing to prevent lubricant leakage.
7   Disconnect the hydraulic fluid line from the clutch release cylinder (see Chapter 8).
8   Disconnect the speedometer cable from the transfer case or transmission (if equipped) (see illustration).

4.8 Remove the bolt and retainer securing the speedometer and disconnect the speedometer cable from the transmission or transfer case

2010 AND EARLIER MODELS

9   Remove the starter motor (see Chapter 5).
10 Disconnect the electrical connections from the backup lamp, shift indicator switch, vehicle speed sensor, heated oxygen sensors or any other nearby electrical connections.
11 Place a jack under the engine and protect the oil pan with a wood block. Apply a slight amount of jack pressure to support the rear of the engine.
12 On 4WD models, remove the transfer case (see Chapter 7C).
13 On V6 engines, remove the exhaust system (see Chapter 4).
14 Place a transmission jack under the transmission. Apply a slight amount of jack pressure to support the transmission. Remove the bolts, lockwashers and plain washers that secure the transmission to the engine.
15 Remove the bolts and nuts securing the transmission mount to the frame crossmember (see illustration 3.3).
16 Remove the nuts securing the frame crossmember to the frame side rails.

➡**Note: If you do not remove the mount from the transmission, it will be necessary to raise the transmission enough to clear the mount bolts, then slide the crossmember toward the rear.**

2011 MODELS

17 On 4WD models, remove the transfer case (see Chapter 7C).
18 Support the transmission with a transmission jack. Disconnect any wiring harnesses from the transmission crossmember, remove the mounting bolts/nuts and remove the crossmember.
19 Remove the HO2S sensor (see Chapter 6) and the transmission

mount (see Section 3).
20 On 4.0L models, remove the exhaust Y-pipe (see Chapter 6, Section 10).
21 Remove all wiring harness/hose/line brackets from the transmission.
22 Disconnect the electrical connectors for the VSS and the back-up light switch, and any remaining wiring harnesses or electrical connectors.
23 Remove the starter motor (see Chapter 5).
24 Disconnect the clutch hydraulic line (see Chapter 8).
25 Place a jack under the engine, placing a wood block between the jack and the oil pan.
26 Remove the bolts securing the transmission to the engine.

ALL MODELS

27 Slowly lower the jack supporting the engine and carefully pull the transmission toward the rear and work it free from the locating dowels. Pull the transmission straight back until the input shaft clears the clutch assembly.
28 Lower the transmission jack and remove the transmission.
29 Installation is the reverse of removal, with the following additions:

   a) *Mount the transmission in a transmission jack and position it under the vehicle.*
   b) *Start the transmission input shaft into the clutch disc. Align the shaft splines with the clutch disc splines and move the transmission forward.*
   c) *Tighten the bolts and nuts to the torque listed in this Chapter's Specifications.*
   d) *Fill the transmission with the proper lubricant (see Chapter 1).*

5   Speedometer pinion gear and seal - removal and installation

▶ **Refer to illustrations 5.3 and 5.4**

➡**Note: Later models have an electronic speedometer and are not equipped with a speedometer cable.**

1   Disconnect the speedometer cable from the transmission.
2   Pull the speedometer pinion gear straight out of the transfer case or extension housing.
3   Use a small screwdriver and remove the retaining clip from the

5.3 Pry the retaining clip from the pinion gear and slide the gear off the cable

5.4 To replace the O-ring, pry off the old O-ring with a small screwdriver

pinion gear, then slide the gear off the cable (see illustration).

4   If necessary, use a small screwdriver and remove the O-ring from the retaining groove (see illustration). Discard the O-ring.

5   Lubricate the new O-ring with transmission lubricant and install it in the retaining groove. Make sure it's seated correctly.

6   Install the pinion gear on the cable and install the retaining clip. Make sure the clip is properly seated in the groove.

7   Install the speedometer pinion gear and cable in the transfer case or rear extension housing and secure it with the bolt and bracket.

6 Extension housing oil seal (2WD models) - replacement

1   Raise the vehicle and support it securely on jackstands.

2   Remove the driveshaft (see Chapter 8). Some transmission lubricant may drain out when the driveshaft slip joint is withdrawn from the extension housing.

3   To remove the oil seal from the end of the extension housing, use a special tool, available at most auto parts stores, and withdraw the oil seal. If the special tool is not available and there is access, use a thin blade screwdriver or chisel and pry the oil seal out.

4   Inspect the sealing surface on the driveshaft slip joint for scoring or burrs that may damage the new oil seal. If the yoke is damaged in any way, replace it.

5   Inspect the extension housing counterbore for burrs. If found, remove them with emery cloth or medium grit wet-and-dry sandpaper. Use a clean cloth dipped in solvent and remove any sanding residue from the counterbore.

6   Apply silicone sealant to the inside diameter of the oil seal and apply grease to the end of the rubber boot portion.

7   Using a seal driver, large socket or section of pipe, install a new oil seal and make sure it is completely seated in the counterbore.

8   Install the driveshaft (see Chapter 8).

9   Lower the vehicle and check the transmission lubricant level. Top up if necessary (see Chapter 1).

7 Transmission overhaul - general information

Overhauling a manual transmission is a difficult job for the do-it-yourselfer. It involves the disassembly and reassembly of many small parts. Numerous clearances must be precisely measured and, if necessary, changed with select-fit spacers and snap-rings. As a result, if transmission problems arise, it can be removed and installed by a competent do-it-yourselfer, but overhaul should be left to a transmission repair shop. Rebuilt transmissions may be available. Check with your dealer's parts department and auto parts stores. At any rate, the time and money involved in an overhaul is almost sure to exceed the cost of a rebuilt unit.

Nevertheless, it's not impossible for an inexperienced mechanic to rebuild a transmission if the special tools are available and the job is done in a deliberate step-by-step manner so nothing is overlooked.

The tools necessary for an overhaul include internal and external snap-ring pliers, bearing puller, slide hammer, set of pin punches, dial indicator and possibly a hydraulic press. In addition, a large, sturdy workbench and a large vise or transmission stand will be required.

During disassembly of the transmission, make careful notes of how each piece comes off, where it fits in relation to other pieces and what holds it in place.

Before taking the transmission apart for repair, it will help if you have some idea what area of the transmission is malfunctioning. Certain problems can be closely tied to specific areas in the transmission, which can make component examination and replacement easier. Refer to the *Troubleshooting* Section at the front of this manual for information regarding possible sources of trouble.

Specifications

General

Transmission type	5-speed synchromesh
Lubricant type	See Chapter 1

Torque specifications

	Ft-lbs
2000 models	
Transmission-to-engine bolts	50 to 68
Mount-to-crossmember nut	65 to 85
Mount-to-transmission bolt	60 to 80
Crossmember-to-frame bracket nut and bolt	65 to 85
2001 through 2005	
Transmission-to-engine bolts	44
Mount-to-crossmember nut	46
Mount-to-transmission bolt	72
Crossmember-to-frame bracket nuts and bolts	46
2006 and later	
Transmission-to-engine bolts	
2006 through 2010	
Four-cylinder engines	35
V6 engines	41
2011 (all engines)	41
Mount-to-crossmember nuts	71 to 72
Mount-to-transmission bolts	71 to 72
Crossmember-to-frame nuts and bolts	
2WD models	74
4WD	46

Notes

Section

Reference to other Chapters

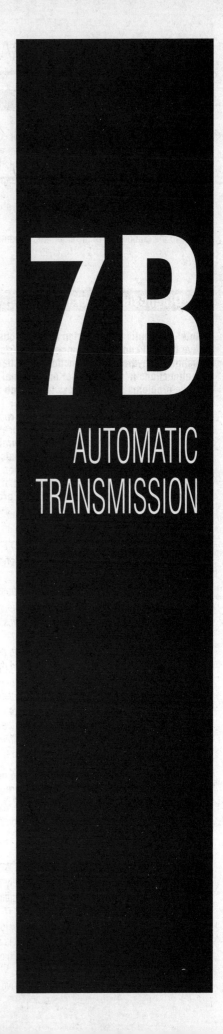

7B

AUTOMATIC
TRANSMISSION

1 General information

Models covered in this manual come equipped with a five-speed manual transmission or an automatic transmission. All information on the automatic transmission is included in this Part of Chapter 7. Information on the manual transmission can be found in Part A of this Chapter.

See the Specifications section at the end of this Chapter for transmission type and application.

Due to the complexity of the automatic transmissions covered in this manual and the need for specialized equipment to perform most service operations, this Chapter contains only general diagnosis, routine maintenance, adjustment and removal and installation procedures.

If the transmission requires major repair work, it should be taken to a dealer service department or an automotive or transmission repair shop. You can, however, remove and install the transmission yourself and save the expense, even if the repair work is done by a transmission shop.

2 Diagnosis - general

➡**Note: Automatic transmission malfunctions may be caused by five general conditions: poor engine performance, improper adjustments, hydraulic malfunctions, mechanical malfunctions or malfunctions in the computer or its signal network. Diagnosis of these problems should always begin with a check of the easily repaired items: fluid level and condition (see Chapter 1) and shift linkage adjustment. Next, perform a road test to determine if the problem has been corrected or if more diagnosis is necessary. If the problem persists after the preliminary tests and corrections are completed, additional diagnosis should be done by a dealer service department or transmission repair shop. Refer to the Troubleshooting Section at the front of this manual for information on symptoms of transmission problems.**

PRELIMINARY CHECKS

1 Drive the vehicle to warm the transmission to normal operating temperature.

2 Check the fluid level as described in Chapter 1:

  a) *If the fluid level is unusually low, add enough fluid to bring the level within the designated area of the dipstick, then check for external leaks (see below).*

  b) *If the fluid level is abnormally high, drain off the excess, then check the drained fluid for contamination by coolant. The presence of engine coolant in the automatic transmission fluid indicates that a failure has occurred in the internal radiator walls that separate the coolant from the transmission fluid (see Chapter 3).*

  c) *If the fluid is foaming, drain it and refill the transmission, then check for coolant in the fluid or a high fluid level.*

3 Check the engine idle speed.

➡**Note: If the engine is malfunctioning, do not proceed with the preliminary checks until it has been repaired and runs normally.**

4 Inspect the shift linkage (see Section 3). Make sure that it's properly adjusted and that the linkage operates smoothly.

FLUID LEAK DIAGNOSIS

5 Most fluid leaks are easy to locate visually. Repair usually consists of replacing a seal or gasket. If a leak is difficult to find, the following procedure may help.

6 Identify the fluid. Make sure it's transmission fluid and not engine oil or brake fluid (automatic transmission fluid is a deep red color when new and may turn light brown after the vehicle has been driven some distance).

7 Try to pinpoint the source of the leak. Drive the vehicle several miles, then park it over a large sheet of cardboard. After a minute or two, you should be able to locate the leak by determining the source of the fluid dripping onto the cardboard.

8 Make a careful visual inspection of the suspected component and the area immediately around it. Pay particular attention to gasket mating surfaces. A mirror is often helpful for finding leaks in areas that are hard to see.

9 If the leak still cannot be found, clean the suspected area thoroughly with a degreaser or solvent, then dry it.

10 Drive the vehicle for several miles at normal operating temperature and varying speeds. After driving the vehicle, visually inspect the suspected component again.

11 Once the leak has been located, the cause must be determined before it can be properly repaired. If a gasket is replaced but the sealing flange is bent, the new gasket will not stop the leak. The bent flange must be straightened.

12 Before attempting to repair a leak, check to make sure that the following conditions are corrected or they may cause another leak.

➡**Note: Some of the following conditions cannot be fixed without highly specialized tools and expertise. Such problems must be referred to a transmission repair shop or a dealer service department.**

Gasket leaks

13 Check the pan periodically. Make sure the bolts are tight, no bolts are missing, the gasket is in good condition and the pan is flat (dents in the pan may indicate damage to the valve body inside).

14 If the pan gasket is leaking, the fluid level or the fluid pressure may be too high, the vent may be plugged, the pan bolts may be too tight, the pan sealing flange may be warped, the sealing surface of the transmission housing may be damaged, the gasket may be damaged or the transmission casting may be cracked or porous. If sealant instead of gasket material has been used to form a seal between the pan and the transmission housing, it may be the wrong sealant.

Seal leaks

15 If a transmission seal is leaking, the fluid level or pressure may be too high, the vent may be plugged, the seal bore may be damaged, the seal itself may be damaged or improperly installed, the surface of the shaft protruding through the seal may be damaged or a loose bearing may be causing excessive shaft movement.

16 Make sure the dipstick tube seal is in good condition and the tube is properly seated. Periodically check the area around the speedometer gear or sensor for leakage. If transmission fluid is evident, check the O-ring for damage.

Case leaks

17 If the case itself appears to be leaking, the casting is porous and will have to be repaired or replaced.

18 Make sure the oil cooler hose fittings are tight and in good condition.

Fluid comes out vent pipe or fill tube

19 If this condition occurs, the transmission is overfilled, there is coolant in the fluid, the case is porous, the dipstick is incorrect, the vent is plugged or the drain back holes are plugged.

---

3   Shift cable - adjustment

1 Raise the vehicle and support it securely on jackstands.

2 Have an assistant position the column shift selector lever in the Drive Overdrive position (if equipped with Overdrive - if not, place the shift lever in Drive) and hold in place during adjustment. If working by yourself, hang a three-pound weight on the gear selector lever.

3 Working under the vehicle, pull down on the lock tab on the shift cable and remove the fitting from the manual shift lever ball stud with a screwdriver (see illustration 6.13).

4 Position the transmission manual shift lever in the Drive Overdrive (or Drive) position by moving the bellcrank lever all the way to the rear (counterclockwise), then forward three detents (clockwise) (or two detents for non-Overdrive models).

5 Connect the cable end fitting to the manual lever ball stud.

6 Push the lock tab all the way down to lock the cable in the correctly adjusted position.

7 If used, remove the weight from the gear selector lever.

8 After adjustment, check for Park engagement. The control lever must move to the right when engaged in Park. Check the control lever in all detent positions with the engine running to ensure correct detent/transmission action and adjust and readjust if necessary.

9 Remove the jackstands and lower the vehicle to the ground.

10 Test drive the vehicle slowly at first to make sure the adjustment is correct.

---

4   Shift cable - replacement

1 Use a screwdriver and pry the end fitting from the steering column lever ball stud.

2 Remove the nuts securing the shift cable bracket to the steering column bracket and remove the bracket.

3 Raise the vehicle and support it securely on jackstands.

4 Working under the vehicle, pull down on the lock tab on the shift cable and remove the fitting from the manual lever ball stud with a screwdriver (see illustration 6.12). Work the cable through the grommet in the firewall.

5 Bend back the retaining tab and disengage the cable from the transmission bracket. Slide the cable down from the transmission bracket and remove the cable.

6 Installation is the reverse of the removal procedure with the following additions:

    a) *Adjust the shift linkage (see Section 3).*

    b) *Remove the jackstands and lower the vehicle to the ground.*

---

5   Extension housing oil seal - replacement

▶ **Refer to illustrations 5.3 and 5.7**

1 Raise the vehicle and support it securely on jackstands.

2 Remove the driveshaft (see Chapter 8). Some transmission fluid may drain out when the driveshaft universal joint is withdrawn from the extension housing.

3 To remove the oil seal from the end of the extension housing, use a special tool made for this purpose, available at most auto parts stores that carry tools, and withdraw the oil seal. If the special tool is not available, and there is access, use a thin blade screwdriver or chisel to remove the oil seal (see illustration). A special tool is also needed to remove the extension housing bushing.

4 Inspect the oil seal contact surface on the universal joint yoke for scoring or burrs that may damage the new oil seal. If the yoke is damaged in any way, replace it.

5 Inspect the extension housing counterbore for burrs. If found, remove them with emery cloth or medium grit wet-and-dry sandpaper. Use a clean cloth dipped in solvent and remove any sanding residue from the counterbore.

5.3 Be extremely careful not to damage the sealing surface on the housing when prying out the rear seal

6   If the extension housing bushing was removed, install a new one with a special tool made for this purpose, available at most auto parts stores that carry tools.

7   Install a new extension housing oil seal and make sure it is completely seated in the counterbore (see illustration).

8   Install the driveshaft (see Chapter 8).

9   Lower the vehicle and check the transmission fluid level. Top up if necessary (see Chapter 1).

5.7 Installing the new extension housing oil seal with a punch and hammer - large socket or length of pipe of the proper diameter may also be used to install the oil seal

6   Automatic transmission - removal and installation

▶ **Refer to illustrations 6.8, 6.12, 6.13, 6.14, 6.15, 6.17, 6.21**

1   Disconnect the negative cable from the battery.

2   Remove the transmission fluid level dipstick. On 2011 4.0L models, also remove the dipstick tube.

3   Raise the vehicle and support it securely on jackstands.

4   On 4WD models, remove the transfer case (see Chapter 7 Part C).

✳✳ CAUTION:

Remove the Vehicle Speed Sensor (VSS) from the transfer case.

5   Drain the transmission fluid only if you will be disassembling the transmission, then reinstall the pan. (see Chapter 1) Otherwise, you are going to have a problem disposing of the lubricant yourself.

6   Unbolt the starter and tie it up out of the way (see Chapter 5).

7   On vehicles with 3.0L V6 engine, remove the transmission access cover from the converter housing to gain access to the torque converter nuts. The starter mounting hole provides access to the torque converter nuts on vehicles with four-cylinder and 4.0L V6 engines.

➡ **Note: On 2001 and later 2.3L engines, it may be easier to get to the torque converter nuts by going through the wheel well.**

8   Mark the driveplate and one of the studs with white paint so they can be installed in the same position (see illustration).

9   Remove the four torque converter-to-driveplate nuts. Turn the crankshaft for access to each nut.

✳✳ CAUTION:

Turn the crankshaft in a clockwise direction only (as viewed from the front). You can remove the spark plugs to make this easier.

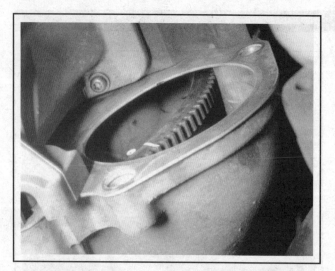

6.8 Mark one of the torque converter studs with white paint and make a corresponding mark on the driveplate so the torque converter and driveplate can be reassembled in the same relative positions

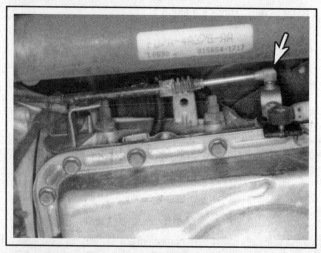

6.12 Disconnect the shift cable from the transmission manual shift lever . . .

6.13 . . . and the kickdown cable from the transmission downshift lever

6.14 Disconnect the electrical connectors for the shift solenoids and neutral start switch

10 On 2WD models, remove the driveshaft (see Chapter 8). Tie a plastic bag over the end of the extension housing to prevent the entry of dirt and to catch any residual transmission fluid.

11 On 2WD models, remove the bolt securing the speedometer cable retaining bracket and remove the bracket and bolt as an assembly. Disconnect the speedometer cable from the transmission (if equipped).

12 Disconnect the shift cable from the transmission manual shift lever (see illustration).

13 Disconnect the transmission range (TR) sensor connector, the 16-pin transmission connector, and any other electrical connectors and brackets attached to the transmission.

14 Place a transmission jack beneath the transmission and apply jack pressure to slightly raise the transmission. Use safety chains to help steady the transmission on the jack.

15 Remove the bolts and nuts securing the rear mount and insulator to the frame crossmember (see illustration).

16 Remove the crossmember-to-frame side support mounting bolts and remove the crossmember insulator, support and damper.

17 Remove the bolts and nuts securing the crossmember to the frame rails (see illustration), raise the transmission slightly and remove the crossmember.

18 Support the engine with a jack. Use a block of wood under the oil pan to spread the load.

19 On V6 engines, remove the catalytic converter (see Chapter 4).

20 Slightly lower the transmission.

⁎⁎ CAUTION:

Do not allow the transmission to hang free.

21 Disconnect the transmission oil cooler lines from the transmission and plug them to prevent the entry of dirt (see illustration). Use a flare nut wrench to avoid rounding off the nuts.

22 Remove the lower converter housing-to-engine bolts.

23 Remove the transmission fluid filler (dipstick) tube (see illustration 6.21).

24 Make sure the transmission is securely mounted on the transmission jack. Remove the two upper converter housing-to-engine bolts.

25 Remove the vent tube attached to the top of the transmission (4WD only).

6.15 Detach the transmission mount from the frame crossmember

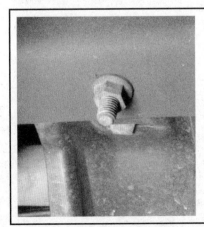

6.17 Detach the front crossmember from the frame rail on each side of the vehicle

6.21 Disconnect the fluid cooler lines and remove the filler tube

26 Remove the four side converter housing-to-engine bolts.

27 Carefully move the transmission to the rear to disengage it from the engine block dowel pins and make sure the torque converter is detached from the driveplate. Secure the torque converter to the transmission so it won't fall out during removal.

28 Installation is the reverse of the removal Steps with the following additions:

a) Install the converter to the transmission, making sure the converter hub is fully engaged in the pump gear.

b) Rotate the converter to align the bolt drive lugs and the drain plug with the holes in the driveplate.

c) With the transmission secured to the jack, raise it into position. Be sure to keep it level so the torque converter does not slide forward and disengage from the pump gear.

d) Turn the torque converter to line up the studs with the holes in the driveplate. The white paint mark on the torque converter and the stud made in Step 5 must line up.

e) Move the transmission forward carefully until the dowel pins and the torque converter are engaged.

f) When installing the driveplate-to-converter nuts, position the driveplate so the pilot hole is in the six o'clock position. First install one nut through the pilot hole and tighten it, then install the remaining nuts. Tighten the nuts to the torque listed in this Chapter's Specifications. Use new nuts.

g) Adjust the shift cable (see Section 3).

h) Lower the vehicle.

i) Fill the transmission with the specified fluid (see Chapter 1), run the engine and check for fluid leaks.

7   Transmission mount - check and replacement

1   Insert a large screwdriver or pry bar into the space between the transmission extension housing and the crossmember and try to pry the transmission up slightly (see illustration 6.15).

2   The transmission should not move away from the mount much at all.

3   To replace the mount, remove the nuts attaching the mount to the crossmember and the bolts attaching the mount to the transmission.

4   Raise the transmission slightly with a jack and remove the mount, noting which holes are used in the crossmember for proper alignment during installation.

5   Installation is the reverse of the removal procedure. Be sure to tighten the nuts/bolts securely.

Specifications

General

Transmission type	
Four-cylinder models	
2000	4R44E
2001 and later	
2.3L engine	5R44E or 5R55E
2.5L engine	4R44E
3.0L V6 models	
2000	4R44E
2001 through 2008	5R44E or 5R55E
4.0L V6 models	5R44E or 5R55E

Torque specifications*   Ft-lbs (unless otherwise indicated)

➡ Note: One foot-pound (ft-lb) of torque is equivalent to 12 inch-pounds (in-lbs) of torque. Torque values below approximately 15 ft-lbs are expressed in inch-pounds, since most foot-pound torque wrenches are not accurate at these smaller values.

Transmission-to-engine fasteners	
2005 and earlier	28 to 38
2006 through 2010 2.3L	35
All others	41
Mount-to-transmission bolts	66
Mount-to-crossmember nuts	66
Digital transmission range sensor bolts	89 in-lbs
Transmission fluid pan bolts	
2010 and earlier	144 in-lbs
2011	89 in-lbs
Torque converter-to-driveplate nuts	
2010 and earlier	26 to 34
2011	26
Neutral start switch (early models)	84 to 120 in-lbs

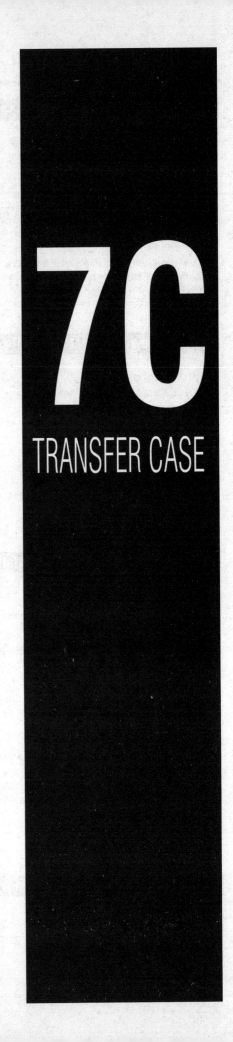

7C

TRANSFER CASE

Section

1   General information

4WD models are equipped with the Borg Warner 13-54 Manual or Electronic Shift transfer case. Manual selection is accomplished with a shift lever that provides neutral, 2-high, 4-high and 4-low. Electronic selection is accomplished with a switch on the instrument panel.

The 13-54 chain-driven transfer case transfers power from the transmission to the rear axle and, when activated, also to the front driveaxle. The unit is lubricated by a positive displacement oil pump that channels oil through drilled holes in the rear output shaft. The pump turns with the rear output shaft and allows towing of the vehicle at maximum legal road speeds for extended distances without disconnecting the front or rear driveshafts.

Although each of the systems differ internally, the external components on the transfer case are similar.

Due to the complexity of the transfer cases covered in this manual and the need for specialized equipment to perform most service operations, this Chapter contains only general diagnosis, routine maintenance, adjustment and removal and installation procedures.

If the transfer case requires major repair work, it should be taken to a dealer service department or an automotive or transmission repair shop. You can, however, remove and install the transfer case yourself and save the expense, even if the repair work is done by a transmission shop.

2   Linkage adjustment - manual shift transfer case

1   The linkage should be adjusted if the transfer case won't engage properly or whenever the transfer case control assembly is removed from the vehicle.
2   Lift up the shift boot so the upper surface of the cam plate is visible.
3   Loosen the lever mounting bolts one turn each.
4   Move the shift lever on the side of the transfer case to the 4L position (down).
5   Pivot the cam plate clockwise around bolt A until the bottom

chamfered corner of the neutral lug just touches the forward right edge of the shift lever on the transfer case.
6   While holding the cam plate from turning, tighten the lever mounting bolts to the torque listed in this Chapter's Specifications.
7   Move the shift lever inside the vehicle to all positions and check for positive engagement. In the 2H, 4H and 4L positions, there should be clearance between the cam plate and the shift lever on the side of the transfer case.
8   When the linkage is adjusted properly, install the shift lever boot.

3   Shift lever - removal and installation

REMOVAL

1   Place the transfer case shift lever in the 4L position.
➡Note: Don't perform Step 2 unless the shift ball, boot or lever is to be replaced.
2   Remove the plastic insert from the shift ball. Warm the ball with a heat gun or portable hair dryer to 140 to 180 degrees F and knock the ball off the lever with a piece of wood and a hammer. Be careful not to damage the finish on the shift lever.
3   Remove the rubber boot and the floor pan cover.
4   Disconnect the vent hose from the control lever.
5   Unscrew the shift lever from the control lever.
6   Remove the large and small housing bolts securing the shifter to the extension housing. Remove the control lever and bushing.

INSTALLATION

7   Adjust the linkage (see Section 2).
8   Install the vent assembly so the white mark on the housing is indexed into the notch in the shifter, if applicable.
➡Note: The upper end of the vent hose should be 3/4-inch above the top of the shifter and positioned just under the vehicle floor.
9   Install the floor pan cover and the rubber boot.
10   If the shift ball was removed, warm it with a heat gun or portable hair dryer to 140 to 180-degrees F and carefully tap the ball onto the lever with a piece of wood and a hammer. Install the plastic insert into the shift ball.
➡Note: The shift ball must be tapped onto the lever until all of the knurled portion of the shaft is covered.
11   Check the transfer case for proper operation.

4   Electronic shift controls - removal and installation

2010 AND EARLIER MODELS

▶ Refer to illustration 4.4

1   Disconnect the cable from the negative terminal of the battery.
2   Remove the instrument cluster trim panel (see Chapter 12).

3   Remove the screws securing the shift control assembly and partially pull the assembly out from the instrument panel.
4   Disconnect the electrical connector from the switch assembly and remove the assembly (see illustration).
5   Installation is the reverse of removal

2011 MODELS

> ※ **CAUTION:**
>
> On these models, the radio unit must be put into Shipment Mode. Follow the procedure in Chapter 12, Section 10 before beginning this procedure.

6   Remove the radio (see Chapter 12).

7   Remove the center instrument bezel by pulling out to release its retainers.

8   Disconnect the 4WD select switch electrical connector.

9   Remove the 4WD select switch knob from the front of the panel.

10   From the rear of the bezel, remove the select switch mounting screws and remove the switch.

11   Installation is the reverse of removal. Make sure the center bezel snaps securely into place. See Chapter 12 to take the radio out of Shipment Mode.

4.4 Lift the connector latch and pull the electrical connector from the electronic shift control switch

---

5   Electronic shift control module - removal and installation

➡**Note: 2000 models are equipped with a Generic Electronic Module (GEM). This module incorporates the functions of several different modules into one and offers diagnostic codes to locate any multitude of failures (see Chapter 6). The 2001 and later models have a 4WD module.**

1   Disconnect the negative cable from the battery.

2000 MODELS

2   Remove the radio (see Chapter 12).

3   Remove the radio trim panel (see Chapter 12).

4   Remove the retaining screw, and slide the GEM off the retaining tabs and toward the front of the vehicle.

5   Disconnect the electrical connectors from the GEM and remove the unit from the dash.

6   Installation is the reverse of removal.

2001 THROUGH 2010 MODELS

7   Remove the driver's side kick panel (see Chapter 11).

8   Remove the two harness connectors from the module by unlocking the connector retainers.

9   Remove the screws, then the module itself.

10   Installation is the reverse of removal.

2011 MODELS

> ※ **CAUTION:**
>
> On these models, the radio unit must be put into Shipment Mode. Follow the procedure in Chapter 12, Section 10 before beginning this procedure.

11   Remove the radio (see Chapter 12).

12   Remove the center instrument bezel (see Section 4), disconnecting any electrical connectors.

13   Remove the module mounting screws and remove the control module.

14   Installation is the reverse of removal. Make sure the center bezel snaps securely into place. See Chapter 12 to take the radio out of Shipment Mode.

---

6   Front output shaft oil seal - replacement

The front output shaft oil seal cannot be serviced externally. If the seal is leaking, have a dealer service department disassemble the transfer case and replace the seal.

---

7   Rear output shaft oil seal - removal and installation

REMOVAL

1   Raise the vehicle and support it securely on jackstands.

2   Remove the rear driveshaft from the transfer case output shaft yoke and wire the driveshaft out of the way (see Chapter 8).

3   Remove and discard the nut securing the flange.

4   Remove and discard the steel washer and rubber seal, then remove the flange.

5   Carefully pry and pull on the outer curved lip of the oil seal and remove it from transfer case.

INSTALLATION

6   Inspect the oil seal contact surface on the housing for scoring or burrs that may damage the new oil seal. If found, remove them with emery cloth or medium grit wet-and-dry sandpaper. Use a clean cloth dipped in solvent and remove any sanding residue from the counterbore.

7   Apply multi-purpose grease to the oil seal. Position the seal into the front output shaft housing bore and make sure the oil seal is not cocked in the bore.

8   To drive the front oil seal into the output housing bore use a special tool available at most auto parts stores that carry special tools, and driver a special tool available at most auto parts stores that carry special tools, or carefully drive the seal into the bore with a hammer and a large socket or piece of pipe of the appropriate size.

9   Clean the transfer case rear output female splines and apply multi-purpose grease to them.

10 Install the output flange onto the output shaft splines.

11 Install the new rubber seal, steel washer and nut. Tighten the nut to the torque listed in this Chapter's Specifications.

12 Connect the front driveshaft to the axle output flange (see Chapter 8).

13 Remove the jackstands and lower the vehicle.

---

8   Transfer case - removal and installation

▶ Refer to illustrations 8.3, 8.5, 8.6 and 8.8

➡Note: On 2011 models, make sure the transfer case is in the 2H position before beginning this procedure.

1   Raise the vehicle and support it securely on jackstands.

2   On models so equipped, remove the four skid plate-to-frame bolts and remove the skid plate.

3   On models so equipped, remove the damper from the transfer case (see illustration).

4   Drain the transfer case lubricant only if you're disassembling it, then reinstall the drain plug.

5   On electronically controlled models, squeeze the locking tabs (the part labeled PUSH) toward each other, then pull the electrical connector apart. This may take some effort, but it shouldn't be necessary to use tools to separate the connector halves. Disconnect the electrical connector from the transfer case motor and from the connector mounting bracket (see illustration).

6   If equipped, disconnect the speed sensor electrical connector and speedometer cable from the transfer case (see illustration).

7   Disconnect the front driveshaft, then the rear driveshaft (see Chapter 8).

8   Disconnect the vent hose from the shift lever bracket (manual shift) or mounting bracket (electronic shift) (see illustration).

✳✳ WARNING:

The catalytic converter is next to the vent hose and is extremely hot after the engine has been run. Be careful when working around the converter and if possible allow the converter to cool down several hours prior to working around it.

9   On manually controlled models, remove the nut from the shift lever and remove the shift lever.

8.3 Some models are equipped with a transfer case damper - this must be removed to remove the transfer case

8.5 Disconnect the shift motor connector (electronic shift models)

8.6 Disconnect the speed sensor connector (if equipped) and speedometer cable

8.8 Disconnect the vent hose from its bracket (electronic shift models)

10 On manually controlled models, remove the large bolt and the small bolt retaining the shifter to the extension housing. Pull on the control lever unit until the bushing slides off the transfer case shift lever pin.

11 Place a transmission jack beneath the transfer case and apply jack pressure to slightly raise the transfer case. Use safety chains to steady the transfer case on the jack.

12 Remove the five bolts securing the transfer case to the transmis-

sion extension housing.

13 Slide the transfer case rearward and off the transmission output shaft, then lower the transfer case from the vehicle. Remove and discard the gasket between the transfer case and the extension housing. Clean and inspect the mating surfaces.

14 Installation is the reverse of the removal Steps with the following additions:

a) *Install a new gasket between the transfer case and the extension housing.*

b) *Slide the transfer case onto the transmission output shaft, making sure the splines align, until the transfer case seats over the dowel pin.*

c) *Install the five bolts securing the transfer case and tighten to the torque listed in this Chapter's Specifications in a clockwise pattern.*

➡**Note: On manually controlled models, always tighten the large bolt securing the shifter to the extension housing before tightening the small bolt.**

d) *Install the vent assembly so the white marking on the hose is positioned in the notch in the shift lever bracket (manual shift) or mounting bracket (electronic shift).*

➡**Note: The upper end of the vent hose should be 3/4 inch above the top of the shifter on manually controlled models.**

e) *Connect the rear driveshaft to the transfer case output flange. Tighten the bolts to the torque listed in the Chapter 8 Specifications.*

f) *Refill the transfer case with the proper type of lubricant (see Chapter 1).*

9 Transfer case overhaul - general information

Overhauling a transfer case is a difficult job for the do-it-yourselfer, not unlike overhauling a transmission. It involves the disassembly and reassembly of many small parts. Numerous clearances must be precisely measured and, if necessary, changed with select-fit spacers and snap-rings. As a result, if transfer case problems arise, it can be removed and installed by a competent do-it-yourselfer, but overhaul should be left to a competent repair shop. Rebuilt transfer cases may be available. Check with your dealer parts department and auto parts stores. At any rate, the time and money involved in an overhaul is almost sure to exceed the cost of a rebuilt unit.

Nevertheless, it's not impossible for an inexperienced mechanic to rebuild a transfer case if the special tools are available and the job is done in a deliberate step-by-step manner so nothing is overlooked.

The tools necessary for an overhaul include internal and external snap-ring pliers, bearing puller, slide hammer, set of pin punches, dial indicator and possibly a hydraulic press. In addition, a large, sturdy workbench and a large vise will be required.

During disassembly, make careful notes of how each piece comes off, where it fits in relation to other pieces and what holds it in place.

Before taking the transfer case apart for repair, it will help if you have some idea what area of the transfer case is malfunctioning. Certain problems can be closely tied to specific areas in the transfer case, which can make component examination and replacement easier. Refer to the *Troubleshooting* Section at the front of this manual for information regarding possible sources of trouble.

10 Transfer case electronic shift motor - general information, diagnosis and replacement

GENERAL INFORMATION AND DIAGNOSIS

1 Some models are equipped with an electronic shift motor which shifts the transfer case from 2-high to 4-high or 4-low in response to an electrical signal from a button on the dash.

2 If the shift motor should malfunction while the vehicle is in 4-low, top speed will be restricted. Should this happen to you, the following procedure will show you how to manually shift the transfer case into 2-high.

3 First, remove the shift motor (see Steps 6 through 12). It isn't necessary to unplug any connectors; just remove the motor mounting

bolts and pull off the motor. To test the motor, have an assistant press the button on the dash (key on) while you watch the motor.

a) *If the motor runs, the problem is in the transfer case.*

b) *If the motor does not run, check for voltage at the shift motor (see Chapter 12, if necessary). If there's voltage, replace the motor. If there's no voltage, the problem lies elsewhere in the shift motor circuit (check the fuse first).*

4 To shift the transfer case into 2-High, rotate the shift shaft on the transfer case clockwise until it stops. Pliers may help rotate the recessed shaft.

5 Reattach the shift motor (see Step 13).

REPLACEMENT

6   Raise the vehicle and place it securely on jackstands.

2010 and earlier models

7   Unplug the electrical connector for the shift motor harness.

8   Remove the two wire harness bracket bolts and detach the harness bracket.

9   Remove the brown wire from the back of the shift motor side of the electrical connector.

10 Remove the motor bracket bolt.

11 Note the position of the triangular shaft protruding from the rear of the transfer case. It must be in this same position when installing the motor.

12 Remove the three motor retaining bolts and remove the motor.

13 Installation is the reverse of removal, with the following additions:

a) Using soft-jaw pliers, rotate the triangular shift shaft so that it's aligned with the triangular slot in the motor.

b) Apply a thin coat of RTV sealant to the motor base.

c) Tighten the shift motor bolts to the torque listed in this Chapter's Specifications.

2011 models

14 Disconnect the electrical connector from the shift motor.

15 Disconnect the coil wire from the electrical connector by releasing the retainer and locking tab.

16 Remove the shift motor bracket bolt, the motor mounting bolts and the shift motor.

17 Installation is the reverse of removal, noting the following:

a) When installing the motor, the transfer case shift rod may need to be rotated to align with the shift motor.

b) Apply a thin coat of RTV sealant to the motor base.

c) Tighten the shift motor bolts to the torque listed in this Chapter's Specifications.

Specifications

Lubricant type	See Chapter 1

Torque specifications   Ft-lbs (unless otherwise indicated)

➡**Note: One foot-pound (ft-lb) of torque is equivalent to 12 inch-pounds (in-lbs) of torque. Torque values below approximately 15 ft-lbs are expressed in inch-pounds, since most foot-pound torque wrenches are not accurate at these smaller values.**

Cam plate bolt A	70 to 90
Cam plate bolt B	31 to 42
Breather vent	72 to 168 in-lbs
Upper shift control and heat shield bolts	27 to 37
Transfer case-to-transmission bolts	
2005 and earlier models	25 to 35
2006 and later models	40
Damper mounting bolts (if equipped)	25
Output shaft nut	
2010 and earlier	150 to 180
2011	155
Skid plate-to-frame bolt	
2010 and earlier	22 to 30
2011	18
Speedometer cable bolt (if equipped)	20 to 25 in-lbs
Bearing retainer bolts	26 to 32
Shift motor bolts	
2010 and earlier	71 to 97 in-lbs
2011	89 in-lbs

Section

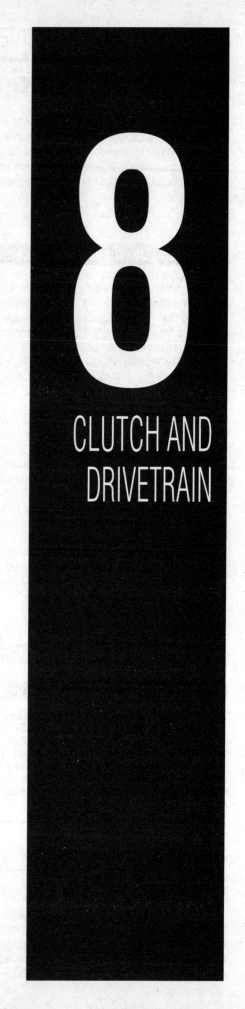

8

CLUTCH AND DRIVETRAIN

1 General information

The information in this Chapter deals with the components that transmit power to the wheels, except for the transmission and transfer case, which are dealt with in Chapter 7. For the purposes of this Chapter, these components are grouped into three categories; clutch, driveshaft and axles. Separate Sections within this Chapter offer general descriptions and checking procedures for components in each of the three groups.

Since nearly all the procedures covered in this Chapter involve working under the vehicle, make sure it's securely supported on sturdy jackstands or on a hoist where the vehicle can be easily raised and lowered.

2 Clutch - description and check

1   All models with a manual transmission use a single dry plate, diaphragm spring type clutch. The clutch disc has a splined hub which allows it to slide along the splines of the transmission input shaft. The clutch and pressure plate are held in contact by spring pressure exerted by the diaphragm in the pressure plate.

2   The clutch release system is operated by hydraulic pressure. The hydraulic release system consists of the clutch pedal, a master cylinder and fluid reservoir, the hydraulic line, an internal release cylinder and the clutch release (or throwout) bearing.

3   The internal release cylinder, mounted concentrically on the transmission input shaft, pushes directly on the release bearing. This eliminates the need for a release lever.

4   Terminology can be a problem when discussing the clutch components because common names are in some cases different from those used by the manufacturer. For example, the driven plate is also called the clutch plate or disc, the clutch release bearing is sometimes called a throwout bearing, the release cylinder is sometimes called the operating or slave cylinder.

5   Other than to replace components with obvious damage, some preliminary checks should be performed to diagnose clutch problems.

a) The first check should be of the fluid level in the clutch master cylinder. If the fluid level is low, add fluid as necessary and inspect the hydraulic system for leaks. If the master cylinder reservoir has run dry, bleed the system as described in Section 9 and retest the clutch operation.

b) To check "clutch spin down time," run the engine at normal idle speed with the transmission in Neutral (clutch pedal up - engaged). Disengage the clutch (pedal down), wait several seconds and shift the transmission into Reverse. No grinding noise should be heard. A grinding noise would most likely indicate a problem in the pressure plate or the clutch disc.

c) To check for complete clutch release, run the engine (with the parking brake applied to prevent movement) and hold the clutch pedal approximately 1/2-inch from the floor. Shift the transmission between 1st gear and Reverse several times. If the shift is hard or the transmission grinds, component failure is indicated. Check the release bearing travel. With the clutch pedal depressed completely, the release cylinder should extend substantially. If it doesn't, check the fluid level in the clutch master cylinder (see Chapter 1). Bleed the system (see Section 9).

d) Visually inspect the pivot bushing at the top of the clutch pedal to make sure there is no binding or excessive play.

3 Clutch components - removal, inspection and installation

✳✳ WARNING:

Dust produced by clutch wear and deposited on clutch components is hazardous to your health. DO NOT blow it out with compressed air and DO NOT inhale it. DO NOT use gasoline or petroleum-based solvents to remove the dust. Brake system cleaner should be used to flush the dust into a drain pan. After the clutch components are wiped clean with a rag, dispose of the contaminated rags and cleaner in a covered, marked container.

REMOVAL

▶ **Refer to illustrations 3.3 and 3.5**

1   Access to the clutch components is normally accomplished by removing the transmission (and transfer case on 4WD models), leaving the engine in the vehicle. If, of course, the engine is being removed for major overhaul, then check the clutch for wear and replace worn components as necessary. However, the relatively low cost of the clutch components compared to the time and trouble spent gaining access to them warrants their replacement anytime the engine or transmission is removed, unless they are new or in near perfect condition. The following procedures are based on the assumption the engine will stay in place.

2   Referring to Chapter 7 Part A and Part C, remove the transmission from the vehicle. Support the engine while the transmission is out. Preferably, an engine hoist should be used to support it from above. However, if a jack is used underneath the engine, make sure a piece of wood is positioned between the jack and oil pan to spread the load.

✳✳ CAUTION:

The pick-up for the oil pump is very close to the bottom of the oil pan. If the pan is bent or distorted in any way, engine oil starvation could occur.

3   To support the clutch disc during removal, install a clutch alignment tool through the clutch disc hub (see illustration).

4   Carefully inspect the flywheel and pressure plate for indexing marks. The marks are usually an X, an O or a white letter. If they cannot

3.3 A clutch alignment tool can be purchased at most auto parts stores and eliminates all guesswork when centering the clutch disc in the pressure plate

3.5 Loosen the pressure plate bolts (arrows) one turn at a time in rotation until they are free

be found, scribe marks yourself so the pressure plate and the flywheel will be in the same alignment during installation.

5   Turning each bolt only 1/4-turn at a time, loosen the pressure plate-to-flywheel bolts (see illustration). Work in a criss-cross pattern until all spring pressure is relieved evenly. Then hold the pressure plate securely and completely remove the bolts, followed by the pressure plate and clutch disc.

INSPECTION

▶ **Refer to illustrations 3.9, 3.11, 3.13a and 3.13b**

6   Ordinarily, when a problem occurs in the clutch, it can be attributed to wear of the clutch driven plate assembly (clutch disc). However, all components should be inspected at this time.

7   Inspect the flywheel for cracks, heat checking, grooves and other obvious defects. If the imperfections are slight, a machine shop can machine the surface flat and smooth, which is highly recommended regardless of the surface appearance. Refer to Chapter 2 for the flywheel removal and installation procedure.

8   Inspect the pilot bearing (see Section 4).

9   Inspect the lining on the clutch disc. There should be at least 1/16-inch of lining above the rivet heads. Check for loose rivets,

distortion, cracks, broken springs and other obvious damage (see illustration). As mentioned above, ordinarily the clutch disc is routinely replaced, so if in doubt about the condition, replace it with a new one.

10   The release bearing should also be replaced along with the clutch disc (see Section 6).

11   Check the machined surfaces and the diaphragm spring fingers of the pressure plate (see illustration). If the surface is grooved or otherwise damaged, replace the pressure plate. Also check for obvious

3.9 The clutch disc

1   **Lining** - *this will wear down in use*
2   **Rivets** - *these secure the lining and will damage the flywheel or pressure plate if allowed to contact the surfaces*
3   **Marks** - *"Flywheel side" or similar*

NORMAL FINGER WEAR

EXCESSIVE WEAR

EXCESSIVE FINGER WEAR

BROKEN OR BENT FINGERS

3.11 Replace the pressure plate if excessive or abnormal wear is noted

3.13a Position the pressure plate on the flywheel and place both components in a hydraulic press as shown, then, using a suitable adapter, depress the clutch diaphragm fingers until the adjusting ring (arrow) moves freely

damage, distortion, cracking, etc. Light glazing can be removed with medium grit emery cloth. If a new pressure plate is required, new and factory-rebuilt units are available.

INSTALLATION

12 Before installation, clean the flywheel and pressure plate machined surfaces with lacquer thinner or acetone. It's important that no oil or grease is on these surfaces or the lining of the clutch disc. Handle the parts only with clean hands.

13 Position the clutch disc and pressure plate against the flywheel with the clutch held in place with an alignment tool (see illustration 3.3). Make sure it's installed properly (most replacement clutch plates will be marked "flywheel side" or something similar - if not marked, install the clutch disc with the flat side of the hub toward the flywheel).

➡**Note: The pressure plate may have an adjustment ring that must be adjusted before installation. Use the following procedure (if equipped):**

   a) *Use a suitable press to press all the fingers on the pressure plate down (see illustration).*

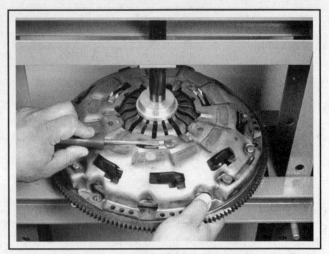

3.13b Using a screwdriver, move the adjusting ring counterclockwise

   b) *There is an adjusting ring integrated within the pressure plate that can be rotated - move it to the extreme counterclockwise position until the springs on the adjuster ring are compressed fully (see illustration).*

   c) *Hold the adjuster ring in position while releasing the tension on the pressure plate fingers.*

   d) *The clutch pressure plate is now adjusted and ready for installation.*

14 Tighten the pressure plate-to-flywheel bolts only finger tight, working around the pressure plate.

15 Center the clutch disc by ensuring the alignment tool extends through the splined hub and into the pilot bearing in the crankshaft. Wiggle the tool up, down or side-to-side as needed to bottom the tool in the pilot bearing. Tighten the pressure plate-to-flywheel bolts a little at a time, working in a criss-cross pattern to prevent distorting the cover. After all of the bolts are snug, tighten them to the torque listed in this Chapter's Specifications. Remove the alignment tool.

16 If removed, install the clutch release bearing as described in Section 6.

17 Install the transmission and all components removed previously. Tighten all fasteners to the torques listed in this Chapter's Specifications.

4 Pilot bearing - inspection and replacement

▶ **Refer to illustrations 4.5 and 4.6**

1   The clutch pilot bearing is a needle roller type bearing which is pressed into the rear of the crankshaft. It is greased at the factory and does not require additional lubrication. Its primary purpose is to support the front of the transmission input shaft. The pilot bearing should be inspected whenever the clutch components are removed from the engine. Due to its inaccessibility, if you are in doubt as to its condition, replace it with a new one.

➡**Note: If the engine has been removed from the vehicle, disregard the following steps which do not apply.**

2   Remove the transmission (see Chapter 7 Part A).

3   Remove the clutch components (see Section 3).

4   Inspect for any excessive wear, scoring, lack of grease, dryness or obvious damage. If any of these conditions are noted, the bearing should be replaced. A flashlight will be helpful to direct light into the recess.

5   Removal can be accomplished with a special puller and slide hammer (see illustration).

6   To install the new bearing, lightly lubricate the outside surface with lithium-based grease, then drive it into the recess with a soft-face hammer (see illustration). The seal must face out.

7   Install the clutch components, transmission and all other components removed previously, tightening all fasteners properly.

4.5 One method of removing the pilot bearing requires an internal puller connected to a slide hammer

4.6 Tap the bearing into place with a bushing driver or a socket slightly smaller than the outside diameter of the bearing

5   Clutch hydraulic line quick-disconnect fittings - general information

♦ **Refer to illustration 5.2**

1   The hydraulic lines are equipped with quick-disconnect fittings and a special tool available at most auto parts stores that carry special tools, is required for separation

2   Depress the white retainer within the quick-disconnect fitting with the special tool while pulling on the hydraulic line, then disconnect the male connector. To install, push the male connector into the female connector until it locks into place (see illustration).

3   There should be no loss of hydraulic fluid during separation of the fittings so there is no need to bleed the system after a fitting has been disconnected unless shifting is hard or there's a lack of clutch reserve travel.

5.2 If you don't have a clutch coupling tool to disconnect the clutch hydraulic line from the transmission, use a screwdriver instead - carefully push the spring-loaded transmission side of the coupling toward the transmission and simultaneously pull straight out on the hydraulic line side of the fitting

6   Clutch release bearing - removal, inspection and installation

♦ **Refer to illustrations 6.2 and 6.3**

❈❈ WARNING:

Dust produced by clutch wear and deposited on clutch components is hazardous to your health. DO NOT blow it out with compressed air and DO NOT inhale it. DO NOT use gasoline or petroleum-based solvents to remove the dust. Brake system cleaner should be used to flush the dust into a drain pan. After the clutch components are wiped clean with a rag, dispose of the contaminated rags and cleaner in a covered, marked container.

REMOVAL AND INSPECTION

1   Remove the transmission (see Chapter 7 Part A).

2   Within the clutch housing, twist the release bearing and carrier assembly until you feel resistance. Keep pushing the assembly and the preload spring down to release bearing off the release cylinder. Remove the retaining ring to separate the release bearing from the release cylinder (see illustration).

3   Hold the center of the bearing and rotate the outer portion while applying pressure. If the bearing doesn't turn smoothly or it's noisy,

6.2 To disengage the clutch release bearing from the release cylinder, push the release bearing against spring pressure and remove the retaining ring

replace it with a new one. Wipe the bearing with a clean rag and inspect it for damage, wear and cracks. Don't immerse the bearing in solvent - it's sealed for life and to do so would ruin it (see illustration).

INSTALLATION

4 Apply a light coat of high-temperature lithium based grease to the face of the release bearing, where it contacts the pressure plate dia-

6.3 To check the clutch release bearing, hold the hub (the center) of the bearing and rotate the outer portion while applying pressure; if the bearing doesn't turn smoothly of if it's noisy or rough, replace it

phragm fingers.

5 Lubricate the inner bore of the bearing and bearing carrier with lithium-based grease. Don't use petroleum-based grease.

6 Push the release bearing and carrier onto the slave cylinder until it bottoms out.

7 Install the transmission (see Chapter 7 Part A).

---

7 Clutch release cylinder - removal and installation

▸ **Refer to illustration 7.4**

➟**Note: Prior to removing the release cylinder, disconnect the master cylinder pushrod from the clutch pedal. If not discon-nected, permanent damage to the master cylinder will occur if the clutch pedal is depressed while the release cylinder is disconnected.**

1 Pry off the retainer bushing and disconnect the master cylinder pushrod from the clutch pedal.

2 Disconnect the hydraulic quick-disconnect fitting from the release cylinder (see Section 5).

3 Remove the transmission (see Chapter 7 Part A).

4 Remove the bolts securing the release cylinder to the transmis-sion and slide the release cylinder assembly off the transmission input shaft (see illustration).

5 Installation is the reverse of the removal Steps with the following additions:

    a) *Install the release cylinder onto the input shaft with the hydraulic line facing toward the left side of the transmission.*

    b) *Install the release cylinder mounting bolts and tighten them to the torque listed in this Chapter's Specifications.*

    c) *If necessary, bleed the clutch hydraulic system (see Section 9).*

7.4 Remove the clutch release cylinder bolts and remove the clutch release cylinder; note the bleeder screw location

8   Clutch master cylinder and reservoir - removal and installation

REMOVAL

1   Disconnect the negative cable from the battery.

2   Disconnect the hydraulic line from the clutch release cylinder (see Section 5).

3   Working inside the vehicle, remove the spring clip or retainer bushing and disconnect the pushrod from the top of the clutch pedal. On later models, the driver's side lower kick panel will have to be removed to access the pushrod.

4   Remove the clutch/starter interlock switch (early models) or Clutch Pedal Position (CPP) sensor (later models) from the pushrod (see Section 11).

5   The clutch master cylinder is retained in an opening in the firewall. From the engine side of the firewall, twist the clutch master cylinder about 45 degrees counterclockwise and remove the clutch master cylinder.

6   On 2011 models, remove the inner fender splash shield and disconnect the hydraulic line-to-frame bracket.

7   Remove the master cylinder mounting bolts from the engine side of the firewall. Be careful not to spill any of the fluid.

8   Remove the master cylinder and reservoir from the engine compartment. On 2011 models, the master cylinder, clutch fluid reservoir and hydraulic line must be removed as a unit.

INSTALLATION

9   Install the master cylinder through the firewall and make sure the pushrod is positioned on the correct side of the clutch pedal so it can be installed onto the pedal's pivot pin.

10 Attach the master cylinder to the firewall and install the mounting bolts. Tighten the bolts to the torque listed in this Chapter's Specifications.

11 Attach the master cylinder reservoir to the firewall and install the mounting bolts, tightening them securely.

12 Connect the hydraulic line to the slave cylinder (see Section 5).

13 Working inside the vehicle, connect the pushrod to the clutch pedal and install the clip or retainer bushing. On 2011 models, use a new clip.

14 Install the clutch/starter interlock switch (see Section 11).

15 Connect the negative cable to the battery.

16 Fill the clutch master cylinder reservoir with brake fluid conforming to DOT 3 specifications and bleed the clutch system (see Section 9).

9   Clutch hydraulic system - bleeding

1   The hydraulic system should be bled to remove all air whenever air enters the system. This occurs if the fluid level has been allowed to fall so low that air has been drawn into the master cylinder. Under normal circumstances, air should not enter the system when the quick-disconnect hydraulic line fittings are disconnected. The procedure is very similar to bleeding a brake system, but depends mainly on gravity, rather than the pumping action of the pedal, for the bleeding effect.

2   Fill the master cylinder to the top with new brake fluid conforming to DOT 3 specifications.

✳✳ CAUTION:

Do not re-use any of the fluid coming from the system during the bleeding operation and don't use fluid which has been inside an open container for an extended period of time.

3   Raise the vehicle and place it securely on jackstands to gain access to the bleeder valve, which is located on the left side of the clutch housing.

4   Remove the dust cap which fits over the bleeder valve and push a length of clear plastic hose over the valve. Place the other end of the hose into a clear container.

5   Open the bleeder valve. Fluid will run from the master cylinder, down the hydraulic line, into the release cylinder and out through the clear plastic tube. Let the fluid run out until it is free of bubbles.

➡**Note: Don't let the fluid level drop too low in the master cylinder, or air will be drawn into the hydraulic line and the whole process will have to be started over.**

6   Close the bleeder valve.

7   Have an assistant slowly depress the clutch pedal and hold it. Open the bleeder valve on the release cylinder, allowing fluid to flow through the clear plastic hose. Close the bleeder valve when the flow stops. Once closed, have the assistant release the pedal.

8   Slowly press and release the pedal five times, waiting for two seconds each time the pedal is released.

9   Fill the fluid reservoir to the step.

10 The clutch should now be completely bled. If it isn't (indicated by failure to disengage completely), repeat Steps 5 through 9.

11 Continue this process until all air is evacuated from the system, indicated by a solid stream of fluid being ejected from the bleeder valve each time with no air bubbles in the hose or container.

12 Install the dust cap and lower the vehicle. Check carefully for proper operation before placing the vehicle in normal service. Check the fluid level.

10   Clutch pedal - removal and installation

1   Disconnect the negative cable from the battery.

2   Disconnect the barbed end of the clutch/starter interlock switch rod from the clutch pedal. Remove the lockpin and remove the master cylinder pushrod from the clutch pedal. Remove the plastic bushing.

3   Remove the plastic side panel on the driver's sidewall.

4   Unbolt the parking brake and move it aside.

5   Pry the retainer from the clip on the pedal support bracket.

6   Slide the pedal out of the bracket.

7   Installation is the reverse of the removal Steps.

11 Clutch/starter interlock switch - removal and installation

➡Note: On later models, this is known as the Clutch Pedal Position (CPP) sensor.

1 Disconnect the cable from the negative terminal of the battery.
2 Disconnect the electrical connector from the switch/sensor.
3 Rotate the switch/sensor so the plastic retainer is visible. Squeeze the retainer tabs together and slide the retainer rearward off the switch/sensor.

4 Detach the switch/sensor from the master cylinder pushrod and remove it.
5 Installation is the reverse of removal. Be sure the switch/sensor is securely seated on the master cylinder pushrod.

12 Driveshaft and universal joints - description and check

1 The driveshaft is a tube running between the transfer case or transmission and the rear axle or front axle. Universal joints are located at either end of the driveshaft(s) and permit power to be transmitted to the rear (and, on 4WD models the front) wheels at varying angles. The driveshaft on long wheelbase models is actually two shafts connected by a universal joint and supported in the middle by a bearing attached to the frame.

2 Some driveshafts feature a splined slip yoke at one end, which fits into the transmission extension housing. Others incorporate a slip yoke as part of the driveshaft. This arrangement allows the length of the driveshaft to change, which compensates for suspension movement.

3 On models with a slip yoke at the front of the driveshaft, an oil seal is used to prevent leakage of fluid and to keep dirt and contaminants from entering the transmission. If leakage is evident at the front of the driveshaft, replace the oil seal, referring to the procedures in Chapter 7.

4 The driveshaft assembly(ies) requires very little service. The universal joints on models not equipped with grease fittings are lubricated for life and must be replaced if problems develop. The driveshaft(s) must be removed from the vehicle for this procedure.

5 Since the driveshaft is a balanced unit, it's important that no undercoating, mud, etc. be allowed to stay on it. When the vehicle is raised for service it's a good idea to clean the driveshaft(s) and inspect it for any obvious damage. Also check that the small weights used to originally balance the driveshaft(s) are in place and securely attached. Whenever a driveshaft is removed it's important that it be reinstalled in the same relative position to preserve the balance.

6 Problems with the driveshaft(s) are usually indicated by a noise or vibration while driving the vehicle. A road test should verify if the problem is the driveshaft(s) or another vehicle component:

a) *On an open road, free of traffic, drive the vehicle and note the engine speed (rpm) at which the problem is most evident.*
b) *With this noted, drive the vehicle again, this time manually keeping the transmission in first, then second, then third gear ranges and running the engine up to the engine speed noted.*
c) *If the noise or vibration decreased or was eliminated, visually inspect the driveshaft(s) for damage, material on the shaft which would effect balance, missing weights and damaged universal joints. Another possibility for this condition would be tires which are out-of-balance or a bent or damaged wheel(s).*
d) *If the noise or vibration occurs at the same engine speed regardless of which gear the transmission is in, the driveshaft is not at fault.*

7 To check for worn universal joints:

a) *On an open road, free of traffic, drive the vehicle slowly until the transmission is in High gear. Let off on the accelerator, allowing the vehicle to coast, then accelerate. A clunking or knocking noise will indicate worn universal joints.*
b) *Drive the vehicle at a speed of about 10 to 15 mph and then place the transmission in Neutral, allowing the vehicle to coast. Listen for abnormal driveline noises.*
c) *Raise the vehicle and support it securely on jackstands. With the transmission in Neutral, manually turn the driveshaft(s), watching the universal joints for excessive play.*

13 Driveshafts - removal and installation

REAR DRIVESHAFT (ONE-PIECE)

▸ **Refer to illustrations 13.3 and 13.4**

1 Disconnect the negative cable from the battery.
2 Raise the vehicle and support it securely on jackstands. Place the transmission in Neutral with the parking brake off.
3 Look for the yellow paint marks made at the factory on the axle companion flange and the driveshaft flange (see illustration). If these aren't visible, use a scribe or white paint to place marks on the driveshaft and the differential flange in line with each other. This is to make sure the driveshaft is reinstalled in the same position to preserve the balance.
4 On 4WD models, repeat Step 3 for the front end of the driveshaft (see illustration).

5 Remove the bolts and lower the rear of the driveshaft. On 4WD models, remove the bolts and detach the front end from the transfer case. On 2WD models, slide the front end out of the transmission.
6 Installation is the reverse of the removal Steps with the following additions:

a) *On 2WD models, slide the front of the driveshaft into the transmission.*
b) *On 4WD models, position the front end of the driveshaft on the transfer case with the alignment marks lined up.*
c) *Raise the rear of the driveshaft into position, checking to be sure the marks are in alignment. If not, make sure the transmission is still in Neutral, then turn the rear wheels to match the pinion flange and the driveshaft.*
d) *On 2011 models, tighten the driveshaft-to-axle bolts in a criss-cross pattern, to the torque listed in this Chapter's Specifications.*

13.3 The rear driveshaft comes from the factory with yellow paint marks that indicate the correct alignment of the driveshaft with the companion flange

13.4 On 4WD models, make alignment marks on the driveshaft and transfer case flanges

REAR DRIVESHAFT (TWO-PIECE)

➡**Note: Ranger SuperCab models are equipped with a two-piece driveshaft.**

7 Disconnect the negative cable from the battery.

8 Raise the vehicle and support it securely on jackstands. Place the transmission in Neutral with the parking brake off.

9 Look for the yellow paint marks made at the factory on the axle companion flange and the driveshaft flange. If these aren't visible, use a scribe or white paint to place marks on the driveshaft and the differential flange in line with each other. This is to make sure the driveshaft is reinstalled in the same position to preserve the balance.

10 Remove bolts that hold the driveshaft center bearing bracket to the frame crossmember. Make note of any spacers and save them for installation. Support the driveshaft with wire or rope. Do not allow it to hang free.

11 Remove the bolts securing the driveshaft to the rear axle circular flange.

12 On 2WD models, disconnect the driveshaft from the rear axle companion flange. Pull the driveshaft toward the rear of the vehicle until the slip yoke clears the extension housing. Plug the extension housing to prevent lubricant from leaking out.

13 On 4WD models, disconnect the driveshaft from the transfer case circular flange, and remove the driveshaft.

14 Installation is the reverse of removal with the following additions:

a) *Lubricate the slip yoke splines with chassis grease.*

b) *Inspect the housing seal for damage and replace it if necessary.*

c) *Do not allow the driveshaft slip yoke to bottom out on the output shaft.*

d) *Make sure that the center bearing bracket is aligned at right angles or "square" with the driveshaft. If there were spacers under*

the bracket, install them again.

e) *Line up the paint marks on the rear yoke and the rear axle companion flange.*

f) *Tighten all fasteners to the torques listed in this Chapter's Specifications.*

FRONT DRIVESHAFT (4WD MODELS)

15 Using a scribe or white paint, place marks on the driveshaft and differential flanges in line with each other (see illustration 13.3). This is to make sure the driveshaft is reinstalled in the same position to preserve the balance.

16 Make alignment marks on the driveshaft and transfer case flanges.

17 Unbolt the flange that secures the driveshaft double cardan joint to the transfer case.

18 Remove the bolts and straps that secure the front end of the driveshaft to the differential yoke.

19 Wrap tape around the universal joint bearings at the axle end of the driveshaft so they won't fall off.

20 Installation is the reverse of the removal Steps with the following additions:

a) *Raise the front of the driveshaft into position, checking to be sure the marks are in alignment. If not, make sure the transmission is still in Neutral, then turn the front wheels to line up the marks.*

b) *Remove the tape securing the bearing cups and install the straps and bolts. Tighten the bolts to the torque listed in this Chapter's Specifications.*

c) *On 2011 models, tighten the driveshaft-to-transfer case bolts in a crisscross pattern, to the torque listed in this Chapter's Specifications.*

14 Universal joints - replacement

➡️**Note: A press or large vise will be required for this procedure. It may be a good idea to take the driveshaft to a repair or machine shop where the universal joints can be replaced for you, normally at a reasonable charge.**

1 Remove the driveshaft as outlined in the previous Section.

SINGLE CARDAN U-JOINT

▸ **Refer to illustrations 14.3, 14.5a and 14.5b**

2 Mark the position of driveshaft components in relation to the driveshaft tube so that all components can be reassembled in the same relationship.

3 Using a small pair of pliers, remove the snap-rings from the spider (see illustration).

4 Supporting the driveshaft, place it in position on either an arbor press or on a workbench equipped with a vise.

5 Place a piece of pipe or a large socket with the same inside diameter over one of the bearing caps. Position a socket which is of slightly smaller diameter than the cap on the opposite bearing cap (see illustration) and use the vise or press to force the cap out (inside the pipe or large socket), stopping just before it comes completely out of the yoke. Use the vise or large pliers to work the cap the rest of the way out (see illustration).

6 Transfer the sockets to the other side and press the opposite bearing cap out in the same manner.

7 Clean all parts that will be reused.

✳️ CAUTION:

A new U-joint must be replaced as an assembly. Do not use old parts if new ones are included with the new U-joint.

8 Pack the new universal joint bearings with chassis grease. Ordinarily, specific instructions for lubrication will be included with the universal joint servicing kit and should be followed carefully.

9 Position the spider in the yoke and partially install one bearing cap in the yoke. If the replacement spider is equipped with a grease fitting, be sure it's offset in the proper direction (toward the driveshaft).

10 Start the spider into the bearing cap and partially install the other cap. Align the spider and press the bearing caps into position, being careful not to damage the dust seals.

11 Install the snap-rings. If difficulty is encountered in seating the snap-rings, strike the driveshaft yoke sharply with a brass or plastic hammer. This will spring the yoke ears slightly and allow the snap-rings to seat in the groove.

✳️ CAUTION:

Do not strike the bearings.

12 Install the grease fitting and fill the joint with grease. Be careful not to overfill the joint, as this could blow out the grease seals.

13 Install the driveshaft. Tighten the flange bolts to the specified torque listed in this Chapter's Specifications.

DOUBLE CARDAN U-JOINT

➡️**Note: The double cardan joint must be replaced as an assembly - don't attempt to replace half of it, even if only one cross-and-roller assembly is worn.**

14 Mark the position of the spiders, the driveshaft center yoke, and the driveshaft centering socket yoke in relation to the stud yoke welded to the front of the driveshaft tube. All components must be reassembled in the same relationship.

15 Using a small pair of pliers, remove the snap-rings from the spider (see illustration 14.3).

16 Supporting the driveshaft, place it in position on either an arbor press or on a workbench equipped with a vise.

17 Place a piece of pipe or a large socket with the same inside diameter over one of the bearing caps. Position a socket which is of slightly smaller diameter than the cap on the opposite bearing cap (see illustrations 14.5a and 14.5b) and use the vise or press to force the cap out (inside the pipe or large socket), stopping just before it comes completely out of the yoke. Use the vise or large pliers to work the cap the rest of the way out.

18 Transfer the sockets to the other side and press the opposite bearing cap out in the same manner.

14.3 Remove the universal joint snap-rings with small pliers

14.5a The universal joint bearing cups can be pressed out with a vise and sockets

14.5b The bearing cup can be extracted with locking pliers

19 Remove the spider from the center yoke.

20 Pull the centering socket yoke off the center stud. Remove the rubber seal from the centering ball stud.

21 Repeat steps 15 through 19 to remove the other spider from the center yoke.

22 Clean all parts that will be reused.

✳✳ CAUTION:

A new U-joint must be replaced as an assembly. Do not use old parts if new ones are included with the new U-joint.

23 Pack the new universal joint bearings with Premium Long-Life Grease XG-1-C, or equivalent grease. Ordinarily, specific instructions for lubrication will be included with the universal joint servicing kit and should be followed carefully.

24 Position the spider in the driveshaft yoke and partially install one bearing cap in the yoke. If the replacement spider is equipped with a grease fitting, be sure it's offset in the proper direction (toward the driveshaft).

25 Start the spider into the bearing cap and then partially install the other cap. Align the spider and press the bearing caps into position, being careful not to damage the dust seals.

26 Install the snap-rings. If difficulty is encountered in seating the snap-rings, strike the driveshaft yoke sharply with a brass or plastic hammer. This will spring the yoke ears slightly and allow the snap-rings to seat in the groove.

✳✳ CAUTION:

Do not strike the bearings.

27 Install the grease fitting (if equipped) and fill the joint with grease. Be careful not to overfill the joint, as this could blow out the grease seals.

28 Pack the socket relief and the ball with chassis grease.

29 Position the driveshaft center yoke over the spider ends and press in the bearing. Install the snap rings.

30 Install a new seal on the centering ball stud. Position the driveshaft centering socket yoke on the stud.

31 Start the front spider into the bearing cap and then partially install the other cap. Align the spider and press the bearing caps into position, being careful not to damage the dust seals. Install the snap-rings.

32 Install the grease fitting (if equipped) and fill the joint with grease. Be careful not to overfill the joint, as this could blow out the grease seals.

33 Install the driveshaft. Tighten the flange bolts to the torque listed in this Chapter's Specifications.

15 Center bearing - replacement

➡Note: A center bearing is used to support the two-piece driveshaft on long wheelbase models.

1 Unbolt the center bearing mount. Save any spacers so that they can be reinstalled. Spin the bearing by hand. If it does not spin freely, replace it.

2 Inspect the rubber insulator. Replace it if there is evidence of hardening, cracking or deterioration before removing the shaft.

3 Remove the driveshaft as outlined in Section 13.

4 Separate the driveshaft from the coupling shaft. Make sure to mark the driveshaft and coupling shaft.

5 Remove the nut securing the half-round yoke to the coupling shaft and remove the yoke.

6 Installation is the reverse of these steps with the following additions:

a) *Make sure the yoke and coupling shaft have the same orientation as originally installed.*

b) *Torque the nut to this Chapter's Specifications.*

c) *Make sure the driveshaft and coupling shaft have the same orientation as originally installed.*

16 Rear axle - description and check

1 The rear axle assembly is a hypoid (the centerline of the pinion gear is below the centerline of the ring gear) semi-floating type. The differential carrier is a casting with a pressed steel cover. The axle tubes are made of steel, pressed and welded into the carrier.

2 An optional Traction-Lok limited slip rear axle is also available. This differential allows for normal operation until one wheel loses traction. The unit utilizes multi-disc clutch packs and a speed sensitive engagement mechanism which locks both axleshafts together, applying equal rotational power to both wheels.

3 In order to undertake certain operations, particularly replacement of the axleshafts, it's important to know the axle identification number. It's located on a small metal tag near one of the cover bolts.

4 Many times a problem is suspected in the rear axle area when, in fact, it lies elsewhere. For this reason, a thorough check should be performed before assuming a rear axle problem.

5 The following noises are those commonly associated with rear axle diagnosis procedures:

a) *Road noise is often mistaken for mechanical faults. Driving the vehicle on different surfaces will show whether the road surface is the cause of the noise. Road noise will remain the same if the vehicle is under power or coasting.*

b) *Tire noise is sometimes mistaken for mechanical problems. Tires which are worn or low on air pressure are particularly susceptible to emitting vibrations and noises. Tire noise will remain about the same during varying driving situations, where rear axle noise will change during coasting, acceleration, etc.*

c) *Engine and transmission noise can be deceiving because it will travel along the driveline. To isolate engine and transmission noises, make a note of the engine speed at which the noise is most pronounced. Stop the vehicle and place the transmission in Neutral and run the engine to the same speed. If the noise is the same, the rear axle is not at fault.*

6 Overhaul and general repair of the rear axle is beyond the scope of the home mechanic due to the many special tools and critical measurements required. Thus, the procedures listed here will involve axleshaft removal and installation, axleshaft oil seal replacement, axleshaft bearing replacement and removal of the entire unit for repair or replacement.

17 Rear axle assembly - removal and installation

♦ **Refer to illustrations 17.6, 17.7, 17.9 and 17.11**

1 Loosen the lug nuts on the rear wheels.
2 Raise the rear of the vehicle, support it securely on jackstands and remove the rear wheels.
3 Remove the axleshafts (see Section 18).
4 Unbolt the brake line junction block from the axle housing and detach the brake lines from the clips on the axle housing. Disconnect the rear anti-lock electrical connector from the sensor on the axle housing (see Chapter 9).
5 Remove the rear brake drums (see Chapter 9).
6 Remove the nuts and bolts that secure the brake backing plate to the axle (see illustration). Separate the backing plates from the axle and tie them up out of the way.
7 Detach the vent hose from the axle housing (see illustration).
8 Place a transmission jack beneath the axle housing. Secure the axle housing to the jack with a safety strap or chain.

17.6 Remove the nuts that secure the brake backing plate to the axle housing, then carefully separate the backing plate from the axle housing and support it with wire - don't bend the brake line or allow the backing plate to hang on the line

17.7 The vent hose is secured to the axle by a crimp-type clamp - you'll need to replace it with a screw-type clamp

17.9 Remove the four nuts that secure the shock mounting bracket to the axle - don't remove the lower shock absorber bolt

17.11 Unbolt the stabilizer bar retainer from the axle housing

➡Note: You'll need to tilt the axle housing on the jack to remove it. Secure the axle so it can't fall off the jack, but position the strap or chain so the axle can be tilted.

9   Remove the U-bolt nuts that secure the shock mounting bracket to the axle (see illustration). Don't detach the shock absorber from the bracket.

10   Lower the bracket away from the spring, then remove the U-bolts.

11   Unbolt the stabilizer bar bracket bolts from the axle housing (see illustration). Move the stabilizer bar out of the way.

12   Jack the axle up off the spring. Move it toward the passenger side of the vehicle until the driver's side end of the axle shaft clears the spring.

13   Tilt the driver's side of the axle housing down. Lower the axle, move it toward the driver's side and remove it from beneath the vehicle.

14   Installation is the reverse of the removal Steps. Be sure to tighten the fasteners to the torque values listed in this Chapter's Specifications. Tighten the wheel lug nuts to the torque listed in the Chapter 1 Specifications.

18   Axleshafts, bearings and oil seals (rear) - removal and installation

AXLESHAFT REMOVAL

▶ **Refer to illustrations 18.6a, 18.6b, 18.6c, 18.7a, 18.7b and 18.8**

1   Loosen the lug nuts on the rear wheels.

2   Raise the rear of the vehicle, support it securely on jackstands and remove the rear wheels.

3   Remove the rear brake drums (see Chapter 9).

4   Clean all dirt from the area surrounding the carrier cover.

5   Drain the differential lubricant (see Chapter 1).

6   Remove the differential shaft lock-bolt and differential pinion shaft (see illustration). On Traction-Lok differentials, it isn't necessary to remove the preload spring (see illustrations).

➡**Note: The pinion gears may be left in place. Once the axleshafts are removed, reinstall the pinion shaft and lock-bolt.**

7   Push the axleshafts toward the center of the vehicle and remove the C-locks from the button end of the axleshafts (see illustration). Don't damage the rubber O-ring which fits in the axle shaft

18.6a   The pinion shaft lock-bolt fits in a recess in the differential housing

18.6b   Remove the bolt with a thinwall socket . . .

18.6c   . . . then pull the pinion shaft out - on Traction-Lok models, the spacer spring (arrow) need not be removed

18.7a   Remove the C-lock from the end of each axleshaft - the differential lubricant is very slippery and makes the C-locks hard to hold with pliers, so be careful not to drop them

18.7b   There's a rubber O-ring in the C-lock groove in the end of each axleshaft

18.8 Lift and pull the axleshaft out of the axle housing - be careful not to damage the oil seal

groove under the C-lock (see illustration).

8   Carefully remove the axleshafts from the housing (see illustration). Don't damage the oil seal at the end of the housing.

18.9b Using the slide hammer and puller attachment to remove the axleshaft bearing and seal

18.9a A typical slide hammer and axleshaft bearing removal attachment

OIL SEAL AND BEARING REPLACEMENT

▶ **Refer to illustrations 18.9a, 18.9b and 18.11**

9   Insert a rear axle bearing remover attached to a slide hammer into the bore of the bearing and position it behind the bearing outer race. Using the slide hammer withdraw the bearing and oil seal as a unit (see illustrations). These tools are available at most auto parts stores.

10 Thoroughly clean the rear axle housing bore with a rag and solvent.

11 Lubricate the new bearing with rear axle lubricant and install the bearing into the housing bore. Use an axle bearing driver tool or a large socket that matches the outer bearing race (see illustration). Tap the bearing in until it's into the full depth of its recess.

✳✳ CAUTION:

Do not tap on the inner bearing race while installing the bearing, as it will be damaged.

12 Apply multi-purpose grease between the lips of the axleshaft seal.

13 Install a new axleshaft seal using an axle seal installation tool, available at most auto parts stores, or a large socket that matches the seal diameter.

18.11 The wheel bearing and seal can be installed with a large socket or piece of pipe of the correct diameter if the special tool isn't available

18.14 The O-ring in the C-lock groove goes toward the wheel end of the axleshaft

18.15 Align the lock-bolt hole in the pinion lock shaft with the hole in the differential housing

❋❋ CAUTION:

If the seal is installed incorrectly or gets cocked during installation it will be damaged, leading to component failure and an oil leak.

AXLESHAFT INSTALLATION

▶ **Refer to illustrations 18.14 and 18.15**

14 Make sure the rubber O-ring is in the groove in the end of the axleshaft. Push the O-ring toward the outer end of the groove (toward the wheel) (see illustration). Carefully insert the axle into the housing and install the C-lock on the button end of the axleshaft splines. Be sure the O-ring is in the axleshaft groove (see illustration 18.7b). Push the shaft out until the C-lock seats in the counterbore of the differential side gear.

15 Position the differential pinion shaft through the case and pinion gears, aligning the hole in the shaft with the lock-bolt hole (see illustration). Apply thread locking compound to the lock-bolt, install the bolt and tighten it to the torque listed in this Chapter's Specifications.

16 Clean the gasket mounting surface on the rear axle housing and cover of all old gasket material residue with lacquer thinner or gasket remover. Apply a continuous bead of silicone sealant. Run the bead to the inside of the bolt holes and install the cover and bolts.

17 Tighten the bolts in a criss-cross pattern to the torque listed in this Chapter's Specifications.

18 Refill the axle with the correct quantity and grade of lubricant (see Chapter 1).

19 Install the brake drums (see Chapter 9).

20 Install the wheels and lug nuts.

21 Lower the vehicle and tighten the lug nuts to the value listed in the Chapter 1 Specifications.

19 Driveaxles (4WD models) - removal and installation

REMOVAL

▶ **Refer to illustrations 19.4, 19.7 and 19.8**

➡ **Note: A special retainer ring/seal installer tool is required to reinstall the driveaxle retainer ring. Be sure this tool is on hand before beginning this procedure.**

1 Loosen the wheel lug nuts, raise the vehicle and support it securely on jackstands. Remove the wheel(s).

2 Remove the hub lock (if equipped) (see Section 4 in Chapter 10).

➡ **Note: Many later model 4WD vehicles do not have front locking hubs; this step may not apply to your vehicle.**

3 Remove the brake caliper (see Chapter 9), then disconnect the ABS sensor, if equipped, and secure the sensor and wire harness aside.

4 On 2000 models with Pulse Vacuum Hubs, remove the plastic retainer ring from the end of the driveaxle using a pair of snap-ring pliers. Discard the retaining ring.

❋❋ CAUTION:

You MUST replace the plastic driveaxle retainer ring every time it's removed. Using an old retainer ring can damage the hub and/or the driveaxle.

On 2000 models without Pulse Vacuum Hubs, and all 2001 and later models, remove the driveaxle/hub nut (see illustration). Discard the nut - a new one must be used during installation.

5 Support the lower control arm with a floor jack. Make sure the control arm is securely supported at its outer end.

6 Remove the upper control arm balljoint-to-steering knuckle nut and pinch bolt and separate the upper arm from the knuckle (see Chapter 10).

❋❋ WARNING:

The jack must remain in this position throughout the entire procedure.

19.4 To remove the driveaxle/hub nut, hold the driveaxle by inserting a large screwdriver or prybar between the wheel studs as shown and use a large breaker bar to loosen the nut

19.7 If the driveaxle does not come out easily, use a puller to press it out

7 To separate the driveaxle assembly from the steering knuckle, simply swing the knuckle out, compress the outer CV joint and pull the driveaxle assembly out of the knuckle. It should come right out. If the driveaxle splines are "frozen" to the hub and bearing assembly, knock the driveaxle loose with a brass hammer, or press the driveaxle out of the hub with a two-jaw puller, using a prybar or large screwdriver to keep the hub from turning (see illustration). Once the driveaxle is loose from the hub splines, pull out on the steering knuckle assembly and guide the outer CV joint out of the hub.

8 Using a prybar or slide hammer with CV joint adapter, pry the inner CV joint assembly from the front differential (see illustration). Be careful not to damage the front differential. Suspend the axle with a piece of wire - don't let it hang, or damage to the outer CV joint may occur.

9 Remove the driveaxle from the vehicle.

INSTALLATION

10 Installation is basically the reverse of removal, except that you MUST install a NEW retainer ring as follows (2000 models with Pulse Vacuum Hubs). Place the new retainer ring on the special retainer ring/ seal installer tool (make sure that the steel band on the retainer faces out), slide the installer tool onto the end of the axleshaft splines, install the snap-ring sleeve on the seal installer and install the seal remover guide on the snap-ring sleeve. (The seal remover guide serves as a pressing handle when used with the seal installer tool and the snap-ring sleeve). Pull out (toward the steering knuckle) on the driveaxle assembly and simultaneously press in with the seal remover guide until the retainer ring seats. You should hear an audible "click" when the retainer snaps into place. Verify that the retainer ring has been correctly seated by pushing and pulling firmly on the driveaxle assembly and on the seal remover guide.

19.8 Using a prybar or slide hammer with a CV joint adapter, disengage the inner CV joint assembly from the front differential

✳✳ CAUTION:

If the retainer ring is not fully seated, the driveaxle seal will leak, the hub and bearing assembly will be contaminated and the vehicle will not operate in 4WD.

11 If you're working on a 2000 model without Pulse Vacuum Hubs, or any 2001 and later model, install a new driveaxle/hub nut and tighten it to the torque listed in this Chapter's Specifications.

12 Installation is otherwise the reverse of removal.

20 Driveaxle boot replacement (4WD models)

INNER CV JOINT AND BOOT REPLACEMENT

Disassembly

▶ **Refer to illustrations 20.6, 20.7 and 20.8**

1 4WD models are equipped with Constant Velocity (CV) joint type driveaxle assemblies. The inboard tripod design CV joint and driveaxle boot are serviceable units. The outer CV joint is not serviceable and must be replaced as an assembly. However, the outer driveaxle boot is serviceable with a similar procedure as the inner boot.

2 Remove the driveaxle from the vehicle (see Section 19).

3 Mount the driveaxle in a vise. The jaws of the vise should be lined with wood or rags to prevent damage to the axleshaft.

4 Cut the boot clamps from the inner boot and discard them, then move the boot toward the center of the shaft.

5 Bend the retaining tabs slightly to allow for tripod removal.

6 Remove the tripod assembly from the outer race (see illustration).

7 Move the inner (exposed) stop ring down the shaft about 1/2-inch (see illustration).

20.6 Bend the retaining tabs back slightly, then remove the outer race from the tripod assembly

20.7 Move the stop ring down the axleshaft

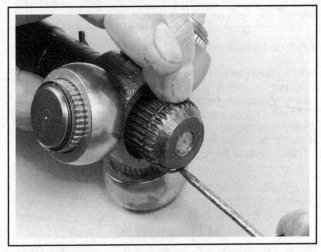

20.8 Remove the circlip and pull the tripod assembly off the axleshaft

8   Move the tripod down the shaft towards the inner stop-ring until the circlip is visible on the end of the driveaxle. Remove the circlip and remove the tripod assembly from the driveaxle (see illustration).

9   No further disassembly of the tripod is possible. Inspect the tripod rollers, roller bearings and races carefully for damage, worn spots and smooth operation. Damaged or worn tripods cannot be rebuilt and must be replaced.

10 Remove the inner stop ring from the axleshaft and remove the old boot.

Reassembly

♦ **Refer to illustrations 20.18 and 20.19**

11 Slide a new clamp and the inner CV joint boot on the axleshaft.

12 Install a new inner stop ring past the second ring groove about 1/2-inch.

13 Install the tripod assembly on the driveaxle with the chamfered side inward.

14 Push the tripod assembly down the axle far enough to allow circlip installation. Install the new circlip and push the tripod assembly towards the axle end until the tripod seats on the circlip and the inner

stop ring groove is exposed.

15 Move the inner stop ring to its groove to secure the tripod assembly.

16 Fill the outer race with CV joint grease and spread some on the inside of the boot as well. The left axle tripods use about 6.5 ounces of grease and the right axles use about 7 ounces. Push the tripod assembly into outer race and bend the six retaining tabs back to their original shape.

17 Wipe any excess grease from the axle boot groove on the outer race. Seat the small diameter of the boot in the recessed area on the axleshaft and install the clamp.

18 Position the CV joint mid-way through its travel, then equalize the pressure in the boot by inserting a dull screwdriver between the boot and the outer race (see illustration). Don't damage the boot with the tool.

19 Install the boot clamp. A pair of special clamp-crimping pliers are required (see illustration).

20 Install a new clip on the stub axle.

21 Install the driveaxle as described in Section 19.

20.18 Equalize the pressure inside the boot by inserting a screwdriver between the boot and outer race . . .

20.19 . . . then secure the boot clamps with special pliers (available at most auto parts stores)

OUTER CV JOINT AND BOOT REPLACEMENT

♦ Refer to illustration 20.27

➡Note: The outer CV joint is a non-serviceable item and is permanently retained to the driveaxle. If any damage or excessive wear occurs to the axle or the outer CV joint, the driveaxle and outer CV joint assembly must be replaced. Complete rebuilt driveaxle assemblies are available at most auto parts stores. If after disassembly and inspection the CV joint is deemed serviceable, replace the boot as described below.

22 Remove the inner CV joint and boot.

23 Cut the boot clamps and remove them from the outer CV joint.

24 Detach the boot from the CV joint and slide it off the axleshaft.

25 Check the grease for contamination by rubbing a small amount between your fingers. If the grease feels gritty, the CV joint is contaminated and must be replaced.

26 If the grease is not contaminated, remove all traces of grease from the CV joint using solvent and a soft bristle brush. Thoroughly dry the CV joint using compressed air, if available. All traces of solvent must be removed or damage to the CV joint may occur.

✳✳ WARNING:

Wear eye protection when using compressed air!

27 Inspect the cage, balls and races for pitting, score marks, cracks and other signs of wear or damage (see illustration). Shiny, polished spots are normal and will not adversely affect CV joint performance.

28 Install the new outer boot and clamps onto the driveaxle shaft.

20.27 After the old grease has been completely removed and the solvent has dried, rotate the outer joint housing through its full range of motion and inspect the bearing surfaces for wear or damage; if the balls, race or cage appear damaged, replace the driveaxle shaft and outer joint assembly

Completely pack the CV joint with the grease provided in the boot kit. Force the grease into the joint and around the balls and races. Spread the remaining grease evenly inside the boot. Total grease fill is approximately 6.0 ounces.

29 Position the outer boot on the CV joint and using the appropriate boot clamp pliers, tighten the clamps.

30 Assemble the inner CV joint and boot and install the driveaxle.

Specifications

Clutch

Fluid type	See Chapter 1
Type	Single dry plate, diaphragm spring
Actuation	Hydraulic

Driveshaft type

Short bed models	One-piece with single or double cardan type joints
Long bed models	Two-piece with single or double cardan type joints

Rear axle

Type	Integral carrier
Ring gear size	7.5, 8.8-inch
Lubricant type	See Chapter 1

Front axle

Type	Dana Model 35 IFS
Hubs	Automatic locking type
Lubricant type	See Chapter 1

Torque specifications   Ft-lbs (unless otherwise indicated)

➡**Note: One foot-pound (ft-lb) of torque is equivalent to 12 inch-pounds (in-lbs) of torque. Torque values below approximately 15 ft-lbs are expressed in inch-pounds, since most foot-pound torque wrenches are not accurate at these smaller values.**

Clutch

Pressure plate-to-flywheel bolts	
2010 and earlier	15 to 24
2011	20
Release cylinder-to-clutch housing bolts	
2010 and earlier	13 to 19
2011	177 in-lbs

Rear driveshaft

Driveshaft-to-transfer case bolts (4WD only)	83
Driveshaft-to-differential bolts	83

Front driveshaft

Driveshaft-to-transfer case flange bolts	22
Driveshaft-to-differential yoke bolts	
2005 and earlier models	15
2006 and later models	168 in-lbs

Rear axle

Cover bolts	See Chapter 1
Pinion shaft lock-bolt	
2010 and earlier	15 to 30
2011	22
Leaf spring U-bolt nuts	See Chapter 10
Rear shock absorber-to-axle bracket bolt or nut	See Chapter 10
Brake backing plate nuts	See Chapter 9

Front axle

Pivot bolt	120 to 150
Pivot bracket-to-frame nut	70 to 92
Axle stud	190 to 230
Lower balljoint nut	95 to 110
Upper balljoint pinch bolt	35
Upper balljoint nut	85 to 100
Carrier-to-axle arm bolts	35 to 53
Carrier shear bolt	75 to 95
Front shock absorber-to-radius arm nut	See Chapter 10
Front spring seat nut	See Chapter 10
Front radius arm bracket bolts	See Chapter 10
Driveaxle/hub nut	
2010 and earlier	162
2011	184
Tie-rod nut	
2010 and earlier	67
2011	59
Axle-to-frame bolts (2011)	49

Notes

Section

Reference to other Chapters

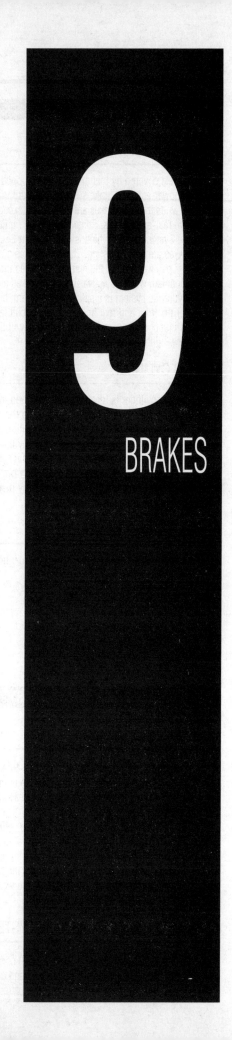

9

BRAKES

1 General information

GENERAL DESCRIPTION

All models covered by this manual are equipped with hydraulically operated, power-assisted brake systems. All front brake systems are disc type, while the rear brakes are drum type, except for 2010 models, which have rear disc brakes. Some models are equipped with an Anti-lock Brake System (ABS), which is described in Section 2.

All brakes are self-adjusting. The disc brakes automatically compensate for pad wear, while the rear drum brakes incorporate an adjustment mechanism which is activated as the brakes are applied.

The hydraulic system is a split design, meaning there are separate circuits for the front and rear brakes. If one circuit fails, the other circuit will remain functional and a warning indicator will light up on the dashboard, showing that a failure has occurred.

MASTER CYLINDER

The master cylinder is located under the hood, mounted to the power brake booster, and is best recognized by the large fluid reservoir on top. The removable plastic reservoir is partitioned to prevent total fluid loss in the event of a front or rear brake hydraulic system failure.

The master cylinder is designed for the "split system" mentioned earlier and has separate primary and secondary piston assemblies, the piston nearest the firewall being the primary piston, which applies hydraulic pressure to the front brakes.

POWER BRAKE BOOSTER

The power brake booster, utilizing engine manifold vacuum and atmospheric pressure to provide assistance to the hydraulically operated brakes, is mounted on the firewall in the engine compartment.

PARKING BRAKE

The parking brake mechanically operates the rear brakes only.
The parking brake cables pull on a lever attached to the brake shoe assembly, causing the shoes to expand against the drum.

PRECAUTIONS

There are some general cautions and warnings involving the brake system on this vehicle:

a) *Use only brake fluid conforming to DOT 3 specifications.*
b) *The dust from brake pads and linings is hazardous to your health if inhaled. Whenever you work on brake system components, clean all parts with brake system cleaner. Do not allow the fine dust to become airborne. Also, wear an approved filtering mask*
c) *Safety should be paramount whenever any servicing of the brake components is performed. Do not use parts or fasteners which are not in perfect condition, and be sure that all clearances and torque specifications are adhered to. If you are at all unsure about a certain procedure, seek professional advice. Upon completion of any brake system work, test the brakes carefully in a controlled area before putting the vehicle into normal service.*

If a problem is suspected in the brake system, don't drive the vehicle until it's fixed.

2 Anti-lock Brake System (ABS) - general information

GENERAL INFORMATION

1 Some models are equipped with an Anti-lock Brake System (ABS). Early models and later 2WD models are equipped with rear wheel anti-lock brake systems while later 4WD models are equipped with 4-wheel anti-lock brake systems.

2 The ABS system is designed to maintain vehicle steerability, directional stability and optimum deceleration under severe braking conditions and on most road surfaces. It does so by monitoring the rotational speed of each wheel and controlling the brake line pressure to each wheel during braking. This prevents the wheel from locking-up and provides maximum vehicle controllability.

REAR WHEEL ANTI-LOCK BRAKE SYSTEM (RABS)

3 The Rear Anti-lock Brake System (RABS) consists of a computer module, anti-lock brake valve, an exciter ring and a sensor.

4 Disconnect the cable from the negative battery terminal.

RABS module

5 Remove the center finish panel from the instrument panel (see Chapter 11).

6 Slide the module's upper tab free of the instrument panel brace, then disconnect the electrical connectors and take it out.

7 Installation is the reverse of the removal steps.

RABS valve

8 Disconnect the two brake lines from the RABS valve. Plug the ends of the lines to prevent the loss of hydraulic fluid and the entry of foreign matter and moisture.

9 Disconnect the electrical connector from the RABS valve.

10 Remove the screw securing the RABS valve to the frame rail and take it out.

11 To install, position the RABS valve on the frame rail. Install the screw and tighten it to the torque listed in this Chapter's Specifications.

12 Connect the electrical connector to the valve.

13 Install the brake lines and tighten the fittings securely.

2.28 Typical hydraulic control unit and electronic control module

2.32 ABS front wheel sensor (arrow)

✳✳ CAUTION:

Do not overtighten the fittings.

14 Bleed the hydraulic system.

Speed sensor

15 The sensor is located on the rear axle housing

16 Disconnect the electrical connector from the sensor.

17 Prior to removing the sensor, thoroughly clean the rear axle housing surrounding the sensor.

18 Unbolt the sensor and remove it from the rear axle housing. Do not allow any dirt to fall into the interior of the rear axle housing.

19 Thoroughly clean the sensor mounting surface on the rear axle housing.

20 Inspect and clean the magnetized sensor pole piece. Remove any small metal particles that could cause erratic system operation.

21 If installing a new sensor, lightly lubricate the O-ring seal with clean engine oil.

22 If installing an old sensor, remove the old O-ring seal, install a new one and lubricate it with clean engine oil.

23 Firmly grasp the sides of the sensor (do not apply pressure to the electrical connector) and push it into the mounting hole.

24 Align the mounting flange bolt hole with that on the rear axle housing and install the hold-down bolt.

25 Tighten the hold-down bolt to the torque listed in this Chapter's Specifications.

26 Connect the electrical connector to the sensor.

Exciter ring

27 To service the exciter ring the rear axle must be disassembled and the ring gear removed with a press. It is recommended that this procedure be performed by a dealer service department or other repair shop.

FOUR WHEEL ANTI-LOCK BRAKE SYSTEM (4WABS)

Hydraulic Control Unit (HCU)

▶ **Refer to illustration 2.28**

28 The hydraulic control unit is located in the left front corner (driver's side) of the engine compartment. It consists of a brake pressure control valve block, a pump motor and a hydraulic control unit reservoir with a fluid level indicator assembly (see illustration).

29 During normal braking conditions, brake hydraulic fluid from the master cylinder enters the hydraulic control unit through two inlet ports and passes through four normally open inlet valves, one to each wheel.

30 When the anti-lock brake control module senses that a wheel is about to lock up, the anti-lock brake control module closes the appropriate inlet. This prevents any more fluid from entering the affected brake. If the module determines that the wheel is still decelerating, the module opens the outlet valve, which bleeds off pressure in the affected brake.

Wheel sensors

▶ **Refer to illustration 2.32**

31 The ABS system uses four "variable-reluctance" sensors to monitor wheel speed ("reluctance" is a term used to indicate the amount of resistance to the passage of flux lines - lines of force in a magnetic field - through a given material). Each sensor contains a small inductive coil that generates an electromagnetic field. When paired with a toothed sensor ring which interrupts this field as the wheels turn, each sensor generates a low-voltage analog (continuous) signal. This voltage signal, which rises and falls in proportion to wheel rotation speed, is continuously sampled (monitored) by the control module, converted into digital data inside the module and processed (interpreted).

32 The front wheel sensors (see illustration) are mounted in the steering knuckle in close proximity to the toothed sensor rings, which are pressed onto the wheel hubs. The rear wheel sensors are mounted in the rear axle housing and the sensor ring is part of the ring gear in the rear axle.

Brake control module

33 The brake control module, which is mounted at the right front of the battery on the radiator support or directly on the hydraulic control unit itself, is the "brain" of the ABS system. The module (referred to as an Electronic Control Unit or ECU) constantly monitors the incoming analog voltage signals from the four ABS wheel sensors, converts these signals to digital form, processes this digital data by comparing it to the map (program), makes decisions, converts these (digital) decisions to analog form and sends them to the hydraulic control unit, which

opens and closes the front and/or rear circuits as necessary.

34 The module also has a self-diagnostic capability which operates during both normal driving as well as ABS system operation. If a malfunction occurs, a red "BRAKE" warning indicator or an amber "CHECK ANTI-LOCK BRAKES" warning indicator will light up on the dash.

a) If the red BRAKE light glows, the brake fluid level in the master cylinder reservoir has fallen below the level established by the fluid level switch. Top up the reservoir and verify that the light goes out.

b) If the amber CHECK ANTI-LOCK BRAKES light glows, the ABS has been turned off because of a symptom detected by the module. Normal power-assisted braking is still operational, but the wheels can now lock up if you're involved in a panic-stop situation. A diagnostic code is also stored in the module when a warning indicator light comes on; when retrieved by a service technician, the code indicates the area or component where the problem is located. Once the problem is fixed, the code is cleared. These procedures, however, are beyond the scope of the home mechanic.

Relays

35 The main relay and pump motor relay are located in a relay box mounted near the master cylinder on the left side of the engine compartment. Refer to Chapter 12 for the locations and designations for the relays.

DIAGNOSIS AND REPAIR

36 Although a special electronic ABS diagnostic tester is necessary to properly diagnose the system, the home mechanic can perform a few preliminary checks before taking the vehicle to a dealer who is equipped with this tester.

a) Check the brake fluid level in the reservoir.
b) Verify that the control module electrical connector is securely connected.
c) Check the electrical connectors at the hydraulic control unit.
d) Check the fuses.
e) Follow the wiring harness to each wheel and check that all connections are secure and that the wiring is not damaged.

If the above preliminary checks do not rectify the problem, the vehicle should be diagnosed by a dealer service department or other qualified repair shop. Due to the rather complex nature of this system, all actual repair work must be done by the dealer service department or repair shop.

3 Brake pads - replacement

▶ **Refer to illustrations 3.3 and 3.6a through 3.6f**

➡ **Note: This procedure applies to both the front and rear brakes.**

1 Remove the cover from the brake fluid reservoir and siphon out about 1/2 of the brake fluid.

2 Loosen the wheel lug nuts, raise the vehicle and support it

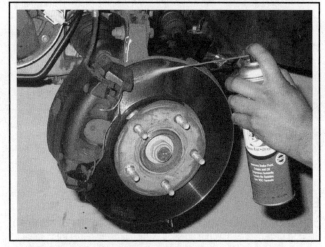

3.3 Before disassembling the brake, wash it thoroughly with brake system cleaner and allow it to dry - position a drain pan under the brake to catch the residue - DO NOT use compressed air to blow off the brake dust!

securely on jackstands.

3 Remove the wheels. Work on one brake assembly at a time, using the assembled brake for reference if necessary. Wash the brake with brake system cleaner before beginning work (see illustration).

3.6a Use a large C-clamp and push the piston(s) back into the bore(s)

4   Inspect the brake disc carefully as outlined in Section 5.
5   If machining is necessary, follow the information in that Section to remove the disc, at which time the pads can be removed from the caliper as well.

3.6c If the caliper isn't going to be removed for service, suspend it with a length of wire to relieve any strain on the brake hose. Now remove the pads from the caliper, noting carefully how they're installed

3.6e Insert a new anti-rattle clip on the lower end of the inner pad

3.6b Remove the two caliper mounting bolts.

➡**Note: Don't wipe the lubricating gel from these pins or the pin boots. At the time of publication there was no substitute for this gel (also read the Warning at the beginning of this Section)**

3.6d Make sure the tabs on the spring clip are positioned correctly and the clip is fully seated

3.6f Compress the anti-rattle clip and slide the upper end of the pad into position. Place the caliper over the disc, then install and tighten the mounting bolts to the torque listed in this Chapter's Specifications

6 Follow the accompanying photos, beginning with illustration 3.6a, for the front brake pad replacement procedure. Be sure to stay in order and read the caption under each illustration.

7 When reinstalling the caliper, be sure to tighten the caliper bolts to the torque listed in this Chapter's Specifications.

8 After the job has been completed, firmly depress the brake pedal a few times to bring the pads into contact with the disc.

9 Check the brake fluid level and add some, if necessary, to bring it to the appropriate level (see Chapter 1).

4 Brake caliper - removal, overhaul and installation

✳✳ WARNING 1:

Dust created by the brake system is harmful to your health. Never blow it out with compressed air and don't inhale any of it. An approved filtering mask should be worn when working on the brakes. Do not, under any circumstances, use petroleum-based solvents to clean brake parts. Use brake system cleaner only!

✳✳ WARNING 2:

These models use a special lubricating gel on certain parts of the brake caliper. This gel is non-toxic under most conditions. If it is heated to a certain point, however, it can give off toxic fumes which can cause health problems or even death. Never apply heat to these calipers and don't smoke around them, either (the gel might get on your cigarette). Always wash your hands thoroughly after working on the brakes.

✳✳ WARNING 3:

If the vehicle is equipped with an Anti-lock Brake System, make sure you plug the brake hose immediately after disconnecting it from the brake caliper, to prevent the fluid from draining out of the line and air entering the Hydraulic Control Unit (HCU). The HCU on the four-wheel ABS system cannot be bled without a very expensive tool.

➡Note: If an overhaul is indicated (usually because of fluid leakage) explore all options before beginning the job. New and factory-rebuilt calipers are available on an exchange basis, which makes this job quite easy. If it is decided to rebuild the calipers, make sure that a rebuild kit is available before proceeding. Always rebuild the calipers in pairs - never rebuild just one of them.

REMOVAL

1 Apply the parking brake and block the wheels opposite the end being worked on. Loosen the wheel lug nuts, raise the vehicle and support it securely on jackstands. Remove the wheel.

2 Unscrew the brake hose banjo bolt and detach the hose from the caliper.

✳✳ CAUTION:

Plug the brake hose immediately to prevent excessive fluid loss and, on models with a four-wheel Anti-lock Brake System, to keep air from getting into the Hydraulic Control Unit (HCU). If air gets into the HCU, you will not be able to bleed the brakes properly at home, since bleeding the brakes on these models requires a very expensive special tool.

➡Note: If the caliper will not be completely removed from the vehicle - as for pad inspection or disc removal - leave the hose connected and suspend the caliper with a length of wire. This will save the trouble of bleeding the brake system.

3 Refer to the first six steps in Section 3 to separate the caliper from the steering knuckle - it's part of the brake pad replacement procedure.

OVERHAUL

◗ Refer to illustrations 4.5, 4.6, 4.7, 4.17, 4.19 and 4.21

4 Clean the exterior of the caliper with brake system cleaner. Never use gasoline, kerosene or other petroleum-based cleaning solvents. Place the caliper on a clean workbench.

5 Position a wood block or rags in the center of the caliper as a cushion, then use compressed air to remove the piston from the caliper (see illustration).

➡Note: These models have two pistons.

Use only enough air to ease the piston out of the bore. If the piston is blown out, even with the cushion in place, it may be damaged.

✳✳ WARNING:

Never place your fingers in front of the piston in an attempt to catch or protect it when applying compressed air, as serious injury could occur.

6 Pull the dust boot(s) out of the caliper bore (see illustration).

4.5 With the caliper padded to catch the piston, use compressed air to force the piston out of its bore - make sure your hands and fingers are not between the piston and the caliper!

4.6 Remove the dust boot from the caliper bore groove

4.7 To remove the seal from the caliper bore, use a plastic or wooden tool, such as a pencil

4.17 Push the new seal into the groove with your fingers, then check to see that it isn't twisted or kinked

4.19 Lubricate the piston and bore with clean brake fluid, insert the piston into the dust boot (NOT the bore) at an angle, then, using a rotating motion, work the piston completely into the dust boot . . .

4.21 Install the lip of the dust boot in the groove on the caliper piston

7   Using a wooden or plastic tool, remove the piston seal(s) from the caliper bore (see illustration). Metal tools may cause bore damage.

8   Carefully examine the piston for nicks, burrs, cracks, loss of plating, corrosion or any signs of damage. If surface defects are present, the parts must be replaced.

9   Check the caliper bore in a similar way. Light polishing with crocus cloth is permissible to remove light corrosion and stains.

10 Remove the bleeder valve and rubber cap.

11 Inspect the caliper pins (bolts) for corrosion and damage. Don't wipe the lubricating gel from the pins or pin boots. At the time of publication there was no suitable substitute for this gel.

12 If the pins (bolts) are in need of addition lubrication, the manufacturer recommends replacing them along with the boots, which come pre-filled with the special lubricating gel. Petroleum or mineral-based greases can destroy the caliper pin boot.

13 Use brake system cleaner to clean all the parts.

✳✳ WARNING:

Do not, under any circumstances, use petroleum-based solvents to clean brake parts. Allow the parts to dry, preferably using compressed air to blow out all passages. Make sure the compressed air is filtered, as a harmful lubricant residue or moisture may be present in unfiltered systems.

14 Examine carefully the bore of the caliper. Replace the caliper if the bore is excessively pitted, damaged or scored.

15 Check the fit of the piston in the bore by sliding it into the caliper. The piston should move easily (don't install it yet).

16 Thread the bleeder valve into the caliper and tighten it securely. Install the rubber cap.

17 Lubricate the new piston seal(s) and caliper bore(s) with clean brake fluid. Position the seal(s) in the caliper bore groove(s), making sure it doesn't twist (see illustration).

18 Lubricate the caliper pistons with clean brake fluid. Push the pistons into the caliper bores by hand as far as possible.

19 Using a C-clamp and a block of wood, push the pistons about two-thirds of the way into the bores. Work slowly, keeping an eye on the side of the pistons, making sure they enter the bore perfectly straight with no resistance.

20 Install the dust boots on the pistons and seat the boots in the caliper. Now push the pistons to the bottom of the bores.

INSTALLATION

21 Refer to Section 3 for the caliper installation procedure, as it is part of the brake pad replacement procedure.

22 Connect the brake hose to the caliper, using new sealing washers. Tighten the banjo bolt to the torque listed in this Chapter's Specifications.

23 Bleed the brakes as outlined in Section 10. This is not necessary if the banjo bolt was not loosened or removed (if the caliper was removed for access to other components, for example).

24 Install the wheel and lower the vehicle. Tighten the lug nuts to the torque listed in the Chapter 1 Specifications. Pump the brake pedal several times to bring the pads into contact with the disc.

25 Test the operation of the brakes before placing the vehicle into normal service.

5   Brake disc - inspection, removal and installation

INSPECTION

▶ Refer to illustrations 5.4a, 5.4b, 5.5a and 5.5b

➡Note: This procedure applies to front and rear disc brake assemblies.

1   Loosen the wheel lug nuts, raise the vehicle and support it securely on jackstands. Remove the wheel.

2   Remove the brake caliper as outlined in Section 4. It isn't necessary to disconnect the brake hose for this procedure. After removing the caliper, suspend the it out of the way with a piece of wire. Don't let the caliper hang by the hose and don't stretch or twist the hose.

3   Visually check the disc surface for score marks and other damage. Light scratches and shallow grooves are normal after use and may not always be detrimental to brake operation, but deep score marks - over 0.015-inch - require disc removal and refinishing by an automotive machine shop. Be sure to check both sides of the disc. If pulsating has been noticed during application of the brakes, suspect disc runout.

4   To check disc runout, place a dial indicator at a point about 1/2-inch from the outer edge of the disc (see illustration). Set the indicator to zero and turn the disc. The indicator reading should not exceed the specified allowable runout limit. If it does, the disc should be refinished by an automotive machine shop.

➡Note: Professionals recommend resurfacing of brake discs regardless of the dial indicator reading (to produce a smooth, flat surface that will eliminate brake pedal pulsations and other undesirable symptoms related to questionable discs). At the very least, if you elect not to have the discs resurfaced, deglaze the surface with emery cloth or sandpaper (use a swirling motion to ensure a non-directional finish) (see illustration).

5.4a To check disc runout, mount a dial indicator as shown and rotate the disc

5   The disc must not be machined to a thickness less than the specified minimum refinish thickness. The minimum wear (or discard) thickness is cast into the inside of the disc (see illustration). The disc thickness can be checked with a micrometer (see illustration).

REMOVAL

6   Remove the disc from the hub. If the disc is stuck to the hub and won't come off, place a block of wood against the rotor and lightly tap the wood with a hammer, until the disc is free. Remove the disc from the hub.

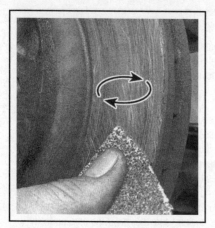

5.4b Using a swirling motion, remove the glaze from the disc withsandpaper or emery cloth

5.5a The minimum thickness limit is cast into the inside of the disc

5.5b Use a micrometer to measure disc thickness at several points, about 1/2-inch from the edge

INSTALLATION

7 Install the disc by reversing the removal procedure.
8 Install the caliper (see Section 4).
9 Install the wheel and lug nuts, lower the vehicle to the ground

and tighten the lug nuts to the torque listed in the Chapter 1 Specifications. Depress the brake pedal a few times to bring the brake pads into contact with the disc. Bleeding of the system will not be necessary unless the brake hose was disconnected from the caliper. Check the operation of the brakes carefully before placing the vehicle into normal service.

6 Brake shoes (rear) - replacement

▶ Refer to illustrations 6.4a through 6.4z and 6.5

✳✳ WARNING:

Drum brake shoes must be replaced on both wheels at the same time - never replace the shoes on only one wheel. Also, the dust created by the brake system is harmful to your health. Never blow it out with compressed air and don't inhale any of it. An approved filtering mask should be worn when working on the brakes. Do not, under any circumstances, use petroleum-based solvents to clean brake parts. Use brake system cleaner only!

✳✳ CAUTION:

Whenever the brake shoes are replaced, the retractor and hold-down springs should also be replaced. Due to the continuous heating/cooling cycle that the springs are subjected to, they lose their tension over a period of time and may allow the shoes to drag on the drum and wear at a much faster rate than normal.

1 Loosen the wheel lug nuts, raise the rear of the vehicle and support it securely on jackstands. Block the front wheels to keep the vehicle from rolling.
2 Release the parking brake.
3 Remove the wheel.

➡Note: All four rear brake shoes must be replaced at the same time, but to avoid mixing up parts, work on only one brake assembly at a time.

4 Follow the accompanying photos (illustrations 6.4a through 6.4z) for the inspection and replacement of the brake shoes. Be sure to stay in order and read the caption under each illustration.

➡Note: If the brake drum cannot be easily pulled off, pry the rubber plug from the backing plate inspection hole and insert a screwdriver and a brake adjusting tool to lift the adjusting lever and rotate the adjusting screw. This will cause the brake shoes

6.4a Components of the rear brake assembly (early models shown, later models similar)

to pull together. Spray the assembly with penetrating oil and allow the oil to soak in if the mechanism is difficult to turn. The drum should now come off.

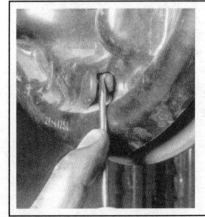

6.4b If the drum is difficult to remove, you may have to retract the brake shoes: Remove the rubber plug from the backing plate . . .

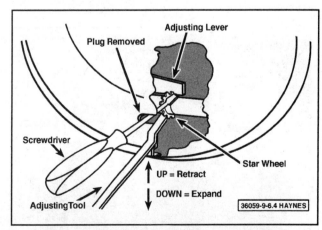

6.4c . . . use a narrow bladed screwdriver to push the adjusting lever away from the adjusting screw star wheel so you can turn the star wheel down with a brake tool (turn the tool handle up) to retract the shoes . . .

6.4d . . . and slide the drum off the shoes

5   Before reinstalling the drum it should be checked for cracks, score marks, deep scratches and hard spots, which will appear as small discolored areas. If the hard spots cannot be removed with fine emery cloth or if any of the other conditions listed above exist, the drum must

6.4f Use a brake spring removal tool to remove the shoe retracting springs

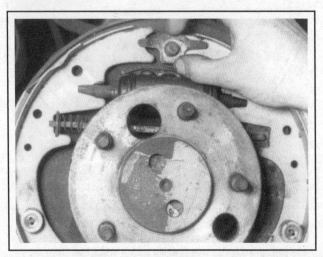

6.4h Remove the anchor pin plate

6.4e Before removing any internal drum brake components, wash them off with brake cleaner and allow them to dry - position a drain pan under the brake to catch the residue - DO NOT USE COMPRESSED AIR TO BLOW THE DUST FROM THE BRAKE PARTS!

6.4g Pull up on the adjusting cable and disconnect the cable eye from the anchor pin

6.4i Remove the shoe retaining springs and pins (one on each shoe)

6.4j Pull the shoes apart and remove the adjusting screw

6.4k Remove the primary shoe, then slide out the parking brake strut and spring

be taken to an automotive machine shop to have it resurfaced.

→Note: Professionals recommend resurfacing the drums whenever a brake job is performed. Resurfacing will eliminate the possibility of out-of-round drums. If the drums are worn so much that they can't be resurfaced without exceeding the maximum allowable diameter, which is stamped into the drum (see

illustration), then new ones will be required. At the very least, if you elect not to have the drums resurfaced, remove the glazing from the surface with medium-grit emery cloth using a swirling motion.

6   Install the brake drum on the hub. Turn the adjuster wheel until

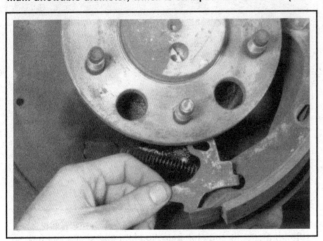

6.4l Remove the adjuster pawl

6.4m Pull the secondary shoe away from the backing plate

6.4n Separate the parking brake cable and spring from the actuating lever

6.4o Remove the retaining clip which holds the parking brake actuating lever to the brake shoes

6.4p Install the parking brake actuator lever on the new brake shoe and install the retaining clip then the brake cable

6.4q Lubricate the threads and end of the adjusting screw assembly with high-temperature brake grease

the brake shoes just drag on the drum when the drum is rotated, then back-off the adjuster wheel until the shoes don't drag.

7   Mount the wheel, install the lug nuts, then lower the vehicle.

8   Make a number of forward and reverse stops to adjust the brakes until satisfactory pedal action is obtained.

6.4r Lightly coat the shoe guide pads on the backing plate with high-temperature brake grease

6.4s Position the shoes on the backing plate, insert the retaining pins through the backing plate and shoes and put the springs over them

6.4t Install the retaining spring caps

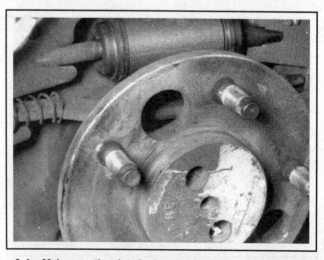

6.4u Make sure the slots in the wheel cylinder pushrods and the parking brake strut properly engage the brake shoes

6.4v Install the adjusting screw with the long end pointing towards the front of the vehicle

6.4w Install the adjusting pawl and spring

6.4x Install the anchor pin plate, cable guide and cable

6.4y Install the shoe guide and adjusting cable eye to the anchor pin, then install the shoe retracting springs

6.4z Connect the cable and spring to the adjuster lever. The cable is hooked to the lever from the back side. Now install the drum and adjust the shoe-to-drum clearance (adjust the shoes so they rub slightly as the drum is turned, then back off the adjuster until they don't rub)

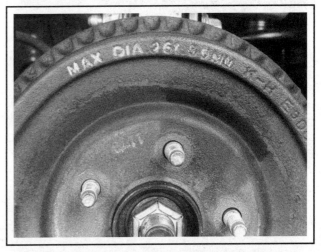

6.5 The maximum permissible diameter specification is cast into the brake drum

7 Wheel cylinder - removal, overhaul and installation

➡Note: If an overhaul is indicated (usually because of fluid leakage or sticky operation) explore all options before beginning the job. New wheel cylinders are available, which makes this job quite easy. If it's decided to rebuild the wheel cylinder, make sure that a rebuild kit is available before proceeding. Never overhaul only one wheel cylinder - always rebuild both of them at the same time.

REMOVAL

▶ Refer to illustration 7.4

1   Raise the rear of the vehicle and support it securely on jackstands. Block the front wheels to keep the vehicle from rolling.
2   Remove the brake shoe assembly (see Section 6).
3   Remove all dirt and foreign material from around the wheel cylinder.
4   Disconnect the brake line (see illustration). Don't pull the brake line away from the wheel cylinder.
5   Remove the wheel cylinder mounting bolts.
6   Detach the wheel cylinder from the brake backing plate and place it on a clean workbench. Immediately plug the brake line to prevent fluid loss and contamination.

OVERHAUL

▶ Refer to illustration 7.7

7   Remove the bleeder screw, cups, pistons, boots and spring assembly from the wheel cylinder body (see illustration).

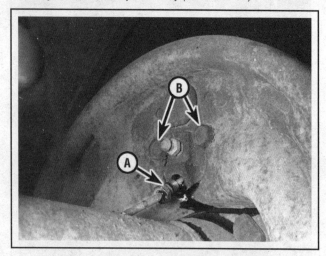

7.4 To remove the wheel cylinder, disconnect the brake line fitting (A) and remove the two mounting bolts (B)

8   Clean the wheel cylinder with brake fluid, denatured alcohol or brake system cleaner.

✳✳ WARNING:

Do not, under any circumstances, use petroleum-based solvents to clean brake parts!

9   Use compressed air to remove excess fluid from the wheel cylinder and to blow out the passages. Make sure the compressed air is filtered and unlubricated.
10 Check the cylinder bore for corrosion and score marks. Crocus cloth can be used to remove light corrosion and stains, but the cylinder must be replaced with a new one if the defects cannot be removed easily, or if the bore is scored.
11 Lubricate the new cups, pistons and cylinder bore with brake fluid.
12 Assemble the brake cylinder components. Make sure the cup lips face in.

INSTALLATION

13 Place the wheel cylinder in position, install the mounting bolts and tighten them to the torque listed in this Chapter's Specifications.
14 Connect the brake line and install the brake shoe assembly.
15 Bleed the brakes (see Section 10).

7.7 Exploded view of a typical wheel cylinder

1   Pushrods
2   Dust boots
3   Pistons
4   Cups
5   Expander spring
6   Wheel cylinder

8 Master cylinder - removal, overhaul and installation

✳✳ WARNING:

If the vehicle is equipped with a four-wheel Anti-lock Brake System (ABS), do not attempt to remove or overhaul the master cylinder. Have the master cylinder removed, rebuilt and installed at a dealer service department or other qualified repair shop. Removing a master cylinder from a four-wheel ABS system can allow air to get into the ABS Hydraulic Control Unit (HCU), which requires a special tool and bleeding procedure which makes it impossible to perform at home.

➡**Note: Before deciding to overhaul the master cylinder, check on the availability and cost of a new or factory rebuilt unit and also the availability of a rebuild kit.**

REMOVAL

1 Place rags under the brake line fittings and prepare caps or plastic bags to cover the ends of the lines once they are disconnected.

8.7 Use a Phillips head screwdriver to push the primary piston into the cylinder, then remove the snap-ring

✳✳ CAUTION:

Brake fluid will damage paint. Cover all body parts and be careful not to spill fluid during this procedure.

2 Unscrew the tube nuts at the ends of the brake lines where they enter the master cylinder. To prevent rounding off the flats on these nuts, a flare-nut wrench, which wraps around the fitting, should be used.

3 Pull the brake lines away from the master cylinder slightly and plug the ends to prevent contamination.

4 Disconnect the brake warning light electrical connector (if equipped), remove the two master cylinder mounting nuts, and detach the master cylinder from the vehicle.

5 Remove the reservoir cap, then discard any fluid remaining in the reservoir.

OVERHAUL

▶ **Refer to illustrations 8.7, 8.8, 8.9, 8.10, 8.14 and 8.18**

6 Mount the master cylinder in a vise with the vise jaws clamping on the mounting flange.

7 Remove the primary piston snap-ring by depressing the piston and extracting the ring with a pair of snap-ring pliers (see illustration).

8 Remove the primary piston assembly from the cylinder bore (see illustration).

9 Remove the secondary piston assembly from the cylinder bore. It may be necessary to remove the master cylinder from the vise and invert it, carefully tapping it against a block of wood to expel the piston (see illustration).

10 If fluid has been leaking past the reservoir grommets, pry the reservoir from the cylinder body with a screwdriver (see illustration). Remove the grommets. Clean the master cylinder body and components with brake system cleaner.

✳✳ WARNING:

DO NOT use petroleum-based solvents to clean brake parts - use brake system cleaner only.

8.8 Remove the primary piston assembly from the cylinder

8.9 Tap the master cylinder against a block of wood to eject the secondary piston assembly

8.10 If you must remove the fluid reservoir to replace leaking seals or a broken reservoir, gently pry it off with a screwdriver or small prybar

11 Inspect the cylinder bore for corrosion and damage. If any corrosion or damage is found, replace the master cylinder with a new one, as abrasives cannot be used on the bore.

12 Lubricate the new reservoir grommets with silicone grease and press them into the master cylinder body. Make sure they're properly seated.

➡**Note: If silicone grease is not available, use clean brake fluid.**

13 Lay the reservoir on a hard surface and press the master cylinder body onto the reservoir, using a rocking motion.

14 Lubricate the cylinder bore and primary and secondary piston assemblies with clean brake fluid. Insert the secondary piston assembly into the cylinder (see illustration).

15 Install the primary piston assembly in the cylinder bore, depress it and install the snap-ring. If equipped with a stop bolt, install it now, using a new sealing washer and tightening it securely.

16 Inspect the reservoir cap and diaphragm for cracks and deformation. Replace any damaged parts with new ones and attach the diaphragm to the cap.

➡**Note: Whenever the master cylinder is removed, the complete hydraulic system must be bled. The time required to bleed the system can be reduced if the master cylinder is filled with fluid and bench bled (refer to Steps 17 through 21) before the master cylinder is installed on the vehicle.**

17 Insert threaded plugs of the correct size into the cylinder outlet holes and fill the reservoirs with brake fluid. The master cylinder should be supported in such a manner that brake fluid will not spill during the bench bleeding procedure.

18 Loosen one plug at a time, starting with the secondary outlet port first, and push the piston assembly into the bore to force air from the master cylinder (see illustration). To prevent air from being drawn back into the cylinder, the appropriate plug must be replaced before allowing the piston to return to its original position.

19 Stroke the piston three or four times for each outlet to ensure that all air has been expelled.

20 Since high pressure is not involved in the bench bleeding procedure, an alternative to the removal and replacement of the plugs with each stroke of the piston assembly is available. Before pushing in on the piston assembly, remove one of the plugs completely. Before releasing the piston, however, instead of replacing the plug, simply put your finger tightly over the hole to keep air from being drawn back into the master cylinder. Wait several seconds for the brake fluid to be

8.14 Coat the secondary piston with clean brake fluid and install it in the master cylinder, spring end first

drawn from the reservoir to the piston bore, then repeat the procedure. When you push down on the piston it will force your finger off the hole, allowing the air inside to be expelled. When only brake fluid is being ejected from the hole, replace the plug and go on to the other port.

21 Refill the master cylinder reservoirs and install the diaphragm and cap assembly.

INSTALLATION

▶ **Refer to illustration 8.22**

➡**Note: Step 22 applies to 2002 and earlier models only.**

22 Using a hand-held vacuum pump, apply a vacuum of about 20-in. Hg to the power booster and check the distance from the outer end of the booster pushrod to the front face of the brake booster assembly (see illustration). Turn the pushrod adjusting screw in or out as required to obtain the correct length.

23 Carefully install the master cylinder by reversing the removal steps, then bleed the brakes (see Section 10).

8.18 When bench bleeding the master cylinder, start with the secondary outlet port

8.22 To adjust the booster master cylinder pushrod on 2002 and earlier models, fabricate a gauge block of the dimensions shown. Place it against the master cylinder mounting surface of the booster and adjust the end of the pushrod so it just touches the slot in the gauge block

9   Brake hoses and lines - inspection and replacement

✳✳ CAUTION:

If the vehicle is equipped with a four-wheel Anti-lock Brake System (ABS), make sure you plug the brake line immediately after disconnecting it from the brake hose, to prevent the fluid from draining out of the line and air from entering the HCU. The HCU on an ABS system cannot be bled without a very expensive tool.

INSPECTION

1   About every six months, with the vehicle raised and supported securely on jackstands, the rubber hoses which connect the steel brake lines with the front and rear brake assemblies should be inspected for cracks, chafing of the outer cover, leaks, blisters and other dam-

9.2 To disconnect the fitting that attaches the flexible brake hose to the metal brake line at the bracket in the wheel well, use a backup wrench on the hose fitting to ensure that the metal line doesn't get twisted

9.3 Once the fitting has been unscrewed, remove this large retainer clip and separate the hose from the bracket

age. These are important and vulnerable parts of the brake system and inspection should be complete. A light and mirror will be helpful for a thorough check. If a hose exhibits any of the above conditions, replace it with a new one.

REPLACEMENT

Flexible hose

♦ **Refer to illustrations 9.2 and 9.3**

2   Using a flare nut wrench, disconnect the brake line from the hose fitting, being careful not to bend the frame bracket or brake line. Hold the fitting on the hose with a wrench to prevent the metal line from twisting and the frame bracket from bending (see illustration).

3   Remove the large retaining clip (see illustration) and detach the hose from the bracket and the body.

✳✳ CAUTION:

Plug the metal brake line immediately. This is especially important on models with four wheel ABS, to prevent air from getting into the Hydraulic Control Unit (HCU). If air gets into the HCU, you will not be able to bleed the brakes properly at home - the vehicle will have to be towed to a dealer service department or other repair shop equipped with the necessary tool.

4   Remove the banjo bolt from the caliper and discard the sealing washers.

5   Connect the hose to the caliper, using new sealing washers. Tighten the banjo bolt to the torque listed in this Chapter's Specifications.

6   Without twisting the hose, connect the other end of the line to the bracket on the chassis.

7   Connect the metal brake line to the hose fitting by hand, then, using a flare nut wrench, tighten the fitting securely. Be sure to use a wrench on the hose fitting to prevent the bracket from bending or the metal line from twisting.

8   When the brake hose installation is complete, there should be no kinks in the hose. Make sure the hose doesn't contact any part of the suspension. Check this by turning the wheels to the extreme left and right positions. If the hose makes contact, remove it and correct the installation as necessary.

Metal brake line

9   When replacing brake lines be sure to use the correct parts. Don't use copper tubing for any brake system components. Purchase steel brake lines from a dealer or auto parts store.

10   Prefabricated brake line, with the tube ends already flared and fittings installed, is available at auto parts stores and dealers. These lines are also sometimes bent to the proper shapes.

11   When installing the new line make sure it's securely supported in the brackets and has plenty of clearance between moving or hot components.

12   After installation, check the master cylinder fluid level and add fluid as necessary. Bleed the brake system as outlined in the next Section and test the brakes carefully before driving the vehicle in traffic.

10 Brake hydraulic system - bleeding

▶ **Refer to illustration 10.8**

➡**Note: Bleeding the hydraulic system is necessary to remove any air that manages to find its way into the system when it's been opened during removal and installation of a hose, line, caliper or master cylinder.**

CONVENTIONAL BRAKES (NON-ABS)

1   It will probably be necessary to bleed the system at all four brakes if air has entered the system due to low fluid level, or if the brake lines have been disconnected at the master cylinder.

2   If a brake line was disconnected only at a wheel, then only that caliper or wheel cylinder must be bled.

3   If a brake line is disconnected at a fitting located between the master cylinder and any of the brakes, that part of the system served by the disconnected line must be bled.

4   Remove any residual vacuum from the brake power booster by applying the brake several times with the engine off.

5   Remove the master cylinder reservoir cover and fill the reservoir with brake fluid. Reinstall the cover.

➡**Note: Check the fluid level often during the bleeding operation and add fluid as necessary to prevent the fluid level from falling low enough to allow air bubbles into the master cylinder.**

6   Have an assistant on hand, as well as a supply of new brake fluid, an empty clear plastic container, a length of 3/16-inch plastic, rubber or vinyl tubing to fit over the bleeder valve and a wrench to open and close the bleeder valve.

7   Beginning at the right rear wheel, loosen the bleeder valve slightly, then tighten it to a point where it is snug but can still be loosened quickly and easily.

8   Place one end of the tubing over the bleeder valve and submerge

10.8 When bleeding the brakes, a hose is connected to the bleed screw at the caliper or wheel cylinder and then submerged in brake fluid - air will be seen as bubbles in the tube and container (all air must be expelled before moving to the next wheel)

the other end in brake fluid in the container (see illustration).

9   Have the assistant pump the brakes slowly a few times to get pressure in the system, then hold the pedal firmly depressed.

10   While the pedal is held depressed, open the bleeder valve just enough to allow a flow of fluid to leave the valve. Watch for air bubbles to exit the submerged end of the tube. When the fluid flow slows after a couple of seconds, close the valve and have your assistant release the pedal.

11   Repeat Steps 9 and 10 until no more air is seen leaving the tube, then tighten the bleeder valve and proceed to the left rear wheel, the right front wheel and the left front wheel, in that order, and perform the same procedure. Be sure to check the fluid in the master cylinder reservoir frequently.

12   Never use old brake fluid. It contains moisture which will deteriorate the brake system components.

13   Refill the master cylinder with fluid at the end of the operation.

14   Check the operation of the brakes. The pedal should feel solid when depressed, with no sponginess. If necessary, repeat the entire process.

ANTI-LOCK BRAKE SYSTEM (ABS)

Rear-wheel Anti-lock Brake System (RABS)

15   Place several rags or newspapers underneath the master cylinder. Using a flare nut wrench, loosen the brake line fittings at the master cylinder. Have an assistant slowly depress the brake pedal and hold it in the depressed position, then tighten the fittings. Repeat this step until the fluid flowing from the fittings is free of air bubbles. This will bleed out any air trapped in the master cylinder.

16   Working underneath the vehicle (raise and support it on jackstands, if necessary) attach a hose to the bleeder valve on the rear-wheel anti-lock brake valve (located on the inside of the driver's side frame rail, behind the front wheel) and place the other end of the hose in a container partially filled with clean brake fluid.

17   Open the bleeder valve and have your assistant slowly depress the brake pedal, holding it in the depressed position, then close the bleeder valve. Repeat this step until the fluid flowing from the valve is free of air bubbles.

18   The remainder of the bleeding procedure is the same as that for the conventional braking system. Follow Steps 7 through 14, making sure to check the fluid level in the master cylinder often.

Four-wheel Anti-lock Brake System

19   Four-wheel ABS-equipped models cannot be bled at home if air gets into the master cylinder and/or the Hydraulic Control Unit (HCU). The first step in the bleeding procedure for these two components requires a special anti-lock test adapter which must be plugged into the control module. Any attempt to bleed the master cylinder and HCU without this special device will trap air in the HCU, which will result in a spongy brake pedal.

20   However, as long as no air has gotten into the master cylinder or the HCU, the brake lines and the calipers can be bled in the conventional manner. Refer to Steps 1 through 14 above.

11 Parking brake - adjustment

The parking brake system on all models is completely self-adjusting. No means of manual adjustment is provided.

12 Parking brake cables - replacement

✳✳ WARNING:

Cable tension must be released before removing any parts of the parking brake system, then reset after installation.

1 This procedure requires a steel pin to be inserted in the parking brake control. Use a 5/32-inch drill bit or fabricate the pin from a piece of stiff wire and bend a loop in one end so you can pull the pin out when you're done with it. You'll also need an assistant to pull on the parking brake cable while you insert the pin.

2 Release the parking brake.

3 Locate the lockout pin hole in the parking brake control.

4 Have an assistant, working beneath the vehicle, pull the front parking brake cable rearward. Insert the pin into the hole in the parking brake control assembly, then have your assistant let go of the cable.

5 To reset cable tension, remove the pin and operate the parking brake pedal several times.

FRONT CABLE

6 Release cable tension as described in Steps 1 through 4.

7 Raise the vehicle and support it securely on jackstands. Disconnect the rear end of the front cable from the parking brake rear cable.

8 From inside the vehicle, disconnect the cable from the pedal assembly.

9 Detach the cable from the mounting bracket on the frame. Remove the cable-to-frame bolt (if equipped) and take the cable out.

10 Installation is the reverse of the removal steps. Be sure the retainer fingers on the cable secure it to the front mounting bracket.

11 After installation, reset cable tension as described in Step 5.

REAR CABLE

12 Release cable tension as described in Steps 1 through 4.

13 Raise the vehicle and support it securely on jackstands. Remove the hubcap, the wheel and tire, and brake drum.

14 Disconnect the front cable from the rear cable.

15 Disconnect the end of the right rear cable from the equalizer, then slip the cable out of the bracket.

16 On the wheel side of the backing plate, compress the retainer fingers so the retainer passes through the hole in the backing plate.

17 Lift the cable out of the slot in the parking brake lever attached to the secondary brake shoe and remove the cable through the backing plate hole.

18 Installation is the reverse of removal.

19 After installation, reset cable tension as described in Step 5.

13 Rear parking brake shoes (2010 models) - replacement

♦ **Refer to illustrations 13.5a and 13.5b**

1 Block the front wheels and release the parking brake.

2 Loosen the rear wheel lug nuts, raise the rear of the vehicle and securely support the rear axle on jackstands. Remove the rear wheels.

3 Remove the rear disc brake pads (see Section 3).

4 Remove the rear brake disc. If disc removal is hindered by the

parking brake shoes, remove the rubber dust plug on the back of the anchor plate and use a brake tool to back off the shoe adjuster mechanism until the disc can be removed.

5 Use needle-nose locking pliers to remove the shoe return springs and adjusting spring (see illustrations). Work on only one side of the vehicle at a time. Refer to the other (assembled) side for reference until your have replaced the shoes on one side.

13.5a Small locking pliers are useful for removing the adjusting spring and shoe-return spring

13.5b Depress the shoe hold-down springs, while rotating and removing the shoe hold-down pins from behind

6 Remove the actuator and press the two shoes together until the parking brake cable eye can be disconnected.

7 Remove the parking brake shoe hold-down springs and the old shoes.

8 Examine the condition of the brake disc, including the inner surface on which the rear parking brake shoes make contact. If there are hard spots or minor grooving, have the disc resurfaced at a brake ser-vice shop. If the disc is worn beyond the thickness cast into the disc, replace both rear discs.

9 Installation is the reverse of the removal procedure. Once the rear brakes are assembled, connect the left and right parking brake cables and adjust the shoes with a brake tool inserted through the adjustment hole on the backside of the assembly. Reinsert the rubber plug to prevent entry of dirt or moisture.

14 Power brake booster - check, removal, installation and adjustment

1 The power brake booster unit requires no special maintenance apart from periodic inspection of the vacuum hose and the case.

2 Dismantling of the brake booster requires special tools and should not be done by the home mechanic. If a problem develops, install a new or factory rebuilt unit.

CHECK

3 Begin the power booster check by depressing the brake pedal several times with the engine running and make sure that there is no change in the pedal reserve distance. The reserve distance is the distance between the pedal and the floor when the pedal is fully depressed.

4 Turn off the engine and depress the brake pedal several times slowly. If the pedal goes down farther the first time but gradually rises after the second or third depression, the booster is airtight.

5 Now, depress the pedal and start the engine. If the pedal goes down slightly, operation is normal. Release the brake pedal and let the engine run for a couple of minutes.

6 Depress the brake pedal, then stop the engine with the pedal still depressed. If there is no change in the reserve distance after holding the pedal for about 30-seconds, the booster is airtight.

7 If the pedal feels "hard" when the engine is running, the booster isn't operating properly or there is a vacuum leak in the hose to the booster.

REMOVAL

▶ Refer to illustrations 14.10 and 14.11

8 Remove the nuts attaching the master cylinder to the booster (see Section 8) and carefully pull the master cylinder forward until it clears the mounting studs. Use caution so as not to bend or kink the brake lines.

9 Detach the manifold vacuum hose from the booster check valve.

10 Working in the passenger compartment under the steering column, unplug the electrical connector from the brake light switch (see illustration) (and cruise control switch, if equipped), then remove the pushrod retaining clip and nylon washer from the brake pedal pin. Slide the pushrod off the pin.

11 Remove the nuts attaching the brake booster to the firewall (see illustration).

12 Carefully detach the booster from the firewall and lift it out of the engine compartment.

INSTALLATION

13 Place the booster into position on the firewall and tighten the mounting nuts to the torque listed in this Chapter's Specifications. Connect the pushrod and brake light switch to the brake pedal. Install the retaining clip in the brake pedal pin.

14 Install the master cylinder to the booster, tightening the nuts to the torque listed in this Chapter's Specifications.

15 Carefully check the operation of the brakes before driving the vehicle in traffic.

ADJUSTMENT

16 Some boosters feature an adjustable pushrod. They are matched to the booster at the factory and most likely will not require adjustment, but if a misadjusted pushrod is suspected, a gauge can be fabricated out of heavy gauge sheet metal (see illustration 8.22).

14.10 Working in the passenger compartment, disconnect the brake light switch and booster pushrod (arrow) . . .

14.11 . . . then pull down the floorboard padding and remove the four booster mounting nuts (arrows)

17 Some common symptoms caused by a misadjusted pushrod include dragging brakes (if the pushrod is too long) or excessive brake pedal travel accompanied by a groaning sound from the brake booster (if the pushrod is too short).

18 To check the pushrod length, unbolt the master cylinder from the booster and position it to one side. It isn't necessary to disconnect the hydraulic lines, but be careful not to bend them.

19 Apply vacuum to the booster with a hand-held vacuum pump, then place the pushrod gauge against the end of the pushrod, exerting a force of approximately five pounds to seat the pushrod in the power unit (see illustration 8.22). The rod should just touch the cutout on the gauge. If it doesn't, adjust it by holding the knurled portion of the pushrod with a pair of pliers and turning the end with a wrench.

20 When the adjustment is complete, reinstall the master cylinder and check for proper brake operation before driving the vehicle in traffic.

15 Brake light switch/Brake Pedal Position (BPP) switch - removal and installation

REMOVAL

▶ **Refer to illustration 15.3**

1   Remove the under dash panel.
2   Locate the brake light switch assembly (see illustration 14.10) near the top of the brake pedal and disconnect the switch from the brake pedal by removing the retaining clip.
3   Use a small screwdriver to unlock the electrical connector, then unplug the connector from the brake light switch (see illustration).

INSTALLATION

4   Install the switch to the electrical connector by snapping the clip into place.
5   Reconnect the assembly to the brake pedal.
6   Install the under dash panel.
7   Check the brake lights for proper operation.

15.3 Use a small screwdriver to disengage the clip inside the electrical connector

Specifications

Brake fluid type	See Chapter 1

Disc brakes

Minimum pad lining thickness	1/8 inch
Front brake disc	
Minimum thickness	Refer to marks stamped on disc
Runout limit	
2010 and earlier	0.003 inch
2011	0.002 inch

Drum brakes

Drum wear limit	Refer to marks stamped on drum
Minimum lining thickness	1/16 inch above rivet heads

Torque specifications   Ft-lbs (unless otherwise indicated)

➡**Note: One foot-pound (ft-lb) of torque is equivalent to 12 inch-pounds (in-lbs) of torque. Torque values below approximately 15 ft-lbs are expressed in inch-pounds, since most foot-pound torque wrenches are not accurate at these smaller values.**

Backing plate-to-axle housing nuts	25 to 40
Brake booster-to-firewall nuts	
2010 and earlier	16 to 21
2011	18
Brake hose-to-caliper banjo bolt	
Front disc	25
Rear disc	26
Front caliper mounting bolts	
2005 and earlier	21 to 26
2006 and later	27
Caliper mounting bracket-to-spindle bolts*	85
Rear disc brake (2010 and later)	
Caliper guide pin bolts	18
Caliper bracket-to-axle bolts	50
Master cylinder-to-brake booster nuts	
2010 and earlier	16 to 21
2011	159 in-lbs
RABS sensor mounting bolt	
2010 and earlier	20 to 29
2011	97 in-lbs
RABS valve mounting bolt	14 to 19
Front wheel sensor mounting bolt	
2010 and earlier	68 to 92 in-lbs
2011	
FWD models	159 in-lbs
RDW models	22
Wheel cylinder-to-backing plate bolts	106 to 159 in-lbs

Use new bolts or apply non-permanent thread locking agent to the threads of the old bolts.

Section

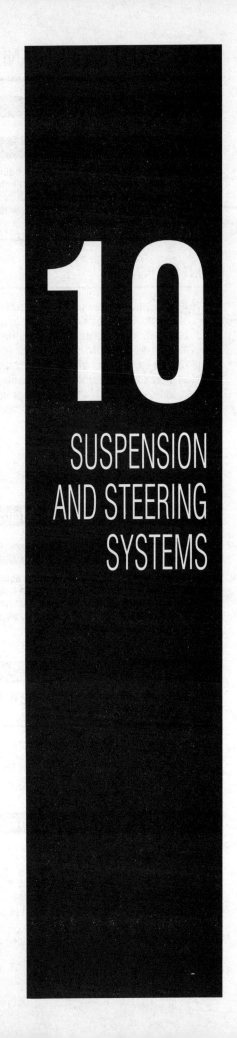

10

SUSPENSION AND STEERING SYSTEMS

1 General information

❉❉ WARNING:

Some models covered by this manual are equipped with airbags. Always disable the airbag system before working in the vicinity of any airbag system component to avoid the possibility of accidental deployment of the airbag(s), which could cause personal injury (see Chapter 12).

FRONT SUSPENSION

The front suspension (see illustration 5.3) consists of upper and lower control arms, shock absorbers, coil springs (2WD models) or torsion bars (4WD models) and a stabilizer bar. The inner ends of the control arms are attached to the frame; the outer ends are attached to the spindle. The upper control arms pivot on eccentric bolts. The lower control arms pivot on two separate, non-adjustable bolts. The shock absorbers and, on 2WD models, the coil springs are mounted between the lower control arms and the frame. On 4WD models, the torsion bars are mounted between the lower control arms and the frame. The front stabilizer bar is attached to the frame with mounting clamps. The balljoints are an integral part of the control arms and cannot be replaced separately; if a balljoint is damaged or worn out, the control arm must be replaced.

REAR SUSPENSION

The rear suspension uses shock absor-bers and semi-elliptical leaf springs. The forward end of each spring is attached to the bracket on the frame side rail. The rear of each spring is shackled to a bracket on the frame rail. The rear shock absorbers are direct, double acting units with staggered mounting positions. The right shock is mounted forward of the axle and the left mounted behind it.

Since most procedures that are dealt with in this Chapter involve jacking up the vehicle and working underneath it, a good pair of jackstands will be needed. A hydraulic floor jack is the preferred type of jack to lift the vehicle, and it can also be used to support certain components during various operations.

2 Suspension systems - working precautions

❉❉ WARNING:

Some models covered by this manual are equipped with airbags. Always disable the airbag system before working in the vicinity of any airbag system component to avoid the possibility of accidental deployment of the airbag(s), which could cause personal injury (see Chapter 12).

❉❉ WARNING:

Never, under any circumstances, rely on a jack to support the vehicle while working under it.

❉❉ WARNING:

Whenever any of the suspension or steering fasteners are loosened or removed they must be inspected and, if necessary, replaced with new ones of the same part number or of original equipment quality and design. Torque specifications must be followed for proper reassembly and component retention.

Use safe practices when working on the suspension and steering systems.

3 Front shock absorber - removal and installation

▶ **Refer to illustrations 3.3 and 3.4**

1   Loosen the front wheel lug nuts, raise the vehicle and support it securely on jackstands. Remove the front wheels.

2   Remove the front disc brake water shield (if necessary) (see Chapter 9).

3   Remove the upper shock absorber mounting nut (see illustra-tion), washer and bushing.

4   Remove the two lower shock absorber mounting nuts (see illustration) and remove the shock.

5   Installation is the reverse of removal. Be sure to tighten the upper and lower shock mounting nuts to the torque listed in this Chapter's Specifications.

3.3 If the shock absorber upper mounting nut is rusted tight, it'll probably be necessary to hold the stem from turning with a pair of locking pliers

3.4 To detach the lower end of the shock absorber, remove these two nuts (2WD model shown, 4WD models similar)

4 Front hub and bearing assembly (4WD models) - removal and installation

2000 MODELS WITH PULSE VACUUM HUB LOCKS

➡**Note:** The hub and bearing assembly is a sealed unit and is neither adjustable nor serviceable. If it's defective, it must be replaced. Also, a number of special tools are needed to remove the hub lock and the hub and bearing assembly, to disassemble and reassemble the hub and bearing, and to install the hub and bearing and hub lock. Before undertaking this procedure, carefully read through the following steps and then obtain the tools you'll need from an auto parts store or specialty tool retailer.

Removal

◆ Refer to illustration 4.8

➡**Note:** To remove the hub lock on these models, you'll need six special hub-lock removal clips, a hub-lock puller and a slide hammer designed to screw into the puller. Before proceeding, check on availability of these special tools.

1   Loosen the front wheel lug nuts, raise the vehicle and support it securely on jackstands. Remove the wheel.

2   Remove the brake caliper and the brake disc (see Chapter 9).

3   Install the hub-lock removal clips and the hub-lock puller. Align the puller with the three slots in the hub lock and hand-tighten the set screw on the side of the puller. Screw the slide hammer into the puller and remove the hub lock assembly.

4   Unbolt and remove the brake disc splash shield from the steering knuckle.

5   Remove the driveaxle retainer ring (see Section 19 in Chapter 8).

6   Detach the clips for the hub-lock system vacuum line, disconnect the vacuum line from the steering knuckle and set the vacuum line aside.

7   On models with ABS, disconnect the ABS electrical wire harness clips, remove the ABS sensor retaining bolt, remove the sensor from the knuckle and set the sensor and wire harness safely aside.

8   Remove the hub assembly-to-steering knuckle bolts (see illustration).

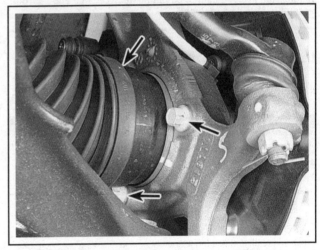

4.8 To detach the hub and bearing assembly from the steering knuckle, remove these three bolts (arrows)

9   Tap the hub assembly from side-to-side to break it loose from the steering knuckle. Pull the hub assembly off the end of the driveaxle. Wrap the end of the driveaxle with a rag to prevent damaging it. If the hub is stuck on the splines on the end of the driveaxle, use a puller to free it.

Disassembly

➡**Note:** To disassemble the hub and bearing assembly, you'll need a special needle bearing puller and a slide hammer designed to screw into the puller (the same slide hammer tool that's used with the hub-lock puller). Before proceeding, consult with auto parts stores or your dealer service department regarding the availability of these special tools.

10 Remove and discard the old O-ring(s) from the hub and bearing assembly. Always use new O-rings when installing the hub and bearing assembly.

✳✳ CAUTION:

You MUST replace the two hub and bearing O-rings every time the hub and bearing assembly is removed. Using an old O-ring can result in a vacuum leak, which could cause a loss of four-wheel-drive and/or contaminate the hub-lock vacuum system.

11 Place the hub and bearing assembly in a bench vise.

12 Remove the old thrust washer and discard it. Always use a new thrust washer when installing the hub and bearing assembly.

✳✳ CAUTION:

You MUST replace the thrust washer every time the hub and bearing assembly is removed. Using an old thrust washer can damage the wheel hub and/or the driveaxle.

13 Install the special needle bearing puller, screw the slide hammer into the puller and remove the caged needle bearing.

✳✳ CAUTION:

Do NOT unscrew the big nut on the hub and bearing assembly! This nut is the bearing retaining nut. The bearing preload is preset at the factory. If you unscrew the bearing retaining nut, the bearing preload cannot be readjusted. The hub and bearing assembly MUST be replaced.

Inspection

14 Wipe off the hub and bearing assembly so that you can inspect the condition of the internal parts.

✳✳ CAUTION:

Do NOT immerse the hub and bearing assembly in any kind of solvent! Doing so will ruin the sealed bearing inside and you will have to replace the hub and bearing assembly.

15 Inspect the bearing preload nut and bore slots to ensure that the slots are aligned. If they're not aligned, or if the slots are damaged, replace the hub and bearing assembly.

16 Inspect the axleshaft bore for scoring and excessive wear. If it's scored or worn, replace the hub and bearing assembly. If there are metal particles in the axleshaft bore, the vacuum system must be flushed out and tested.

17 Inspect the needle bearing bore for scoring, bluing and excessive wear. If it's scored, blued or worn, replace the hub and bearing assembly.

18 Inspect the sealed hub bearing for excessive looseness or binding. If it's loose or binding, replace the hub and bearing assembly.

Reassembly

➡Note: To reassemble the hub and bearing assembly, you'll need a special needle bearing installation tool and a driver designed to screw into the installation tool. Before proceeding, consult with your local Ford dealer or auto parts store regarding the availability of these special tools.

19 Install the caged needle bearing into the hub and bearing assembly as follows: Place the caged needle bearing in position with the stamped part number side of the bearing race facing up. Position the bearing installation tool on the caged needle bearing and screw the driver handle into the installation tool. Using a hammer, tap the driver until the installation tool seats against the wheel hub and bearing. To verify that the caged needle bearing is correctly seated, measure the distance between the face of the hub and bearing assembly and the face of the needle bearing. It should be within the range of 23/64 to 25/64-inch.

20 Lubricate the caged needle bearings with wheel bearing grease. Install a new thrust washer. Make sure that all eight locking tabs on the thrust washer are correctly seated in the groove in the hub and bearing assembly.

✳✳ CAUTION:

If the thrust washer locking tabs are not fully seated in the groove in the hub and bearing assembly, the thrust washer can come loose from the hub and bearing, allowing the bearing pre-load nut to back off and destroying the wheel hub bearing.

Installation

➡Note: To install the hub and bearing assembly, you'll need a special main seal replacer tool, a main seal depth setting tool, a driveaxle seal installer tool, a seal remover guide and a snapring sleeve. Before proceeding, consult with auto parts stores or a dealer service department regarding the availability of these special tools.

21 Wipe off and inspect the steering knuckle main seal. If it's damaged or worn, the wheel end of the vacuum system will leak and the vehicle will not operate in 4WD. If the main seal looks marginal, now is the time to replace it. Knock out the old main seal with a hammer and punch. Clean the seal bore thoroughly and blow out the steering knuckle vacuum chamber and vacuum hose. Inspect the bore for burrs, nicks and other damage. If necessary, clean up the bore with crocus or emery cloth. Apply a thin coat of multi-purpose grease to the seal bore, place the new main seal in the special seal replacer, install the seal replacer tool and the depth setting tool on the steering knuckle, then drive the seal into position until it seats against the knuckle. Lubricate the sealing surface of the new seal with a liberal amount of wheel bearing grease. Lubricate the driveaxle splines with multi-purpose grease.

22 Install the hub and bearing assembly in the steering knuckle, install the three hub and bearing mounting bolts and tighten them to the torque listed in this Chapter's Specifications.

23 Install a new retainer ring on the driveaxle (see Section 19 in Chapter 8).

24 Reattach the vacuum line clips and, if equipped, the ABS harness clips to the frame.

25 If the vehicle is equipped with ABS, reconnect the ABS harness electrical connector.

26 Before reconnecting the vacuum line to the steering knuckle, check the wheel-end for vacuum leaks as follows: Hook up a hand-operated vacuum pump/gauge to the wheel-end of the vacuum line and apply 15 in-Hg of vacuum (you may have to pump rapidly for as much as 10 seconds). The line must not leak more than 0.50 in-Hg in 30 seconds. If the line holds vacuum satisfactorily, proceed to the next Step. If the line is leaking more than 0.50 in-Hg over 30 seconds, carefully inspect the line and connections between the wheel end and the pulse vacuum hub-lock solenoid (on the transfer case) for leaks. Repair or replace any leaking lines and/or connections.

27 Reconnect the vacuum line to the steering knuckle.

28 Install the brake disc splash shield.

29 Place the hub lock in position on the wheel, then use a soft-tipped rubber mallet to tap it all the way on. Make sure that the hub-lock locking arms are fully seated in the hub groove.

30 Install the brake disc and caliper (see Chapter 9).

31 Install the wheel, remove the vehicle from all jacks and stands and lower the vehicle. Tighten the wheel lug nuts to the torque listed in the Chapter 1 Specifications.

MODELS WITHOUT PULSE VACUUM HUB LOCKS

➡Note: These hubs have sealed wheel bearings that are not serviceable. If they are defective, the hub must be replaced.

32 Loosen the front wheel lug nuts, raise the vehicle and support it securely on jackstands. Remove the wheel

33 Remove the brake caliper and the brake disc (see Chapter 9).

34 Remove the driveaxle/hub nut and discard it.

35 Loosen the driveaxle from the wheel hub. Use a puller tool if it is stuck (see Section 19 in Chapter 8).

36 Remove the dust shield from the steering knuckle.

37 Remove the ABS sensor from the wheel hub (if equipped).

38 Remove the three bolts that attach the wheel hub to the steering knuckle and then remove the wheel hub (see illustration 4.8).

➡Note: Be careful not to overextend the CV joint while removing the wheel hub and bearing.

39 Installation is the reverse of removal. Tighten the hub and bearing assembly mounting bolts to the torque listed in this Chapter's Specifications.

➡Note: A new driveaxle/hub nut must be used and tightened to the torque listed in this Chapter's Specifications.

5 Front wheel spindle - removal and installation

⬦ Refer to illustrations 5.3, 5.8a and 5.8b

➡Note: On 4WD models, the spindle is referred to as the steering knuckle.

1 Loosen the front wheel lug nuts, position the front wheels in the straight ahead position, raise the vehicle and support it securely on jackstands. Remove the front wheel.

2 Remove the disc brake caliper, brake disc and, on 2WD models, the disc brake splash shield (see Chapter 9). Wire the caliper to the underbody to prevent damage to the brake hose. On 2WD models with ABS, remove the ABS sensor.

3 On 2WD models, place a jack under the lower arm at the balljoint area (see illustration). Raise the jack until it supports the spring load on the lower arm. The jack must remain in this position throughout the remainder of this procedure.

5.3 Front suspension and steering components (2WD model shown, 4WD models similar)

1	Stabilizer bar	3	Shock absorber (lower mount)	4	Steering knuckle	6	Lower control arm
2	Tie-rod end			5	Lower balljoint	7	Torsion bar

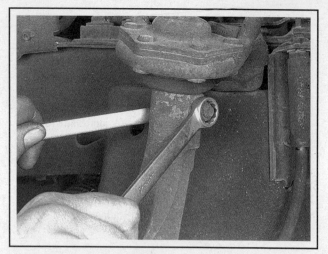

5.8a To separate the spindle from the upper control arm, remove the pinch bolt . . .

5.8b . . . then carefully pry the ballstud out of the spindle

✳✳ WARNING:

Failure to place a jack under the lower control arm could result in serious injury.

4   On 4WD models, remove the hub lock assembly (if equipped) and disconnect the driveaxle from the hub and bearing assembly (see Section 4).

5   On 4WD models, remove the disc brake splash shield. If the vehicle is equipped with ABS, remove the ABS sensor from the steering knuckle.

6   On 4WD models, unload the torsion bar (see Section 7), then support the lower control arm with a jack.

7   Remove the upper shock absorber mounting nut, washer and bushing (see illustration 3.3).

8   Remove the upper balljoint pinch bolt nut and pinch bolt (see illustrations).

9   Disconnect the lower shock absorber mounting nuts (see illustration 3.4) and remove the shock absorber.

10 Disconnect the tie-rod end from the spindle (see Section 16).

11 On 2WD models, compress the coil spring with a coil spring compressor (see illustration 8.5).

12 Remove the lower balljoint cotter pin and loosen the castellated nut, install a small puller and separate the lower control arm balljoint from the spindle.

13 Remove the spindle/steering knuckle.

✳✳ CAUTION:

To prevent damage to the CV joints on 4WD models, support the driveaxle assembly while the steering knuckle is removed.

14 Installation is the reverse of removal with the following additions:

a) *Be sure to tighten all fasteners to the torque values listed in this Chapter's Specifications.*

b) *Have the front-end alignment checked by a dealer service department or an alignment shop.*

6   Front stabilizer bar - removal and installation

1   Position the front wheels in the straight-ahead position. Raise the vehicle and support it securely on jackstands.

2   To disconnect the stabilizer bar from the lower control arms, remove the nuts from the links that attach the bar to the arms. Discard the fasteners; new ones will be used on installation.

3   To detach the stabilizer bar from the frame, remove the four stabilizer bar bracket bolts (two per bracket). Discard the fasteners; new ones will be used on installation.

4   Remove the stabilizer bar assembly.

5   Inspect all rubber bushings for cracks, tears and other damage. Replace any bushings that are worn, damaged or deteriorated.

6   Installation is the reverse of removal. Be sure to tighten the bolts and nuts to the torque listed in this Chapter's Specifications.

➡Note: The stabilizer-to-frame bracket bolts are self-tapping. If they can no longer be tightened to the correct torque, obtain a kit with special fasteners from your dealer. Use new stabilizer bar link nuts and bracket bolts.

7   Torsion bar - removal and installation

➡**Note: A special tool designed for torsion bar removal and installation is required to safely perform the following procedures.**

REMOVAL

1   Position the front wheels in the straight-ahead position. Raise the vehicle and support it securely on jackstands.

2   Remove the torsion bar cover plate from the frame.

3   Before removing or adjusting the torsion bar, measure the distance that the torsion bar adjustment bolt protrudes from the adjustment nut. Jot down this dimension; you'll need it to readjust the torsion bar during installation.

4   Install the special tool on the crossmember and the torsion bar adjuster.

5   Tighten the torsion bar tool until the torsion bar adjuster lifts off the adjustment bolt.

6   Unscrew the adjustment bolt from the torsion bar nut while counting the number of turns to remove the bolt. Record this number on a piece of paper for installation purposes. Remove the adjustment bolt and nut. Discard the old adjustment bolt.

❊❊ CAUTION:

Do NOT reuse the old adjustment bolt. The bolt is coated with a special adhesive to prevent it from backing out. When the bolt is backed out, this adhesive is removed from the threads. Using an old bolt without this adhesive could allow it to back out, resulting in the front end lowering substantially.

7   Loosen the torsion bar tool until there's no tension on the torsion bar.

8   Mark the relationship of the torsion bar to the torsion bar adjuster.

9   Lower the torsion bar adjuster, remove the torsion bar insulator and pull the torsion bar out of the lower control arm.

10   Remove the torsion bar adjuster from the torsion bar.

INSTALLATION

11   Installation is the reverse of removal, with the following points:

a)   *Be sure to use a new adjustment bolt, factory-coated with the special adhesive.*

b)   *When installing the new adjustment bolt, screw it in the same number of turns it took to remove the old one, then measure the height of the bolt from the adjustment nut and compare this measurement to the measurement you made before removing the old adjustment bolt.*

c)   *After lowering the vehicle to the ground, turn the torsion bar adjustment bolt in or out to adjust the ride height so the vehicle is level from side-to-side, with the vehicle sitting on its suspension. Also, roll the vehicle back and forth and jounce the suspension before adjusting and in between adjustments.*

d)   *Have the front-end alignment checked by a dealer service department or an alignment shop.*

8   Lower control arm - removal, inspection and installation

REMOVAL

◗ **Refer to illustration 8.5**

1   Loosen the wheel lug nuts. Raise the front of the vehicle and support it securely on jackstands. Remove the front wheel.

2   On 2WD models, remove the brake disc and dust shield (see Chapter 9).

3   Remove the shock absorber (see Section 3).

4   Disconnect the stabilizer bar from the lower control arm (see Section 6).

5   On 2WD models, compress the coil spring (see illustration).

6   On 4WD models, remove the torsion bar (see Section 7).

7   Position the floor jack under the lower control arm to give support during removal.

8   Remove and discard the cotter pin from the lower control arm balljoint stud, loosen the castellated nut on the stud and install a suitable small puller. Separate the lower control arm balljoint from the spindle/steering knuckle. On 2WD models, carefully remove the compressed coil spring and set it and the spring compressor aside.

8.5 A typical aftermarket internal spring compressor tool: The hooked arms grip the upper coils of the spring, the plate is inserted below the lower coil, and the nut on the threaded rod is turned to compress the spring

9   Loosen the two control arm pivot nuts and bolts and remove the lower control arm.

❋❋ CAUTION:

To prevent damage to the CV joints on 4WD models, support the steering knuckle and driveaxle assembly while the control arm is removed

INSPECTION

10   Inspect the bushings for cracks and tears. If they're damaged or worn, take the control arm to an automotive machine shop to have new bushings installed. This procedure requires a number of specialized tools, so it's not worth tackling at home. If the balljoint is worn out the entire control arm must be replaced.

11   Inspect the lower control arm balljoint and boot seal for damage.

If the balljoint or the boot is damaged, replace the lower control arm. The balljoint cannot be serviced.

INSTALLATION

12   Installation is the reverse of removal, with the following additions:

a) During assembly, tighten the pivot bolts and nuts finger-tight only. Do not tighten them to the specified torque until the vehicle is lowered to the ground.
b) On 2WD models, make sure that the end of the coil spring covers the first hole in the lower control arm, but is not visible through the second hole.
c) After the vehicle is back on the ground, tighten the lower control arm pivot bolts and nuts to the torque listed in this Chapter's Specifications.
d) Have the front-end alignment checked by a dealer service department or an alignment shop.

9   Coil spring - removal and installation

1   To remove the coil spring, you will need a suitable coil spring compressor (see illustration 8.5). These tools are available at most auto parts stores.

2   Removing the coil spring is an integral part of removing the lower control arm (see Steps 1 through 8 in Section 8).

10   Upper control arm - removal, inspection and installation

➡Note: The upper control arm and balljoint cannot be separated and must be replaced as a single unit.

REMOVAL

1   Loosen the wheel lug nuts, raise the vehicle, support it securely on jackstands and remove the wheel.

2   On early 2WD models, remove the brake disc and dust shield (see Chapter 9).

3   Place a floor jack under the lower control arm and raise the control arm slightly. The jack must remain in this position during the entire operation.

4   On 2WD models, mark the position of the cams on the upper control arm cam bolts.

5   Before separating the upper control arm from the spindle/steering knuckle on 4WD models, support the spindle/knuckle to prevent it from tilting out (away from the vehicle) to protect the driveaxle assembly.

6   Remove the pinch bolt nut and pinch bolt that secure the upper balljoint stud to the spindle/steering knuckle (see illustration 5.8a and 5.8b).

7   Using a puller, separate the upper control arm from the spindle/steering knuckle.

8   Remove the upper control arm cam bolts and detach the arm from the frame.

INSPECTION

9   Inspect the control arm bushings for cracks and tears. If they're damaged or worn, take the control arm to an automotive machine shop to have new bushings installed. This procedure requires a number of specialized tools, so it's not worth tackling at home. If the balljoint is worn out, the control arm must be replaced.

INSTALLATION

10   Installation is the reverse of removal, with the following additions:

a) On 2WD models, be sure to align the marks you made on the upper control arm adjustment cams before tightening the pivot nuts and bolts. Don't tighten the pivot nuts and bolts until the vehicle is on the ground.
b) On 4WD models, replace all four alignment plates with new alignment cams. Tighten the pivot nuts and bolts to the torque listed in this Chapter's Specifications.
c) After a 2WD model is lowered to the ground, tighten the pivot nuts and bolts to the torque listed in this Chapter's Specifications. Tighten the forward bolt and nut first, then the rear bolt and nut.

11 Rear shock absorbers - removal and installation

▶ **Refer to illustrations 11.2 and 11.3**

1   Place a floor jack under the axle adjacent to shock absorber being removed. Apply just enough pressure with the jack to take the load off the shock absorber.

2   Remove the nut and bolt securing the lower end of the shock absorber to the spring plate (see illustration).

3   Remove the nut securing the top of the shock absorber to the upper mounting bracket on the frame (see illustration).

4   Installation is the reverse of the removal Steps. Tighten the nuts and bolts to the torque listed in this Chapter's Specifications.

11.2 Remove the shock absorber lower bolt and nut (arrow) . . .

11.3 . . . and the upper nut (arrow)

12 Leaf spring - removal and installation

REMOVAL

1   Raise the rear of the vehicle until the weight is off the rear springs but the tires are still touching the ground.

2   Support the vehicle securely on jackstands and support the rear axle with a jack. DO NOT get under a vehicle that's supported only by a jack, even if the tires are still installed.

3   Remove the nut and bolt securing the lower end of the shock absorber to the spring plate (see illustration 11.2). Compress the shock up and out of the way.

4   Remove the nuts from the U-bolts and remove the U-bolts and the spring plate from the spring.

5   Remove the bolts and nuts securing the shackle assembly at the rear of the spring. Let the spring pivot down and rest on the floor.

6   Remove the spring hanger bolt and nut at the front of the spring. Remove the spring.

7   Inspect the spring eye bushings for wear or distortion. If worn or damaged have them replaced by a dealership service department or properly equipped shop.

INSTALLATION

8   Place the spring in the rear shackle. Install the bolt and nut and tighten them finger-tight.

9   Install the spring in the front bracket. Tighten the bolt and nut finger-tight.

10 Position the rear shackle on the frame. Install the bolt and nut and tighten them finger-tight.

11 Position the axle on the spring and install the spring seat. Make sure the spring tie-bolt is positioned in the hole in the spring, then install the U-bolts and nuts. Tighten the nuts finger-tight.

12 Lower the vehicle to the ground so its weight is resting on the tires. Tighten the spring bracket bolt and nut, shackle bolts and nuts and U-bolt nuts in a criss-cross pattern to the torque listed in this Chapter's Specifications.

13 Rear stabilizer bar - removal and installation

REMOVAL

1   Remove the nut and washer securing the rear stabilizer bar ends to the link at each end.
2   Unbolt the retainers from the rear axle housing.
3   Remove the mounting brackets, retainer and the stabilizer bar from the vehicle.
4   Inspect the rubber isolators on the stabilizer bar and replace if necessary.

INSTALLATION

5   Position the stabilizer bar onto the rear axle assembly. Position the retainer with the UP mark facing up.
6   Install the stabilizer bar and retainer onto the mounting brackets. Make sure the UP mark on the retainer is facing up toward the truck bed.
7   Install the U-bolts and nuts. Tighten the nuts finger-tight.
8   Move the stabilizer bar ends up into position and connect them to the links. Install the bolt, washer and nut on each end. Tighten the bolts and nuts to the torque listed in this Chapter's Specifications.
9   Tighten the retainer bolts and link nuts to the torque listed in this Chapter's Specifications.

14 Steering system - general information

The steering system consists of a power-assisted rack-and-pinion type steering gear which is connected to the spindle/steering knuckles by tie-rod ends. The power steering system is similar to earlier systems, except that it uses a power steering fluid cooler.

15 Steering wheel - removal and installation

✳ WARNING:

Some models covered by this manual are equipped with airbags. Always disable the airbag system before working in the vicinity of any airbag system component to avoid the possibility of accidental deployment of the airbag(s), which could cause personal injury (see Chapter 12).

✳ WARNING:

On models equipped with a driver's side airbag, put the wheels in the straight ahead position and lock the steering column. The steering column must not be rotated while the steering wheel is removed.

REMOVAL

▶ **Refer to illustrations 15.2a, 15.2b, 15.3a, 15.3b, 15.4, 15.5 and 15.7**

1   Disconnect the negative cable from the battery (also disconnect the positive cable if equipped with an airbag).
2   On non-airbag systems, remove the screws securing the horn pad to the steering wheel (see illustration). On airbag systems, pry the two plugs covering the driver's side airbag module screws on the sides of the steering wheel (see illustration).
3   On non-airbag systems, partially pull the horn pad away from the steering wheel, unplug the electrical connector then

15.2a Remove the horn pad screws and take the horn pad off

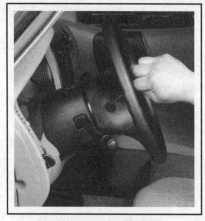

15.2b Remove the plugs from the sides of the steering wheel on models equipped with an airbag

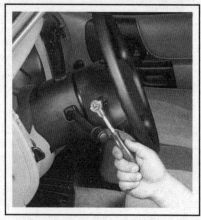

15.3a Remove the airbag module retaining screw from each side of the steering wheel . . .

15.3b . . . lift the module up and disconnect the airbag electrical connector

15.4 Loosen the steering wheel bolt (arrow) two or three turns

remove the horn pad. On models with airbags, remove the two screws from the side of the steering wheel, lift the airbag off and detach the electrical connector (see illustrations). Store the airbag in a safe place until needed.

❋❋ WARNING:

Whenever handling an airbag module, always keep the airbag opening pointed away from your body. Never place the airbag module on a bench or other surface with the airbag opening facing the surface. Always place the airbag module in a safe location with the airbag opening facing up.

4   Loosen the steering wheel bolt two or three turns, but don't remove it yet (see illustration).
5   Use a steering wheel puller to remove the steering wheel. On airbag equipped models, use a two-jaw puller (tool no. T77F-4220-B1 or equivalent). Attach it to the areas on the steering wheel marked Pull (see illustration).

❋❋ CAUTION:

Don't hammer on the shaft to remove the steering wheel. Once the steering wheel is loose, remove the bolt and discard it. Use a new bolt on installation.

6   Lift off the damper (if equipped).
7   Look for alignment marks on the steering wheel and column (see illustration). If they aren't visible, use white paint and make your own marks. These marks will be used during installation to align the wheel and column. Remove the steering wheel from the column. On airbag systems, guide the sliding contact/clockspring wires through the steering wheel.

INSTALLATION

▶ Refer to illustration 15.8

8   Make sure the horn spring is in position (see illustration). Align the mark on the steering wheel hub with the mark on the steering shaft and slip the wheel onto the shaft. Install the new mounting bolt and tighten it to the torque listed in this Chapter's Specifications.
9   The remainder of installation is the reverse of the removal Steps.

❋❋ CAUTION:

On airbag systems, make sure the airbag wiring does not get pinched between the airbag sliding contact/clockspring and the steering wheel.

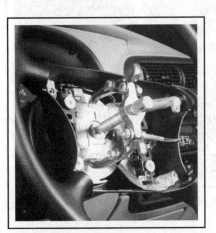

15.5 Position the puller against the steering wheel bolt, then tighten the puller to free the steering wheel - DO NOT pound on the wheel to loosen it

15.7 There should be alignment marks on the steering wheel and shaft (arrow); if not, make your own

15.8 Make sure the horn spring is in position before installing the wheel

16 Tie-rod ends - removal and installation

✳✳ WARNING:

Whenever any of the suspension or steering fasteners are loosened or removed, discard the originals and don't re-use them. They must be replaced with new fasteners of the same part number or of original equipment quality and design. Torque specifications must be followed for proper reassembly and component retention.

REMOVAL

▶ Refer to illustrations 16.4, 16.5 and 16.6

1 Loosen the front wheel lug nuts on the side to be dismantled. Raise the front of the vehicle, support it securely on jackstands, block the rear wheels and set the parking brake.

2 Remove the front wheel.

3 Remove the cotter pin and loosen the nut on the tie-rod end stud. Discard the cotter pin.

4 Loosen the tie-rod end jam nut and back it off several turns (see illustration).

5 Disconnect the tie-rod from the steering spindle with a Pitman arm puller (see illustrations).

6 If you're going to install a new tie-rod end, count and record the number of turns it takes to back the tie-rod end off the connecting rod. If you're going to re-use the same tie-rod end, simply apply a paint mark on the threads adjacent to the tie-rod end and unscrew the tie-rod end from the connecting rod (see illustration).

INSTALLATION

7 If you're installing the old tie-rod end, simply screw the tie-rod into the connecting rod until the tie-rod end is adjacent to the paint

16.4 Hold the tie-rod with a pair of locking pliers and loosen the jam nut

mark you made in Step 6. If you're installing a new tie-rod end, screw it in the same number of turns noted during removal.

8 Install the tie-rod onto the steering spindle. Make sure the front wheels and steering wheel are in the straight ahead position. Make sure the tie-rod stud is seated in the taper to prevent it from rotating while tightening the nut.

9 Install a new nut on the stud and tighten it to the torque listed in this Chapter's Specifications. Install a new cotter pin and bend the ends over completely.

10 Tighten the jam nut securely.

11 Install the wheel and lug nuts. Lower the vehicle and tighten the lug nuts to the torque listed in Chapter 1.

12 Have the front end alignment checked by a dealership service department or an alignment shop.

16.5 Remove the tie-rod end using a Pitman arm puller (earlier models)

16.6 Mark the position of the tie-rod end on the tie-rod

17 Steering gear - removal and installation

✳✳ WARNING:

Some models covered by this manual are equipped with airbags. Always disable the airbag system before working in the vicinity of any airbag system component to avoid the possibility of accidental deployment of the airbag(s), which could cause personal injury (see Chapter 12).

✳✳ WARNING:

On models equipped with airbags, DO NOT rotate the steering shaft while the steering gear is removed from the vehicle or damage to the airbag coil will occur. To prevent the shaft from turning, turn the ignition key to the Lock position before beginning work or run the seat belt through the steering wheel and clip the seat belt into place.

✳✳ WARNING:

Whenever any of the suspension or steering fasteners are loosened or removed discard the originals and don't re-use them. They must be replaced with new fasteners of the same part number or of original equipment quality and design. Torque specifications must be followed for proper reassembly and component retention.

REMOVAL

1 Set the front wheels to the straight-ahead position. Raise and securely support the vehicle on jackstands.

2 Disconnect the cable from the negative battery terminal.

3 Secure the steering wheel in the straight-ahead position, but do not lock the column. On 2011 models, DO lock the column.

4 On V6 2WD models, disconnect the hoses from the power steering fluid cooler, drain the fluid into a suitable container and remove the cooler.

5 On 4WD models so equipped, remove the air deflector retaining screws, pull down on the deflector to disengage the retaining pins.

6 Separate the tie-rod ends from the spindle/steering knuckle (see Section 16).

7 On 4WD models, remove the front stabilizer bar (see Section 6).

8 On early 4WD models, remove the power steering fluid cooler-to-crossmember nuts, then disconnect the fluid return line hose, allow the fluid to drain into a suitable container, disconnect the return hose and remove the cooler.

9 Disconnect the power steering pressure and return lines at the steering gear. Plug the lines and the steering gear inlet and outlet ports to prevent the entry of dirt or moisture.

10 Remove the pinch bolt retaining the lower steering column intermediate shaft to the steering gear input shaft. Turn the ignition switch to the LOCK position, then disconnect the intermediate shaft from the steering gear input shaft.

✳✳ CAUTION:

Do not rotate the steering wheel while the intermediate shaft is disconnected from the steering column or damage to the airbag sliding contact will result.

11 Remove the nuts and mounting stud, nut, washer and stop assemblies.

12 On 2WD models, remove the steering gear assembly.

13 On 4WD models, remove the insulator bushings from the steering gear.

14 On 4WD models, rotate the steering gear control valve housing forward, turn the steering gear input shaft clockwise until it stops, move the steering gear as far to the right as possible, move the left tie-rod forward to clear the crossmember, then pull out the steering gear.

INSTALLATION

15 Installation is the reverse of removal, with the following additions:

a) Replace any insulators that are cracked, torn or deteriorated.

b) Be sure to tighten all fasteners to the torque listed in this Chapter's Specifications.

c) Using a special seal installation tool, install new seals on the power steering fluid pressure and return hose fittings.

d) Have the vehicle's alignment checked when you're done.

18 Power steering pump - removal and installation

➡Note: Refer to Section 19 for information on quick disconnect fittings used on the power steering system.

REMOVAL

◗ Refer to illustration 18.5

1 Disconnect the cable from the negative battery terminal.

2 Remove the drivebelt from the power steering pulley (see Chapter 1).

3 Disconnect the return hose at the pump and drain the fluid into a container.

4 Disconnect the pressure hose from the pump. Discard the seal (if equipped).

5 Remove the drivebelt pulley as follows:

a) Install a pump pulley removal tool, available at most auto parts stores, onto the pulley (see illustration).

b) Hold onto the pulley and rotate the tool nut counterclockwise to remove the pulley from the pump. Do not apply excessive force on the pulley shaft as it may damage the internal parts of the pump.

6 Remove the bolts securing the pump to the mounting bracket.

7 Remove the pump and pulley through the mounting bracket.

18.5 This special tool is needed to remove the power steering pump pulley

18.9 This tool is used to install the power steering pump pulley

INSTALLATION

▶ Refer to illustration 18.9

8   Place the pump in the bracket and install the mounting bolts. Tighten the bolts to the torque listed in this Chapter's Specifications.

9   Install the pulley onto the pump using a special pulley installation tool, available at most auto parts stores (see illustration). Press

the pulley onto the shaft until the hub is flush with the end of the shaft (within 0.010-inch).

10 Install the pump drivebelt (see Chapter 1).

11 Install the pressure and return hoses to the proper fittings on the pump. Install a new seal on the pressure hose (if equipped with replaceable seals).

12 Fill the pump reservoir with the specified fluid and bleed the system (see Section 20).

19 Power steering line quick disconnect fittings

1   If a fitting leaks, note whether the leak is between the tubing and the flare nut or between the flare nut and the pump. If it's between the tubing and the flare nut, replace the hose as an assembly. If it's between the flare nut and the pump, repair the leak (see Steps 2 and 3).

2   Make sure the nut is tightened to the torque listed in this Chapter's Specifications.

3   If the fitting still leaks, unscrew the nut and check the Teflon washer. Replace the washer if its condition is in doubt.

➡ **Note: It may be necessary to stretch the washer with a center punch or similar tapered tool so it will fit over the flare nut. The washer will slowly return to its original size after being stretched.**

4   The O-ring in the fitting can't be replaced. If it's causing the leak, the hose must be replaced as an assembly.

5   If a quick-disconnect fitting disconnects while the pump is in operation, replace the hose as an assembly.

20 Power steering system - bleeding

1   The power steering system must be bled whenever a line is disconnected. Bubbles can be seen in power steering fluid which has air in it and the fluid will often have a tan or milky appearance. Low fluid level can cause air to mix with the fluid, resulting in a noisy pump as well as foaming of the fluid.

2   Open the hood and check the fluid level in the reservoir, add-

ing the specified fluid necessary to bring it up to the proper level (see Chapter 1).

3   Start the engine and slowly turn the steering wheel several times from left-to-right and back again. Do not turn the wheel completely from lock-to-lock. Check the fluid level, topping it up as necessary until it remains steady and no more bubbles are visible.

21 Wheels and tires - general information

▶ **Refer to illustration 21.1**

All vehicles covered by this manual are equipped with metric-sized fiberglass or steel-belted radial tires (see illustration). Use of other size or type of tires may affect the ride and handling of the vehicle. Don't mix different types of tires, such as radials and bias belted, on the same vehicle as handling may be seriously affected. It's recommended that tires be replaced in pairs on the same axle, but if only one tire is being replaced, be sure it's the same size, structure and tread design as the other.

Because tire pressure has a substantial effect on handling and wear, the pressure on all tires should be checked at least once a month or before any extended trips (see Chapter 1).

Wheels must be replaced if they are bent, dented, leak air, have elongated bolt holes, are heavily rusted, out of vertical symmetry or if the lug nuts won't stay tight. Wheel repairs that use welding or peening are not recommended.

Tire and wheel balance is important to the overall handling, braking and performance of the vehicle. Unbalanced wheels can adversely affect handling and ride characteristics as well as tire life. Whenever a tire is installed on a wheel, the tire and wheel should be balanced by a shop with the proper equipment.

21.1 Metric tire size code

22 Front end alignment - general information

▶ **Refer to illustration 22.1**

A front end alignment refers to the adjustments made to the front wheels so they are in proper angular relationship to the suspension and the ground (see illustration). Front wheels that are out of proper alignment not only affect steering control, but also increase tire wear. The only front end adjustments possible on these vehicles are caster and toe-in.

Getting the proper front wheel alignment is a very exacting process, one in which complicated and expensive machines are necessary to perform the job properly. Because of this, you should have a technician with the proper equipment perform these tasks. We will, however, use this space to give you a basic idea of what is involved with front end alignment so you can better understand the process and deal intelligently with the shop that does the work.

Toe-in is the turning in of the front wheels (see illustration). The purpose of a toe specification is to ensure parallel rolling of the front wheels. In a vehicle with zero toe-in, the distance between the front edges of the wheels will be the same as the distance between the rear edges of the wheels. The actual amount of toe-in is normally only a fraction of an inch. Toe-in adjustment is controlled by the tie-rod end position on the tie-rod. Incorrect toe-in will cause the tires to wear improperly by making them scrub against the road surface.

Caster is the tilting of the top of the front steering axis from the vertical. A tilt toward the rear is positive caster and a tilt toward the front is negative caster. Caster is adjusted by means of eccentric cams on the upper control arm pivot bolts.

Camber is the tilting of the front wheels from vertical when viewed from the front of the vehicle. Camber is adjusted by means of eccentric cams on the upper control arm pivot bolts.

22.1 Front end alignment details

A minus B = C (degrees camber)
D = degrees caster
E minus F = toe-in (measured in inches)
G = toe-in (expressed in degrees)

Specifications

General

Power steering fluid type and capacity	See Chapter 1

Torque specifications

	Ft-lbs
Front suspension	
Driveaxle/hub nut (4WD)	
2010 and earlier	162
2011	184
Front stabilizer bar link nuts	
2007 and earlier	18
2008 and later	26
Front stabilizer bar bracket bolts	30
Hub and bearing-to-steering knuckle	
mounting bolts (4WD)	85
Lower balljoint castellated nut	83 to 113
Lower balljoint nuts (2011)	98
Lower control arm pivot bolts/nuts	
2010 and earlier	110 to 148
2011	148
Shock absorber-to-lower control arm mounting nuts	
2010 and earlier	15 to 21
2011	18
Shock absorber upper mounting nut	
2010 and earlier	30 to 41
2011	35
Upper control arm-to-spindle pinch bolt/nut	35 to 46
Upper control arm-to-balljoint nuts (2011)	46
Upper control arm pivot bolts	
2010 and earlier	83 to 113
2011	98
Rear suspension (2005 and earlier)	
Rear leaf spring U-bolt nut	65 to 87
Shock-to-lower bracket nut	39 to 53
Shock-to-upper bracket nut	39 to 53
Shackle-to-spring nut and bolt	65 to 87
Spring shackle-to-rear bracket bolt	65 to 87
Spring-to-front bracket bolt	65 to 87
Stabilizer-to-axle bracket	25 to 34
Stabilizer-to-link nut	55 to 59
Stabilizer link-to-frame bolt	55 to 59

Torque specifications   Ft-lbs (unless otherwise indicated)

Rear suspension (2006 and later models)

Frame bracket bolts/nut	30
Lower shock absorber nuts	59
Spring shackle-to-frame bracket bolts	85
Rear shackle-to-spring nut	98
Front spring eye-to-frame bolt	148
U-bolt nuts	
Step 1	22
Step 2	44
Step 3	66
Step 4	85
Upper shock absorber nuts (2011)	46

Steering system

Steering column-to-gear bolt	
2010 and earlier	30 to 40
2011	41
Steering gear-to-frame bolts/nuts	
2010 and earlier	102 to 127
2011	111
Power steering pump-to-bracket bolts	
2.3L DOHC engine	
2010 and earlier	156 in-lbs
2011	17
2.3L/2.5L SOHC engines	32 to 38
3.0L engine	30 to 40
4.0L engines	
2010 and earlier	15 to 21
2011	18
Steering wheel bolt	
2010 and earlier	25 to 34
2011	30
Tie-rod end-to-spindle nut	44 to 59

NOTES

Section

11

BODY

1 General information

These models feature a welded body that is attached to a separate frame. Certain components are particularly vulnerable to accident damage and can be unbolted and repaired or replaced. Among these parts are the body moldings, bumpers, hood, doors, tailgate and all glass.

Only general body maintenance procedures and body panel repair procedures within the scope of the do-it-yourselfer are included in this Chapter.

2 Body - maintenance

1 The condition of your vehicle's body is very important, because the resale value depends a great deal on it. It's much more difficult to repair a damaged body than it is to repair mechanical components. The hidden areas of the body, such as the fenderwells, the frame and the engine compartment, are equally important, although they don't require as frequent attention as the rest of the body.

2 Once a year, or every 12,000 miles, it's a good idea to have the underside of the body steam cleaned. All traces of dirt and oil will be removed and the area can then be inspected carefully for rust, damaged brake lines, frayed electrical wires, damaged cables and other problems. The front suspension components should be greased after completion of this job.

3 At the same time, clean the engine and the engine compartment with a steam cleaner or water soluble degreaser.

4 The fenderwells should be given close attention, since undercoating can peel away and stones and dirt thrown up by the tires can cause the paint to chip and flake, allowing rust to set in. If rust is found, clean down to the bare metal and apply an anti-rust paint.

5 The body should be washed about once a week (or when dirty). Wet the vehicle thoroughly to soften the dirt, then wash it down with a soft sponge and plenty of clean soapy water. If the surplus dirt is not washed off very carefully, it can wear down the paint.

6 Spots of tar or asphalt thrown up from the road should be removed with a cloth soaked in solvent.

7 Once every six months, wax the body and chrome trim. If a chrome cleaner is used to remove rust from any of the vehicle's plated parts, remember that the cleaner also removes part of the chrome, so use it sparingly.

3 Vinyl trim - maintenance

Don't clean vinyl trim with detergents, caustic soap or petroleum-based cleaners. Plain soap and water works just fine, with a soft brush to clean dirt that may be ingrained. Wash the vinyl as frequently as the rest of the vehicle.

After cleaning, application of a high quality rubber and vinyl protectant will help prevent oxidation and cracks. The protectant can also be applied to weatherstripping, vacuum lines and rubber hoses, which often fail as a result of chemical degradation, and to the tires.

4 Upholstery and carpets - maintenance

1 Every three months remove the carpets or mats and clean the interior of the vehicle (more frequently if necessary). Vacuum the upholstery and carpets to remove loose dirt and dust.

2 Leather upholstery requires special care. Stains should be removed with warm water and a very mild soap solution. Use a clean, damp cloth to remove the soap, then wipe again with a dry cloth. Never use alcohol, gasoline, nail polish remover or thinner to clean leather upholstery.

3 After cleaning, regularly treat leather upholstery with a leather wax. Never use car wax on leather upholstery.

4 In areas where the interior of the vehicle is subject to bright sunlight, cover leather seats with a sheet if the vehicle is to be left out for any length of time.

5 Body repair - minor damage

See photo sequence

REPAIR OF MINOR SCRATCHES

1   If the scratch is superficial and does not penetrate to the metal of the body, repair is very simple. Lightly rub the scratched area with a fine rubbing compound to remove loose paint and built up wax. Rinse the area with clean water.

2   Apply touch-up paint to the scratch, using a small brush. Continue to apply thin layers of paint until the surface of the paint in the scratch is level with the surrounding paint. Allow the new paint at least two weeks to harden, then blend it into the surrounding paint by rubbing with a very fine rubbing compound. Finally, apply a coat of wax to the scratch area.

3   If the scratch has penetrated the paint and exposed the metal of the body, causing the metal to rust, a different repair technique is required. Remove all loose rust from the bottom of the scratch with a pocket knife, then apply rust inhibiting paint to prevent the formation of rust in the future. Using a rubber or nylon applicator, coat the scratched area with glaze-type filler. If required, the filler can be mixed with thinner to provide a very thin paste, which is ideal for filling narrow scratches. Before the glaze filler in the scratch hardens, wrap a piece of smooth cotton cloth around the tip of a finger. Dip the cloth in thinner and then quickly wipe it along the surface of the scratch. This will ensure that the surface of the filler is slightly hollow. The scratch can now be painted over as described earlier in this Section.

REPAIR OF DENTS

✳✳ WARNING:

Some models covered by this manual are equipped with airbags. Always disable the airbag system before working in the vicinity of any airbag system component to avoid the possibility of accidental deployment of the airbag(s), which could cause personal injury (see Chapter 12).

4   When repairing dents, the first job is to pull the dent out until the affected area is as close as possible to its original shape. There is no point in trying to restore the original shape completely as the metal in the damaged area will have stretched on impact and cannot be restored to its original contours. It is better to bring the level of the dent up to a point about 1/8-inch below the level of the surrounding metal. In cases where the dent is very shallow, it is not worth trying to pull it back out at all.

5   If the back side of the dent is accessible, it can be hammered out gently from behind using a soft-face hammer. While doing this, hold a block of wood firmly against the opposite side of the metal to absorb the hammer blows and prevent the metal from being stretched.

6   If the dent is in a section of the body which has double layers, or some other factor makes it inaccessible from behind, a different technique is required. Drill several small holes through the metal inside the damaged area, particularly in the deeper sections. Screw long, self tapping screws into the holes just enough for them to get a good grip in the metal. Now the dent can be pulled out by pulling on the protruding heads of the screws with locking pliers.

7   The next stage of repair is the removal of the paint from the dam-

aged area and from an inch or so of the surrounding metal. This is easily done with a wire brush or sanding disk in a drill motor, although it can be done just as effectively by hand with sandpaper. To complete the preparation for filling, score the surface of the bare metal with a screwdriver or the tang of a file or drill small holes in the affected area. This will provide a good grip for the filler material. To complete the repair, see the Section on filling and painting.

REPAIR OF RUST HOLES OR GASHES

8   Remove all paint from the affected area and from an inch or so of the surrounding metal using a sanding disk or wire brush mounted in a drill motor. If these are not available, a few sheets of sandpaper will do the job just as effectively.

9   With the paint removed, you will be able to determine the severity of the corrosion and decide whether to replace the whole panel, if possible, or repair the affected area. New body panels are not as expensive as most people think and it is often quicker to install a new panel than to repair large areas of rust.

10 Remove all trim pieces from the affected area except those which will act as a guide to the original shape of the damaged body, such as headlight shells, etc. Using metal snips or a hacksaw blade, remove all loose metal and any other metal that is badly affected by rust. Hammer the edges of the hole in to create a slight depression for the filler material.

11 Wire brush the affected area to remove the powdery rust from the surface of the metal. If the back of the rusted area is accessible, treat it with rust inhibiting paint.

12 Before filling is done, block the hole in some way. This can be done with sheet metal riveted or screwed into place, or by stuffing the hole with wire mesh.

13 Once the hole is blocked off, the affected area can be filled and painted. See the following subsection on filling and painting.

FILLING AND PAINTING

14 Many types of body fillers are available, but generally speaking, body repair kits which contain filler paste and a tube of resin hardener are best for this type of repair work. A wide, flexible plastic or nylon applicator will be necessary for imparting a smooth and contoured finish to the surface of the filler material. Mix up a small amount of filler on a clean piece of wood or cardboard (use the hardener sparingly). Follow the manufacturer's instructions on the package, otherwise the filler will set incorrectly.

15 Using the applicator, apply the filler paste to the prepared area. Draw the applicator across the surface of the filler to achieve the desired contour and to level the filler surface. As soon as a contour that approximates the original one is achieved, stop working the paste. If you continue, the paste will begin to stick to the applicator. Continue to add thin layers of paste at 20-minute intervals until the level of the filler is just above the surrounding metal.

16 Once the filler has hardened, the excess can be removed with a body file. From then on, progressively finer grades of sandpaper should be used, starting with a 180-grit paper and finishing with 600-grit wet-or-dry paper. Always wrap the sandpaper around a flat rubber or wooden block, otherwise the surface of the filler will not be completely flat. During the sanding of the filler surface, the wet-or-dry paper should be periodically rinsed in water. This will ensure that a very

These photos illustrate a method of repairing simple dents. They are intended to supplement Body repair - minor damage in this Chapter and should not be used as the sole instructions for body repair on these vehicles.

1   If you can't access the backside of the body panel to hammer out the dent, pull it out with a slide-hammer-type dent puller. In the deepest portion of the dent or along the crease line, drill or punch hole(s) at least one inch apart . . .

2   . . . then screw the slide-hammer into the hole and operate it. Tap with a hammer near the edge of the dent to help 'pop' the metal back to its original shape. When you're finished, the dent area should be close to its original contour and about 1/8-inch below the surface of the surrounding metal

3   Using coarse-grit sandpaper, remove the paint down to the bare metal. Hand sanding works fine, but the disc sander shown here makes the job faster. Use finer (about 320-grit) sandpaper to feather-edge the paint at least one inch around the dent area

4   When the paint is removed, touch will probably be more helpful than sight for telling if the metal is straight. Hammer down the high spots or raise the low spots as necessary. Clean the repair area with wax/silicone remover

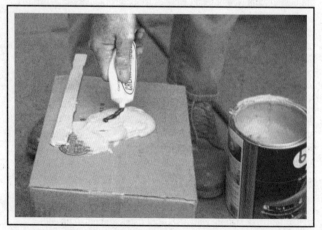

5   Following label instructions, mix up a batch of plastic filler and hardener. The ratio of filler to hardener is critical, and, if you mix it incorrectly, it will either not cure properly or cure too quickly (you won't have time to file and sand it into shape)

6   Working quickly so the filler doesn't harden, use a plastic applicator to press the body filler firmly into the metal, assuring it bonds completely. Work the filler until it matches the original contour and is slightly above the surrounding metal

7   Let the filler harden until you can just dent it with your fingernail. Use a body file or Surform tool (shown here) to rough-shape the filler

8   Use coarse-grit sandpaper and a sanding board or block to work the filler down until it's smooth and even. Work down to finer grits of sandpaper - always using a board or block - ending up with 360 or 400 grit

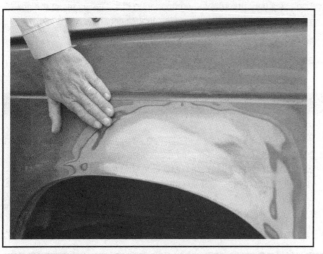

9   You shouldn't be able to feel any ridge at the transition from the filler to the bare metal or from the bare metal to the old paint. As soon as the repair is flat and uniform, remove the dust and mask off the adjacent panels or trim pieces

10   Apply several layers of primer to the area. Don't spray the primer on too heavy, so it sags or runs, and make sure each coat is dry before you spray on the next one. A professional-type spray gun is being used here, but aerosol spray primer is available inexpensively from auto parts stores

11   The primer will help reveal imperfections or scratches. Fill these with glazing compound. Follow the label instructions and sand it with 360 or 400-grit sandpaper until it's smooth. Repeat the glazing, sanding and respraying until the primer reveals a perfectly smooth surface

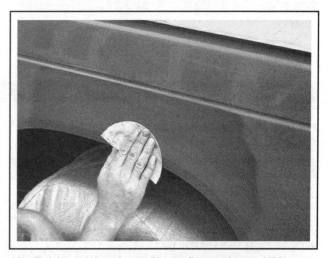

12   Finish sand the primer with very fine sandpaper (400 or 600-grit) to remove the primer overspray. Clean the area with water and allow it to dry. Use a tack rag to remove any dust, then apply the finish coat. Don't attempt to rub out or wax the repair area until the paint has dried completely (at least two weeks)

smooth finish is produced in the final stage.

17 At this point, the repair area should be surrounded by a ring of bare metal, which in turn should be encircled by the finely feathered edge of good paint. Rinse the repair area with clean water until all of the dust produced by the sanding operation is gone.

18 Spray the entire area with a light coat of primer. This will reveal any imperfections in the surface of the filler. Repair the imperfections with fresh filler paste or glaze filler and once more smooth the surface with sandpaper. Repeat this spray-and-repair procedure until you are satisfied that the surface of the filler and the feathered edge of the paint are perfect. Rinse the area with clean water and allow it to dry completely.

19 The repair area is now ready for painting. Spray painting must be carried out in a warm, dry, windless and dust free atmosphere. These conditions can be created if you have access to a large indoor work area, but if you are forced to work in the open, you will have to pick the day very carefully. If you are working indoors, dousing the floor in the work area with water will help settle the dust which would otherwise be in the air. If the repair area is confined to one body panel, mask off the surrounding panels. This will help minimize the effects of a slight mis-

match in paint color. Trim pieces such as chrome strips, door handles, etc. will also need to be masked off or removed. Use masking tape and several thicknesses of newspaper for the masking operations.

20 Before spraying, shake the paint can thoroughly, then spray a test area until the spray painting technique is mastered. Cover the repair area with a thick coat of primer. The thickness should be built up using several thin layers of primer rather than one thick one. Using 600-grit wet-or-dry sandpaper, rub down the surface of the primer until it is very smooth. While doing this, the work area should be thoroughly rinsed with water and the wet-or-dry sandpaper periodically rinsed as well. Allow the primer to dry before spraying additional coats.

21 Spray on the top coat, again building up the thickness by using several layers of paint. Begin spraying in the center of the repair area and then, using a circular motion, work out until the whole repair area and about two inches of the surrounding original paint is covered. Remove all masking material 10 to 15 minutes after spraying on the final coat of paint. Allow the new paint at least two weeks to harden, then use a very fine rubbing compound to blend the edges of the new paint into the existing paint. Finally, apply a coat of wax.

6   Body repair - major damage

1 Major damage must be repaired by an auto body shop. These shops have the specialized equipment required to do the job properly.

2 If the damage is extensive, the frame must be checked for proper alignment or the vehicle's handling characteristics may be adversely affected and other components may wear at an accelerated rate.

3 Due to the fact that all of the major body components (hood,

fenders, etc.) are separate and replaceable units, any seriously damaged components should be replaced rather than repaired. Sometimes the components can be found in a wrecking yard that specializes in used vehicle components, often at a considerable savings over the cost of new parts.

7   Hinges and locks - maintenance

Once every 3,000 miles, or every three months, the hinges and latch assemblies on the doors, hood and the tailgate should be given a few drops of light oil or lock lubricant. The door latch strikers should also

be lubricated with a thin coat of grease to reduce wear and ensure free movement. Lubricate the door locks with spray-on graphite lubricant.

8   Hood - removal, installation and adjustment

▶ **Refer to illustrations 8.3 and 8.4**

✳✳ WARNING:

Some models covered by this manual are equipped with airbags. Always disable the airbag system before working in the vicinity of any airbag system component to avoid the possibility of accidental deployment of the airbag(s), which could cause personal injury (see Chapter 12).

➡**Note: The hood is heavy and somewhat awkward to remove and install - at least two people should perform this procedure.**

REMOVAL AND INSTALLATION

1 Open the hood and support it in the open position with a long piece of wood.

2 Cover the fenders and cowl with blankets or heavy cloths to protect the paint.

3 Scribe or draw alignment marks around the hinge and bolt heads to ensure proper alignment on reinstallation (see illustration).

4 Disconnect the underhood light connector on the driver's side and the ground strap on the passenger side of the hood (if equipped) (see illustration).

5 Have an assistant hold onto the hood on one side while you hold

8.3 Scribe or draw alignment marks on the hood to ensure proper alignment on reinstallation

8.4 Detach the ground strap from the hood (if equipped)

the other side.

6   Remove the hood-to-hinge assembly bolts on your side of the hood, then hold your side of the hood while your assistant removes the hood-to-hinge bolts on the other side.

7   Lift the hood off.

8   Installation is the reverse of the removal steps with the following additions:

   a) *Align the hood and hinges using the alignment marks made in Step 3.*

   b) *Be sure to tighten the bolts securely.*

ADJUSTMENT

9   The hood can be adjusted to obtain a flush fit between the hood and fenders.

10 Loosen the hood retaining bolts.

11 Move the hood from side-to-side or front-to-rear until the hood is properly aligned with the fenders at the front. Tighten the bolts securely.

12 Loosen the bolts securing the hood latch assembly.

13 Move the latch until alignment is correct with the hood latch striker. Tighten the latch bolt securely.

9   Hood latch control cable - removal and installation

▶ **Refer to illustration 9.2**

✳✳ WARNING:

Some models covered by this manual are equipped with airbags. Always disable the airbag system before working in the vicinity of any airbag system component to avoid the possibility of accidental deployment of the airbag(s), which could cause personal injury (see Chapter 12).

1   Open the hood and support it in the open position with a long piece of wood.

2   Scribe or draw alignment marks around the hood latch to ensure proper alignment on reinstallation (see illustration).

3   Remove the bolts securing the hood latch and take the latch out.

4   Detach the cable bushing and lift the cable eye off the anchor post.

5   Note the routing of the cable within the engine compartment and remove any fasteners that secure the cable.

6   Remove the screws that secure the hood release handle to the instrument panel.

7   Remove the tie wrap that secures the cable to the steering column bracket.

8   Working in the passenger compartment, remove the cable grommet from the firewall, then pull the cable through.

9.2 Mark the position of the hood latch for proper installation

9   Installation is the reverse of the removal steps with the following additions:

   a) *Insert the cable through the grommet in the firewall and make sure the grommet is properly seated within the firewall hole.*

   b) *Before closing the hood, operate the control cable and make sure the latch control operates correctly.*

10 Door - removal, installation and alignment

REMOVAL AND INSTALLATION

1   With the door in the open position, place a jack under the door or have an assistant hold the door while the hinge bolts are removed.

➡**Note: Place thick padding on top of the jack to protect the door's painted finish.**

2   On models so equipped, remove the upper and lower hinge access cover plates. Disconnect the electrical connectors to the door wiring harness.

3   Scribe or paint lines around the door hinges to ensure proper alignment on reinstallation.

4   Remove the hinge-to-door bolts and carefully lift off the door.

5   Installation is the reverse of the removal steps. Align the door.

ALIGNMENT

6   Check the alignment of the door all around the edge. The door should be evenly spaced in the opening and should be flush with the body.

7   Adjust if necessary as follows:

a) *Note how the door is misaligned and determine which bolts need to be loosened to correct it.*

b) *Loosen the bolts just enough so the door can be moved with a padded prybar. Reposition the door as necessary, then tighten the bolts securely.*

c) *The door lock striker can also be adjusted both up-and-down and sideways to provide positive engagement with the lock mechanism (see Section 12).*

8   Tighten the hinge-to-body bolts securely.

11 Door hinge - removal and installation

➡**Note: If both hinges are to be replaced, it is easier to leave the door in place and replace one hinge at a time.**

1   With the door in the open position, place a jack under the door or have an assistant hold the door while the door hinge bolts are removed.

➡**Note: If a jack is used, place thick padding on top of the jack to protect the door's painted finish.**

2   On models so equipped, remove the upper and lower hinge access cover plates.

3   Scribe or draw lines around the door hinges to ensure proper

alignment on reinstallation.

4   Remove the hinge-to-door bolts, then the hinge-to-body bolts. Carefully remove the hinge(s) or lift off the door.

5   Installation is the reverse of the removal Steps with the following additions:

a) *Apply a body sealant to the hinge before installing it onto the body panel.*

b) *Adjust the door if necessary (see Section 10).*

12 Door latch striker - removal, installation and adjustment

REMOVAL AND INSTALLATION

1   Use a Torx bit to unscrew the door latch striker stud from the door jamb.

2   Installation is the reverse of removal. Adjust if necessary.

ADJUSTMENT

3   The door latch striker can be adjusted vertically and laterally as well as fore-and-aft.

➡**Note: Don't use the door latch striker to compensate for door misalignment.**

4   The door latch striker can be shimmed to obtain the correct clearance between the latch and the striker. Don't use more than one shim per door.

5   To check the clearance between the latch jamb and the striker area, spread a layer of dark grease on the striker.

6   Open and close the door several times and note the pattern in the grease.

7   Move the door striker assembly laterally to provide a flush fit at the door and pillar or at the quarter panel.

8   Securely tighten the door latch striker after adjustment is complete.

13 Inner door handle and latch assembly - removal and installation

➡**Note 1: The interior door handle is secured by a single rivet that must be drilled out for handle removal. A rivet gun is necessary to replace the drilled out rivet and to secure the handle in its original position.**

➡**Note 2: The interior door handle uses a cable to actuate the door latch instead of a hard link or rod. The cable must be detached to remove the door handle.**

1   Remove the door trim panel and watershield (see Section 16).

2   Remove the fastener(s) securing the inner door handle assembly to the door.

3   Disconnect the handle link from the handle and lock cylinder.

➡**Note: The rear run channel for the window glass must be removed to gain access to the door latch. Simply remove the fastener and move the run channel aside.**

4 Detach the rods or any electrical connectors from the latch, then remove the latch screws and take it out.

5 Installation is the reverse of the removal steps, plus the following additions:

a) If a new latch is being installed, install the rod retaining clips in it.

b) Attach the control rod and lock cylinder rod to the latch before installing the latch.

c) Tighten the latch screws securely.

d) Check operation of the handle and lock before installing the watershield and door panel.

14 Outer door handle - removal and installation

→Note: This Section is specific to front door handles, but the procedure can be applied to vertical rear door handles.

1 Remove the door trim panel and pull away the watershield (see Section 16).

2 Disconnect the door latch actuator rod from the latch.

3 Support the door handle in the open position. Make sure the window is in the fully up position.

4 Drill out both rivets that secure the handle to the door and remove the handle.

5 Installation is the reverse of the removal steps. Position the handle in the door and install the two pop-rivets.

15 Door lock cylinder - removal and installation

1 Raise the window all the way.

2 Remove the door trim panel and watershield (see Section 16).

3 Disconnect the door latch control-to-cylinder rod.

4 Use a pair of pliers and slide the cylinder retainer clip away from the lock cylinder and door.

5 Remove the lock cylinder from the door.

6 Install the lock cylinder into the door opening from the outside and push the retainer clip into place. Make sure it's seated correctly.

7 Reconnect the lock cylinder rod-to-door latch control.

8 Check for proper lock operation, then install the watershield and the door trim panel.

16 Door trim panel and watershield - removal and installation

▶ Refer to illustrations 16.1, 16.3a, 16.3b and 16.5

1 If the truck is equipped with manual windows, remove the window regulator handle (see illustration).

2 If the truck is equipped with power windows or door locks, remove the switches by removing the screws for the power window switch and the other switch connectors on the back side of the door trim finish panel.

3 Remove the screws from the armrest area of the door panel (see illustrations).

4 Remove the inner door handle (see Section 13).

5 Remove the screw (if equipped) at the lower rear of the door

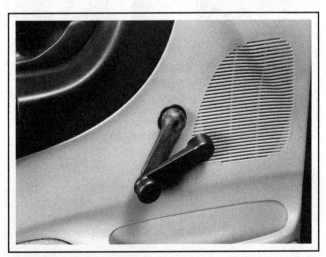

16.1 Pull back the window crank trim and remove the screw (manual windows)

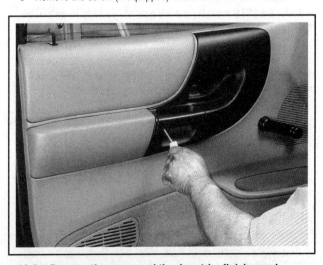

16.3a Remove the screw and the door trim finish panel . . .

16.3b . . . and remove the panel screws from the armrest area

16.5 Remove one screw (if equipped) that secures the lower rear corner of the panel

panel (see illustration).

6   Lift the panel at least 1-1/2 inches to disengage it from the slots along the bottom of the door, then remove it.

7   If necessary, carefully peel the watershield from the door. Be careful not to tear it.

8   Installation is the reverse of the removal Steps.

17   Front door window glass - replacement and adjustment

REPLACEMENT

▶ **Refer to illustration 17.5**

1   Remove the door trim panel and watershield (see Section 16).

2   On 2010 and ealier models, remove the door speakers (if equipped) (see Chapter 12).

3   Raise the window all the way.

➡**Note: On 2011 models, the window only needs to be raised halfway to expose the glass run retainer.**

4   Detach the rear glass run retainer from the door and take it out.

5   Lower the window enough to provide access to the glass bracket and retention rivets (see illustration). Tap the center pin out of each rivet with a punch, then drill out the rivets with a 1/4-inch drill.

6   Lift the glass out through the top of the door.

7   Installation is the reverse of the removal Steps, with the following additions:

   a) *Lubricate the regulator rollers, shafts and tracks with multi-purpose grease.*

   b) *Raise and lower the window to check its operation before installing the speakers (if equipped), watershield and door trim panel.*

ADJUSTMENT

8   Lower the glass two-to-three inches from the full-up position.

9   Loosen the three guide assembly nut and washer assemblies.

10   Push the glass toward the rear until it bottoms out within the

17.5 Drill out the rivets to detach the glass

door frame.

11   Move the window guide post toward the rear within the retention slot in the door inner panel. Tighten the three guide assembly nuts securely.

12   Raise and lower the window several times and check for proper fit.

13   Install the watershield and door trim panel.

18 Front door window regulator - replacement

1 If you're working on a vehicle with power windows, disconnect the negative cable from the battery.

2 Remove the door trim panel and watershield (see Section 16).

3 Remove the window glass (see Section 17).

4 If you're working on a vehicle with power windows, disconnect the window motor electrical connector.

5 Carefully drill-out the rivets that secure the regulator base plate to the inner door panel.

6 Remove the nuts that secure the glass guide channel to the door.

7 Remove the regulator from the door, together with the power window motor (if equipped). If necessary, detach the window motor from the regulator.

✳✳ WARNING:

Before removing the motor from the regulator, secure the regulator arm to the regulator body to prevent the arm from unloading violently when the motor is detached.

8 Attach the regulator to the inner door panel. This can be done with rivets, or with suitable bolts, nuts and washers. If you use nuts and bolts, tighten them securely.

9 The remainder of installation is the reverse of the removal Steps.

19 Front bumper and valance - removal and installation

✳✳ WARNING:

Some models covered by this manual are equipped with airbags. Always disable the airbag system before working in the vicinity of any airbag system component to avoid the possibility of accidental deployment of the airbag(s), which could cause personal injury (see Chapter 12).

➡Note: The bumper is heavy and somewhat awkward to remove and install - at least two people should perform this procedure.

2010 AND EARLIER MODELS

1 If you're working on a vehicle with fog lights, unbolt their brackets and remove them from the bumper.

2 Support the bumper with a jack and block of wood. Remove the mounting nuts on each side and detach the bumper from the vehicle.

3 Remove the screws and pushpins and detach the valance panel from the bumper.

4 Installation is the reverse of removal. Tighten the fasteners securely.

2011 MODELS

➡Note: The bumper and bumper covers must be removed as an assembly.

5 If equipped with fog lights, disconnect the electrical connectors.

6 Remove the nuts, and remove the front bumper and bumper cover as an assembly.

7 The lower bumper cover is attached to the bumper with clips. Detach the clips to remove the lower cover. If you are replacing the lower bumper cover, remove the fog lights from the cover.

8 The upper bumper cover is attached to the bumper with plastic rivets. Use a punch to drive out the rivets and remove the upper cover from the bumper.

9 Installation is the reverse of removal. Tighten the bumper fasteners to 41 ft-lbs.

20 Rear bumper - removal and installation

➡Note: The bumper is heavy and somewhat awkward to remove and install - at least two people should perform this procedure.

1 Support the rear bumper with a jack.

2 Unbolt the bumper brackets from the vehicle and lower it clear.

3 Detach the brackets from the vehicle as necessary.

4 Installation is the reverse of the removal steps. Tighten the nuts and bolts securely.

21 Radiator grille - removal and installation

✳✳ WARNING:

Some models covered by this manual are equipped with airbags. Always disable the airbag system before working in the vicinity of any airbag system component to avoid the possibility of accidental deployment of the airbag(s), which could cause personal injury (see Chapter 12).

1 Open the hood.

➡Note: The panel that the radiator grille is mounted to must be removed before the next step. The headlight assemblies must also be removed to get this panel out.

2 Remove the screws or retaining fasteners and detach the grille from the vehicle.

3 Installation is the reverse of the removal procedure. Be careful not to overtighten the screws.

22 Front fender - removal and installation

※ WARNING:

Some models covered by this manual are equipped with airbags. Always disable the airbag system before working in the vicinity of any airbag system component to avoid the possibility of accidental deployment of the airbag(s), which could cause personal injury (see Chapter 12).

1   Before you start, it's a good idea to check the fender fasteners for dirt, especially in the wheel well. The job will be easier if you wash off the dirt first with a high-pressure hose.

➡Note: It may be necessary to remove the front bumper.

2   Remove the front side marker lamp (see Chapter 12).
3   Unbolt the lower rear corner of the fender from the rocker panel.
4   Open the door and remove the single cowl-to-fender bolt.

➡Note: The panel that the radiator grille is mounted to must be removed before the next step. The headlight assemblies must also be removed to get this panel out.

5   Remove the fasteners and detach the inner fender panel.
6   Open the hood and remove the bolts across the top of the fender.
7   Unbolt the fender brace from the radiator support. Carefully detach the fender from the vehicle.
8   Installation is the reverse of the removal procedure. Don't tighten any of the bolts until they are all installed.

23 Windshield and fixed glass - removal and installation

Replacement of the windshield and fixed glass requires the use of special fast-setting adhesive/caulk materials and some specialized tools and techniques. These operations should be left to a dealer service department or a shop specializing in automotive glass work.

24 Console - removal and installation

※ WARNING:

Some models covered by this manual are equipped with airbags. Always disable the airbag system before working in the vicinity of any airbag system component to avoid the possibility of accidental deployment of the airbag(s), which could cause personal injury (see Chapter 12).

2010 AND EARLIER MODELS

1   Carefully pry out the trim covers for access to the console rear mounting bolts, then remove the bolts.
2   Lift off the armrest and remove the single screw beneath it.
3   Remove the cup holder screws, lift off the cup holder and remove the two screws beneath it.
4   Lift the console away from the mounting brackets and remove it from the vehicle.
5   Installation is the reverse of the removal steps.

2011 MODELS

6   On consoles with a speaker housing, lift the mats from the storage tray and cup holder and remove the screw(s) beneath the mats.
7   On consoles with a speaker housing, remove the pushpin fasteners and remove the front section of the console.
8   Position the seats fully forward.
9   Remove the armrest bolt covers and remove the bolts. Remove the armrest.
10 Remove the rear screw from the console.
11 Slide the seats all the way to the rear. On consoles with a speaker housing, remove the cup holder.
12 Remove the front screws and remove the console. On consoles with a speaker housing, tilt the rear of the housing up slightly.
13 Installation is the reverse of removal.

25 Steering column covers - removal and installation

※ WARNING:

Some models covered by this manual are equipped with airbags. Always disable the airbag system before working in the vicinity of any airbag system component to avoid the possibility of accidental deployment of the airbag(s), which could cause personal injury (see Chapter 12).

2010 AND EARLIER MODELS

▸ Refer to illustrations 25.3a and 25.3b

1   Remove the steering column cover screws and remove the cover and opening reinforcement.

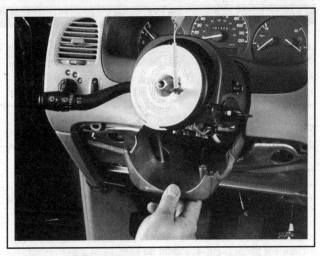

25.3a Remove the screws from the underside of the shroud . . .

25.3b . . . and lower it away from the steering column

2   If equipped, unscrew the tilt lever. Squeeze the top and bottom of the tilt lever collar and remove it.

3   Remove the screws from the underside of the lower column shroud and lower the shroud away from the column (see illustrations). On vehicles with automatic transmission, you may need to move the shift lever.

4   Lift the upper shroud half off the column.

5   Installation is the reverse of removal.

2011 MODELS

6   Remove the key lock cylinder (see Chapter 12).

7   If equipped, unscrew the tilt lever. Squeeze the top and bottom of the tilt lever collar and remove it.

8   Remove the cover mounting screws from below the steering column and remove the upper and lower covers.

9   Installation is the reverse of removal.

26 Instrument cluster bezel - removal and installation

2010 AND EARLIER MODELS

▶ **Refer to illustration 26.2**

1   Remove the steering column cover and reinforcement (see Section 25).

2   Remove the cluster bezel screws and take the bezel out (see illustration). On 2006 and later models, unbolt the hood release lever before removing the cluster finish panel.

3   Installation is the reverse of removal.

2011 MODELS

4   Disconnect the retainers from the lower trim panel and remove the panel, then remove the bolts securing the opening reinforcement to remove it.

5   Remove the radio (see Chapter 12), then remove the center bezel retaining screws. Remove the center bezel and disconnect the electrical connectors.

6   Remove the upper and lower cluster bezel screws and remove the

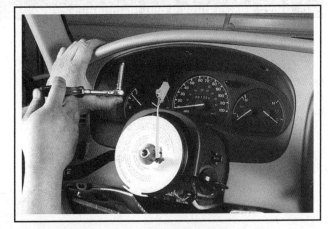

26.2 Remove the cluster bezel screws and withdraw the bezel

bezel (see illustration 26.2). Disconnect the electrical connectors.

7   Installation is the reverse of removal.

27 Instrument panel - removal and installation

✷✷ WARNING:

Some models covered by this manual are equipped with airbags. Always disable the airbag system before working in the vicinity of any airbag system component to avoid the possibility of accidental deployment of the airbag(s), which could cause personal injury (see Chapter 12).

➡Note: Removal of the instrument panel is a difficult procedure not recommended for the home mechanic. There are many hidden fasteners and electrical connectors that must be located and disconnected. Take notes and digital pictures before disconnecting anything. Unless you have a high skill level and experience with procedures such as this and have an assistant to help you, instrument panel removal should be handled at a dealership.

1   Lock or clamp the steering column in the straight-ahead position. Remove the steering wheel (see Chapter 10).
2   Inside the engine compartment, move the fuse box aside by releasing the retaining tabs.
3   Open the hood. Locate the instrument cluster electrical connectors in the engine compartment and disconnect them.
4   Unbolt the hood release handle and parking brake control from the instrument panel.
5   If the vehicle is equipped with a center console, remove it (see Section 24).
➡Note: The instrument panel procedure is easier if the front seats are removed first (see Section 29).
6   Remove the knee bolster from below the steering column.
7   If you're working on a 4WD model with shift levers, push the transfer case control all the way forward.
8   Remove the steering column cover and reinforcement from the instrument panel (see Section 25).

9   Disconnect the connector above the brake pedal near the booster pushrod. Also, disconnect the connector above the clutch pedal that's attached to the rod that actuates the clutch.
10   Unbolt the steering column from the crossmember of the instrument panel and carefully lower the column.
11   Unbolt the bracket at the right of the accelerator pedal.
12   Remove the trim covers at the edge of the carpet on the bottom of the door jam (scuff plates), the kick panels, and the trim on each the side of the windshield (the A-pillar interior trim). Do this on both sides of the vehicle.
13   Remove the passenger compartment fuse panel on the LH side of the instrument panel.
14   Disconnect the electrical connectors behind the center, right side and then left side of the instrument panel (connectors for the radio, climate control, electrical modules, etc.)
15   Working inside the fuse box opening, remove two bolts that secure the instrument panel to the cowl.
16   Remove the single mounting bolt at the lower right of the instrument panel.
17   Remove the sound deadener from the lower right of the instrument panel (if equipped).
18   Carefully pry up the edge of the defroster grille with a wooden tool and detach its clips, then lift it out.
19   Remove the mounting bolts at the top of the panel. Mark and unplug any remaining electrical connectors.
20   Check carefully to make sure the panel is completely detached from the vehicle, then lift it out.
➡Note: It's best to use an assistant to help move the instrument panel out of the vehicle.

21   Installation is the reverse of the removal steps.

28 Glove box - removal and installation

▶ Refer to illustration 28.1

1   Open the glove box. Squeeze the sides of the glove box together to disengage the tabs and let the glove box hang down. Remove its mounting screws and take it out of the instrument panel (see illustration).
2   Installation is the reverse of the removal steps.

28.1 Swing the glove box down and remove the screws

29 Seats - removal and installation

WARNING:

Some models covered by this manual are equipped with airbags. Always disable the airbag system before working in the vicinity of any airbag system component to avoid the possibility of accidental deployment of the airbag(s), which could cause personal injury (see Chapter 12).

BUCKET AND BENCH SEATS

1 Remove the seat track shield (if equipped). Disconnect any electrical connectors under the seat.

2 Remove the four bolts securing the seat track to the floorpan. On some bench seat models, the center seat belt anchor must be unbolted from the floor to remove the seat.

3 Carefully tilt the seat up and disconnect any electrical connectors

underneath which may prevent removal, then lift the seat away from the vehicle.

4 Installation is the reverse of the removal steps. Tighten the retaining bolts securely.

TILT-SLIDE SEATS (SUPERCAB MODELS)

5 Tilt the seat back and slide it all the way forward.

6 Pull the lock tabs or pushpins on the seat track insulators clear of the tracks and unbolt the rear ends of the seat tracks from the floorpan. On later models, remove the pushpins securing the seat front trim panel for access to the seat mounting bolts.

7 Tilt the seat upright and slide it to the rear.

8 Disconnect the seat electrical connector (if equipped). Unbolt the front ends of the seat tracks and remove the seat from the vehicle.

9 Installation is the reverse of the removal steps. Tighten the retaining bolts securely.

30 Seat belt check

WARNING:

Some models covered by this manual are equipped with airbags. Always disable the airbag system before working in the vicinity of any airbag system component to avoid the possibility of accidental deployment of the airbag(s), which could cause personal injury (see Chapter 12).

1 Check the seat belts, buckles, latch plates and guide loops for

obvious damage and signs of wear.

2 Check that the seat belt reminder light comes on when the ignition key is turned to the Run or Start position.

3 The seat belts are designed to lock up during a sudden stop or impact, yet allow free movement during normal driving. Check that the retractors return the belt against your chest while driving and rewind the belt fully when the buckle is unlatched.

4 If any of the above checks reveal problems with the seat belt system, replace parts as necessary.

31 Mirrors (exterior) - removal and installation

▶ **Refer to illustration 31.4**

1 Remove the door trim panel (see Section 16).

2 Disconnect the electrical connector for the power mirror (if equipped).

➡**Note: Remove the watershield and speaker to access the electrical connector for power mirrors, if necessary.**

3 Where necessary, lower the window for access to the mirror mounting nuts.

4 Remove the mounting nuts and remove the mirror (see illustration).

5 Installation is the reverse of removal.

31.4 Remove the fasteners to detach the mirror

Notes

Section

12

CHASSIS ELECTRICAL SYSTEM

1 General information

➡Note: Whenever the battery is disconnected, the powertrain control module must reset itself. This may cause driveability problems until the vehicle has been driven 10 miles or more.

The chassis electrical system of this vehicle is a 12-volt, negative ground type. Power for the lights and all electrical accessories is supplied by a lead/acid-type battery which is charged by the alternator.

This Chapter covers repair and service procedures for various chassis (non-engine related) electrical components. For information regarding the engine electrical system components (battery, alternator, distributor and starter motor), see Chapter 5.

2 Electrical troubleshooting - general information

A typical electrical circuit consists of an electrical component, any switches, relays, motors, fuses, fusible links or circuit breakers, etc. related to that component and the wiring and connectors that link the components to both the battery and the chassis. To help you pinpoint an electrical circuit problem, wiring diagrams are included at the end of this book.

Before tackling any troublesome electrical circuit, first study the appropriate wiring diagrams to get a complete understanding of what makes up that individual circuit. Trouble spots, for instance, can often be isolated by noting if other components related to that circuit are often routed through the same fuse and ground connections.

Electrical problems usually stem from simple causes such as loose or corroded connectors, a blown fuse, a melted fusible link or a bad relay. Visually inspect the condition of all fuses, wires and connectors in a problem circuit before troubleshooting it.

The basic tools needed for electrical troubleshooting include a circuit tester, a high impedance (10 K-ohm) digital voltmeter, a continuity tester and a jumper wire with an inline circuit breaker for bypassing electrical components. Before attempting to locate or define a problem with electrical test instruments, use the wiring diagrams to decide where to make the necessary connections.

VOLTAGE CHECKS

Perform a voltage check first when a circuit is not functioning properly. Connect one lead of a circuit tester to either the negative battery terminal or a known good ground.

Connect the other lead to a connector in the circuit being tested, preferably nearest to the battery or fuse. If the bulb of the tester lights up, voltage is present, which means that the part of the circuit between the connector and the battery is problem free. Continue checking the rest of the circuit in the same fashion.

When you reach a point at which no voltage is present, the problem lies between that point and the last test point with voltage. Most of the time the problem can be traced to a loose connection.

➡Note: Keep in mind that some circuits receive voltage only when the ignition key is in the Accessory or Run position.

FINDING A SHORT CIRCUIT

One method of finding shorts in a circuit is to remove the fuse and connect a test light or voltmeter in its place. There should be no voltage present in the circuit. Move the electrical connectors from side-to-side while watching the test light. If the bulb goes on, there is a short to ground somewhere in that area, probably where the insulation has been rubbed through. The same test can be performed on each component in a circuit, even a switch.

GROUND CHECK

Perform a ground test to check whether a component is properly grounded. Dis-connect the battery and connect one lead of a self-powered test light, known as a continuity tester, to a known good ground. Connect the other lead to the wire or ground connection being tested. If the bulb goes on, the ground is good. If the bulb does not go on, the ground is not good.

CONTINUITY CHECK

A continuity check determines if there are any breaks in a circuit - if it is conducting electricity properly. With the circuit off (no power in the circuit), a self-powered continuity tester can be used to check the circuit. Connect the test leads to both ends of the circuit, and if the test light comes on the circuit is passing current properly. If the light doesn't come on, there is a break somewhere in the circuit. The same procedure can be used to test a switch, by connecting the continuity tester to the power in and power out sides of the switch. With the switch turned on, the test light should come on.

FINDING AN OPEN CIRCUIT

When diagnosing for possible open circuits it is often difficult to locate them by sight because oxidation or terminal misalignment are hidden by the connectors. Merely wiggling a connector on a sensor or in the electrical connector may correct the open circuit condition. Remember this if an open circuit is indicated when troubleshooting a circuit. Intermittent problems may also be caused by oxidized or loose connections.

Electrical troubleshooting is simple if you keep in mind that all electrical circuits are basically electricity running from the battery, through the wires, switches, relays, fuses and fusible links to each electrical component (light bulb, motor, etc.) and then to ground, from which it is passed back to the battery. Any electrical problem is an interruption in the flow of electricity to and from the battery.

3 Connectors - general information

Always release the lock lever(s) before attempting to unplug inline type connectors. There are a variety of lock lever configurations. Although nothing more than a finger is usually necessary to pry lock levers open, a small pocket screwdriver is effective for hard-to-release levers. Once the lock levers are released, try to pull on the connectors themselves when unplugging two connector halves (there are times, however, when this is not possible - use good judgment).

It is usually necessary to know which side, male or female, of the connector you're checking. Male connectors are easily distinguished from females by the shape of their internal pins.

When checking continuity or voltage with a circuit tester, insertion of the test probe into the receptacle may open the fitting to the connector and result in poor contact. Instead, insert the test probe from the wire harness side of the connector (known as "backprobing").

4 Fuses - general information

▶ **Refer to illustration 4.5**

The electrical circuits are protected by a combination of fuses, fusible links and circuit breakers. There are two fuse panels; one on the power distribution box in the engine compartment and one above the driver's footwell.

The fuse panels are equipped with miniaturized fuses because their compact dimensions and convenient blade-type terminal design allow fingertip removal and installation.

Each fuse protects one or more circuits. A fuse guide is included

here but consult your owner's manual - it will have the most accurate guide for your vehicle.

The cover of the footwell fuse panel contains spare fuses. The fuse puller is mounted in the fuse box.

If an electrical component fails, always check the fuse first. The best way to check the fuses is with a test light. Check for power at the exposed terminal tips of each fuse. If power is present at one side of the fuse but not the other, the fuse is blown. A blown fuse can also be identified by visually inspecting it (see illustration).

Use the fuse puller tool to remove and insert fuses. Don't twist the fuses during removal or installation. Twisting could force the terminal open too far, resulting in a bad connection.

Be sure to replace blown fuses with the correct type and amp rating. Fuses of different ratings are physically interchangeable, but replacing a fuse with one of a higher or lower value than specified is not recommended. Each electrical circuit needs a specific amount of protection. The amperage value of each fuse is molded into the fuse body. Different colors are also used to denote fuses of different amperage types.

4.5 When a fuse blows, the element between the terminals melts - the fuse on the left is blown, the fuse on the right is good

✳✳ CAUTION:

Always turn off all electrical components and the ignition switch before replacing a fuse. Never bypass a fuse with pieces of metal or foil. Serious damage to the electrical system, or even a fire, could result.

If the replacement fuse immediately fails, do not replace it again until the cause of the problem is isolated and corrected. In most cases, this will be a short circuit in the wiring caused by a broken or deteriorated wire.

5 Fusible links - general information

Some circuits are protected by fusible links. These links are used in circuits which are not ordinarily fused, such as the ignition circuit.

Although fusible links appear to be of heavier gauge than the wire they are protecting, their appearance is due to thicker insulation. All fusible links are several wire gauges smaller than the wire they are designed to protect.

Fusible links cannot be repaired, but a new link of the same size wire can be put in its place. The procedure is as follows:

a) *Disconnect the negative cable at the battery.*
b) *Disconnect the fusible link from the electrical connectors.*
c) *Cut the damaged fusible link out of the wiring just behind the connector.*

d) *Strip the insulation back approximately 1/2-inch.*
e) *Position the connector on the new fusible link and crimp it into place.*
f) *Splice and solder the new fusible link to the wires from which the old link was cut. Use rosin core solder at each end of the new link to obtain a good solder joint.*
g) *Wrap the splices completely with vinyl electrical tape around the soldered joint. No wires should be exposed.*
h) *Install the repaired wiring as before, using existing clips, if provided.*
i) *Connect the battery ground cable.*
j) *Test the circuit for proper operation.*

6 Circuit breakers - general information

Circuit breakers protect accessories such as the windshield wipers, windshield washer pump, interval wiper, low washer fluid, etc. Circuit breakers are located in the fuse box. Refer to the fuse panel guide in Section 4 and the fuse panel guide in your owner's manual for the location of the circuit breakers used in your vehicle.

Because a circuit breaker resets itself automatically, an electrical overload in a circuit breaker protected system will cause the circuit to fail momentarily, then come back on. If the circuit does not come back on, check it immediately.

a) *Remove the circuit breaker from the fuse panel.*
b) *Using an ohmmeter, verify that there is continuity between both terminals of the circuit breaker. If there is no continuity, replace the circuit breaker.*
c) *Install the old or new circuit breaker. If it continues to cut out, a short circuit is indicated. Troubleshoot the appropriate circuit (see the Wiring Diagrams at the back of this book) or have the system checked by a professional mechanic.*

7 Steering column switches - replacement

◆ **Refer to illustrations 7.4a, 7.4b and 7.5**

✳✳ WARNING:

Some models covered by this manual are equipped with airbags. Always disable the airbag system before working in the vicinity of any airbag system component to avoid the possibility of accidental deployment of the airbag(s), which could cause personal injury (see Section 28).

1 Disconnect the negative cable from the battery (and if equipped with an airbag, the positive cable, too).
2 On 2011 models, remove the key lock cylinder (see Section 9); if equipped, remove the tilt lever handle.

3 Remove the steering column lower cover and shrouds (see Chapter 11).

➡**Note: On 2011 models, remove the upper and lower steering column covers.**

4 Remove the two screws securing the switch assembly to the steering column (see illustrations).
5 Use a small screwdriver and release the tangs, then pull the electrical connector(s) from the switch (see illustration).
6 Remove the switch assembly.
7 Installation is the reverse of the removal steps. Be sure the horn harness grommet (if equipped) is positioned correctly (see illustration 7.4a). Check the steering column and switch for proper operation.

7.4a Remove the lower screw . . .   **7.4b . . . and the upper screw**   **7.5 Use a small screwdriver and release the tangs to allow connector removal**

8 Turn signal/hazard flasher relay - replacement

◆ **Refer to illustration 8.2**

1 Disconnect the negative cable from the battery.
2 The flasher relay is located under the instrument panel to the right of the steering column (see illustration). Remove the flasher by pulling straight out.
3 Install the new flasher unit. Be sure to line up the metal contacts with the slots in the fuse panel. Press the flasher firmly into place.

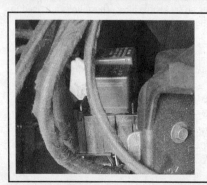

8.2 The flasher relay is located under the instrument panel to the right of the steering column

9   Ignition switch/key lock cylinder - replacement

▶ **Refer to illustrations 9.6a and 9.6b**

✳✳ WARNING:

Some models covered by this manual are equipped with airbags. Always disable the airbag system before working In the vicinity of any airbag system component to avoid the possibility of accidental deployment of the airbag(s), which could cause personal injury (see Section 28).

1   The ignition switch is secured to the underside of the steering column by two screws.

2   Disconnect the negative cable from the battery (and if equipped with an airbag, the positive cable, too).

3   Remove the steering column cover and shrouds (see Chapter 11). Disconnect the electrical connector from the ignition switch.

4   Disconnect the negative cable from the battery (and if equipped with an airbag, the positive cable, too).

5   Remove the steering column cover and reinforcement (see Chapter 11).

➡**Note: On some late models, it may be necessary to remove the multi-function switch and electrical connector to gain access to the ignition switch (see Section 7).**

6   Remove the ignition switch screws and take it off the column (see illustrations). Disconnect the ignition switch electrical connector.

7   Installation is the reverse of the removal steps, with the following additions:

   a) *Place the ignition key and the ignition switch in the Run positions.*

   b) *Align the ignition switch pin with the slot in the steering column, then install the switch and tighten the screws.*

   c) *Check to make sure the switch operates correctly in all of the key positions.*

KEY LOCK CYLINDER REPLACEMENT

8   Disconnect the negative cable from the battery. Disconnect the positive cable as well.

9.6b . . . lower the switch and unplug the electrical connector

2010 and earlier models

9   Remove the steering column lower cover and shroud (see Chapter 11).

10   Turn the steering lock to the Run position.

2011 models

11   Remove the upper and lower steering column covers (see Chapter 11).

12   Turn the ignition key to the Run position.

All models

▶ **Refer to illustration 9.13**

13   Insert a 1/8-inch diameter wire, punch or small screwdriver into the lock cylinder housing and release the actuator pin while pulling out on the cylinder (see illustration).

14   Installation is the reverse of the removal steps.

9.6a Remove the nuts . . .

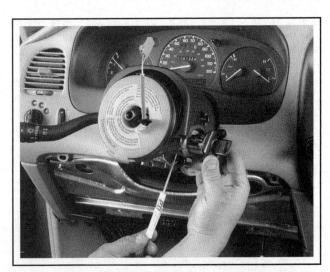

9.13 Push in on the actuator pin and pull the lock cylinder out

10 Horn - check and replacement

→**Note: Check the fuse and relay before beginning electrical diagnosis.**

1 Disconnect the electrical connector from the horn.
2 Test the horn by connecting battery voltage to the terminal with a jumper wire.

3 If the horn doesn't sound, replace it. If it does sound, the problem lies in the switch, relay or the wiring between components.
4 Disconnect the electrical connector(s) and remove the mounting bolt.
5 Installation is the reverse of removal.

11 Windshield wiper motor - removal and installation

1 Turn the windshield wiper switch On.
2 Turn the ignition switch on and keep your hand on the key. When the wiper arms move to the straight up position, turn the ignition switch Off.
3 Disconnect the negative cable from the battery.

2010 AND EARLIER MODELS

4 Remove the right side wiper arm and blade assembly (see Section 12).
5 Remove the pivot nut from the right side linkage post. Allow the linkage to drop down into the cowl.
6 Remove the wiper linkage access cover. Reach through the access opening and unsnap the wiper motor clip.
7 Push the clip away from the linkage until it clears the crank pin nib, then push the clip off the linkage.
8 Remove the wiper linkage from the motor crankpin.

9 Disconnect the electrical connector from the motor.
10 Remove the screws securing the motor and remove the motor.
11 Make sure the wiper blades are in the parked position, then attach the linkage to the motor.
12 Installation is the reverse of removal.

2011 MODELS

13 Disconnect the electrical connector from the wiper motor.
14 Remove the wiper arms (see Section 12).
15 Remove the mounting bolts and stud, then remove the wiper motor.
16 Installation is the reverse of removal, noting the following:
   a) Install the left wiper arm first, then the right arm.
   b) Make sure the wiper motor clip is fully seated on the pivot shaft to prevent damage.
   c) Tighten the wiper motor fasteners to 80 in-lbs.

12 Windshield wiper arm - removal and installation

2010 AND EARLIER MODELS

♦ **Refer to illustrations 12.2a and 12.2b**

→**Note: To prevent damage to the windshield and also to make sure the wipers are operating under normal conditions, keep the windshield wet during Step 1.**

1 Prior to removing the wiper arm, turn the windshield wipers switch On, allow the wipers to travel through several cycles, then turn it Off. This will ensure that the wiper arm is in the parked position parallel to the base of the windshield.
2 Lift the wiper arm and blade assembly away from the windshield and pull-out the small latch on the wiper arm near the spindle (see illustrations). Lower the arm and allow it to rest on the latch. The blade will rest several inches away from the windshield. Grasp the arm, wiggle it back-and-forth and remove it from the spindle.
3 Installation is the reverse of the removal steps with the following additions.
   a) Position the arm back onto the post in the parked position. Do not position the arm too low as it will hit the base of the windshield during normal wiper operation.
   b) Make sure the latch is correctly seated in the groove in the wiper spindle.

2011 MODELS

4 Pull up on each wiper pivot arm, pull out the retaining tab and remove the arms.
5 Remove the PCM mounting fasteners, and set the PCM and harness aside.
6 Remove the right wiper arm access cover screws and remove the cover.
7 Remove the Power Distribution Box (PDB) mounting fasteners, and set the PDB aside.
8 Remove the left wiper arm access cover screws and remove the cover.
9 Reaching through the access opening, unsnap the wiper motor clip from the mounting bracket and pivot shaft.
10 Remove the right wiper arm, then the left wiper arm from the pivot shafts and disconnect them from the wiper motor.
11 Remove the pivot nuts from each side, then, reaching through the right access opening, remove the left and right mounting brackets and pivot shafts.
12 Installation is the reverse of removal, noting the following:
   a) Install the left wiper arm first, then the right arm.
   b) Make sure the wiper motor clip is fully seated on the pivot shaft to prevent damage.
   c) Tighten the fasteners securely.

12.2a Lift the wiper blade away from the windshield, pull the latch out and allow the arm to rest on the latch - this prevents the arm from binding on the spindle

12.2b Be sure to pull the latch back far enough to clear the spindle

13 Windshield washer reservoir and pump assembly - removal and installation

▶ **Refer to illustration 13.1**

1   Use a small screwdriver to unlock the electrical connector tabs, then unplug the washer pump's electrical connector (see illustration).

2   Remove the two screws securing the washer reservoir and pump motor assembly to the fenderwell.

3   Lift the washer reservoir up and disconnect the small hose from the base of the reservoir. Place your finger over the end of the small hose fitting on the reservoir to prevent spilling the washer fluid in the engine compartment. Remove the reservoir.

4   Drain the washer fluid from the reservoir into a clean container. If the fluid is kept clean it can be reused.

5   Use a small screwdriver and carefully pry out the retaining ring securing the pump motor in the reservoir receptacle.

➡**Note: On later models, the pump motor is retained by a rubber grommet only. Simply pull the pump from the reservoir being careful not to damage the grommet, motor or reservoir.**

6   Grasp one wall surrounding the electrical terminal with a pair of pliers, then pull the motor, seal and impeller assembly out of the reservoir.

➡**Note: If the impeller and seal separate from the motor they can be reassembled after removal.**

7   Flush out the reservoir with clean water to remove any residue. Inspect it for any foreign matter.

8   Inspect the reservoir pump chamber prior to installing an old motor into a new reservoir. Clean it if necessary.

9   Lubricate the outer surface of the seal with powdered graphite to make installation easier.

10   Align the small projection on the motor end cap with the slot in the reservoir and push it in until the seal seats against the bottom of the motor receptacle in the reservoir.

11   Use a 1-inch 12-point socket and hand press the retaining ring securely against the motor and plate.

13.1 Disconnect the electrical connector for the pump motor (arrow)

12   Connect the hose to the fitting on the base of the reservoir.

13   Install the reservoir in the engine compartment and secure with the two screws.

14   Connect the electrical connector.

✳✳ CAUTION:

Do not operate the pump without fluid in the reservoir, as it would be damaged. Fill the reservoir with fluid, operate the pump and check for leaks.

14 Headlight switch - replacement

▶ **Refer to illustration 14.3**

1 Disconnect the negative cable from the battery.
2 Remove the instrument cluster bezel (see Chapter 11).
3 Remove the switch screws and detach the switch from the bezel (see illustration). Later models use retaining tabs instead of screws. To remove the switch, depress the tabs and pull out the switch.
4 Installation is the reverse of removal.

14.3 The light switch (right arrow) and instrument panel dimmer (left arrow) are mounted on the back of the instrument cluster bezel

15 Headlight bulb and housing - replacement

BULB REPLACEMENT

> ✳✳ **WARNING:**
>
> **Bulbs can remain hot for up to twenty minutes after they're turned off. Be sure bulbs are off and cool before you touch them.**

> ✳✳ **WARNING:**
>
> **Halogen bulbs are gas-filled and under pressure and may shatter if the surface is scratched or the bulb is dropped. Wear eye protection and handle the bulbs carefully, grasping only the base whenever possible. Don't touch the surface of the bulb with your fingers because the oil from your skin could cause it to overheat and fail prematurely. If you do touch the bulb surface, clean it with rubbing alcohol.**

1 Open the hood.

Early models

▶ **Refer to illustrations 15.2 and 15.3**

2 Unscrew the retainer from the back of the headlight (see illustration).
3 Pull the bulb socket out of the headlight assembly (see illustration).
4 Carefully pull the bulb straight out of the socket (see illustration 15.3). Do not rotate the bulb during removal.
5 Without touching the glass with bare fingers, insert the bulb into the socket. Position the flat on the plastic base up.
6 Align the socket locating tabs with the notches in the headlight housing, then push the socket firmly into the housing. Make sure the socket mounting flange contacts the housing.
7 Slide the retainer on. Turn it clockwise until it hits the stop.

Later models

8 Remove the headlight assembly (see Steps 16 and 17).
9 Turn the bulb socket counterclockwise, then pull it out of the

15.2 Unscrew the retainer from the headlight

15.3 Pull the socket out of the housing, then pull the bulb straight out of the socket and push the new one in - don't touch the bulb glass with your bare fingers

15.15 The headlight housing is secured by clips

headlight assembly.

10 Carefully pull the bulb straight out of the socket.

11 Installation is the reverse of removal

All models

12 Test headlight operation, then close the hood.

13 Have the headlight alignment checked and, if necessary, adjusted by a dealer service department or service station at the earliest opportunity (see Section 16).

HOUSING REMOVAL AND INSTALLATION

Early models

▶ **Refer to illustration 15.15**

14 Perform Steps 1 through 3 to detach the bulb and wiring from the housing.

15 Pull out the housing clips and remove the housing from the grille opening panel (see illustration).

Later models

16 Remove the headlight housing retainers.

17 Pull out the headlight assembly, disconnecting the electrical connectors.

All models

18 Installation is the reverse of removal.

19 Have the headlight alignment checked and, if necessary, adjusted by a dealer service department or service station at the earliest opportunity (see Section 16).

16 Headlights - adjusting

▶ **Refer to illustrations 16.1 and 16.6**

➡Note: The headlights must be aimed correctly. If adjusted incorrectly they could momentarily blind the driver of an oncoming vehicle and cause a serious accident or seriously reduce your ability to see the road. The headlights should be checked for proper aim every 12 months and any time a new headlight is installed or front end body work is performed. It should be emphasized that the following procedure is only an interim step which will provide temporary adjustment until the headlights can be adjusted by a properly equipped shop.

1 Headlights have two hex-head adjusting screws, one controlling up-and-down movement and one controlling left-and-right movement (see illustration).

2 There are several methods of adjusting the headlights. The simplest method requires a blank wall 25 feet in front of the vehicle and a level floor.

3 Position masking tape vertically on the wall in reference to the vehicle centerline and the centerline of both headlights.

4 Position a horizontal line in reference to the centerline of all headlights.

➡Note: It may be easier to position the tape on the wall with the vehicle parked only a few inches away.

5 Adjustment should be made with the vehicle sitting level, the gas tank half-full and no unusually heavy load in the vehicle.

6 Starting with the low beam adjustment, position the high intensity zone so it is two inches below the horizontal line and two inches to the side of the headlight vertical line away from oncoming traffic. Turn the vertical adjusting screw as necessary to raise or lower the beam. The other adjusting screw should be used in the same manner to move the beam left or right (see illustration).

7 With the high beams on, the high intensity zone should be vertically centered with the exact center just below the horizontal line.

➡Note: It may not be possible to position the headlight aim exactly for both high and low beams. If a compromise must be made, keep in mind that the low beams are the most used and have the greatest effect on driver safety.

8 Have the headlights adjusted by a dealer service department or service station at the earliest opportunity.

16.1 The headlight adjusting screws (arrows) are accessible from the rear

16.6 Turn the adjusting screws with a socket

17 Bulb replacement

PARKING/TURN SIGNAL/FRONT SIDE MARKER LIGHTS

▶ **Refer to illustrations 17.1a, 17.1b, 17.1c, 17.2 and 17.3**

➡**Note: On some later models, the front side marker light is in a separate housing. To remove it, remove the headlight housing, then unbolt and remove the side marker light housing. The remainder of the procedure is the same.**

1   Remove the screw(s) from the top of the light housing and the nut(s) from the back. On later models, position the bumper trim panel out of the way, if necessary (see illustrations). On later models, remove the headlight housing (see Section 15).

2   Pull the assembly straight out and detach the bulb socket (see illustration). On later models, rotate the socket counterclockwise, then pull it from the housing.

3   Pull the bulb out of the socket (see illustration).

4   Installation is the reverse of removal.

REAR TURN SIGNAL/STOP/TAIL AND BACKUP LIGHTS

▶ **Refer to illustrations 17.5, 17.7 and 17.8**

5   Remove the light housing screws (see illustration).

6   Remove the housing from the fender (see illustration 17.5).

7   Rotate the bulb socket (counterclockwise on later models) to align the lugs and remove the socket from the housing (see illustration).

8   On early models, carefully pry off the retaining clip and pull the bulb out of the socket (see illustration). On later models, simply pull the bulb out of the socket.

9   Installation is the reverse of removal.

LICENSE PLATE BULB

▶ **Refer to illustrations 17.11a and 17.11b**

10   On vehicles without a rear bumper, twist the socket counterclockwise and remove it from the housing. Pull the bulb out of the socket.

11   On early models with a rear bumper, carefully pry the bulb socket out of the bumper (see illustration). On later models with a rear bumper, the bulb socket is accessed from the back of the bumper; turn the bulb socket counterclockwise, then pull it out. On all models, pull the bulb out of the socket (see illustration).

12   Installation is the reverse of removal.

17.1a Remove the screw that secures the top of the lamp housing . . .

17.1b . . . and the nut from the back

17.1c Remove the two screws at the bottom of the housing (late models)

17.2 Pull the housing out of the body and detach the bulb socket

17.3 Pull the bulb out of the socket

17.5 Remove the lamp housing screws

17.7 Rotate the bulb socket and remove it from the housing

17.8 Pry the retainer off and pull the bulb out of the socket

17.11a Carefully pry one side of the light out - if it won't go, try the other side - don't force it

17.11b Pull the socket out and pull out the bulb

17.13 Remove the light housing screws

17.14 Lift the housing away from the body, detach the socket and pull out the bulb

CARGO LIGHT AND HIGH-MOUNT BRAKE LIGHT

◗ **Refer to illustrations 17.13 and 17.14**

13 Remove the mounting screws (see illustration) and remove the light housing.

14 On early models, pull out the bulb socket, then pull the bulb from the socket (see illustration). On later models, turn the bulb socket counterclockwise to remove it from the housing, then pull the bulb out of the socket.

15 Installation is the reverse of removal.

INSTRUMENT CLUSTER BULBS

◗ **Refer to illustration 17.17**

❉ **CAUTION:**

The instrument cluster printed circuit board is fragile. Be careful when removing the bulb assemblies.

➡Note: It may be necessary to remove the instrument cluster to gain access to the bulbs (see Section 21).

16 Reach up under the instrument panel and turn the bulb/socket assembly 1/4-turn counterclockwise.

17 Remove the bulb from the socket (see illustration). Installation is the reverse of removal.

17.17 Twist the socket and pull it out of the cluster, then pull the bulb straight out of the socket

DOME LIGHT

▶ **Refer to illustration 17.18**

18 Snap the lens free from the dome light assembly and remove the bulb (see illustration).

19 Installation is the reverse of removal.

FOG LIGHTS

➡**Note: Not all models are equipped with fog lights.**

20 Turn the bulb socket counterclockwise to remove it from the housing. Disconnect the electrical connector, if necessary.

21 Pull the bulb straight out of the socket to replace it.

22 Installation is the reverse of removal.

17.18 Squeeze the retainer tabs on the light assembly and pull it out

18 Radio - removal and installation

▶ **Refer to illustration 18.2**

✳✳ CAUTION:

On 2011 models with CD6 (six-disc) audio units, the Shipment Mode must be entered before removing the unit (see Steps 6 through 8).

1 Remove the instrument cluster trim panel (see Chapter 11).

2 Insert a radio removal tool, available at most auto parts stores, or equivalent, into the radio face plate (see illustration). Push the tool in about 1-inch to release the retaining clips on each side.

3 Using the special tool, pull the radio partially out of the instrument panel, then disconnect the power, speaker and antenna wires from the radio.

4 Pull the radio assembly out of the instrument panel.

5 Installation is the reverse of removal. On 2011 models with CD6 audio units, exit Shipment Mode (see Steps 9 through 11).

ENTERING AND EXITING SHIPMENT MODE

➡**Note: This procedure is for 2011 models with six-disc changers only.**

6 Eject all CDs from the unit, then turn the ignition key to OFF.

7 While holding down radio preset buttons 2 and 5, turn the ignition key to ACC or RUN. The display should flash "SHIPMENT," then

18.2 Insert the two radio removal tools to release the clips, then pull the radio out with the tools (push the tools toward each other to grip the radio)

display "SHIPMENT ON."

8 Turn the ignition key back to OFF. You may now remove the radio.

9 Once the radio has been reinstalled, turn the ignition key to the ACC or RUN position, then turn on the radio.

10 Press the LOAD button, holding for 2 seconds.

11 Turn the radio off. Shipment mode should be exited. Make sure that the radio works normally.

19 Antenna and cable - removal and installation

2010 AND EARLIER MODELS

1 Reach under the instrument panel and disconnect the antenna cable at the lead-in connector.

2 Detach the antenna cable from the plastic clips under the instrument panel.

3 Unscrew the antenna from the base. Use a small screwdriver and

carefully pry the antenna cap from the base and remove the cap.

4 Tie a piece of string or wire onto the radio end of the antenna cable. This will be used to pull the new antenna cable back through the same path as the old one.

5 Remove the screws securing the antenna base to the body and slowly pull the antenna cable out through the body opening. Remove the antenna base and gasket.

6   If necessary, disconnect the antenna lead-in cable from the radio and detach it from its clips.

2011 MODELS

7   Unscrew the antenna from the base.

8   Use a small screwdriver to carefully pry off the base cover, then remove the screws and the antenna base from the cowl.

9   Disconnect the antenna cable connector from the base. Tie a piece of string or wire onto the end of the cable. This will be used to pull the new antenna cable back through the same path as the old one.

10 Remove the radio (see Section 18). Disconnect the antenna cable from the back of the radio unit.

11 Open the glove box and lower it to its fully open position (see Chapter 11).

12 Remove the gasket at the back of the glove box, then pull the cable out through the opening in the glove box.

ALL MODELS

13 Installation is the reverse of the removal steps with the following additions:

   a) Be sure to install a new gasket.

   b) Untie the string or wire and attach it to the new antenna cable. Slowly pull the string and antenna cable back through the body opening and into place. Remove the string or wire.

20 Speakers - removal and installation

➡Note: The models covered by this manual come equipped from the factory with speakers in the doors, with additional rear speakers on vehicles equipped with AM/FM sound systems. Your particular model may vary from the following procedure due to the size and configuration of aftermarket speakers in-stalled in some models.

DOOR SPEAKERS

1   Remove the door trim panel (see Chapter 11).

2   Remove the screws securing the speaker to the door.

3   Lift out the speaker and disconnect the electrical connector at the speaker.

✳✳ CAUTION:

Do not operate the radio with the speakers disconnected.

4   Installation is the reverse of the removal steps.

REAR SPEAKERS

5   Remove the screws and lift the speaker out of the trim panel.

6   Disconnect the electrical connector at the speaker.

✳✳ CAUTION:

Do not operate the radio with the speakers disconnected.

7   Installation is the reverse of the removal steps.

21 Instrument cluster - removal and installation

✳✳ WARNING:

Some models covered by this manual are equipped with airbags. Always disable the airbag system before working in the vicinity of any airbag system component to avoid the possibility of accidental deployment of the airbag(s), which could cause personal injury (see Section 28).

REMOVAL

1   Take note of the preceding **Warning**, then disconnect the battery cables.

2   Remove the radio (see Section 18).

3   Remove the center and lower trim panels, the knee bolster and the instrument cluster bezel (see Chapter 11).

4   Remove the screws securing the instrument cluster.

5   On automatic transmission models, remove the screws securing the gear indicator to the instrument cluster and slide the indicator down and out of the cluster. It is not necessary to disconnect the indicator.

6   Carefully pull the instrument cluster assembly partially out from the instrument panel.

7   If the vehicle has a speedometer cable, reach under the instrument panel, press on the flat portion of the quick-disconnect plastic connector and detach the cable from the instrument cluster.

➡Note: If there isn't enough slack in the speedometer cable to pull the cluster out far enough, disconnect the cable at the transmission or transfer case under the vehicle, then push it inside the vehicle while an assistant tugs on the cluster. Once there is enough slack in the cable, reach behind the cluster and disconnect it.

8   Squeeze the locking tabs on the printed circuit electrical connectors, then disconnect them from the printed circuit board.

9   Remove the instrument cluster assembly.

INSTALLATION

10 Installation is the reverse of the removal steps, with the following addition: If the vehicle has a speedometer cable, apply a 3/16-inch diameter ball of silicone dielectric compound to the drive hole of the speedometer head prior to installing the cable.

22 Gauges - replacement

➡**Note: US Federal law requires that the odometer in any replacement speedometer must register the same mileage as that on the removed speedometer.**

1 Remove the instrument cluster (see Section 21).
2 Remove the lens and mask from the instrument cluster.
3 Gently push on the back of the speedometer to loosen it from the

retainer clips in the cluster housing.
4 Lift the gauges with a gentle rocking motion to separate them from the retainer prongs in the cluster housing.
5 Installation is the reverse of the removal steps. Apply a 3/16-inch diameter ball of silicone dielectric compound to the drive hole of the speedometer head prior to installing the cable.

23 Speedometer cable - replacement

➡**Note: Later model vehicles are equipped with electronic speedometers and do not have a speedometer cable.**

1 Perform Steps 1 through 9 of Section 21.
2 To remove the cable only, pull out the cable core from the casing and install a new one by reversing the removal steps.
3 Remove the casing as follows:

a) *Remove the screw and clamp securing the speedometer cable to the firewall.*

b) *Working under the vehicle, remove the clamp screw and remove the cable and casing from the transmission or transfer case.*

4 Connect the speedometer casing to the head and (if removed) install the casing to the transmission using a new O-ring.
5 Install the instrument cluster (see Section 21).

24 Power window system - description and check

1 The power window system operates the electric motors mounted in the doors which lower and raise the windows. The system consists of the control switches, the motors (regulators), glass mechanisms and associated wiring.
2 The windows can be lowered and raised from the master control switch by the driver or by a remote switch located at the passenger window. Each window has a separate motor which is reversible. The position of the control switch determines the polarity and therefore the direction of operation. Some systems are equipped with relays that control current flow to the motors.
3 Each motor is equipped with a separate circuit breaker in addition to the fuse or circuit breaker protecting the whole circuit. This prevents one stuck window from disabling the whole system.
4 The power window system will only operate when the ignition switch is ON. In addition, when activated the window lockout switch at the master control switch disables the switches at the passenger's window also. Always check these items before troubleshooting a window problem.
5 These procedures are general in nature, so if you can't find the problem using them, take the vehicle to a dealer service department.
6 If the power windows don't work at all, check the fuse or circuit breaker.
7 If only the rear windows are inoperative, or if the windows only operate from the master control switch, check the rear window lockout

switch for continuity in the unlocked position. Replace it if it doesn't have continuity.
8 Check the wiring between the switches and fuse panel for continuity. Repair the wiring, if necessary.
9 If the passenger window is inoperative from the master control switch, try the other control switch at the window.
➡**Note: This doesn't apply to the driver's door window.**
10 If the same window works from one switch, but not the other, check the switch for continuity.
11 If the switch tests OK, check for a short or open in the wiring between the affected switch and the window motor.
12 If the passenger window is inoperative from both switches, remove the trim panel from the door and check for voltage at the motor while the switch is operated.
13 If voltage is reaching the motor, disconnect the glass from the regulator (see Chapter 11). Move the window up and down by hand while checking for binding and damage. Also check for binding and damage to the regulator. If the regulator is not damaged and the window moves up and down smoothly, replace the motor. If there's binding or damage, lubricate, repair or replace parts, as necessary.
14 If voltage isn't reaching the motor, check the wiring in the circuit for continuity between the switches and motors. You'll need to consult the wiring diagram for the vehicle.
15 Test the windows after you are done to confirm proper repairs.

25 Power mirrors - check, removal and installation

1   The electric rear view mirrors use two motors to move the glass; one for up and down adjustments and one for left-right adjustments.

2   The control switch has a selector portion which sends voltage to the left or right side mirror. With the ignition switch in the ACC position, roll down the windows and operate the mirror control switch through all functions (left-right and up-down) for both the left and right side mirrors.

3   Listen carefully for the sound of the electric motors running in the mirrors.

4   If the motors can't be heard or if the mirror glass doesn't move, there's probably a problem with the drive mechanism inside the mirror. Remove and disassemble the mirror to locate the problem.

5   If the mirrors don't operate and no sound comes from them, check the mirror fuse in the fuse block (see Section 4).

6   If the fuse is OK, remove the switch bezel (see Chapter 11) for access to the back of the mirror control switch without disconnecting the wire attached to it. Turn the ignition On and check for voltage at the switch. There should be voltage at one terminal. If there's no voltage at

the switch, check for an open or short in the wiring between the fuse panel and switch.

7   If there's voltage at the switch, disconnect it. Check the switch for continuity in all its operating positions. If the switch does not have continuity, replace it.

8   Re-connect the switch. Locate the wire going from the switch to ground. Leaving the switch connected, connect a jumper wire between this wire and ground. If the mirror works normally with this wire in place, repair the faulty ground connection.

9   If the mirror still doesn't work, remove the mirror (see Chapter 11) and check the wires at the mirror for voltage. Check with the ignition On and the mirror selector switch on the appropriate side. Operate the mirror switch in all its positions. There should be voltage at one of the switch-to-mirror wires in each switch position (except the neutral "off" position).

10 If there's not voltage in each switch position, check the wiring between the mirror and switch for opens and shorts.

11 If there's voltage, remove the mirror and test it off the vehicle with jumper wires. Replace the mirror if it fails this test.

26 Power door lock system - description and check

The power door lock system operates the door lock actuators mounted in each door. The system consists of the switches, actuators and associated electrical wiring.

Diagnosis can usually be limited to simple checks of the wiring connectors and actuators for minor faults which can be easily repaired. These include:

a) *Check the system fuse and circuit breaker.*
b) *Check the switch wiring for damage or loose connections.*
c) *Check the switch for continuity in the closed position. Also check the switches for sticking. If a switch sticks closed the actuator internal circuit breaker will trip and stay tripped until voltage is removed.*

d) *Remove the door panel(s) and check the actuator electrical connections for looseness or damage. Inspect the actuator rods and door lock linkage to make sure they are not bent, damaged or binding.*
e) *Remove the electrical connector at the actuator and with a test light or voltmeter, check for available voltage to the actuator as you cycle the switch. If voltage is present, but the actuator doesn't operate when connected, the actuator is probably defective. If no voltage is present at the connector, the switch, relay (if equipped) or wiring is probably defective.*

27 Cruise control system - description and check

1   The cruise control system maintains vehicle speed with an electric servo motor mounted in the engine compartment, which is connected to the throttle linkage by a cable. The system consists of the servo motor, brake switch, clutch switch (manual transmission models), control switches and a relay.

2   Cruise controls all work by the same basic principles. However, the hardware used varies considerably depending on model and year or manufacture. Some later systems require special testers and diagnostic procedures which are beyond the scope of the home mechanic. Listed below are some general procedures that may be used to locate common problems.

3   Locate and check the fuse (see Section 4).

4   Have an assistant operate the brake lights while you check their operation (voltage from the brake switch deactivates the cruise control).

5   If the brake lights don't come on or don't shut off, correct the problem and retest the cruise control.

6   Inspect the actuator cable between the cruise control servo and the throttle linkage. The cruise control servo is usually fist-sized or slightly larger and is located on the right front fender.

7   Cruise controls use a variety of speed sensing devices. On these models the speed sensor pick-up is located at the transmission.

8   Test drive the vehicle to determine if the cruise control is now working. If it isn't, take it to a dealer service department or an automotive electrical specialist for further diagnosis and repair.

28 Airbag - general information

Later models are equipped with a Supplemental Inflatable Restraint (SIR) System, more commonly known as an airbag. This system is designed to protect the driver (and front seat passenger on some models) from serious injury in the event of a head-on or frontal collision. It consists of an airbag module in the center of the steering wheel (driver) and the right side of the instrument panel (passenger), two crash sensors mounted at the front of the vehicle and a diagnostic monitor which also contains a backup power supply located in the passenger compartment.

On 2010 and later models, side-impact airbags are optional. The modules are located in the top of the seatbacks (driver and passenger front seats), facing the exterior of the vehicle.

AIRBAG MODULE

Steering wheel-mounted

The airbag inflator module contains a housing incorporating the cushion (airbag) and inflator unit, mounted in the center of the steering wheel. The inflator assembly is mounted on the back of the housing over a hole through which gas is expelled, inflating the bag almost instantaneously when an electrical signal is sent from the system. A coil assembly on the steering column under the module carries this signal to the module.

This coil assembly can transmit an electrical signal regardless of steering wheel position. The igniter in the airbag converts the electrical signal to heat and ignites the sodium azide/copper oxide powder, producing nitrogen gas, which inflates the bag.

Instrument panel-mounted

The passenger airbag (if equipped) is mounted above the glove compartment and designated by the letters SRS (Supplemental Restraint System). It consists of an inflator containing an igniter, a bag assembly, a reaction housing and a trim cover.

This airbag is considerably larger than the steering wheel-mounted unit and is supported by the steel reaction housing. The trim cover is textured and painted to match the instrument panel and has a molded seam which splits when the bag inflates. As with the steering-wheel-mounted airbag, the igniter electrical signal converts to heat, converting sodium azide/iron oxide powder to nitrogen gas, inflating the bag.

RESTRAINT CONTROL MODULE (RCM) DIAGNOSTIC UNIT

The Restraint Control Module (RCM) is the microprocessor that monitors and operates the airbag system. The RCM checks the system every time the vehicle is started. When you start the car, an AIRBAG indicator light comes on for about six seconds, then goes off, if the system is operating properly. If there is a fault in the system, the RCM stores a Diagnostic Trouble Code (DTC) and illuminates the AIRBAG indicator light, which remains on until the problem is repaired and the RCM memory is cleared of any DTCs. If the AIRBAG indicator light comes on at any time other than the bulb test and remains on, or doesn't come on at all, there's a problem in the system. A DRBIII scan tool is the only means by which the system can be diagnosed. Take the vehicle to your dealer immediately and have the system professionally diagnosed and repaired.

The RCM controls the operation of the standard driver and passenger airbags, and on later models, the optional side-impact modules

located in the outside-top of the driver and passenger front seats.

SERVICING COMPONENTS NEAR THE SRS SYSTEM

There are times when you need to remove the steering wheel, the instrument cluster, the radio, the heater/air conditioning control assembly or other components that are near airbag components. At these times you'll be working around components and wire harnesses for the SRS system. Do not use electrical test equipment on airbag system wires; it could cause the airbag(s) to deploy. ALWAYS DISABLE THE SRS SYSTEM BEFORE WORKING NEAR THE SRS SYSTEM COMPONENTS OR RELATED WIRING.

SENSORS

The system on early models has three sensors: two forward sensors at the front of the vehicle and a safing sensor inside the electronic diagnostic monitor. Later models have four sensors: two forward sensors and one mounted in each front door, behind the trim panel.

The forward and passenger compartment sensors are basically pressure sensitive switches that complete an electrical circuit during an impact of sufficient G force. The electrical signal from these sensors is sent to the electronic diagnostic monitor which then completes the circuit and inflates the airbag(s).

ELECTRONIC DIAGNOSTIC MONITOR

The electronic diagnostic monitor supplies the current to the airbag system in the event of the collision, even if battery power is cut off. It checks this system every time the vehicle is started, causing the "AIR BAG" light to go on then off, if the system is operating properly. If there is a fault in the system, the light will go on and stay on, flash, or the dash will make a beeping sound. If this happens, the vehicle should be taken to your dealer immediately for service.

DISABLING AND ENABLING THE SYSTEM

2005 and earlier models

Disabling

Whenever working in the vicinity of the steering wheel, steering column or near other components of the airbag system, the system should be disarmed. To do this, perform the following steps:

a) *Turn the ignition switch to Off.*
b) *Detach the cable from the negative battery terminal, then detach the positive cable. Wait two minutes for the electronic module backup power supply to be depleted.*

Enabling

a) *Turn the ignition switch to the Off position.*
b) *Connect the positive battery cable first, then connect the negative cable.*

On models equipped with a passenger side airbag, a switch is included that can be used to disable the airbag when an infant or small child is being transported in a rear-facing child safety seat. The switch is located in the center of the dash and can be operated by inserting any Ford ignition key.

2006 and later models

Disabling

a) *Turn Off all accessories on the vehicle and disconnect any memory-saver devices.*

b) *Turn Off the ignition switch.*

c) *At the interior fuse/relay box under the right side of the instrument panel, remove the fuse marked RCM.*

d) *Turn the ignition switch to On. Observe the airbag warning light on the instrument panel for 30 seconds. If you have removed the correct fuse, the warning light should be steady (no blinking).*

e) *Turn the ignition switch Off.*

f) *Disconnect the negative battery cable and wait two minutes before doing any work around SRS components.*

Enabling

a) *Turn the ignition switch from Off to On.*

b) *Reinstall the RCM fuse.*

c) *Connect the battery cable.*

✷✷ WARNING:

When the battery cable is connected, no one should be in front of any airbag module, in case of accidental deployment.

To test if the SRS system is working properly, turn the ignition switch from On to Off for ten seconds, then back to On. The warning light should illuminate for six seconds and go out.

The warning light indicates a problem with the SRS system if: the light blinks, stays illuminated continuously, or fails to illuminate in one minute. If one of these conditions exists, have your system checked with a scan tool at a dealership.

29 Wiring diagrams - general information

Since it isn't possible to include all wiring diagrams for every model year covered by this manual, the following diagrams are those that are typical and most commonly needed.

Prior to troubleshooting any circuit, check the fuses and circuit breakers to make sure they're in good condition. Make sure the battery is fully charged and check the cable connections (see Chapter 1). Make sure all connectors are clean, with no broken or loose terminals.

Notes

Sample diagram - how to read and interpret wiring

WIRING DIAGRAM SYMBOLS

BATTERY · CONNECTOR OR SPLICE · CIRCUIT BREAKER · CAPACITOR · COIL · DIODE · FUSE · FUSIBLE LINK

GROUND · LED · RESISTOR · SINGLE FILAMENT BULB · DUAL FILAMENT BULB · HEATING ELEMENT · SOLENOID OR COIL · VARIABLE RESISTOR

CRYSTAL · POTENTIOMETER · HORN OR SPEAKER · ALTERNATOR · DISTRIBUTOR ASSEMBLY · IGNITION COIL

SPARK PLUG · STEPPER MOTOR · HEAT ACTIVATED SWITCH · RELAY · NORMALLY OPEN SWITCH · NORMALLY CLOSED SWITCH

GANGED SWITCH · 3-POSITION SWITCH · REED SWITCH · MOTOR OR ACTUATOR · SPEED SENSOR · JUNCTION BLOCK · MODEL OPTIONS BRACKET

Common wiring diagram symbols

Engine wiring - four-cylinder models

V6 engine wiring

Starting and charging system wiring

Body wiring

GLOSSARY

AIR/FUEL RATIO: The ratio of air-to-gasoline by weight in the fuel mixture drawn into the engine.

AIR INJECTION: One method of reducing harmful exhaust emissions by injecting air into each of the exhaust ports of an engine. The fresh air entering the hot exhaust manifold causes any remaining fuel to be burned before it can exit the tailpipe.

ALTERNATOR: A device used for converting mechanical energy into electrical energy.

AMMETER: An instrument, calibrated in amperes, used to measure the flow of an electrical current in a circuit. Ammeters are always connected in series with the circuit being tested.

AMPERE: The rate of flow of electrical current present when one volt of electrical pressure is applied against one ohm of electrical resistance.

ANALOG COMPUTER: Any microprocessor that uses similar (analogous) electrical signals to make its calculations.

ARMATURE: A laminated, soft iron core wrapped by a wire that converts electrical energy to mechanical energy as in a motor or relay. When rotated in a magnetic field, it changes mechanical energy into electrical energy as in a generator.

ATMOSPHERIC PRESSURE: The pressure on the Earth's surface caused by the weight of the air in the atmosphere. At sea level, this pressure is 14.7 psi at 32°F (101 kPa at 0°C).

ATOMIZATION: The breaking down of a liquid into a fine mist that can be suspended in air.

AXIAL PLAY: Movement parallel to a shaft or bearing bore.

BACKFIRE: The sudden combustion of gases in the intake or exhaust system that results in a loud explosion.

BACKLASH: The clearance or play between two parts, such as meshed gears.

BACKPRESSURE: Restrictions in the exhaust system that slow the exit of exhaust gases from the combustion chamber.

BAKELITE: A heat resistant, plastic insulator material commonly used in printed circuit boards and transistorized components.

BALL BEARING: A bearing made up of hardened inner and outer races between which hardened steel balls roll.

BALLAST RESISTOR: A resistor in the primary ignition circuit that lowers voltage after the engine is started to reduce wear on ignition components.

BEARING: A friction reducing, supportive device usually located between a stationary part and a moving part.

BIMETAL TEMPERATURE SENSOR: Any sensor or switch made of two dissimilar types of metal that bend when heated or cooled due to the different expansion rates of the alloys. These types of sensors usually function as an on/off switch.

BLOWBY: Combustion gases, composed of water vapor and unburned fuel, that leak past the piston rings into the crankcase during normal engine operation. These gases are removed by the PCV system to prevent the buildup of harmful acids in the crankcase.

BRAKE PAD: A brake shoe and lining assembly used with disc brakes.

BRAKE SHOE: The backing for the brake lining. The term is, however, usually applied to the assembly of the brake backing and lining.

BUSHING: A liner, usually removable, for a bearing; an anti-friction liner used in place of a bearing.

CALIPER: A hydraulically activated device in a disc brake system, which is mounted straddling the brake rotor (disc). The caliper contains at least one piston and two brake pads. Hydraulic pressure on the piston(s) forces the pads against the rotor.

CAMSHAFT: A shaft in the engine on which are the lobes (cams) which operate the valves. The camshaft is driven by the crankshaft, via a belt, chain or gears, at one half the crankshaft speed.

CAPACITOR: A device which stores an electrical charge.

CARBON MONOXIDE (CO): A colorless, odorless gas given off as a normal byproduct of combustion. It is poisonous and extremely dangerous in confined areas, building up slowly to toxic levels without warning if adequate ventilation is not available.

CARBURETOR: A device, usually mounted on the intake manifold of an engine, which mixes the air and fuel in the proper proportion to allow even combustion.

CATALYTIC CONVERTER: A device installed in the exhaust system, like a muffler, that converts harmful byproducts of combustion into carbon dioxide and water vapor by means of a heat-producing chemical reaction.

CENTRIFUGAL ADVANCE: A mechanical method of advancing the spark timing by using flyweights in the distributor that react to centrifugal force generated by the distributor shaft rotation.

CHECK VALVE: Any one-way valve installed to permit the flow of air, fuel or vacuum in one direction only.

CHOKE: A device, usually a moveable valve, placed in the intake path of a carburetor to restrict the flow of air.

CIRCUIT: Any unbroken path through which an electrical current can flow. Also used to describe fuel flow in some instances.

CIRCUIT BREAKER: A switch which protects an electrical circuit from overload by opening the circuit when the current flow exceeds a predetermined level. Some circuit breakers must be reset manually, while most reset automatically.

COIL (IGNITION): A transformer in the ignition circuit which steps up the voltage provided to the spark plugs.

COMBINATION MANIFOLD: An assembly which includes both the intake and exhaust manifolds in one casting.

COMBINATION VALVE: A device used in some fuel systems that routes fuel vapors to a charcoal storage canister instead of venting them into the atmosphere. The valve relieves fuel tank pressure and allows fresh air into the tank as the fuel level drops to prevent a vapor lock situation.

COMPRESSION RATIO: The comparison of the total volume of the cylinder and combustion chamber with the piston at BDC and the piston at TDC.

CONDENSER: 1. An electrical device which acts to store an electrical charge, preventing voltage surges. 2. A radiator-like device in the air conditioning system in which refrigerant gas condenses into a liquid, giving off heat.

CONDUCTOR: Any material through which an electrical current can be transmitted easily.

CONTINUITY: Continuous or complete circuit. Can be checked with an ohmmeter.

COUNTERSHAFT: An intermediate shaft which is rotated by a mainshaft and transmits, in turn, that rotation to a working part.

CRANKCASE: The lower part of an engine in which the crankshaft and related parts operate.

CRANKSHAFT: The main driving shaft of an engine which receives reciprocating motion from the pistons and converts it to rotary motion.

CYLINDER: In an engine, the round hole in the engine block in which the piston(s) ride.

CYLINDER BLOCK: The main structural member of an engine in which is found the cylinders, crankshaft and other principal parts.

CYLINDER HEAD: The detachable portion of the engine, usually fastened to the top of the cylinder block and containing all or most of the combustion chambers. On overhead valve engines, it contains the valves and their operating parts. On overhead cam engines, it contains the camshaft as well.

DEAD CENTER: The extreme top or bottom of the piston stroke.

DETONATION: An unwanted explosion of the air/fuel mixture in the combustion chamber caused by excess heat and compression, advanced timing, or an overly lean mixture. Also referred to as "ping".

DIAPHRAGM: A thin, flexible wall separating two cavities, such as in a vacuum advance unit.

DIESELING: A condition in which hot spots in the combustion chamber cause the engine to run on after the key is turned off.

DIFFERENTIAL: A geared assembly which allows the transmission of motion between drive axles, giving one axle the ability to turn faster than the other.

DIODE: An electrical device that will allow current to flow in one direction only.

DISC BRAKE: A hydraulic braking assembly consisting of a brake disc, or rotor, mounted on an axle, and a caliper assembly containing, usually two brake pads which are activated by hydraulic pressure. The pads are forced against the sides of the disc, creating friction which slows the vehicle.

DISTRIBUTOR: A mechanically driven device on an engine which is responsible for electrically firing the spark plug at a predetermined point of the piston stroke.

DOWEL PIN: A pin, inserted in mating holes in two different parts allowing those parts to maintain a fixed relationship.

DRUM BRAKE: A braking system which consists of two brake shoes and one or two wheel cylinders, mounted on a fixed backing plate, and a brake drum, mounted on an axle, which revolves around the assembly.

DWELL: The rate, measured in degrees of shaft rotation, at which an electrical circuit cycles on and off.

ELECTRONIC CONTROL UNIT (ECU): Ignition module, module, amplifier or igniter. See Module for definition.

ELECTRONIC IGNITION: A system in which the timing and firing of the spark plugs is controlled by an electronic control unit, usually called a module. These systems have no points or condenser.

END-PLAY: The measured amount of axial movement in a shaft.

ENGINE: A device that converts heat into mechanical energy.

EXHAUST MANIFOLD: A set of cast passages or pipes which conduct exhaust gases from the engine.

FEELER GAUGE: A blade, usually metal, or precisely predetermined thickness, used to measure the clearance between two parts.

FIRING ORDER: The order in which combustion occurs in the cylinders of an engine. Also the order in which spark is distributed to the plugs by the distributor.

FLOODING: The presence of too much fuel in the intake manifold and combustion chamber which prevents the air/fuel mixture from firing, thereby causing a no-start situation.

FLYWHEEL: A disc shaped part bolted to the rear end of the crankshaft. Around the outer perimeter is affixed the ring gear. The starter drive engages the ring gear, turning the flywheel, which rotates the crankshaft, imparting the initial starting motion to the engine.

FOOT POUND (ft. lbs. or sometimes, ft.lb.): The amount of energy or work needed to raise an item weighing one pound, a distance of one foot.

FUSE: A protective device in a circuit which prevents circuit overload by breaking the circuit when a specific amperage is present. The device is constructed around a strip or wire of a lower amperage rating than the circuit it is designed to protect. When an amperage higher than that stamped on the fuse is present in the circuit, the strip or wire melts, opening the circuit.

GEAR RATIO: The ratio between the number of teeth on meshing gears.

GENERATOR: A device which converts mechanical energy into electrical energy.

HEAT RANGE: The measure of a spark plug's ability to dissipate heat from its firing end. The higher the heat range, the hotter the plug fires.

HUB: The center part of a wheel or gear.

HYDROCARBON (HC): Any chemical compound made up of hydrogen and carbon. A major pollutant formed by the engine as a byproduct of combustion.

HYDROMETER: An instrument used to measure the specific gravity of a solution.

INCH POUND (inch lbs.; sometimes in.lb. or in. lbs.): One twelfth of a foot pound.

INDUCTION: A means of transferring electrical energy in the form of a magnetic field. Principle used in the ignition coil to increase voltage.

INJECTOR: A device which receives metered fuel under relatively low pressure and is activated to inject the fuel into the engine under relatively high pressure at a predetermined time.

INPUT SHAFT: The shaft to which torque is applied, usually carrying the driving gear or gears.

INTAKE MANIFOLD: A casting of passages or pipes used to conduct air or a fuel/air mixture to the cylinders.

JOURNAL: The bearing surface within which a shaft operates.

KEY: A small block usually fitted in a notch between a shaft and a hub to prevent slippage of the two parts.

MANIFOLD: A casting of passages or set of pipes which connect the cylinders to an inlet or outlet source.

MANIFOLD VACUUM: Low pressure in an engine intake manifold formed just below the throttle plates. Manifold vacuum is highest at idle and drops under acceleration.

MASTER CYLINDER: The primary fluid pressurizing device in a hydraulic system. In automotive use, it is found in brake and hydraulic clutch systems and is pedal activated, either directly or, in a power brake system, through the power booster.

MODULE: Electronic control unit, amplifier or igniter of solid state or integrated design which controls the current flow in the ignition primary circuit based on input from the pick-up coil. When the module opens the primary circuit, high secondary voltage is induced in the coil.

NEEDLE BEARING: A bearing which consists of a number (usually a large number) of long, thin rollers.

OHM: (Ω) The unit used to measure the resistance of conductor-to-electrical flow. One ohm is the amount of resistance that limits current flow to one ampere in a circuit with one volt of pressure.

OHMMETER: An instrument used for measuring the resistance, in ohms, in an electrical circuit.

OUTPUT SHAFT: The shaft which transmits torque from a device, such as a transmission.

OVERDRIVE: A gear assembly which produces more shaft revolutions than that transmitted to it.

OVERHEAD CAMSHAFT (OHC): An engine configuration in which the camshaft is mounted on top of the cylinder head and operates the valve either directly or by means of rocker arms.

OVERHEAD VALVE (OHV): An engine configuration in which all of the valves are located in the cylinder head and the camshaft is located in the cylinder block. The camshaft operates the valves via lifters and pushrods.

OXIDES OF NITROGEN (NOx): Chemical compounds of nitrogen produced as a byproduct of combustion. They combine with hydrocarbons to produce smog.

OXYGEN SENSOR: Use with the feedback system to sense the presence of oxygen in the exhaust gas and signal the computer which can reference the voltage signal to an air/fuel ratio.

PINION: The smaller of two meshing gears.

PISTON RING: An open-ended ring with fits into a groove on the outer diameter of the piston. Its chief function is to form a seal between the piston and cylinder wall. Most automotive pistons have three rings: two for compression sealing; one for oil sealing.

PRELOAD: A predetermined load placed on a bearing during assembly or by adjustment.

PRIMARY CIRCUIT: the low voltage side of the ignition system which consists of the ignition switch, ballast resistor or resistance wire, bypass, coil, electronic control unit and pick-up coil as well as the connecting wires and harnesses.

PRESS FIT: The mating of two parts under pressure, due to the inner diameter of one being smaller than the outer diameter of the other, or vice versa; an interference fit.

RACE: The surface on the inner or outer ring of a bearing on which the balls, needles or rollers move.

REGULATOR: A device which maintains the amperage and/or voltage levels of a circuit at predetermined values.

RELAY: A switch which automatically opens and/or closes a circuit.

RESISTANCE: The opposition to the flow of current through a circuit or electrical device, and is measured in ohms. Resistance is equal to the voltage divided by the amperage.

RESISTOR: A device, usually made of wire, which offers a preset amount of resistance in an electrical circuit.

RING GEAR: The name given to a ring-shaped gear attached to a differential case, or affixed to a flywheel or as part of a planetary gear set.

ROLLER BEARING: A bearing made up of hardened inner and outer races between which hardened steel rollers move.

ROTOR: 1. The disc-shaped part of a disc brake assembly, upon which the brake pads bear; also called, brake disc. 2. The device mounted atop the distributor shaft, which passes current to the distributor cap tower contacts.

SECONDARY CIRCUIT: The high voltage side of the ignition system, usually above 20,000 volts. The secondary includes the ignition coil, coil wire, distributor cap and rotor, spark plug wires and spark plugs.

SENDING UNIT: A mechanical, electrical, hydraulic or electro-magnetic device which transmits information to a gauge.

SENSOR: Any device designed to measure engine operating conditions or ambient pressures and temperatures. Usually electronic in nature and designed to send a voltage signal to an on-board computer, some sensors may operate as a simple on/off switch or they may provide a variable voltage signal (like a potentiometer) as conditions or measured parameters change.

SHIM: Spacers of precise, predetermined thickness used between parts to establish a proper working relationship.

SLAVE CYLINDER: In automotive use, a device in the hydraulic clutch system which is activated by hydraulic force, disengaging the clutch.

SOLENOID: A coil used to produce a magnetic field, the effect of which is to produce work.

SPARK PLUG: A device screwed into the combustion chamber of a spark ignition engine. The basic construction is a conductive core inside of a ceramic insulator, mounted in an outer conductive base. An electrical charge from the spark plug wire travels along the conductive core and jumps a preset air gap to a grounding point or points at the end of the conductive base. The resultant spark ignites the fuel/air mixture in the combustion chamber.

SPLINES: Ridges machined or cast onto the outer diameter of a shaft or inner diameter of a bore to enable parts to mate without rotation.

TACHOMETER: A device used to measure the rotary speed of an engine, shaft, gear, etc., usually in rotations per minute.

THERMOSTAT: A valve, located in the cooling system of an engine, which is closed when cold and opens gradually in response to engine heating, controlling the temperature of the coolant and rate of coolant flow.

TOP DEAD CENTER (TDC): The point at which the piston reaches the top of its travel on the compression stroke.

TORQUE: The twisting force applied to an object.

TORQUE CONVERTER: A turbine used to transmit power from a driving member to a driven member via hydraulic action, providing changes in drive ratio and torque. In automotive use, it links the driveplate at the rear of the engine to the automatic transmission.

TRANSDUCER: A device used to change a force into an electrical signal.

TRANSISTOR: A semi-conductor component which can be actuated by a small voltage to perform an electrical switching function.

TUNE-UP: A regular maintenance function, usually associated with the replacement and adjustment of parts and components in the electrical and fuel systems of a vehicle for the purpose of attaining optimum performance.

TURBOCHARGER: An exhaust driven pump which compresses intake air and forces it into the combustion chambers at higher than atmospheric pressures. The increased air pressure allows more fuel to be burned and results in increased horsepower being produced.

VACUUM ADVANCE: A device which advances the ignition timing in response to increased engine vacuum.

VACUUM GAUGE: An instrument used to measure the presence of vacuum in a chamber.

VALVE: A device which control the pressure, direction of flow or rate of flow of a liquid or gas.

VALVE CLEARANCE: The measured gap between the end of the valve stem and the rocker arm, cam lobe or follower that activates the valve.

VISCOSITY: The rating of a liquid's internal resistance to flow.

VOLTMETER: An instrument used for measuring electrical force in units called volts. Voltmeters are always connected parallel with the circuit being tested.

WHEEL CYLINDER: Found in the automotive drum brake assembly, it is a device, actuated by hydraulic pressure, which, through internal pistons, pushes the brake shoes outward against the drums.

A

MASTER INDEX

B

C

Notes